ADVANCED COURSE IN
ALGEBRA

CW00821305

MAVEN BOOKS

ADVANCED COURSE IN
ALGEBRA

WEBSTER WELLS, S.B.

Professor of Mathematics in the Massachusetts
Institute of Technology

MAVEN BOOKS

Chennai   Trichy   Tirunelveli   New Delhi

MAVEN BOOKS

An Imprint of **MJP Publishers**

ISBN 978-93-88191-22-7   **MAVEN Books**

All rights reserved   No. 44, Nallathambi Street,
Printed and bound in India   Triplicane, Chennai 600 005

MJP   596   © Publishers, 2019

Publisher :   **C. Janarthanan**

PUBLISHER'S NOTE

The legacy of a country is in its varied cultural heritage, historical literature, developments in the field of economy and science. The top nations in the world are competing in the field of science, economy and literature. This vast legacy has to be conserved and documented so that it can be bestowed to the future generation. The knowledge of this legacy is slowly getting perished in the present generation due to lack of documentation.

Keeping this in mind, the concern with retrospective acquiring of rare books has been accented recently by the burgeoning reprint industry. MAVEN Books is gratified to retrieve the rare collections with a view to bring back those books that were landmarks in their time.

In this effort, a series of rare books would be republished under the banner, "MAVEN Books". The books in the reprint series have been carefully selected for their contemporary usefulness as well as their historical importance within the intellectual. We reconstruct the book with slight enhancements made for better presentation, without affecting the contents of the original edition.

Most of the works selected for republishing covers a huge range of subjects, from history to anthropology. We believe this reprint edition will be a service to the numerous researchers and practitioners active in this fascinating field. We allow readers to experience the wonder of peering into a scholarly work of the highest order and seminal significance.

MAVEN Books

PREFACE

In preparing the present work, the author has endeavored to meet the needs of Colleges and Scientific Schools of the highest rank.

The development of the subject follows in the main the author's College Algebra; but numerous improvements have been introduced.

Attention is especially invited to the following:

1. The development of the fundamental laws of Algebra for the positive and negative integer, the positive and negative fraction, and zero, in Chaps. I and II.

In the above treatment, the author has followed to a certain extent *The Number·System of Algebra*, by Professor H. B. Fine; who has very courteously permitted this use of his treatise.

2. The development of the principles of equivalence of equations, and systems of equations, both linear and of higher degrees; see §§ 116–123, 182, 233–6, 396, 442, 470, 477, and 478.

3. The prominence given to graphical representation.

In Chap. XIV, the student learns how to obtain the graphs of linear equations with two unknown numbers, and of linear expressions with one unknown number. He also learns how to represent graphically the solution of a system of two linear equations, involving two unknown numbers, and sees how indeterminate and inconsistent systems are represented graphically.

The graphical representation of quadratic expressions, with one unknown number, is taken up in § 465; and, in § 467, the graphical representation of equal and imaginary roots.

The principles are further developed for simultaneous quadratics, in §§ 482 and 483; and for expressions of any degree, with one unknown number, in §§ 744 and 745.

At the end of Chap. XVIII, the student is taught the graphical representation of the fundamental laws of Algebra for pure imaginary and complex numbers.

In Chap. XXXVII, the graphical representation is given of Derivatives (§ 751), of Multiple Roots (§ 755), of Sturm's Theorem (§ 762), and of a Discontinuous Function (§ 766).

4. In Chap. VII, there are given the Remainder and Factor Theorems, and the principles of Symmetry.

5. In Chap VIII will be found every method of factoring which can be done advantageously by inspection, including factoring of symmetrical expressions. In this chapter is also given Solution of Equations by Factoring (§ 182).

6. In the earlier portions of Chap. XI, the pupil is shown that additional solutions are introduced by multiplying a fractional equation by an expression which is not the L.C.M. of the given denominators; and is shown how such additional solutions are discovered.

7. In §§ 264 and 265, the student is taught how to find the values of expressions taking the indeterminate forms $\frac{0}{0}$, $\frac{\infty}{\infty}$, $0 \times \infty$, and $\infty - \infty$.

8. All work coming under the head of the Binomial Theorem for positive integral exponents is taken up in the chapter on Involution.

9. In developing the principles of Evolution, all roots are restricted to their principal values.

10. In the examples of § 398, the pupil is taught to reject all solutions which do not satisfy the given equation, when the roots have their principal values.

11. The development of the theory of the Irrational Number, and its graphical representation (§§ 399–406).

12. The development of the fundamental laws of Algebra for Pure Imaginary and Complex Numbers (Chap. XVIII).

13. The use of the general form $ax^2 + bx + c = 0$, in the theory of quadratic equations (§§ 454–6).

14. The discussion of the maxima and minima values of quadratic expressions (§ 461).

15. The chapter on Convergency and Divergency of Series (Chap. XXVI).

16. In Chap. XXVIII is given Euler's proof of the Binomial Theorem, for any Rational Exponent.

17. The solution of logarithmic equations (§ 604).

18. The proof of the formula for the number of permutations of n different things, taken r at a time (§ 624).

19. The chapter on Theory of Numbers (Chap. XXXV).

20. In the chapter on Determinants, the double-suffix notation is used only in demonstrations which would not otherwise be complete.

Each demonstration of a general principle is preceded by an illustration showing the truth of the principle for a determinant of the third order.

Multiplication of determinants is taken up only for determinants of the second and third orders.

21. In Chap. XXXVII will be found Symmetrical Functions of the Roots (§ 721); a shorter proof of Descartes' Rule (§ 735); improved methods for finding limits to the roots (§§ 739, 740); the demonstration of two theorems used in the proof of Sturm's Theorem (§ 757); and a discussion of Continuous Functions (§ 765).

22. Chap. XXXVIII contains the solution of Cubic Equations by Trigonometry, in Cardan's Irreducible Case (§ 788); also, an improved discussion of Newton's Method for determining incommensurable roots (§ 801).

The examples and problems have been selected with great care, and include many varieties not found in the College Algebra; no example is a duplicate of any in the College Algebra.

The manuscript was read in the most careful manner by Professor George D. Olds, of Amherst College, who offered many suggestions; these have added materially to the value of the work.

The author would be under great obligations to any one who will bring to his attention any error which may be found in the book.

WEBSTER WELLS.

Boston, 1904.

CONTENTS

vii

ALGEBRA

I. DEFINITIONS. NOTATION. POSITIVE INTEGERS

1. In **Algebra**, the operations of Arithmetic are abridged and generalized by means of **Symbols**.

SYMBOLS REPRESENTING NUMBERS

2. The symbols usually employed to represent numbers are the *Arabic Numerals*, and the *Letters of the Alphabet*.

The numerals denote known or determinate numbers.

The letters denote numbers which may have any values whatever, or numbers whose values are to be determined.

Numbers occupying similar relations in the same investigation are often represented by the same letter, distinguished by different *accents*; as a', a'', a''', read "*a prime*," "*a second*," "*a third*," etc.

They may also be distinguished by different *subscript numbers*; as a_1, a_2, a_3, read "*a sub one*," "*a sub two*," "*a sub three*," etc.

SYMBOLS REPRESENTING OPERATIONS

3. The **Sign of Addition**, $+$, is read "*plus.*"

The **Sign of Subtraction**, $-$, is read "*minus.*"

The **Sign of Multiplication**, $\times$, is read "*times*," "*into*," or "*multiplied by.*"

A *point* is sometimes used instead of the sign $\times$; thus, $2 \cdot 3 \cdot 4$ signifies $2 \times 3 \times 4$.

The **Sign of Division**, $\div$, is read "*divided by.*"

SYMBOLS OF RELATION

4. The **Sign of Equality,** $=$, is read *"equals,"* or *"is equal to."*

The sign $\neq$ is sometimes used for the words *" is not equal to."*

The **Signs of Inequality,** $>$ and $<$, stand for *" is greater than "* and *" is less than,"* respectively.

The signs $\not>$ and $\not<$ are sometimes used for the words *" is not greater than "* and *" is not less than,"* respectively.

SYMBOLS OF ABBREVIATION

5. The **Signs of Aggregation,** the *parentheses* ( ), the *brackets* [ ], the *braces* { }, and the *vinculum* ‾, indicate that what is enclosed by them is to be taken as a whole.

The **Sign of Deduction,** $\therefore$, is read *" therefore "* or *" hence."*

The **Sign of Continuation,** · , is read *" and so on."*

THE POSITIVE INTEGER

6. By the *number* of things in a group, we mean that attribute of the group which remains unchanged however the group may be changed, provided no thing is divided into two or more things, and that two or more things are not merged into a single thing.

That is, the number of things in a group is independent of their character, of the order in which they may be arranged, and of the way in which they may be associated in smaller groups.

7. The numbers of things in two groups are said to be *equal* when for every thing in either group there is a thing in the other.

8. The number of things in one group is said to be *greater than* the number in another, or the number in the second group *less than* the number in the first, when for every thing in the second group there is a thing in the first, but not one in the second for every thing in the first.

9. The Positive Integer.

We define a *positive integer* as the number of things in a group.

A positive integer is also called a *whole number.*

To ensure generality in the results, we represent numbers by letters.

In the remainder of the present chapter, the letters a, b, c, etc., will be understood as representing positive integers.

10. If a and b stand for the numbers in any two groups (that is, for any two positive integers), we use the statement

$$a = b$$

to signify that the numbers are equal (§ 7).

The statement $a = b$ is called an **Equation.**

Again, we use the statements

$$a > b, \text{ and } a < b$$

to signify that the number in the first group is greater or less, respectively, than the number in the second (§ 8).

These statements are called **Inequalities.**

ADDITION OF POSITIVE INTEGERS

11. Let two or more groups contain a, b, c, $\cdots$ things, respectively.

If the second group be joined to the first, we represent the number in the resulting group by $a + b$.

If to the latter group the third group be joined, we represent the number in the resulting group by $a + b + c$; and so on.

After all the groups have been united in a single group, the number in the latter group is expressed

$$a + b + c + \cdots.$$

This result is called the **Sum** of the positive integers a, b, c, etc.

The operation of finding the sum is called **Addition.**

12. The Commutative and Associative Laws for Addition.

Addition of positive integers is subject to the following laws:

I. *The Commutative Law.*

To add b to a is the same as to add a to b.

Expressed in symbols,

$$a + b = b + a.$$

II. *The Associative Law.*

To add the sum of b and c to a is the same as to add b to a, and then add c to the result.

Expressed in symbols,

$$a + (b + c) = a + b + c.$$

To indicate the addition of $b + c$, it must be enclosed in *parentheses* (§ 5).

The Commutative and Associative Laws follow from § 6; for the number of things in the sum-group is independent of the order in which they may be arranged, and of the way in which they may be associated in smaller groups.

The Commutative and Associative Laws evidently hold for the sum of any number of positive integers.

MULTIPLICATION OF POSITIVE INTEGERS

13. Finding the sum of b positive integers, each equal to a, is called *multiplying* a by b.

The result is expressed $a \times b$, or simply ab; thus,

$$ab = a + a + \cdots \text{ to } b \text{ terms.}$$

The sign of multiplication is usually omitted in Algebra, except between Arabic numerals.

We call a the **Multiplicand**, and b the **Multiplier**.

If ab be multiplied by another positive integer, c, the result is expressed abc; and so on.

If any number of positive integers be multiplied together, the result is called their **Product**.

The operation of finding the product is called **Multiplication.**

14. The Commutative, Associative, and Distributive Laws for Multiplication.

Multiplication of positive integers is subject to the following laws:

I. *The Commutative Law.*

To multiply a by b is the same as to multiply b by a.

Expressed in symbols, $ab = ba$.

II. *The Associative Law.*

To multiply a by the product of b by c, is the same as to multiply a by b, and then multiply the result by c.

Expressed in symbols, $a(bc) = abc$.

III. *The Distributive Law.*

To multiply a by the sum of b and c is the same as to multiply a by b, and then a by c, and add the results.

Expressed in symbols, $a(b + c) = ab + ac$.

15. Proof of the Commutative Law.

Let there be, in the figure, a units in each row, and b rows.

We may find the entire number of units by multiplying the number in each row, a, by the number of rows, b.

Thus, the entire number of units is ab.

We may also find the entire number by multiplying the number in each vertical column, b, by the number of columns, a.

a in a row.

1 1 1 1 ⋯
1 1 1 1 ⋯
1 1 1 1 ⋯
⋯⋯⋯⋯⋯

b rows.

Thus, the entire number of units is ba.

Therefore, $ab = ba$.

16. Proof of the Associative Law.

By the definition of § 13,

$$abc = ab + ab + \cdots \text{ to } c \text{ terms}$$
$$= (a + a + \cdots \text{ to } b \text{ terms}) + (a + a + \cdots \text{ to } b \text{ terms})$$
$$+ \cdots \text{ to } c \text{ terms}$$
$$= a + a + \cdots \text{ to } bc \text{ terms,}$$
$$\text{by the Associative Law for Addition (§ 12)}$$
$$= a(bc), \text{ by the definition of § 13.}$$

17. Proof of the Distributive Law.

By the definition of § 13,

$a(b + c) = a + a + \cdots$ to $(b + c)$ terms

$\qquad = (a + a + \cdots$ to b terms) $+ (a + a + \cdots$ to c terms),

$\qquad\qquad$ by the Associative Law for Addition (§ 12),

$\qquad = ab + ac$, by the definition of § 13.

18. We will now show that the Commutative and Associative Laws for Multiplication hold for the product of any number of positive integers.

We will first prove the Commutative Law for the product of *three* positive integers, a, b, and c.

By § 14, II, $\quad abc = a(bc) = (cb)a$, by § 14, I,

$\qquad\qquad\qquad = cba$ (§ 13).

In like manner, we may prove abc equal to the product of a, b, and c in any other order.

19. We will now prove the Associative Law for the product of *four* positive integers, a, b, c, and d.

By § 14, I, $a(bcd) = (bcd)a = (bc)da = a(bc)d$ (§ 18)

$\qquad\qquad\qquad = [a(bc)]d = (abc)d$ (§ 14, II) $= abcd$.

By continuing the foregoing, the Commutative and Associative Laws may be proved for the product of any number of positive integers.

The Distributive Law for Multiplication holds for the sum of any number of positive integers, as is evident from the nature of the demonstration in § 17.

SUBTRACTION OF POSITIVE INTEGERS

20. We define **Subtraction** as the process of finding one of two positive integers (the **Remainder**), when their sum (the **Minuend**) and the other positive integer (the **Subtrahend**) are given.

Thus, subtraction is the inverse of addition.

21. The remainder, when b is subtracted from a, is expressed $a - b$.

Since, by the definition of § 20, the sum of the remainder and the subtrahend equals the minuend, we have

$$(a - b) + b = a. \tag{1}$$

22. If $\qquad a + c = b + c$, then $a = b$.

For if the numbers of units in the sums $a + c$ and $b + c$ are equal, the result of subtracting the units in c from each sum will be the same; that is, $a = b$.

23. It follows, precisely as in § 22, that

If $\qquad a + c > b + c$, then $a > b$.

If $\qquad a + c < b + c$, then $a < b$.

24. Rules for Subtraction.

The following rules, together with the laws of §§ 12 and 14, are sufficient, if suitably combined, to determine the result of any operation with positive integers, involving only addition, subtraction, and multiplication:

(1) $a - (b + c) = a - b - c$.

(2) $a - b - c \quad = a - c - b$.

(3) $a - (b - c) = a - b + c$.

(4) $a + b - b \quad = a$.

(5) $a + (b - c) = a + b - c$.

(6) $a + b - c \quad = a - c + b$.

(7) $a(b - c) \quad = ab - ac$.

25. Proofs of the Rules for Subtraction.

Proof of (1).

If we add c, and then b, to $a - b - c$, or (§ 12, I), if we add b, and then c, or (§ 12, II), if we add $b + c$, the result is a.

That is, $\qquad a - b - c + (b + c) = a$.

Regarding a as the minuend, $b + c$ as the subtrahend, and $a - b - c$ as the remainder, we have

$$a - (b + c) = a - b - c.$$

Proof of (2).

By (1), $a - c - b = a - (c + b) = a - (b + c)$ (§ 12, I)
$$= a - b - c, \text{ by (1)}.$$

Proof of (3).

By § 21, (1), $a - b + c = a - [(b - c) + c] + c$
$$= a - (b - c) - c + c, \text{ by (1)},$$
$$= a - (b - c).$$

Proof of (4).

We have $a + b - b + b = a + b.$

Then, by § 22, $a + b - b = a.$

Proof of (5).

By § 21, $a + b - c = a + [(b - c) + c] - c$
$$= a + (b - c) + c - c \ (\S 12, \text{ II})$$
$$= a + (b - c), \text{ by (4)}.$$

Proof of (6).

By § 12, I, $a + b - c = b + a - c = b + (a - c)$, by (5),
$$= (a - c) + b \ (\S 12, \text{ I}) = a - c + b.$$

Proof of (7).

By § 21, $ab - ac = a[(b - c) + c] - ac$
$$= a(b - c) + ac - ac(\S 14, \text{ III}) = a(b - c), \text{ by (4)}.$$

It is important to observe that the results of § 24 are simply formal consequences of §§ 12, 14, 21, and 22; they must follow from these whatever meaning is attached to the symbols, a, b, c, $+$, $-$, and $=$.

26. Equations (2) and (6), § 24, show that a set of subtractions, or of additions and subtractions, can be performed in any order.

Equation (4) shows that addition is the inverse of subtraction.

Equations (1), (3), and (5), with § 12, II, give complete associative laws for addition and subtraction.

Equation (7), with § 14, III, give a complete distributive for multiplication.

DIVISION OF POSITIVE INTEGERS

27. We define **Division** of positive integers as the process of finding one of two positive integers (the **Quotient**), which when multiplied by another positive integer (the **Divisor**), gives a third positive integer (the **Dividend**).

Thus, division is the inverse of multiplication.

28. The quotient when a is divided by b is expressed $a \div b$, or $\dfrac{a}{b}$.

Since, by the definition of § 27, the product of the quotient by the divisor gives the dividend, we have

$$\left(\frac{a}{b}\right)b = a. \tag{1}$$

29. If $\qquad ac = bc$, then $a = b$.

For, if $a + a + \cdots$ to c terms $= b + b + \cdots$ to c terms, we must have $a = b$.

30. Rules for Division.

(1) $\dfrac{a}{b} \cdot \dfrac{c}{d} = \dfrac{ac}{bd}.$

For by § 14, I and II, $\dfrac{a}{b} \cdot \dfrac{c}{d} \cdot bd = \left(\dfrac{a}{b} \cdot b\right) \cdot \left(\dfrac{c}{d} \cdot d\right)$

$$= ac, \text{ by § 28, (1).}$$

Also, $\qquad\qquad \dfrac{ac}{bd} \cdot bd = ac, \text{ by § 28, (1).}$

Then, by § 29, $\qquad \dfrac{a}{b} \cdot \dfrac{c}{d} = \dfrac{ac}{bd}.$

(2) $\dfrac{\frac{a}{b}}{\frac{c}{d}} = \dfrac{ad}{bc}.$

For by § 28, (1), $\qquad \dfrac{\frac{a}{b}}{\frac{c}{d}} \cdot \dfrac{c}{d} = \dfrac{a}{b}. \tag{A}$

Also, by (1), $\dfrac{ad}{bc} \cdot \dfrac{c}{d} = \dfrac{a}{b} \cdot \dfrac{d}{c} \cdot \dfrac{c}{d} = \dfrac{a}{b}\left(\dfrac{d}{c} \cdot \dfrac{c}{d}\right)$, by § 14, II,

$$= \dfrac{a}{b}\left(\dfrac{dc}{cd}\right), \text{ by (1)}.$$

But by § 28, $\qquad\qquad \dfrac{dc}{cd} \cdot cd = dc = 1 \times cd.$

Whence, by § 29, $\qquad\qquad \dfrac{dc}{cd} = 1, \text{ and } \dfrac{ad}{bc} \cdot \dfrac{c}{d} = \dfrac{a}{b}. \qquad$ (B)

From (A) and (B), by § 29, $\dfrac{\frac{a}{b}}{\frac{c}{d}} = \dfrac{ad}{bc}.$

(3) $\dfrac{a}{b} + \dfrac{c}{d} = \dfrac{ad + bc}{bd}.$

For by § 14, I, II, and III,

$$\left(\dfrac{a}{b} + \dfrac{c}{d}\right)bd = \dfrac{a}{b}\left(bd\right) + \dfrac{c}{d}\left(bd\right) = \left(\dfrac{a}{b}b\right)d + \left(\dfrac{c}{d}d\right)b$$

$$= ad + bc, \text{ by § 28, (1)}. \qquad\qquad \text{(C)}$$

Also, $\dfrac{ad + bc}{bd} \cdot bd = ad + bc$, by § 28, (1). $\qquad\qquad$ (D)

From (C) and (D), by § 29, $\dfrac{a}{b} + \dfrac{c}{d} = \dfrac{ad + bc}{bd}.$

(4) $\dfrac{a}{b} - \dfrac{c}{d} = \dfrac{ad - bc}{bd}.$

This is proved in the same manner as (3).

The results of § 30 are simply formal consequences of §§ 14, 24, 28, and 29; and must follow from these whatever meaning is attached to the symbols a, b, c, $+$, $-$, $=$, ab, and $\dfrac{a}{b}$.

31. If $ad = bc$, then $\left(\dfrac{a}{b} \cdot b\right)d = b\left(\dfrac{c}{d} \cdot d\right)$, by § 28, (1).

Then, by § 14, I and II, $\dfrac{a}{b}\left(bd\right) = \dfrac{c}{d} \cdot b \cdot d = \dfrac{c}{d}\left(bd\right).$

Then, by § 29, $\qquad\qquad\qquad\qquad \dfrac{a}{b} = \dfrac{c}{d}.$

II. RATIONAL NUMBERS

32. The proofs in § 25 hold only when the result of every indicated subtraction is a *positive integer;* for the laws of §§ 12 and 14 have only been proved for the case in which all the letters involved represent positive integers.

A result like (1) has, at present, no meaning unless $b + c$ is $< a$; and in the remainder of the work we should be compelled to limit every subtraction to cases where it was arithmetically possible.

Unless, then, subtraction is to be very much restricted, we must consider the cases where the subtrahend equals, or is greater than, the minuend; this leads to the introduction into Algebra of *Zero* and the *Negative Number.*

SYMBOLIC EQUATIONS

33. The equation (1), § 21, is not an equation as defined in § 10, unless a and b are positive integers, and $a > b$.

But if we agree to define an equation as simply *a statement that two symbols, or combinations of symbols, are of such a character that one may be substituted for the other in any operation,* then (1), § 21, may be an equation whatever the values of a and b.

In this symbolic definition of an equation, it is unnecessary that there should be any real things to which the symbols correspond.

We shall attach this meaning to every equation throughout the remainder of the work which does not express the equality of two positive integers.

34. Symbolic Subtraction.

If we regard equation (1), § 21, as defining $a - b$, *whatever the values of a and b,* we have in this way a *symbolic* definition of subtraction which holds universally.

This defines subtraction in terms of *symbolic addition ;* for the sign $+$ cannot indicate numerical addition, unless the symbols which it connects are positive integers.

It is perfectly logical to define an operation by means of an equation.

ZERO AND THE NEGATIVE INTEGER

35. In determining the definitions and rules of operation of *zero* and the *negative integer*, we make the assumption that the results of §§ 12, 14, 22, and 23 hold for these symbols.

If all the letters do not represent positive integers, the results of §§ 12, 14, 22, and 23 are regarded as symbolic statements.

36. Since the results of § 24 are simply formal consequences of §§ 12, 14, and 22, and the definition of subtraction, it follows from § 35 that they hold for the above symbols.

If the results of § 24 do not have a positive integral interpretation, they are regarded as symbolic statements.

In this way they become definitions of symbolic addition, subtraction, and multiplication, and their relations.

37. Zero.

Every letter in §§ 37 to 42, inclusive, will be understood as representing a *positive integer.*

Putting $b = a$, in (1), § 28, we have

$$(a - a) + a = a. \tag{1}$$

The symbol $a - a$, if a is any positive integer, is represented by the symbol 0, called *zero.*

Then (1) becomes $0 + a = a.$ $\qquad(2)$

Since the Commutative Law for Addition (§ 12) is assumed to hold if either letter equals 0 (§ 35), we may write equation (2), $a + 0 = a.$ $\qquad(3)$

Again, by definition, $a - 0$ means a symbol such that when 0 is added to it, the sum is a.

That is, $(a - 0) + 0 = a.$

Then, by (3), $\qquad a - 0 = a.$ $\hfill (4)$

Again, by the definition of 0,

$$a \times 0 = a(b - b) = ab - ab, \text{ by § 24, (7)},$$
$$= 0, \text{ by definition.} \hfill (5)$$

We can use § 24, (7), in the above proof; for we know from § 36 that it holds, even if the result does not have a positive integral interpretation.

From (5), by the Commutative Law for Multiplication,

$$0 \times a = 0. \hfill (6)$$

38. The Negative Integer.

Let b be greater than a; and suppose $b = a + d$, where d is a positive integer.

Then, by the definition of subtraction, $b - a = d$.

Then, $\quad a - b = a - (a + d) = a - a - d$, by § 24, (1),
$$= 0 - d, \text{ by the definition of 0.}$$

We can use § 24, (1), in the above, for we know that it holds, even if the result does not have a positive integral interpretation.

We then define $a - b$, if b is $> a$, as being equal to $0 - d$.

It is usual to write $- d$ instead of $0 - d$.

Thus, $\qquad 0 - d = - d.$ $\hfill (1)$

The symbol $- d$ is called a **Negative Integer**; in contradistinction, the positive integer d may be written $+ d$.

39. The signs $+$ and $-$, when used in the above manner, are no longer signs of operation; they are called signs of *Affection*, *Quality*, or *Opposition*.

If no sign is written, the sign $+$ is understood.

40. Rules for Addition, Subtraction, and Multiplication, involving Negative Integers.

(1) $a + (- b) = a - b$.

For, by the definition of § 38,

$$a + (- b) = a + (0 - b) = a + 0 - b, \text{ by § 24, (5)},$$
$$= a - b, \text{ by § 37, (3)}.$$

(2) $-a + (-b) = -(a+b)$.

For, $-a + (-b) = -a + (0-b) = -a + 0 - b$
$$= 0 - a - b, \text{ by § 12, I,}$$
$$= 0 - (a+b), \text{ by § 24, (1),}$$
$$= -(a+b), \text{ by § 38.}$$

(3) $a - (-b) = a + b$.

For, $a - (-b) = a - (0-b) = a - 0 + b, \text{ by § 24, (3),}$
$$= a + b, \text{ by § 37, (4).}$$

(4) $-a - (-b) = -a + b = b - a$.

For, $-a - (-b) = -a - (0-b) = -a - 0 + b = -a + b - 0$
$$= -a + b, \text{ by § 37, (4),}$$
$$= b - a, \text{ by § 12, I.}$$

Putting b for a in (1) and (4), we have

(5) $b + (-b) = 0$.

(6) $-b + b = 0$.

(7) $-b - (-b) = 0$.

(8) $a(-b) = -ab$.

By § 37, (5), $0 = a \times 0 = a[b + (-b)]$, by (5),
$$= ab + a(-b), \text{ by § 14, III.}$$

Then, $ab - ab = ab + a(-b)$.

Whence, by § 22, $-ab = a(-b)$.

(9) $(-b)a = -ab = -ba$.

This follows from (8) by § 14, I.

(10) $(-a) \times 0 = 0$.

For, by the definition of 0,

$(-a) \times 0 = (-a)(b-b) = (-a)b - (-a)b, \text{ by § 24, (7),}$
$$= (-ab) - (-ab), \text{ by (9),}$$
$$= 0, \text{ by (7).}$$

(11) $0 \times (-a) = 0$.

This follows from (10) by § 14, I.

(12) $(-a)(-b) = ab$.

By (10), $0 = (-a) \times 0 = (-a)[b + (-b)]$, by (5),

$\qquad\qquad\qquad = (-a)b + (-a)(-b)$, by § 14, III,

$\qquad\qquad\qquad = -ab + (-a)(-b)$, by (9).

Then by (6), $\quad -ab + ab = -ab + (-a)(-b)$.

Then by § 22, $\qquad ab = (-a)(-b)$.

41. If b is $> a$, $\quad 0 + b > 0 + a$, by § 37, (2).

Then, $\qquad -a + a + b > -b + b + a$, by § 40, (6).

Then by § 23, $\qquad -a > -b$. $\hfill$ (1)

In like manner, if b is $< a$, $-a$ is $< -b$.

These may be regarded as defining greater and less inequality in negative integers.

42. If a and b are positive integers,

$\qquad a < a + b$; or, $0 + a < a + b$, by § 37, (2).

Then, by § 23, $\qquad 0 < b$.

Then, $\qquad\qquad -b + b < b + 0$, by §§ 37, (3), and 40, (6).

Whence, by § 23, $\quad -b < 0$.

SYMBOLIC DIVISION

43. It is important to observe that the result of § 29 does not hold when $c = 0$; for by § 37, (5), $a \times 0 = b \times 0$, when a and b are not equal.

It follows from this that the proofs in §§ 30 and 31 do not hold if $b = 0$ or $d = 0$.

44. Symbolic Division. The Fraction.

The proofs in §§ 30 and 31 hold only when the result of every indicated division is a *positive integer*.

A result like that of § 30, (1), has, at present, no meaning unless $\frac{a}{b}$, $\frac{c}{d}$, and $\frac{ac}{bd}$ are positive integers.

But if we regard equation (1), § 28, as defining $\frac{a}{b}$, whatever the values of a and b, provided b is not 0 (§ 43), we have a *symbolic* definition of division, which holds universally.

The symbol $\frac{a}{b}$, with the above meaning of a and b, is called a **Fraction**.

The symbols $\frac{a}{0}$ and $\frac{0}{0}$ are considered in Chap. XIII.

If a and b are positive integers, and $\frac{a}{b}$ is not a positive integer, $\frac{a}{b}$ is called a **Positive Fraction**, and $-\frac{a}{b}$ a **Negative Fraction**.

45. We make the assumption that the results of §§ 12, 14, and 22 hold for the symbol $\frac{a}{b}$ as defined in § 44; whence, it follows that the results of § 24 hold for the symbol $\frac{a}{b}$.

We also assume that the result of § 29 holds for all the symbols considered in the present chapter, provided b is not 0.

46. Since the results of §§ 30 and 31 are simply formal consequences of §§ 14, 24, and 29, and the definition of division, it follows from § 45 that they hold, provided b and d are not 0, even if the results do not have a positive integral interpretation.

In this way, the results of § 30 become definitions of addition, subtraction, multiplication, and division, for the symbol $\frac{a}{b}$.

47. Since the results of §§ 12, 14, 22, and 24 hold for any of the symbols considered in the present chapter (§§ 35, 36, 45), the results of §§ 37 and 40 hold for any of these symbols; for they are simply formal consequences of §§ 12, 14, 22, and 24, and the definition of subtraction.

48. Since the symbolic definition of division (§ 44) holds for any values of the letters involved, we have

$$\left(\frac{a}{-b}\right)(-b) = a. \tag{A}$$

Again, (12), § 40, holds when we replace a by $\frac{a}{b}$ (§ 47).

Then, $$\left(-\frac{a}{b}\right)(-b) = \frac{a}{b} \cdot b = a. \tag{B}$$

From (A) and (B), by § 29, which is supposed to hold for the symbol $-b$ (§ 45),

$$\frac{a}{-b} = -\frac{a}{b}. \tag{1}$$

Again,
$$\left(\frac{-a}{b}\right)b = -a. \tag{C}$$

And by (9), § 40,
$$\left(-\frac{a}{b}\right)b = -\left(\frac{a}{b}\cdot b\right) = -a. \tag{D}$$

From (C) and (D),
$$\frac{-a}{b} = -\frac{a}{b}. \tag{2}$$

Also,
$$\left(\frac{-a}{-b}\right)(-b) = -a. \tag{E}$$

And by (8), § 40,
$$\frac{a}{b}(-b) = -\left(\frac{a}{b}\cdot b\right) = -a. \tag{F}$$

From (E) and (F),
$$\frac{-a}{-b} = \frac{a}{b}. \tag{3}$$

The results (1), (2), and (3) hold for any values of the letters, provided b is not 0.

49. Consider the equation $ab = 0$;

where a and b may be positive integers, or any of the symbols considered in the present chapter.

By § 37, (2), whatever the value of c,

$$0 + ac = ac.$$

Putting ab for 0, we have

$$ab + ac = ac, \text{ or } a(b + c) = ac, \text{ by § 14, III.}$$

Then by § 29, if a is not 0 (compare § 43),

$$b + c = c, \text{ or } b = 0 \text{ (§ 22).}$$

Therefore, either $a = 0$, or else $b = 0$.

50. It is advantageous, at this point, to consider the nature of the argument which has been developed.

In Chap. I, we defined the positive integer, and the operations of Addition, Subtraction, Multiplication, and Division with positive integers; and we showed how the fundamental laws of §§ 12, 14, 22, and 29 followed from the definitions of Addition and Multiplication, and the results of §§ 24 and 30 from the above general laws, and the definitions of Subtraction and Division.

In Chap. II, we *assumed* the fundamental laws of §§ 12, 14, 22, and 29, and the symbolic definitions of Subtraction and Division, to hold universally; and from these assumptions, we derived the definitions of zero, the negative integer, and the positive and negative fraction, and the rules for their operation, the assumptions being just sufficient to determine these meanings without ambiguity.

51. Rational Numbers.

In the present chapter, we have considered four symbols — zero, the negative integer, and the positive and negative fraction — which are subject to the same rules as positive integers.

The result of every operation involving only addition, subtraction, multiplication, and division — whether performed on positive integers, or on the symbols themselves — can be expressed either as a positive integer, or as one of the symbols.

For this reason, we shall regard these symbols as *numbers;* and we shall term the entire system of positive and negative integers, and positive and negative fractions, *Rational Numbers.*

Zero, the negative integer, and the positive and negative fraction, are essentially *artificial* numbers, in contrast to the *natural* numbers (positive integers) considered in Chap. I.

It must be clearly understood that they are simply *symbols* for the results of operations on actual groups of things, which cannot be expressed in positive integers.   (Compare § 6.)

We shall use the term *positive number*, in Chaps. II to XVII, inclusive, to denote a *positive integer* or a *positive fraction ;* and the term *negative number* to denote a *negative integer* or a *negative fraction*. The term *number*, without a qualifying adjective, will be understood as signifying a *positive* or *negative integer*, or a *positive* or *negative fraction*.

Every letter will be understood as representing a positive or negative integer, or a positive or negative fraction, unless the contrary is stated.

52. It is important to observe that the results of §§ 24 and 30, and all the results of Chap. II, follow from the fundamental laws of §§ 12, 14, 22, 23, and 29, and the symbolic definitions of subtraction and division, *entirely irrespective of whether or no the symbols have any numerical meaning*.

Thus, all the results of the text hold for any symbols which satisfy the fundamental laws, no matter what their meaning.

53. The *absolute value* of a number is the number taken independently of the sign affecting it.

Thus, the absolute value of -3 is 3.

54. The results of § 42 hold when b is any positive number.

Hence, *zero is less than any positive number, and any negative number is less than zero.*

55. Again, by § 47, the result (1), § 41, also holds when a and b are positive fractions.

Hence, *of two negative numbers, that is the greater which has the smaller absolute value.*

56. Any two magnitudes which are *opposite* to each other may be represented by positive and negative numbers, in Algebra.

Thus, in financial transactions, we may represent *assets* by the sign $+$, and *liabilities* by the sign $-$; thus, the statement that a man's assets are $-\$100$, means that he has liabilities to the amount of $\$100$.

Again, we may represent motion along a straight line in a certain direction by the sign $+$, and in the opposite direction by the sign $-$; and so on.

57. Graphical Representation of Positive and Negative Numbers.

The entire series of positive and negative numbers may be represented by the above scale, in which the divisions are one unit in length.

Distances measured to the right of 0 represent positive numbers, and to the left of 0, negative.

Every positive or negative fraction will be represented by the distance from 0 to a point between two consecutive scale-marks.

Thus, the number $-3\frac{2}{3}$ will be represented by the distance from 0 to a point two-thirds the way from C' to D'.

58. If any number, positive or negative, be denoted by the symbol a, $-a$ will represent a number of the same absolute value, but opposite sign.

It follows from this that $+(-a)$ and $-(-a)$ signify numbers of the same absolute value as $-a$, and of the same sign, and opposite sign, respectively.

That is, $+(-a) = -a$, and $-(-a) = +a.$ (1)

Similarly, $-(+a) = -a$, and $+(+a) = +a.$ (2)

From (1) and (2),

$$+(-a) = -(+a), \text{ and } -(-a) = +(+a).$$

DEFINITIONS

59. Addition, Subtraction, Multiplication, and Division of any algebraic numbers are expressed in the same manner as in §§ 11, 13, 20, and 28.

For example, $2\,ab$ signifies $2 \times a \times b$.

60. If a number be multiplied by itself any number of times, the product is called a **Power** of the number.

An **Exponent** is a number written at the right of, and above another number, to indicate what power of the latter is to be taken; thus,

a^2, read "*a square*," or "*a second power*," denotes $a \times a$;

a^3, read "*a cube*," or "*a third power*," denotes $a \times a \times a$;

a^4, read "*a fourth*," or "*a fourth power*," denotes $a \times a \times a \times a$;
    and so on.

If no exponent is expressed, the *first* power is understood.

Thus, a is the same as a^1.

61. Algebraic Expressions.

An **Algebraic Expression**, or simply an **Expression**, is a number expressed in algebraic symbols; as,

$$2, \ a, \ \text{or} \ 2\,x^2 - 3\,ab + 5.$$

A **Monomial**, or **Term**, is an expression whose parts are not separated by the signs $+$ or $-$; as $2\,x^2$, $-3\,ab$, 5, or $\dfrac{m}{n}$.

A monomial is sometimes called a *simple expression*.

$2\,x^2$, $-3\,ab$, and $+5$ are called the terms of the expression $2\,x^2 - 3\,ab + 5$.

A **Positive Term** is one preceded by a *plus* sign; as $+5\,a$.

For this reason the sign $+$ is often called the *positive sign*.

If no sign is expressed, the term is understood to be positive; thus, $2\,x^2$ is the same as $+2\,x^2$.

A **Negative Term** is one preceded by a *minus* sign; as $-3\,ab$.

For this reason the sign $-$ is often called the *negative sign ;* it can never be omitted before a negative term.

A **Polynomial** is an expression consisting of more than one term; as $a + b$, or $2\,x^2 - 3\,xy - 5\,y^2$.

A polynomial is also called a *multinomial*, or a *compound* expression.

A **Binomial** is a polynomial of *two* terms; as $a + b$.

A **Trinomial** is a polynomial of *three* terms; as $a + b - c$.

62. The **Numerical Value** of an expression is the result obtained by substituting particular numerical values for the letters involved in it, and performing the operations indicated.

Thus, if $a = 4$, $b = 3$, $c = 5$, and $d = 2$, the numerical value of

$$4\,a + \frac{6\,c}{b} - d^3 = 4 \times 4 + \frac{6 \times 5}{3} - 2^3 = 16 + 10 - 8 = 18.$$

63. A monomial is said to be *rational and integral* when it is either a number expressed in Arabic numerals, or a single letter with unity for its exponent, or the product of two or more such numbers or letters.

It is also said to be rational and integral when it can be reduced to either of the above forms.

Thus, $3\,a^2b^3$, being equivalent to $3 \cdot a \cdot a \cdot b \cdot b \cdot b$, is rational and integral.

A polynomial is said to be rational and integral when each term is rational and integral; as $2\,x^2 - \dfrac{3}{4}\,ab + c^3$.

64. If a term has a literal portion which consists of a single letter with unity for its exponent, the term is said to be of the *first degree*.

The *degree* of any rational and integral monomial (§ 63) is the number of terms of the first degree which are multiplied together to form its literal portion.

Thus, $2\,a$ is of the *first* degree; $5\,ab$, of the *second* degree; $3\,a^2b^3$, being equivalent to $3\,aabbb$, is of the *fifth* degree; etc.

The degree of a rational and integral monomial equals the sum of the exponents of the letters involved in it.

Thus, ab^4c^3 is of the *eighth* degree.

The degree of a rational and integral polynomial is the degree of its term of highest degree.

Thus, $2\,a^2b - 3\,c + d^2$ is of the *third* degree.

65. Homogeneous Terms are terms of the same degree.

Thus, a^4, $3\,b^3c$, and $-5\,x^2y^2$ are homogeneous.

A polynomial is said to be homogeneous when its terms are homogeneous; as $a^3 + 3\,b^2c - 4\,xyz$.

66. An **Axiom** is a self-evident truth.

The following are assumed as axioms:

1. *Any number equals itself.*
2. *Any number equals the sum of all its parts.*
3. *Any number is greater than any of its parts.*
4. *Two numbers which are equal to the same number, or to equal numbers, are equal.*
5. *If for any number in an expression an equal number be substituted, the value of the expression is not changed.*

III. ADDITION AND SUBTRACTION OF ALGEBRAIC EXPRESSIONS. PARENTHESES

67. Addition of Positive and Negative Numbers.

If a and b represent any positive numbers,

$$a + (-b) = a - b; \tag{1}$$

for by § 47, the result (1), § 40, also holds when either a or b is a positive fraction.

If b is $> a$, $\qquad a - b = - (b - a);$

for the result of § 38 also holds when either a or b is a positive fraction (§ 47).

Then, $\qquad a + (-b) = - (b - a). \tag{2}$

From (1) and (2), we have the following rule:

To add a positive and a negative number, subtract the smaller absolute value (§ 53) from the greater, and place before the result the sign of the number having the greater absolute value.

Thus, $5\frac{1}{4} + (-3\frac{1}{2}) = 1\frac{3}{4}; \ 2 + (-5) = -3.$

68. Addition of Negative Numbers.

If a and b represent positive numbers, we have by § 40, (2),

$$(-a) + (-b) = - (a + b).$$

We then have the following rule:

To add two negative numbers, add their absolute values, and put a negative sign before the result.

Thus, $(-1\frac{2}{3}) + (-2\frac{1}{5}) = -3\frac{13}{15}.$

69. Addition of Monomials.

The sum of a and b is $a + b$; and by § 40, (1), the sum of a and $-b$ is $a - b$; hence,

The addition of monomials is effected by uniting them with their respective signs.

Thus, the sum of a, $-b$, c, $-d$, and $-e$ is
$$a - b + c - d - e.$$

Since the Commutative Law for Addition holds for any rational numbers (§§ 47, 51), the terms may be united in any order, provided each has its proper sign.

70. Definitions. If two or more numbers are multiplied together, each of them, or the product of any number of them, is called a **Factor** of the product.

Thus, a, b, c, ab, ac, and bc are factors of the product abc.

71. If a number be expressed as the product of two factors, each is called the **Coefficient** of the other.

Thus in $2\,ab$, 2 is the coefficient of ab; $2\,a$ of b; a of $2\,b$; etc.

72. If one factor of a product is expressed in *Arabic numerals*, and the other in *letters*, the former is called the *numerical coefficient* of the latter.

Thus in $2\,ab$, 2 is the numerical coefficient of ab.

If no numerical coefficient is expressed, the coefficient unity is understood.

Thus, a is the same as $1\,a$.

By § 47, the result (9), § 40, also holds when b is a positive fraction.

That is, $-3\,a$ is the product of -3 and a, and $-\frac{2}{3}\,ab$ is the product of $-\frac{2}{3}$ and ab.

Then, -3 is the *numerical coefficient* of a in $-3\,a$, and $-\frac{2}{3}$ is the numerical coefficient of ab in $-\frac{2}{3}\,ab$.

Thus, in a negative term (§ 61), the numerical coefficient includes the *sign*.

73. Similar or **Like Terms** are those which either do not differ at all, or differ only in their numerical coefficients; as $2\,x^2y$ and $-7\,x^2y$.

Dissimilar or **Unlike Terms** are those which are not similar; as $3\,x^2y$ and $3\,xy^2$.

74. Addition of Similar Terms.

1. Find the sum of $5\,a$ and $3\,a$.

Since the Distributive Law for Multiplication (§ 14, III) holds for any rational numbers (§ 47), we have

$$5\,a + 3\,a = (5+3)\,a = 8\,a.$$

2. Find the sum of $5\,a$ and $-3\,a$.

By § 72,
$$5\,a + (-3\,a) = 5\,a + (-3)a$$
$$= [5 + (-3)]a \qquad (§ 14, III)$$
$$= 2\,a. \qquad (§ 67)$$

3. Find the sum of $-5\,a$ and $3\,a$.

$$(-5)a + 3\,a = [(-5)+3]a = -2\,a. \qquad (§ 67)$$

4. Find the sum of $-5\,a$ and $-3\,a$.

$$(-5)a + (-3)a = [(-5)+(-3)]a = -8\,a. \qquad (§ 68)$$

Therefore, *to add two similar terms, find the sum of their numerical coefficients* (§§ 67, 68, 72), *and affix to the result the common letters.*

5. Find the sum of $2\,a$, $-a$, $3\,a$, $-12\,a$, and $6\,a$.

Since the additions may be performed in any order, we may add the positive terms first, and then the negative terms, and finally combine these two results.

The sum of $2\,a$, $3\,a$, and $6\,a$ is $11\,a$.

The sum of $-a$ and $-12\,a$ is $-13\,a$.

Hence, the required sum is $11\,a + (-13\,a)$, or $-2\,a$.

6. Add $3(a-b)$, $-2(a-b)$, $6(a-b)$, and $-4(a-b)$.

The sum of $3(a-b)$ and $6(a-b)$ is $9(a-b)$.

The sum of $-2(a-b)$ and $-4(a-b)$ is $-6(a-b)$.

Then, the result is $[9 + (-6)](a-b)$, or $3(a-b)$.

75. If the terms are not all similar, we may combine the similar terms, and unite the others with their respective signs (§ 69).

Ex. Required the sum of $12\,a$, $-5\,x$, $-3\,y^2$, $-5\,a$, $8\,x$, and $-3\,x$.

The sum of $12\,a$ and $-5\,a$ is $7\,a$.

The sum of $-5\,x$, $8\,x$, and $-3\,x$ is 0; for the result, (5), § 40, holds for any value of b (§ 47).

Hence, the required sum is $7\,a - 3\,y^2$.

76. A polynomial is said to be *arranged* according to the *descending* powers of any letter, when the term containing the highest power of that letter is placed first, that having the next lower immediately after, and so on.

Thus, $\qquad x^4 + 3\,x^3y - 2\,x^2y^2 + 3\,xy^3 - 4\,y^4$

is arranged according to the descending powers of x.

The term $-4\,y^4$, which does not involve x at all, is regarded as containing the lowest power of x in the above expression.

A polynomial is said to be arranged according to the *ascending* powers of any letter, when the term containing the lowest power of that letter is placed first, that having the next higher immediately after, and so on.

Thus, $\qquad x^4 + 3\,x^3y - 2\,x^2y^2 + 3\,xy^3 - 4\,y^4$

is arranged according to the ascending powers of y.

77. Addition of Polynomials.

It follows from § 12, II, and § 24, (5), that the addition of polynomials is effected by uniting their terms with their respective signs.

1. Required the sum of

$$6\,a - 7\,x^2,\ 3\,x^2 - 2\,a + 3\,y^3,\ \text{and}\ 2\,x^2 - a - mn.$$

We set the expressions down one underneath the other, similar terms being in the same vertical column.

We then find the sum of the terms in each column, **and** write the results with their respective signs; thus,

$$
\begin{array}{l}
6\,a - 7\,x^2 \\
-2\,a + 3\,x^2 + 3\,y^3 \\
-\ \ a + 2\,x^2 \qquad\quad - mn \\
\hline
3\,a - 2\,x^2 + 3\,y^3 - mn.
\end{array}
$$

2. Add $4x - 3x^2 - 11 + 5x^3$, $12x^2 - 7 - 8x^3 - 15x$, and $14 + 6x^3 + 10x - 9x^2$.

It is convenient to arrange each expression in *descending* powers of x (§ 76); thus,

$$\begin{array}{r} 5x^3 - \ 3x^2 + \ 4x - 11 \\ -8x^3 + 12x^2 - 15x - \ 7 \\ 6x^3 - \ 9x^2 + 10x + 14 \\ \hline 3x^3 \qquad - \quad x - \ 4. \end{array}$$

3. Add $9(a+b) - 8(b+c)$, $-3(b+c) - 7(c+a)$, and $4(c+a) - 5(a+b)$.

$$\begin{array}{l} 9(a+b) - \ 8(b+c) \\ \quad - \ 3(b+c) - 7(c+a) \\ -5(a+b) \qquad\qquad + 4(c+a) \\ \hline 4(a+b) - 11(b+c) - 3(c+a). \end{array}$$

4. Add $\frac{3}{4}a + \frac{2}{5}b - \frac{1}{3}c$ and $\frac{1}{6}a - \frac{4}{3}b + \frac{5}{7}c$.

$$\begin{array}{l} \frac{3}{4}a + \ \frac{2}{5}b - \ \frac{1}{3}c \\[4pt] \frac{1}{6}a - \ \frac{4}{3}b + \ \frac{5}{7}c \\[4pt] \hline \frac{11}{12}a - \frac{14}{15}b + \frac{8}{21}c. \end{array}$$

SUBTRACTION

78. Subtraction of Monomials.

By § 47, the result (3), § 40, holds for any values of a and b.

Hence, *to subtract a monomial, we change its sign and add the result to the minuend.*

1. Subtract $5a$ from $2a$.

Changing the sign of the subtrahend, and adding the result to the minuend, we have

$$2a - 5a = 2a + (-5a) = -3a \ (\S 74).$$

2. Subtract $-2\,a$ from $5\,a$.

$$5\,a - (-2\,a) = 5\,a + 2\,a = 7\,a.$$

3. Subtract $5\,a$ from $-2\,a$.

$$-2\,a - 5\,a = -7\,a.$$

4. Subtract $-5\,a$ from $-2\,a$.

$$-2\,a - (-5\,a) = -2\,a + 5\,a = 3\,a.$$

5. From $-23\,a$ take the sum of $19\,a$ and $-5\,a$.

It is convenient to *change the sign of each expression which is to be subtracted*, and then add the results.

We then have $-23\,a - 19\,a + 5\,a$, or $-37\,a$.

79. Subtraction of Polynomials.

By § 36, (1) and (3), § 24, hold for any values of the letters.

Hence, *to subtract a polynomial, we change the sign of each of its terms, and add the result to the minuend.*

1. Subtract $7\,ab^2 - 9\,a^2b + 8\,b^3$ from $5\,a^3 - 2\,a^2b + 4\,ab^2$.

It is convenient to place the subtrahend under the minuend, so that similar terms shall be in the same vertical column.

We then change the sign of each term of the subtrahend, and add the result to the minuend; thus,

$$5\,a^3 - 2\,a^2b + 4\,ab^2$$
$$\underline{\quad\ \ -9\,a^2b + 7\,ab^2 + 8\,b^3}$$
$$5\,a^3 + 7\,a^2b - 3\,ab^2 - 8\,b^3.$$

The student should perform *mentally* the operation of changing the sign of each term of the subtrahend.

2. Subtract the sum of $9\,x^2 - 8\,x + x^3$ and $5 - x^2 + x$ from $6\,x^3 - 7\,x - 4$.

We change the sign of each expression which is to be subtracted, and add the results.

$$6\,x^3 \qquad\quad\ -7\,x - 4$$
$$-x^3 - 9\,x^2 + 8\,x$$
$$\underline{\quad +\ \ x^2 -\ \ x - 5}$$
$$5\,x^3 - 8\,x^2 \qquad\quad\ -9.$$

80. By § 78, subtracting $+a$ is the same thing as adding $-a$, and subtracting $-a$ the same thing as adding $+a$.

That is, $-(+a) = +(-a)$, and $-(-a) = +(+a)$.

In these results, the signs within the parentheses are signs of *affection* (§ 39), and those without signs of *operation.*

Comparing the results with those of § 58, where all the signs are signs of affection, we see that the signs $+$ and $-$, when used as signs of affection, are subject to the same laws as when used as signs of operation.

Thus the meaning attached to the signs $+$ and $-$, in § 39, is consistent with their meaning as symbols of operation.

PARENTHESES

81. Removal of Parentheses.

It follows from § 12, II, and § 24, (5), that:

Parentheses preceded by a $+$ sign may be removed without changing the signs of the terms enclosed.

Again, it follows from § 24, (1) and (3), that:

Parentheses preceded by a $-$ sign may be removed if the sign of each term enclosed be changed, from $+$ to $-$, or from $-$ to $+$.

The above rules apply equally to the removal of the *brackets, braces,* or *vinculum* (§ 5).

It should be noticed, in the case of the latter, that the sign apparently prefixed to the first term underneath is in reality prefixed to the vinculum. Thus, $+\overline{a-b}$ and $-\overline{a-b}$ are equivalent to $+(a-b)$ and $-(a-b)$, respectively.

Parentheses often enclose others; in this case they may be removed in succession by the rules of § 81.

Beginners should remove one at a time, commencing with the *innermost* pair; but after a little practice they should be able to remove several signs of aggregation at one operation, in which case they should commence with the outermost pair.

Ex. Simplify $4x - \{3x + (-2x - \overline{x-a})\}$.

We remove the vinculum first, then the parentheses, and finally the braces.

Thus,
$$4x - \{3x + (-2x - \overline{x-a})\}$$
$$= 4x - \{3x + (-2x - x + a)\}$$
$$= 4x - \{3x - 2x - x + a\}$$
$$= 4x - 3x + 2x + x - a = 4x - a.$$

82. Insertion of Parentheses.

To *enclose* terms in parentheses, we take the converse of the rules of § 81.

Any number of terms may be enclosed in parentheses preceded by a + sign, without changing their signs.

Any number of terms may be enclosed in parentheses preceded by a − sign, if the sign of each term be changed, from + to −, or from − to +.

Ex. Enclose the last three terms of $a - b + c - d + e$ in parentheses preceded by a − sign.

Result, $a - b - (-c + d - e).$

EXERCISE I

1. Add $5(a+b)$, $-4(x-y)$, $-6(a+b)$, $3(x-y)$, $-7(x-y)$, and $8(a+b)$.

2. Add $7m^2 - 2p - 8n^3$, $5n^3 - m^2$, and $3xy - 4m^2 + 2n^3$.

3. Add $a - 9 - 8a^2 + 16a^3$, $5 + 15a^3 - 12a - 2a^2$, and $6a^2 - 10a^3 + 11a - 13$.

4. Add $14(x+y) - 17(y+z)$, $4(y+z) - 19(z+x)$, and $-7(z+x) - 3(x+y)$.

5. Add $\frac{3}{2}x - \frac{4}{3}y - \frac{5}{4}z$, $-\frac{1}{4}x + y + \frac{2}{5}z$, and $-\frac{7}{8}x - \frac{6}{7}y + \frac{1}{2}z$.

6. Subtract the sum of $8(m+n)$ and $-15(m+n)$ from $-19(m+n)$.

7. Subtract $3b - 6d - 10c + 7a$ from $4d + 12a - 13c - 9b$.

8. Subtract $41x^3 - 2x^2 + 13$ from $15x^3 + x - 18$.

9. Subtract $\frac{7}{3}p - \frac{5}{2}m - \frac{3}{4}n$ from $\frac{3}{5}m - \frac{2}{7}p - \frac{1}{3}n$.

10. Subtract the sum of $4x^2 - 9y^2 + 6z^2$ and $2x^2 + 8y^2 - 11z^2$ from $7x^2 - 3y^2 - 5z^2$.

11. From the sum of $2a + 3b - 4c$ and $3b + 4c - 5d$ subtract the sum of $5c - 6d - 7a$ and $-7d + 8a + 9b$.

Simplify the following :

12. $9\,m - (3\,n + \{4\,m - [n - 6\,m]\} - [m + 7\,n])$.

13. $2\,a + (-6\,b - \{3\,c + (-4\,b - \overline{6\,c + a})\}]$.

14. $7\,x - (-6\,x - \{-5\,x - [-4\,x - \overline{3\,x - 2}]\})$.

15. $5\,n - [8\,n - (3\,n + 6) - \{-6\,n + \overline{7\,n - 5}\}]$.

16. $4\,a - [a - \{-7\,a - (8\,a - \overline{5\,a + 3}) - (-6\,a - \overline{2\,a - 9})\}]$.

17. $x - \{-12\,y - [2\,x + (-4\,y - \{-7\,x - 5\,y\} - \overline{6\,x - 9\,y}) - \overline{8\,x + y}]\}$.

18. Enclose the last three terms of $a + b - c + d - e$ in parentheses preceded by a − sign, and in the result enclose the last two terms in parentheses in brackets preceded by a − sign.

IV. MULTIPLICATION OF ALGEBRAIC EXPRESSIONS

83. **The Rule of Signs.**

The results (8), (9), and (12), § 40, hold when a and b are any positive numbers.

From these results we may state what is called the **Rule of Signs** in multiplication, as follows :

The product of two terms of like sign is positive; the product of two terms of unlike sign is negative.

84. We have by § 40, (12),

$$(-a) \times (-b) \times (-c) = (ab) \times (-c)$$
$$= -abc; \tag{1}$$
$$(-a) \times (-b) \times (-c) \times (-d) = (-abc) \times (-d), \text{ by (1)},$$
$$= abcd; \text{ etc.}$$

That is, the product of three negative terms is negative; the product of four negative terms is positive; and so on.

In general, *the product of any number of terms is positive or negative according as the number of negative terms is even or odd.*

85. **The Index Law.**

Let it be required to multiply a^3 by a^2.

By § 60, $\qquad\qquad a^3 = a \times a \times a,$

and $\qquad\qquad\qquad a^2 = a \times a.$

Whence, $\qquad\qquad a^3 \times a^2 = a \times a \times a \times a \times a = a^5.$

We will now consider the general case.

Let it be required to multiply a^m by a^n, where m and n are any positive integers.

We have $\qquad a^m = a \times a \times \cdots$ to m factors,

and, $\qquad\qquad a^n = a \times a \times \cdots$ to n factors.

Then, $\quad a^m \times a^n = a \times a \times \cdots$ to $m + n$ factors $= a^{m+n}$.

Hence, *the exponent of a letter in the product is equal to its exponent in the multiplicand plus its exponent in the multiplier.*

This is called the *Index Law for Multiplication.*

A similar result holds for the product of three or more powers of the same letter.

Thus, $a^3 \times a^4 \times a^5 = a^{3+4+5} = a^{12}$.

86. Multiplication of Monomials.

1. Let it be required to multiply $7\,a$ by $-2\,b$.

By § 72, $\qquad -2\,b = (-2) \times b$.

Then, $\qquad 7\,a \times (-2\,b) = 7\,a \times (-2) \times b$.

Then by the Commutative Law for Multiplication (§ 14),

$7\,a \times (-2\,b) = 7 \times (-2) \times a \times b = -14\,ab$ (§ 83).

2. Required the product of $-2\,a^2b^3$, $6\,ab^5$, and $-7\,a^4c$.

$(-2\,a^2b^3) \times 6\,ab^5 \times (-7\,a^4c)$

$\qquad = (-2)\,a^2b^3 \times 6\,ab^5 \times (-7)\,a^4c$

$\qquad = (-2) \times 6 \times (-7) \times a^2 \times a \times b^3 \times b^5 \times c$

$\qquad = 84\,a^3b^8c$, by §§ 84 and 85.

We then have the following rule for the product of any number of monomials:

To the product of the numerical coefficients (§§ 72, 84, 85) *annex the letters; giving to each an exponent equal to the sum of its exponents in the factors.*

3. Multiply $-5\,a^3b$ by $-8\,ab^3$.

$(-5\,a^3b) \times (-8\,ab^3) = 40\,a^{3+1}b^{1+3} = 40\,a^4b^4$.

4. Find the product of $4\,n^2$, $-3\,n^5$, and $2\,n^4$.

$4\,n^2 \times (-3\,n^5) \times 2\,n^4 = -24\,n^{2+5+4} = -24\,n^{11}$.

5. Multiply $-x^m$ by $7\,x^6$, m being a positive integer.

$(-x^m) \times 7\,x^6 = -7\,x^{m+6}$.

6. Multiply $6\,(m+n)^4$ by $7\,(m+n)^3$.

$6\,(m+n)^4 \times 7\,(m+n)^3 = 42\,(m+n)^7$.

87. Multiplication of Polynomials by Monomials.

By §§ 14, III, and 24, (7), we have the following rule for the product of a polynomial by a monomial:

Multiply each term of the multiplicand by the multiplier, and add the partial products.

Ex. Multiply $2\,x^2 - 5\,x + 7$ by $-8\,x^3$.

$$(2\,x^2 - 5\,x + 7) \times (-8\,x^3)$$
$$= (2\,x^2) \times (-8\,x^3) + (-5\,x) \times (-8\,x^3) + (7) \times (-8\,x^3)$$
$$= -16\,x^5 + 40\,x^4 - 56\,x^3.$$

The student should endeavor to put down the final result in one operation.

88. Multiplication of Polynomials by Polynomials.

By the Distributive Law for Multiplication (§ 14),

$$(a + b) \times (c + d) = (a + b) \times c + (a + b) \times d$$
$$= ac + bc + ad + bd;$$

and a similar result holds whatever the number of terms in the multiplicand or multiplier.

We then have the following rule:

Multiply each term of the multiplicand by each term of the multiplier, and add the partial products.

1. Multiply $3\,a - 4\,b$ by $2\,a - 5\,b$.

In accordance with the rule, we multiply $3\,a - 4\,b$ by $2\,a$, and then by $-5\,b$, and add the partial products.

A convenient arrangement of the work is shown below, similar terms being in the same vertical column.

$$\begin{array}{r} 3\,a - 4\,b \\ 2\,a - 5\,b \\ \hline 6\,a^2 - 8\,ab \\ -15\,ab + 20\,b^2 \\ \hline 6\,a^2 - 23\,ab + 20\,b^2. \end{array}$$

The work may be *verified* by performing the example with the multiplicand and multiplier interchanged.

2. Multiply $4\,ax^2 + a^3 - 8\,x^3 - 2\,a^2x$ by $2\,x + a$.

It is convenient to arrange the multiplicand and multiplier in the same order of powers of some common letter (§ 76), and write the partial products in the same order.

Arranging the expressions according to the descending powers of a, we have

$$a^3 - 2\,a^2x + 4\,ax^2 - 8\,x^3$$
$$a + 2\,x$$
$$\overline{a^4 - 2\,a^3x + 4\,a^2x^2 - 8\,ax^3}$$
$$2\,a^3x - 4\,a^2x^2 + 8\,ax^3 - 16\,x^4$$
$$\overline{a^4 \qquad\qquad\qquad\qquad\quad - 16\,x^4.}$$

If the multiplicand and multiplier are arranged in order of powers of a certain letter, with *literal* coefficients, the operation may sometimes be abridged by the use of parentheses.

3. Multiply $x^2 - ax - bx - ab$ by $x - a$.

By § 87, $-ax - bx$ can be written $-(a + b)x$.

$$x^2 - \quad (a + b)x - ab$$
$$x - a$$
$$\overline{x^3 - \quad (a + b)x^2 - \qquad abx}$$
$$- \qquad\quad ax^2 + (a^2 + ab)x + a^2b$$
$$\overline{x^3 - (2\,a + b)x^2 + \qquad\quad a^2x + a^2b.}$$

4. Multiply $x - m$ by $x + n$.

$$x - m$$
$$x + n$$
$$\overline{x^2 - \qquad\quad mx}$$
$$+ \qquad\quad nx - mn$$
$$\overline{x^2 + (-m + n)x - mn.}$$

It is convenient to write the coefficient of x in parentheses, when adding the terms $-mx$ and nx.

89. Homogeneity.

If the multiplicand and multiplier are *homogeneous* (§ 65), the product will also be homogeneous, and its degree equal to the sum of the degrees of the multiplicand and multiplier.

For if each term of the multiplicand is of the mth degree (§ 64), and each term of the multiplier of the nth degree, each term of the product will be of the $(m + n)$th degree (§ 85).

The examples in § 88 are instances of the above law; thus in Ex. 2, the multiplicand, multiplier, and product are homogeneous, and of the third, first, and fourth degrees, respectively.

The student should always, when possible, apply the principles of homogeneity to test the accuracy of algebraic work.

Thus, if two homogeneous expressions be multiplied together, and the product obtained is not homogeneous, it is evident that the work is not correct.

90. Multiplication by Detached Coefficients.

In finding the product of two expressions which are arranged according to the same order of powers of some common letter, the operation may be abridged by writing only the *numerical coefficients* of the terms.

1. Multiply $3\,x^2 + 5\,x - 4$ by $2\,x^2 - 7\,x + 1$.

$$
\begin{array}{r}
3 + 5 - 4 \\
2 - 7 + 1 \\
\hline
6 + 10 - 8 \\
-21 - 35 + 28 \\
3 + 5 - 4 \\
\hline
6 - 11 - 40 + 33 - 4.
\end{array}
$$

We know that the exponent of x in the first term is 4.

Then, the product is $6\,x^4 - 11\,x^3 - 40\,x^2 + 33\,x - 4$.

If the term involving any power be wanting, it may be supplied with the coefficient 0.

2. Multiply $4\,a^3 + 6\,ax^2 - 7\,x^3$ by $2\,a^2 - 3\,x^2$.

In this case the term involving a^2x in the multiplicand and the term involving ax in the multiplier are wanting.

$$\begin{array}{r} 4+0+ 6- 7 \\ 2+0- 3 \\ \hline 8+0+12-14 \\ -12+.0-18+21 \\ \hline 8+0+ 0-14-18+21. \end{array}$$

We know that the product is homogeneous (§ 89), and that the exponent of a in the first term is 5.

Then, the product is $8\,a^5 - 14\,a^2x^3 - 18\,ax^4 + 21\,x^5$.

3. Find the value of $(2\,x - 3)(3\,x + 5)(6\,x - 1)$.

$$\begin{array}{r} 2\ -\ 3 \\ 3\ +\ 5 \\ \hline 6\ -\ 9 \\ +10-15 \\ \hline 6\ +\ 1-15 \\ 6\ -\ 1 \\ \hline 36\ +\ 6-90 \\ -\ 6-\ 1\ +15 \\ \hline 36\,x^3\qquad -91\,x+15. \end{array}$$

Result,

91. By § 83,

$$(+a) \times (+b) = +ab,\ (+a) \times (-b) = -ab,$$
$$(-a) \times (-b) = +ab,\ (-a) \times (+b) = -ab.$$

Hence, in the indicated product of two monomial expressions, *the signs of both expressions may be changed without altering the product; but if the sign of either one be changed, the sign of the product will be changed.*

The above is true for the product of a monomial and a polynomial, or of two polynomials.

If either expression is a polynomial, care must be taken, on changing its sign, to change the sign of *each of its terms*.

For by § 81, $-(a - b + c) = -a + b - c.$

Thus, $(a - b)(c - d)$ may be written in the forms

$$(b - a)(d - c),\quad -(b - a)(c - d),\quad \text{or}\quad -(a - b)(d - c).$$

In like manner it may be shown that, in the indicated product of more than two expressions, *the signs of any* **even** *number of them may be changed without altering the product; but if the signs of any* **odd** *number of them be changed, the sign of the product will be changed* (§ 84).

Thus, $(a-b)(c-d)(e-f)$ may be written in the forms

$$(a-b)(d-c)(f-e),$$
$$(b-a)(c-d)(f-e),$$
$$-(b-a)(d-c)(f-e), \text{ etc.}$$

EXERCISE 2

Multiply the following:

1. $x^3 - 6x^2 + 12x - 8$ and $x^2 + 4x + 4$.
2. $n - 5n^2 + 2 + n^3$ and $5n + n^2 - 10$.
3. $3(a+b)^2 - (a+b) + 2$ and $4(a+b)^2 - (a+b) - 5$.
4. $4x^{3m+2}y^{n-5} + 5x^{m+5}y^{3n-7}$ and $3x^{2m-1}y^3 - 7x^2y^{2n+1}$.
5. $x^2 - (m-n)x - mn$ and $x - p$.
6. $x^2 + ax - bx - ab$ and $x + b$.
7. $a^3 + 3 + 5a^4 - 6a - 2a^2$ and $6 + 2a^2 - a$.
8. $mx + my - nx - ny$ and $mx - my + nx - ny$.
9. $2x - 3y$, $3x + 2y$, $2x + 3y$, and $3x - 2y$.
10. $x + a$, $x + b$, and $x - c$.
11. $\frac{2}{3}m^2 - \frac{3}{4}m - 1$ and $\frac{1}{2}m^2 + \frac{1}{3}m - \frac{4}{9}$.
12. $x^2 - (a+b)x + ab$ and $x^2 - (c-d)x - cd$.
13. $a + b + c$, $a - b + c$, and $a + b - c$.

Simplify the following:

14. $[3x - (5y + 2z)][3x - (5y - 2z)]$.
15. $[(m+2n) - (2m-n)][(2m+n) - (m-2n)]$.
16. $[2x^2 + (3x-1)(4x+5)][5x^2 - (4x+3)(x-2)]$.
17. $(a-b)(a^3+b^3)[a(a+b)+b^2]$.

V. DIVISION OF ALGEBRAIC EXPRESSIONS

In the present chapter, we shall consider those cases only in which the Dividend, Divisor, and Quotient are rational and integral (§ 63).

In such cases, the division is said to be *exact*, and the dividend is said to be *divisible* by the divisor.

92. The **Reciprocal** of a number is 1 divided by that number.

Thus, the reciprocal of a is $\frac{1}{a}$.

93. We have $\qquad a \times 1 = a.$

Regarding a as the quotient, 1 as the divisor, and a as the dividend, we have

$$\frac{a}{1} = a.$$

94. By § 30, (1), $\quad \dfrac{a}{b} = \dfrac{a}{1} \times \dfrac{1}{b} = a \times \dfrac{1}{b}$ (§ 93).

Hence, *to divide by a number is the same thing as to multiply by its reciprocal* (§ 92).

95. The **Commutative Law for Division.**

By § 94, every operation in Division can be expressed as an operation in Multiplication.

Thus, if a is to be divided by b, c, · , in succession, the result is

$$a \times \frac{1}{b} \times \frac{1}{c} \times \cdots.$$

It follows from this, by § 14, I, that if a number is to be divided by any number of numbers in succession, the divisions can be performed in any order.

This is the *Commutative Law for Division*.

It may be expressed as follows:

$$(a \div b) \div c \cdots = (a \div c) \div b \cdots, \text{ etc.}$$

96. By § 14, I, II, $\quad b(ac) = a(bc).$

Then by § 31, $\dfrac{ac}{bc} = \dfrac{a}{b}.$ (1)

That is, *a factor common to the dividend and divisor can be removed, or cancelled.*

Putting $b = 1$, in (1), we have

$$\frac{ac}{c} = \frac{a}{1} = a \quad (\text{§ 93}).$$

That is, *if a number be both multiplied and divided by another, the value of the former will not be changed.*

97. The Rule of Signs.

From the results (1), (2), and (3), § 48, we may state the **Rule of Signs** in Division, as follows:

The quotient of two terms of like sign is positive; the quotient of two terms of unlike sign is negative.

98. The Index Law for Division.

Let it be required to divide a^5 by a^2.

By § 60, $\dfrac{a^5}{a^2} = \dfrac{a \times a \times a \times a \times a}{a \times a}.$

Cancelling the common factor $a \times a$ (§ 96), we have

$$\frac{a^5}{a^2} = a \times a \times a = a^3.$$

We will now consider the general case:

Let it be required to divide a^m by a^n, where m and n are any positive integers such that m is $> n$.

We have, $\dfrac{a^m}{a^n} = \dfrac{a \times a \times a \times \ \cdots \ \text{to } m \text{ factors}}{a \times a \times a \times \ \cdots \ \text{to } n \text{ factors}}.$

Cancelling the common factor $a \times a \times a \times \ \cdots$ to n factors,

$$\frac{a^m}{a^n} = a \times a \times a \times \ \cdots \ \text{to } m - n \text{ factors}$$
$$= a^{m-n}.$$

Then, *the exponent of a letter in the quotient is equal to its exponent in the dividend, minus its exponent in the divisor.*

This is called the *Index Law for Division.*

99. Division of Monomials.

1. Let it be required to divide $-14\,a^2b$ by $7\,a^2$.

By § 86, $\qquad \dfrac{-14\,a^2b}{7\,a^2} = \dfrac{(-2)\times 7\times a^2\times b}{7\times a^2}.$

Cancelling the common factors 7 and a^2, we have

$$\frac{-14\,a^2b}{7\,a^2} = (-2)\times b = -2\,b.$$

We then have the following rule for the quotient of two monomials :

To the quotient of the numerical coefficients annex the letters, giving to each an exponent equal to its exponent in the dividend minus its exponent in the divisor, and omitting any letter having the same exponent in the dividend and divisor.

2. Divide $54\,a^5b^3c^2$ by $-9\,a^4b^3$.

$$\frac{54\,a^5b^3c^2}{-9\,a^4b^3} = -6\,a^{5-4}c^2 = -6\,ac^2.$$

3. Divide $-2\,x^{2m}y^nz^r$ by $-x^my^nz^5$; m, n, and r being positive integers, and $r > 5$.

$$\frac{-2\,x^{2m}y^nz^r}{-x^my^nz^5} = 2\,x^{2m-m}z^{r-5} = 2\,x^mz^{r-5}.$$

4. Divide $35\,(a-b)^7$ by $7\,(a-b)^4$.

$$\frac{35\,(a-b)^7}{7\,(a-b)^4} = 5\,(a-b)^3.$$

100. Division of Polynomials by Monomials.

By § 94,

$$\frac{b+c-d}{a} = (b+c-d)\frac{1}{a}$$

$$= b\cdot\frac{1}{a} + c\cdot\frac{1}{a} - d\cdot\frac{1}{a}, \text{ by §§ 14, III, and 24, (7)},$$

$$= \frac{b}{a} + \frac{c}{a} - \frac{d}{a}, \text{ by § 94}.$$

Hence, *to divide a polynomial by a monomial, we divide each term of the dividend by the divisor, and add the results.*

This is called the *Distributive Law for Division.*

1. Divide $9\,a^2b^2 - 6\,a^4c + 12\,a^3bc^3$ by $-3\,a^2$.

$$\frac{9\,a^2b^2 - 6\,a^4c + 12\,a^3bc^3}{-3\,a^2} = \frac{9\,a^2b^2}{-3\,a^2} + \frac{-6\,a^4c}{-3\,a^2} + \frac{12\,a^3bc^3}{-3\,a^2}$$

$$= -3\,b^2 + 2\,a^2c - 4\,abc^3.$$

The student should endeavor to put down the result in one operation.

2. Divide $35\,(x+y)^5 - 20\,(x+y)^4$ by $5\,(x+y)^3$.

$$\frac{35\,(x+y)^5 - 20\,(x+y)^4}{5\,(x+y)^3} = 7\,(x+y)^2 - 4\,(x+y).$$

101. Division of Polynomials by Polynomials.

Ex. Let it be required to divide $12 + 10\,x^3 - 11\,x - 21\,x^2$ by $2\,x^2 - 4 - 3\,x$.

Arranging the expressions according to the descending powers of x (§ 76), we are to find an expression which, when multiplied by $2\,x^2 - 3\,x - 4$, will produce $10\,x^3 - 21\,x^2 - 11\,x + 12$.

It is evident that the term containing the highest power of x in the product is the product of the terms containing the highest powers of x in the multiplicand and multiplier.

Therefore, $10\,x^3$ is the product of $2\,x^2$ and the term containing the highest power of x in the quotient.

Whence, the term containing the highest power of x in the quotient is $10\,x^3$ divided by $2\,x^2$, or $5\,x$.

Multiplying the divisor by $5\,x$, we have the product $10\,x^3 - 15\,x^2 - 20\,x$; which, when subtracted from the dividend, leaves the remainder $-6\,x^2 + 9\,x + 12$.

This remainder must be the product of the divisor by the rest of the quotient; therefore, to obtain the next term of the quotient, we regard $-6\,x^2 + 9\,x + 12$ as a new dividend.

Dividing the term containing the highest power of x, $-6\,x^2$, by the term containing the highest power of x in the divisor, $2\,x^2$, we obtain -3 as the second term of the quotient.

Multiplying the divisor by -3, we have the product $-6\,x^2 + 9\,x + 12$; which, when subtracted from the second dividend, leaves no remainder.

Hence, $5\,x - 3$ is the required quotient.

DIVISION

DIVISION 43

It is customary to arrange the work as follows:

$$10\,x^3 - 21\,x^2 - 11\,x + 12 \mid 2\,x^2 - 3\,x - 4,\ \text{Divisor.}$$
$$\underline{10\,x^3 - 15\,x^2 - 20\,x} \mid \overline{5\,x - 3,\ \text{Quotient.}}$$
$$-\ 6\,x^2 +\ 9\,x + 12$$
$$-\ 6\,x^2 +\ 9\,x + 12$$

The example might have been solved by arranging the dividend and divisor according to *ascending* powers of x.

102. From § 101, we derive the following rule:

Arrange the dividend and divisor in the same order of powers of some common letter.

Divide the first term of the dividend by the first term of the divisor, and write the result as the first term of the quotient.

Multiply the whole divisor by the first term of the quotient, and subtract the product from the dividend.

If there be a remainder, regard it as a new dividend, and proceed as before; arranging the remainder in the same order of powers as the dividend and divisor.

1. Divide $9\,ab^2 + a^3 - 9\,b^3 - 5\,a^2b$ by $3\,b^2 + a^2 - 2\,ab$.

Arranging according to the descending powers of a,

$$a^3 - 5\,a^2b + 9\,ab^2 - 9\,b^3 \mid a^2 - 2\,ab + 3\,b^2$$
$$\underline{a^3 - 2\,a^2b + 3\,ab^2} \mid \overline{a - 3\,b}$$
$$-\ 3\,a^2b + 6\,ab^2$$
$$-\ 3\,a^2b + 6\,ab^2 - 9\,b^3$$

In the above example, the last term of the second dividend is omitted, as it is merely a repetition of the term directly above.

The work may be verified by multiplying the quotient by the divisor, which should of course give the dividend.

2. Divide $4 + 9\,x^4 - 28\,x^2$ by $-3\,x^2 + 2 + 4\,x$.

Arranging according to the ascending powers of x,

$$4 - 28\,x^2 +\ 9\,x^4 \mid 2 + 4\,x - 3\,x^2$$
$$\underline{4 +\ 8\,x -\ 6\,x^2} \mid \overline{2 - 4\,x - 3\,x^2}$$
$$-\ 8\,x - 22\,x^2 +\ 9\,x^4$$
$$-\ 8\,x - 16\,x^2 + 12\,x^3$$
$$-\ 6\,x^2 - 12\,x^3 + 9\,x^4$$
$$-\ 6\,x^2 - 12\,x^3 + 9\,x^4$$

3. Divide $x^3 + (a + b - c)x^2 + (ab - bc - ca)x - abc$ by $x + a$.

$$
\begin{array}{l|l}
x^3 + (a + b - c)x^2 + (ab - bc - ca)x - abc & \;x\; + a \\
\underline{x^3 + \qquad\qquad ax^2} & \;x^2 + (b - c)x - bc \\
\quad (b - c)x^2 \\
\quad \underline{(b - c)x^2 + (ab \qquad\quad - ca)x} \\
\qquad\qquad\qquad\quad -\;bcx \\
\qquad\qquad\qquad\quad \underline{-\;bcx\; - abc}
\end{array}
$$

103. It is evident from § 89 that, if the dividend and divisor are *homogeneous*, the quotient will also be homogeneous, and its degree equal to the degree of the dividend minus the degree of the divisor.

104. Division by Detached Coefficients.

In finding the quotient of two expressions which are arranged according to the same order of powers of some common letter,' the operation may be abridged by writing only the *numerical coefficients* of the terms.

If the term involving any power is wanting, it may be supplied with the coefficient 0.

Ex. Divide $6\,x^6 + 2\,x^5 - 9\,x^4 + 5\,x^2 + 18\,x - 30$ by $3\,x^3 + x^2 - 6$.

$$
\begin{array}{l|l}
6 + 2 - 9 + \;\;0 + 5 + 18 - 30 & 3 + 1 + 0 - 6 \\
\underline{6 + 2 + 0 - 12} & 2 + 0 - 3 + 5 \\
\quad -9 + 12 \\
\quad \underline{-9 - \;\;3 + 0 + 18} \\
\qquad\quad 15 + 5 \\
\qquad\quad \underline{15 + 5 + \;\;0 - 30}
\end{array}
$$

Then the quotient is $2\,x^3 - 3\,x + 5$.

105. By § 37, (6), if a is any number,

$$0 \times a = 0.$$

Regarding 0 as the quotient, a as the divisor, and 0 as the dividend, we have

$$\frac{0}{a} = 0.$$

Divide the following :

1. $x^6 + 37 x^2 - 70 x + 50$ by $x^2 - 2 x + 10$.

2. $6(x - y)^2 - 7(x - y) - 20$ by $3(x - y) + 4$.

3. $a^{3p+1}b^2 + ab^{3q+2}$ by $a^{p+1}b^2 + ab^{q+2}$; p and q being positive integers.

4. $a^5 - b^5 - 5 a^4 b + 5 ab^4 + 10 a^3 b^2 - 10 a^2 b^3$ by $a^3 - b^3 - 3 a^2 b + 3 ab^2$.

5. $6 n^5 + 25 n^4 - 7 n^3 - 81 n^2 - 3 n + 28$ by $2 n^3 + 5 n^2 - 8 n - 7$.

6. $23 x^2 - 5 x^4 - 12 + 12 x^5 + 8 \dot{x} - 14 x^3$ by $x - 2 + 3 x^2$.

7. $16(a + b)^4 - 81$ by $2(a + b) - 3$.

8. $8 x^6 - 4 x^5 - 2 x^4 + 15 x^3 + 3 x^2 - 5 x - 15$ by $4 x^3 - x - 3$.

9. $a^3 + b^3 - c^3 + 3 abc$ by $a + b - c$.

10. $\dfrac{4}{9} m^4 - 2 m^3 + \dfrac{9}{4} m^2 - \dfrac{1}{16}$ by $\dfrac{2}{3} m^2 - \dfrac{3}{2} m - \dfrac{1}{4}$.

11. $52 x^3 + 64 + 18 x^4 - 200 x^2 + x^5$ by $6 x^2 - 8 + x^3 - 12 x$.

12. $a^6 - 6 a^4 n^2 + 9 a^2 n^4 - 4 n^6$ by $a^3 - 2 a^2 n - an^2 + 2 n^3$.

13. $x^3 - (a - b + c)x^2 - (ab - ac + bc)x + abc$ by $x^2 - (a - b)x - ab$.

14. $x^3 + (a - b + c)x^2 + (- ab + ac - bc)x - abc$ by $x + c$.

15. $x^3 + (4 a + 2 b + 3 c)x^2 + (8 ab + 12 ac + 6 bc)x + 24 abc$ by $x^2 + (4 a + 3 c)x + 12 ac$.

16. $x^3 - (a + 3 b + 2 c)x^2 + (3 ab + 2 ac + 6 bc)x - 6 abc$ by $x - 3 b$.

17. $(2 m^2 + 10 mn) x^2 + (8 m^2 - 9 mn - 15 n^2) x - (12 mn - 9 n^2)$ by $2 mx - 3 n$.

18. $x^4 - (4 a + 3)x^3 + (12 a - 5 b + 2)x^2 - (8 a - 15 b)x - 10 b$ by $x^2 - 3 x + 2$.

VI. INTEGRAL LINEAR EQUATIONS

106. The *First Member* of an equation is the expression to the left of the sign of equality, and the *Second Member* the expression to the right of that sign.

Thus, in $2\,x-3=3\,x+5$, the first member is $2\,x-3$ and the second member $3\,x+5$.

Any term of either member of an equation is called a *term* of the equation.

The *sides* of an equation are its two members.

107. An **Identical Equation**, or **Identity**, is an equation whose members are the same, or become the same after all the indicated operations have been performed; as,

$$5=5, \text{ or } (a+b)(a-b)=a^2-b^2.$$

The sign $\equiv$, read "*is identically equal to*," is frequently used in place of the sign of equality in an identity.

It is evident that, in an identity involving letters, the members are equal whatever values are given to the letters, provided the same value is given to the same letter wherever it occurs.

All equations considered up to the present time have been identical equations.

108. An equation is said to be *satisfied* by a set of values of certain letters involved in it when, on substituting the value of each letter in place of the letter wherever it occurs, the equation becomes identical.

Thus, the equation $x-y=5$ is satisfied by the set of values $x=8$, $y=3$; for, on substituting 8 for x, and 3 for y, the equation becomes

$$8-3=5, \text{ or } 5=5; \text{ which is identical.}$$

109. An **Equation of Condition** is an equation involving one or more letters, called **Unknown Numbers**, which is satisfied only by particular values, or sets of values, of these letters.

Thus, the equation $x + 2 = 5$ is satisfied by the value $x = 3$; but nòt by the value $x = 5$.

Again, the equation $x + y = 7$ is satisfied by the set of values $x = 4$, $y = 3$; but not by the set of values $x = 6$, $y = 9$.

An equation of condition is usually called an *equation*.

Any letter in an equation of condition may represent an unknown number; but it is usual to represent unknown numbers by the last letters of the alphabet.

110. Any letter, or set of letters, which satisfies an equation is called a **Solution** of the equation.

If the equation contains but one unknown number, its solutions are called **Roots**.

A solution is *verified* when, on substituting the values of the unknown numbers, and performing the operations indicated, the equation becomes identical.

To *solve* an equation, or a system of equations, is to find its solutions.

111. A **Numerical Equation** is one in which all the known numbers are represented by Arabic numerals; as,

$$2x - 7 = x + 6.$$

A **Literal Equation** is one in which some or all of the known numbers are represented by letters; as,

$$3x + a = 5x - 2b.$$

An **Integral Equation** is one each of whose members is a rational and integral expression (§ 63); as,

$$4x - 5 = \frac{2}{3}y + 1.$$

112. If a rational and integral monomial (§ 63) involves a certain letter, its *degree with respect to it* is denoted by its exponent.

If it involves two letters, its *degree with respect to them* is denoted by the sum of their exponents; etc.

Thus, $2ab^4x^2y^3$ is of the *second* degree with respect to x, and of the *fifth* with respect to x and y.

113. If an integral equation (§ 111) contains one or more unknown numbers, the *degree* of the equation is the degree of its term of highest degree.

Thus, if x and y represent unknown numbers,

$ax - by = c$, is an equation of the *first* degree;

$x^2 + 4\,x = -2$, an equation of the *second* degree;

$2\,x^2 - 3\,xy^2 = 5$, an equation of the *third* degree; etc.

A **Linear Equation** is an equation of the first degree.

114. Two equations, each involving one or more unknown numbers, are said to be **Equivalent** when every solution of the first is a solution of the second, and every solution of the second a solution of the first.

115. The following are of use in solving equations:

1. *If the same number (or equal numbers) be added to equal numbers, the sums will be equal.*

2. *If the same number (or equal numbers) be subtracted from equal numbers, the remainders will be equal.*

These follow from § 22.

3. *If equal numbers be multiplied by the same number (or equal numbers), the products will be equal* (§ 29).

4. *If equal numbers be divided by the same number (or equal numbers), the quotients will be equal, provided the divisor is not* 0.

This follows from § 29; compare § 43.

PRINCIPLES USED IN SOLVING INTEGRAL EQUATIONS

116. Addition.

If the same expression be added to both members of an equation, the resulting equation will be equivalent to the first.

Consider, for example, the equation

$$A = B. \tag{1}$$

To prove that the equation

$$A + C = B + C, \tag{2}$$

where C is any expression, is equivalent to (1).

Any solution of (1), when substituted for the unknown numbers, makes A identically equal to B (§ 108).

It then makes $A + C$ identically equal to $B + C$ (§ 115, 1).

Then it is a solution of (2).

Again, any solution of (2), when substituted for the unknown numbers, makes $A + C$ identically equal to $B + C$.

It then makes A identically equal to B (§ 115, 2).

Then it is a solution of (1).

Therefore, (1) and (2) are equivalent.

The above demonstration proves that *if the same expression be subtracted from both members of an equation, the resulting equation will be equivalent to the first.*

117. Transposing Terms.

Consider the equation $x + a - b = c$.

Adding $-a$ and $+b$ to both members (§ 116), we have the equivalent equation

$$x + a - b - a + b = c - a + b.$$

Or, $\qquad\qquad x = c - a + b.$

In this case, the terms a and $-b$ are said to be *transposed* from the first member to the second.

Hence, *if any term be transposed from one member of an equation to the other by changing its sign, the resulting equation will be equivalent to the first.*

If the same term appears in both members of an equation affected with the same sign, it may be cancelled.

118. Consider the equation

$$a - x = b - c. \tag{1}$$

Transposing each term, we have the equivalent equation

$$-b + c = -a + x, \text{ or } x - a = c - b;$$

which is the same as (1) with the sign of every term changed.

Hence, *if the signs of all the terms of an equation be changed, the resulting equation will be equivalent to the first.*

119. Multiplication.

If the members of an equation be multiplied by the same expression, which is not zero, and does not involve the unknown numbers, the resulting equation will be equivalent to the first.

Consider the equation $A = B.$ (1)

To prove that the equation

$$A \times C = B \times C,   (2)$$

where C is not zero, and does not involve the unknown numbers, is equivalent to (1).

Any solution of (1), when substituted for the unknown numbers, makes A identically equal to B.

It then makes $A \times C$ identically equal to $B \times C$ (§ 115, 3).

Then it is a solution of (2).

Again, any solution of (2), when substituted for the unknown numbers, makes $A \times C$ identically equal to $B \times C$.

It then makes A identically equal to B (§ 115, 4).

Then it is a solution of (1).

Therefore, (1) and (2) are equivalent.

The reason why the above does not hold for the multiplier zero is, that the principle of § 115, 4, is restricted to cases where the divisor is not zero.

120. The necessity for limiting the principle of § 119 to cases where the multiplier does not involve the unknown numbers is that, if C contains the unknown numbers, the equation $A \times C = B \times C$ is satisfied by certain values of the unknown numbers which make $C = 0$.

But these values do not, in general, satisfy $A = B$.

Consider, for example, the equation

$$x + 2 = 3\,x - 4.   (1)$$

Now the equation

$$(x + 2)\,(x - 1) = (3\,x - 4)\,(x - 1),   (2)$$

which is obtained from (1) by multiplying both members by $x - 1$, is satisfied by the value $x = 1$, which does not satisfy (1).

Then (1) and (2) are not equivalent.

It follows from this that it is never allowable to multiply both members of an integral equation by an expression which involves the unknown numbers; for in this way additional solutions are introduced.

121. Clearing of Fractions.

Consider the equation

$$\frac{2}{3}x - \frac{5}{4} = \frac{5}{6}x - \frac{9}{8}.$$

Multiplying each term by 24, the lowest common multiple of the denominators (§ 119), we have the equivalent equation

$$16\,x - 30 = 20\,x - 27,$$

where the denominators have been removed.

Removing the fractions from an equation by multiplication is called "*clearing the equation of fractions.*"

122. Division.

If the members of an equation be divided by the same expression, which is not zero, and does not involve the unknown numbers, the resulting equation will be equivalent to the first.

Consider the equation $\quad A = B.$ $\hfill (1)$

To prove that the equation

$$A \div C = B \div C, \hfill (2)$$

where C is not zero, and does not involve the unknown numbers, is equivalent to (1).

Any solution of (1), when substituted for the unknown numbers, makes A identically equal to B.

It then makes $A \div C$ identically equal to $B \div C$ (§ 115, 4).

Then it is a solution of (2).

Again, any solution of (2), when substituted for the unknown numbers, makes $A \div C$ identically equal to $B \div C$.

It then makes A identically equal to B.

Then it is a solution of (1).

Therefore, (1) and (2) are equivalent.

123. The necessity for limiting the principle of § 122 to cases where the divisor does not involve the unknown numbers is that, if C contains the unknown numbers, the solution of $A = B$ contains certain numbers which do not, in general, satisfy $A \div C = B \div C$.

Consider, for example, the equation

$$(x + 2)\,(x - 1) = (3\,x - 4)\,(x - 1). \tag{1}$$

Also the equation $\quad x + 2 = 3\,x - 4, \tag{2}$

which is obtained from (1) by dividing both members by $x - 1$.

Now equation (1) is satisfied by the value $x = 1$, which does not satisfy (2).

Then (1) and (2) are not equivalent.

It follows from this that it is never allowable to divide both members of an integral equation by an expression which involves the unknown numbers; for in this way solutions are lost.

SOLUTION OF INTEGRAL LINEAR EQUATIONS

124. To solve an equation containing one unknown number, we put it into a succession of forms, which lead finally to a knowledge of the root or roots.

This process is called *transforming* the equation.

If every transformation is effected by means of the principles of §§ 116 to 122, the successive equations will have the same roots as the given equation, and no solutions will be introduced nor lost.

EXAMPLES

125. 1. Solve the equation

$$5\,x - 7 = 3\,x + 1.$$

Transposing $3\,x$ to the first member, and $- 7$ to the second (§ 117), we have $\quad 5\,x - 3\,x = 7 + 1.$

Uniting similar terms, $\;2\,x = 8.$

Dividing both members by 2 (§ 122),

$$x = 4.$$

To *verify* the result, put $x = 4$ in the given equation.

Thus, $20 - 7 = 12 + 1$; which is identical.

2. Solve the equation

$$\frac{7}{6} x - \frac{5}{3} = \frac{3}{5} x - \frac{1}{4}.$$

Clearing of fractions by multiplying each term by 60, the L. C. M. of 6, 3, 5, and 4, we have

$$70 x - 100 = 36 x - 15.$$

Transposing $36 x$ to the first member, and -100 to the second, and uniting similar terms,

$$34 x = 85.$$

Dividing by 34, $\quad x = \dfrac{85}{34} = \dfrac{5}{2}.$

3. Solve the equation

$$(5 - 3 x)(3 + 4 x) = 62 - (7 - 3 x)(1 - 4 x).$$

Expanding, $15 + 11 x - 12 x^2 = 62 - (7 - 31 x + 12 x^2)$

$$= 62 - 7 + 31 x - 12 x^2.$$

Cancelling the $-12 x^2$ terms (§ 117), and transposing,

$$11 x - 31 x = 62 - 7 - 15.$$

Uniting terms, $\quad -20 x = 40.$

Dividing by -20, $\quad x = -2.$

To *expand* an algebraic expression is to perform the operations indicated.

4. Solve the equation

$$.2 x + .001 - .03 x = .113 x - .0161.$$

Transposing,

$$.2 x - .03 x - .113 x = -.0161 - .001.$$

Uniting terms, $\quad .057 x = -.0171.$

Dividing by .057, $\quad x = -.3.$

From the above examples, we have the following rule for solving an integral linear equation with one unknown number:

Clear the equation of fractions, if any, by multiplying each term by the L. C. M. of the denominators of the fractional coefficients.

Remove the parentheses, if any.

Transpose the unknown terms to the first member, and the known to the second; cancelling any term which has the same coefficient in both members.

Unite similar terms, and divide both members by the coefficient of the unknown number.

The student should endeavor to apply more than one principle at one operation.

He will also find it excellent practice to verify his solutions.

EXERCISE 4

Solve the following :

1. $\dfrac{2}{5}x + \dfrac{4}{3}x - \dfrac{8}{9}x = \dfrac{38}{15}$.

2. $.05x - 1.82 - .7x = .008x - 504$.

3. $4(x+14) - 4(3x-32) = 6(x+12) - 7(x-12)$.

4. $\dfrac{5}{6}x - \dfrac{7}{8}x = \dfrac{7}{9}x - \dfrac{1}{18}x - \dfrac{55}{48}$.

5. $(5-3x)(3+4x) - (7+3x)(1-4x) = -1$.

6. $.07(8x - 5.7) = .8(5x + .86) + 1.321$.

7. $(1+3x)^2 - (5-x)^2 - 4(1-x)(3-2x) = 0$.

8. $6(x-4)^2 = 5 - (3-2x)^2 - 5(2+x)(7-2x)$.

9. $(3x-2)^3 - 9x(x-1)(3x-8) = 45x^2 - 38$.

10. $(x+4)^3 - (x-4)^3 = 2(3x-2)(4x+1)$.

11. $\dfrac{1}{3}(4+x) - \dfrac{7}{12}(1-5x) = \dfrac{3}{8}(1+2x) - \dfrac{5}{16}(2-3x)$.

12. $\dfrac{3}{4}\left[x - \dfrac{1}{2}(5x+1)\right] = \dfrac{5}{6}\left[x - \dfrac{2}{3}(3x+4)\right] + \dfrac{7}{4}$.

PROBLEMS INVOLVING INTEGRAL LINEAR EQUATIONS WITH ONE UNKNOWN NUMBER

126. For the solution of a problem by algebraic methods no general rule can be given.

The following suggestions will be found of service :

1. Represent the unknown number, or one of the unknown numbers if there are several, by x.

2. Every problem contains, explicitly or implicitly, *just as many distinct statements as there are unknown numbers involved.*

Use all but one of these to express the other unknown numbers in terms of x.

3. Use the remaining statement to form an equation.

ILLUSTRATIVE PROBLEMS

127. 1. Divide 45 into two parts such that the less part shall be one-fourth the greater.

Here there are *two* unknown numbers; the greater part and the less.

In accordance with the first suggestion of § 126, we represent the greater part by x.

The first statement of the problem is, implicitly:
The sum of the greater part and the less is 45.

The second statement is:
The less part is one-fourth the greater.

In accordance with the second suggestion of § 126, we use the *second statement* to express the less part in terms of x.

Thus, the less part is represented by $\frac{1}{4}x$.

We now, in accordance with the third suggestion, use the *first statement* to form an equation.

Thus,	$x + \frac{1}{4}x = 45.$
Clearing of fractions,	$4x + x = 180.$
Uniting terms,	$5x = 180.$
Dividing by 5,	$x = 36$, the greater part.
Then,	$\frac{1}{4}x = 9$, the less part.

2. A is 3 times as old as B, and 8 years ago he was 7 times as old. Required their ages at present.

Let	$x =$ number of years in B's age.
Then,	$3x =$ number of years in A's age.
Also,	$x - 8 =$ number of years in B's age 8 years ago,
and	$3x - 8 =$ number of years in A's age 8 years ago.

But A's age 8 years ago was 7 times B's age 8 years ago.

Whence, $3x - 8 = 7(x - 8)$.

Expanding, $3x - 8 = 7x - 56$.

Transposing, $-4x = -48$.

Dividing by -4, $x = 12$, the number of years in B's age.

Then, $3x = 36$, the number of years in A's age.

It must be carefully borne in mind that x can only represent an *abstract number*.

Thus, in Ex. 2, we do not say "let x represent B's *age*," but "let x represent the *number of years* in B's age."

3. A sum of money, amounting to \$4.32, consists of 108 coins, all dimes and cents; how many are there of each kind?

Let $x =$ the number of dimes.

Then, $108 - x =$ the number of cents.

Also, the x dimes are worth $10x$ cents.

But the entire sum amounts to 432 cents.

Whence, $10x + 108 - x = 432$.

Transposing, $9x = 324$.

Whence, $x = 36$, the number of dimes;

and $108 - x = 72$, the number of cents.

4. At what time between 3 and 4 o'clock are the hands of a watch opposite to each other?

Let $x =$ the number of minute-spaces passed over by the minute-hand from 3 o'clock to the required time.

Then since the hour-hand is 15 minute-spaces in advance of the minute-hand at 3 o'clock, $x - 15 - 30$, or $x - 45$ will represent the number of minute-spaces passed over by the hour-hand.

But the minute-hand moves 12 times as fast as the hour-hand.

Then, $x = 12(x - 45)$

                          $= 12x - 540$.

Transposing, $-11x = -540$.

Whence, $x = 49\frac{1}{11}$.

Then, the required time is $49\frac{1}{11}$ minutes after 3 o'clock.

5. Two persons, A and B, 63 miles apart, start at the same time, and travel towards each other. A travels at the rate of 4 miles an hour, and B at the rate of 3 miles an hour. How far will each have travelled when they meet?

Let $4x$ = number of miles that A travels.

Then, $3x$ = number of miles that B travels.

By the conditions, $4x + 3x = 63$.

$$7x = 63$$
$$x = 9$$

Then, $4x = 36$, number of miles that A travels,

and $3x = 27$, number of miles that B travels.

It is often advantageous, as in Ex. 5, to represent the unknown number by some *multiple* of x, instead of by x itself.

EXERCISE 5

1. Divide 66 into two parts such that $\frac{6}{7}$ the greater shall exceed $\frac{5}{8}$ the less by 21.

2. In 9 years, B will be $\frac{5}{6}$ as old as A ; and 12 years ago he was $\frac{3}{5}$ as old. What are their ages?

(Let x represent number of years in A's age 12 years ago.)

3. Divide 197 into two parts such that the smaller shall be contained in the greater 5 times, with a remainder 23.

4. After A has travelled 7 hours at the rate of 10 miles in 3 hours, B sets out to overtake him, travelling at the rate of 9 miles in 2 hours. How far will each have travelled when B overtakes A?

5. At what time between 8 and 9 o'clock are the hands of a watch together?

6. Find four consecutive odd numbers such that the product of the first and third shall be less than the product of the second and fourth by 86.

7. A sum of money, amounting to $19.30, consists of $2 bills, 25-cent pieces, and 5-cent pieces. There are 13 more 5-cent pieces than $2 bills, and $\frac{7}{3}$ as many 5-cent pieces as 25-cent pieces. How many are there of each?

8. At what times between 4 and 5 o'clock are the hands of a watch at right angles to each other?

9. A woman sells half an egg more than half her eggs. She then sells half an egg more than half her remaining eggs. A third time she does the same, and now has 3 eggs left. How many had she at first ?

10. A train leaves A for B, 210 miles distant, travelling at the rate of 28 miles an hour. After it has been gone 1 hour and 15 minutes, another train starts from B for A, travelling at the rate of 22 miles an hour. How many miles from B will they meet ?

11. A man puts a certain sum in a savings bank paying 4 % interest. At the end of a year he deposits the interest, receiving interest on the entire amount. At the end of a second year and a third year he does the same, and now has $2812.16 in the bank. What was his original deposit ?

12. A fox is pursued by a hound, and has a start of 77 of her own leaps. The fox makes 5 leaps while the hound makes 4 ; but the hound in 5 leaps goes as far as the fox in 9. How many leaps does each make before the hound catches the fox ?

13. A clock has an hour-hand, a minute-hand, and a second-hand, all turning on the same centre. At 12 o'clock all the hands point at 12. How many seconds will it be before the hour-hand is between the other two hands and equally distant from them ?

14. A freight train travels from A to B at the rate of 12 miles an hour. After it has been gone $3\frac{1}{2}$ hours, an express train leaves A for B, travelling at the rate of 45 miles an hour, and reaches B 1 hour and 5 minutes ahead of the freight. Find the distance from A to B and the time taken by the express train.

15. A merchant increases his capital each year by one-third, and at the end of each year sets aside $1350 for expenses. At the end of three years, after setting aside his expenses, he finds that he has $\frac{14_5}{108}$ of his original capital. What was his original capital ?

VII. SPECIAL METHODS IN MULTIPLICATION AND DIVISION

128. Any Power of a Power.

Required the value of $(a^m)^n$, where m and n are any positive integers.

We have, $(a^m)^n = a^m \times a^m \times \cdots$ to n factors (§ 60)

$$= a^{m+m+\cdots \text{ to } n \text{ terms}} = a^{mn}.$$

129. Any Power of a Product.

Required the value of $(abc \cdots)^n$, where n is any positive integer.

We have, $(abc \cdot)^n$

$= (abc \cdots) \times (abc \cdots) \times \cdots$ to n factors

$= (a \times a \times \cdots$ to n factors) $(b \times b \times \cdots$ to n factors) $\cdots$

$= a^n b^n c^n \cdots$

130. Any Power of a Monomial.

1. Required the value of $(5\,a^2b)^3$.

We have, $(5\,a^2b)^3 = 5\,a^2b \times 5\,a^2b \times 5\,a^2b = 125\,a^6b^3$.

2. Required the value of $(-m)^4$.

We have, $(-m)^4 = (-m) \times (-m) \times (-m) \times (-m) = m^4$.

3. Required the value of $(-3\,n^3)^3$.

We have, $(-3\,n^3)^3 = (-3\,n^3) \times (-3\,n^3) \times (-3\,n^3) = -27\,n^9$.

From §§ 128 and 129, and the above examples, we have the following rule for raising a rational and integral monomial (§ 63) to any power whose exponent is a positive integer:

Raise the absolute value of the numerical coefficient to the required power, and multiply the exponent of each letter by the exponent of the required power.

*Give to every power of a positive term, and to every **even** power of a negative term, the positive sign ; and to every **odd** power of a negative term the negative sign.*

131. Square of a Binomial.

We find by actual multiplication,

$$(a + b)^2 = (a + b) \times (a + b) = a^2 + 2\,ab + b^2, \qquad (1)$$

$$(a - b)^2 = (a - b) \times (a - b) = a^2 - 2\,ab + b^2. \qquad (2)$$

That is,

The square of the sum of two numbers equals the square of the first, plus twice the product of the first by the second, plus the square of the second.

The square of the difference of two numbers equals the square of the first, minus twice the product of the first by the second, plus the square of the second.

In the remainder of the book, we shall, for the sake of brevity, use the expression " the *difference* of a and b " to denote the *remainder obtained by subtracting b from a*.

1. Square $3\,a^2 - 2\,b$.

By (2), $(3\,a^2 - 2\,b)^2 = (3\,a^2)^2 - 2\,(3\,a^2)\,(2\,b) + (2\,b)^2$

$$= 9\,a^4 - 12\,a^2 b + 4\,b^2 \ (\S\ 130).$$

If the first term of the binomial is negative, it should be enclosed, negative sign and all, in parentheses, before applying the rule.

2. Square $-4\,x^3 + 9$.

$$(-4\,x^3 + 9)^2 = [(-4\,x^3) + 9]^2$$
$$= (-4\,x^3)^2 + 2\,(-4\,x^3)\,(9) + 9^2, \text{ by } (1)$$
$$= 16\,x^6 - 72\,x^3 + 81.$$

132. Product of the Sum and Difference of Two Numbers.

We find by actual multiplication,

$$(a + b)(a - b) = a^2 - b^2.$$

That is, *the product of the sum and difference of two numbers equals the difference of their squares.*

1. Multiply $6\,a + 5\,b^3$ by $6\,a - 5\,b^3$.

By the rule,

$$(6\,a + 5\,b^3)(6\,a - 5\,b^3) = (6\,a)^2 - (5\,b^3)^2 = 36\,a^2 - 25\,b^6.$$

2. Multiply $-x^2+4$ by $-x^2-4$.
$$(-x^2+4)(-x^2-4)=[(-x^2)+4][(-x^2)-4]$$
$$=(-x^2)^2-4^2=x^4-16.$$

3. Expand $(a+b-c)(a-b+c)$.

To *expand* an algebraic expression is to perform the operations indicated.

By § 82, $(a+b-c)(a-b+c)=[a+(b-c)][a-(b-c)]$
$$=a^2-(b-c)^2, \text{ by the rule,}$$
$$=a^2-(b^2-2bc+c^2)$$
$$=a^2-b^2+2bc-c^2.$$

4. Expand $(x+y+z)(x-y+z)$.
$$(x+y+z)(x-y+z)=[(x+z)+y][(x+z)-y]$$
$$=(x+z)^2-y^2$$
$$=x^2+2xz+z^2-y^2.$$

133. Product of Two Binomials having the Same First Term.
We find by actual multiplication
$$(x+a)(x+b)=x^2+(a+b)x+ab.$$
That is,

The product of two binomials having the same first term equals the square of the first term, plus the algebraic sum of the second terms multiplied by the first term, plus the product of the second terms.

1. Multiply $x-5$ by $x+3$.

By the above rule, the coefficient of x is the sum of -5 and $+3$, or -2, and the last term is the product of -5 and $+3$, or -15.

Whence, $\qquad (x-5)(x+3)=x^2-2x-15.$

2. Multiply $x-5$ by $x-3$.

The coefficient of x is the sum of -5 and -3, or -8, and the last term is the product of -5 and -3, or 15.

Whence, $\qquad (x-5)(x-3)=x^2-8x+15.$

3. Multiply $ab - 4$ by $ab + 7$.

By the rule, $(ab - 4)(ab + 7) = a^2b^2 + 3\,ab - 28$.

4. Multiply $m + n + 6$ by $m + n + 8$.

$$(m + n + 6)(m + n + 8) = [(m + n) + 6][(m + n) + 8]$$
$$= (m + n)^2 + 14\,(m + n) + 48.$$

134. Square of a Polynomial.

By § 131,. (1), $(a_1 + a_2)^2 = a_1^2 + a_2^2 + 2\,a_1a_2.$ $\hspace{2cm}$ (1)

We also have,

$$\begin{aligned}
(a_1 + a_2 + a_3)^2 &= [(a_1 + a_2) + a_3]^2 \\
&= (a_1 + a_2)^2 + 2\,(a_1 + a_2) \times a_3 + a_3^2 \\
&= a_1^2 + 2\,a_1a_2 + a_2^2 + 2\,a_1a_3 + 2\,a_2a_3 + a_3^2 \\
&= a_1^2 + a_2^2 + a_3^2 + 2\,a_1a_2 + 2\,a_1a_3 + 2\,a_2a_3. \hspace{1cm} (2)
\end{aligned}$$

The results (1) and (2) are in accordance with the following law :

The square of a polynomial equals the sum of the squares of its terms, plus twice the product of each term by each of the following terms.

We will now prove that this law holds for the square of any polynomial.

Assume that the law holds for the square of a polynomial of m terms, where m is any positive integer; that is,

$$\begin{aligned}
&(a_1 + a_2 + a_3 + \cdots + a_{m-1} + a_m)^2 \\
&= a_1^2 + a_2^2 + \cdots + a_m^2 + 2\,a_1\,(a_2 + \cdots + a_m) \\
&\quad + 2\,a_2(a_3 + \cdots + a_m) + \cdots + 2\,a_{m-1}a_m. \hspace{1cm} (3)
\end{aligned}$$

Then, $(a_1 + a_2 + a_3 + \cdots + a_m + a_{m+1})^2$

$$\begin{aligned}
&= [(a_1 + a_2 + \cdots + a_m) + a_{m+1}]^2 \\
&\doteq (a_1 + a_2 + \cdots + a_m)^2 \\
&\quad + 2\,(a_1 + a_2 + \cdots + a_m)a_{m+1} + a_{m+1}^2,\ \text{by (1)} \\
&= a_1^2 + a_2^2 + \cdots + a_m^2 + a_{m+1}^2 \\
&\quad + 2\,a_1(a_2 + \cdots + a_m + a_{m+1}) \\
&\quad + 2\,a_2(a_3 + \cdots + a_m + a_{m+1}) + \cdots + 2\,a_m a_{m+1},\ \text{by (3)}.
\end{aligned}$$

This result is in accordance with the above law.

Hence, if the law holds for the square of a polynomial of m terms, where m is any positive integer, it also holds for the square of a polynomial of $m + 1$ terms.

But we know that the law holds for the square of a polynomial of three terms, and therefore it holds for the square of a polynomial of four terms; and since it holds for the square of a polynomial of four terms, it also holds for the square of a polynomial of five terms; and so on.

Hence, the law holds for the square of any polynomial.

The above method of proof is known as *Mathematical Induction.*

Ex. Expand $(2\,x^2 - 3\,x - 5)^2$.

In accordance with the law, we have

$$(2\,x^2 - 3\,x - 5)^2$$
$$= (2\,x^2)^2 + (-3\,x)^2 + (-5)^2$$
$$+ 2\,(2\,x^2)\,(-3\,x) + 2\,(2\,x^2)\,(-5) + 2\,(-3\,x)\,(-5)$$
$$= 4\,x^4 + 9\,x^2 + 25 - 12\,x^3 - 20\,x^2 + 30\,x$$
$$= 4\,x^4 - 12\,x^3 - 11\,x^2 + 30\,x + 25.$$

135. Cube of a Binomial.

We find by actual multiplication,

$$(a + b)^3 = a^3 + 3\,a^2b + 3\,ab^2 + b^3, \tag{1}$$
$$(a - b)^3 = a^3 - 3\,a^2b + 3\,ab^2 - b^3. \tag{2}$$

That is,

The cube of the sum of two numbers equals the cube of the first, plus three times the square of the first times the second, plus three times the first times the square of the second, plus the cube of the second.

The cube of the difference of two numbers equals the cube of the first, minus three times the square of the first times the second, plus three times the first times the square of the second, minus the cube of the second.

1. Find the cube of $a + 2\,b$.

By (1), $(a + 2\,b)^3 = a^3 + 3\,a^2(2\,b) + 3\,a(2\,b)^2 + (2\,b)^3$
$$= a^3 + 6\,a^2b + 12\,ab^2 + 8\,b^3.$$

2. Find the cube of $2\,x^3 - 5\,y^2$.

By (2), $(2\,x^3 - 5\,y^2)^3$
$$= (2\,x^3)^3 - 3\,(2\,x^3)^2(5\,y^2) + 3\,(2\,x^3)(5\,y^2)^2 - (5\,y^2)^3$$
$$= 8\,x^9 - 60\,x^6y^2 + 150\,x^3y^4 - 125\,y^6.$$

136. Cube of a Polynomial.

By § 135, (1), $(a_1 + a_2)^3 = a_1^3 + a_2^3 + 3\,a_1^2a_2 + 3\,a_1a_2^2.$ (1)

We also have, $(a_1 + a_2 + a_3)^3$
$$= [(a_1 + a_2) + a_3]^3$$
$$= (a_1 + a_2)^3 + 3\,(a_1 + a_2)^2a_3 + 3\,(a_1 + a_2)a_3^2 + a_3^3$$
$$= a_1^3 + 3\,a_1^2a_2 + 3\,a_1a_2^2 + a_2^3 + 3\,a_1^2a_3 + 6\,a_1a_2a_3$$
$$+ 3\,a_2^2a_3 + 3\,a_1a_3^2 + 3\,a_2a_3^2 + a_3^3$$
$$= a_1^3 + a_2^3 + a_3^3 + 3\,a_1^2a_2 + 3\,a_1^2a_3 + 3\,a_2^2a_1 + 3\,a_2^2a_3$$
$$+ 3\,a_3^2a_1 + 3\,a_3^2a_2 + 6\,a_1a_2a_3. \tag{2}$$

The results (1) and (2) are in accordance with the following law:

The cube of a polynomial equals the sum of the cubes of its terms, plus three times the product of the square of each term by each of the other terms, plus six times the product of every three different terms.

We will now prove by *Mathematical Induction* (see § 134), that this law holds for the cube of any polynomial.

Assume that the law holds for the cube of a polynomial of m terms, where m is any positive integer; that is,

$$(a_1 + a_2 + a_3 + \cdots + a_{m-2} + a_{m-1} + a_m)^3$$
$$= a_1^3 + a_2^3 + \cdots + a_m^3$$
$$+ 3\,a_1^2(a_2 + a_3 + \cdots + a_m) + 3\,a_2^2(a_1 + a_3 + \cdots + a_m)$$
$$+ \cdots + 3\,a_m^2(a_1 + a_2 + \cdots + a_{m-1})$$
$$+ 6\,a_1a_2a_3 + \cdots + 6\,a_{m-2}a_{m-1}a_m. \tag{3}$$

Then, $(a_1 + a_2 + a_3 + \cdots + a_{m-1} + a_m + a_{m+1})^3$
$$= [(a_1 + a_2 + a_3 + \cdots + a_{m-1} + a_m) + a_{m+1}]^3$$
$$= (a_1 + a_2 + a_3 + \cdots + a_{m-1} + a_m)^3$$
$$+ 3(a_1 + a_2 + a_3 + \cdots + a_{m-1} + a_m)^2 a_{m+1}$$
$$+ 3(a_1 + a_2 + a_3 + \cdots + a_{m-1} + a_m)a_{m+1}^2 + a_{m+1}^3 \ (\S\,135).$$

Then, by (3) and § 134,

$(a_1 + a_2 + a_3 + \cdots + a_{m-1} + a_m + a_{m+1})^3$
$$= a_1^3 + a_2^3 + \cdots + a_m^3$$
$$+ 3\,a_1^2(a_2 + a_3 + \cdots + a_m)$$
$$+ 3\,a_2^2(a_1 + a_3 + \cdots + a_m) + \cdots$$
$$+ 3\,a_m^2(a_1 + a_2 + \cdots + a_{m-1})$$
$$+ 6\,a_1 a_2 a_3 + \cdots + 6\,a_{m-2} a_{m-1} a_m$$
$$+ 3\,a_{m+1}(a_1^2 + a_2^2 + \cdots + a_m^2 + 2\,a_1 a_2 + \cdots + 2\,a_1 a_m$$
$$+ 2\,a_2 a_3 + \cdots + 2\,a_2 a_m + \cdots + 2\,a_{m-1}a_m)$$
$$+ 3\,a_{m+1}^2(a_1 + a_2 + a_3 + \cdots + a_m) + a_{m+1}^3$$

or, $\quad a_1^3 + a_2^3 + \cdots + a_m^3 + a_{m+1}^3$
$$+ 3\,a_1^2(a_2 + \cdots + a_m + a_{m+1})$$
$$+ 3\,a_2^2(a_1 + a_3 + \cdots + a_{m+1}) + \cdots$$
$$+ 3\,a_{m+1}^2(a_1 + a_2 + \cdots + a_m)$$
$$+ 6\,a_1 a_2 a_3 + \cdots + 6\,a_{m-1} a_m a_{m+1}.$$

This result is in accordance with the above law.

Hence, if the law holds for the cube of a polynomial of m terms, where m is any positive integer, it also holds for the cube of a polynomial of $m + 1$ terms.

But we know that the law holds for the cube of a polynomial of three terms, and therefore it holds for the cube of a polynomial of four terms; and since it holds for the cube of, a polynomial of four terms, it also holds for the cube of a polynomial of five terms; and so on.

Hence, the law holds for the cube of any polynomial.

Ex. Expand $(2\,x^3 - x^2 + 2\,x - 3)^3$.

In accordance with the above law, we have

$(2\,x^3 - x^2 + 2\,x - 3)^3$.

$$= (2\,x^3)^3 + (-x^2)^3 + (2\,x)^3 + (-3)^3 + 3\,(2\,x^3)^2(-x^2 + 2\,x - 3)$$
$$+ 3\,(-x^2)^2(2\,x^3 + 2\,x - 3) + 3\,(2\,x)^2(2\,x^3 - x^2 - 3)$$
$$+ 3\,(-3)^2(2\,x^3 - x^2 + 2\,x)$$
$$+ 6\,(2\,x^3)(-x^2)(2\,x) + 6\,(2\,x^3)(-x^2)(-3)$$
$$+ 6\,(2\,x^3)(2\,x)(-3) + 6\,(-x^2)(2\,x)(-3)$$

$$= 8\,x^9 - x^6 + 8\,x^3 - 27 - 12\,x^8 + 24\,x^7 - 36\,x^6 + 6\,x^7 + 6\,x^5 - 9\,x^4$$
$$+ 24\,x^5 - 12\,x^4 - 36\,x^2 + 54\,x^3 - 27\,x^2 + 54\,x - 24\,x^6$$
$$+ 36\,x^5 - 72\,x^4 + 36\,x^3$$

$$= 8\,x^9 - 12\,x^8 + 30\,x^7 - 61\,x^6 + 66\,x^5 - 93\,x^4 + 98\,x^3 - 63\,x^2$$
$$+ 54\,x - 27.$$

EXERCISE 6

Write by inspection the values of the following :

1. $(6\,a^3x^2)^3$.   **2.** $(-4\,ab^5c^4)^4$.   **3.** $(-3\,x^3yz^2)^5$.

4. $(3 + 7\,x^2)^2$.   **7.** $(-6\,xy - 11\,xz)^2$.

5. $(2\,a^3 - 5\,b^2c)^2$.   **8.** $(8\,x^p - 9\,x^q)^2$; p and q being

6. $(-m^4n^6 + 4\,p^6)^2$.   positive integers.

Write by inspection the values of the following :

9. $(5\,a^2 + 12\,b^3c)(5\,a^2 - 12\,b^3c)$.

10. $(-10\,m^4n + 13\,x^5)(-10\,m^4n - 13\,x^5)$.

11. $(a^{2m} + x^{3n})(a^{2m} - x^{3n})$; m and n being positive integers.

Expand the following :

12. $(a - b + c)(a - b - c)$.   **14.** $(x^2 + xy + y^2)(x^2 - xy + y^2)$.

13. $(x + y + 3)(x - y - 3)$.   **15.** $(a^2 + 5\,a - 4)(a^2 - 5\,a + 4)$.

16. $(4\,x^2 + 3\,x + 7)(4\,x^2 + 3\,x - 7)$.

17. $(m^4 + 5\,m^2n^2 + 2\,n^4)(m^4 - 5\,m^2n^2 - 2\,n^4)$.

Write by inspection the values of the following :

18. $(x + 2)(x + 10)$.   **22.** $(mn + 11)(mn + 2)$.

19. $(x - 5)(x + 7)$.   **23.** $(a^2b + 3\,c^3)(a^2b - 8\,c^3)$.

20. $(x^2 - 4)(x^2 - 14)$.   **24.** $(a - b - 5)(a - b - 9)$.

21. $(x + 7\,a)(x - 15\,a)$.   **25.** $(x + y - 6\,z^2)(x + y + 12\,z^2)$.

Expand the following:

26. $(3x^2 + 5x - 4)^2$.

27. $(a - b - c + d)^2$.

28. $(2x^3 - 3x^2 + x - 2)^2$.

29. $(a^4 + 3a^3 - 4a^2 - 2a + 1)^2$.

Write by inspection the values of the following:

30. $(a + 3b)^3$.

31. $(7x^4 - x^3)^3$.

32. $(3a^2b + 2c^3)^3$.

33. $(5mx^2 - 4ny^3)^3$.

Expand the following:

34. $(a^2 + a - 2)^3$.

35. $(2x^2 - 4x + 3)^3$.

36. $(a - b + c - d)^3$.

37. $(3x^3 - 4x^2 - 2x + 1)^3$.

Simplify the following:

38. $(3a^2 + 5b)^2(3a^2 - 5b)^2$.

39. $(x + 5)(x - 2)(x - 5)(x + 2)$.

40. $(2 - x)(2 + x)(4 + x^2)$.

41. $(x + 1)^3(x - 1)^3$.

42. $(x + y - z)^2(x - y + z)^2$.

43. $(a + b + c)^3(a + b - c)^3$.

44. $(x + y + z)^2 + (y + z - x)^2 + (z + x - y)^2 + (x + y - z)^2$.

45. $(a + b + c)(b + c - a)(c + a - b)(a + b - c)$.

46. $(m + n)^3 - (m - n)^3 - 3(m + n)^2(m - n) + 3(m + n)(m - n)^2$.

137. We find by actual division,

$$\frac{a^2 - b^2}{a + b} = a - b. \quad (1) \qquad \frac{a^2 - b^2}{a - b} = a + b. \quad (2)$$

That is,

If the difference of the squares of two numbers be divided by the sum of the numbers, the quotient is the difference of the numbers.

If the difference of the squares of two numbers be divided by the difference of the numbers, the quotient is the sum of the numbers.

Ex. Divide $25y^2z^4 - 9$ by $5yz^2 + 3$.

By § 130, $25y^2z^4$ is the square of $5yz^2$.

Then, by (1), $\quad \dfrac{25y^2z^4 - 9}{5yz^2 + 3} = 5yz^2 - 3$.

138. We find by actual division,

$$\frac{a^3 + b^3}{a + b} = a^2 - ab + b^2. \quad (1) \qquad \frac{a^3 - b^3}{a - b} = a^2 + ab + b^2. \quad (2)$$

That is,

*If the sum of the cubes of two numbers be divided by the sum
of the numbers, the quotient is the square of the first number,
minus the product of the first by the second, plus the square of the
second number.*

*If the difference of the cubes of two numbers be divided by the
difference of the numbers, the quotient is the square of the first
number, plus the product of the first by the second, plus the square
of the second number.*

Ex. Divide $27\,a^3 - b^3$ by $3\,a - b$.

By § 130, $27\,a^3$ is the cube of $3\,a$.

Then, by (2), $\dfrac{27\,a^3 - b^3}{3\,a - b} = 9\,a^2 + 3\,ab + b^2.$

139. The Remainder Theorem.

Let it be required to divide $2\,x^3 - 7\,x^2 + 10\,x - 3$ by $x - 2$.

$$
\begin{array}{l}
2\,x^3 - 7\,x^2 + 10\,x - 3\,\big|\underline{x - 2}\\
\underline{2\,x^3 - 4\,x^2}\qquad\quad\ \big|\,2\,x^2 - 3\,x + 4\\
\quad -3\,x^2\\
\quad \underline{-3\,x^2 +\ 6\,x}\\
\qquad\qquad 4\,x\\
\qquad\quad\ \underline{4\,x - 8}\\
\qquad\qquad\quad 5
\end{array}
$$

The division is not exact, and there is a final remainder 5.

Now if we substitute 2 for x in the dividend, we have

$$2 \times 2^3 - 7 \times 2^2 + 10 \times 2 - 3, \text{ which equals } 5.$$

This exemplifies the following law:

*If any rational integral polynomial, involving x, be not divisible
by $x - a$, the remainder of the division equals the result obtained
by substituting a for x in the given polynomial.*

The above is called *The Remainder Theorem.*

To prove the theorem, let D be any rational integral polynomial, involving x, not divisible by $x - a$.

Let the division be carried out until a remainder is obtained which does not contain x.

Let Q denote the quotient, and R the remainder.

Since the dividend equals the product of the divisor and quotient, plus the remainder, we have

$$Q(x - a) + R = D.$$

Substitute in this equation a for x.

The term $Q(x - a)$ becomes zero; and since R does not contain x, it is not changed, whatever value is given to x.

Then, R must equal the result obtained by substituting a for x in D.

140. The Factor Theorem.

If any rational integral polynomial, involving x, becomes zero when x is put equal to a, the polynomial has $x - a$ as a factor.

For by § 139, the remainder obtained by dividing the polynomial by $x - a$ is zero.

141. It follows from § 140 that,

If any rational integral polynomial, involving x, becomes zero when x is put equal to $- a$, the polynomial has $x + a$ as a factor.

142. We will now prove that, if n is any positive integer,

I. $a^n - b^n$ *is always divisible by $a - b$.*

II. $a^n - b^n$ *is divisible by $a + b$ if n is even.*

III. $a^n + b^n$ *is divisible by $a + b$ if n is odd.*

IV. $a^n + b^n$ *is divisible by neither $a + b$ nor $a - b$ if n is even.*

Proof of I.

If b be substituted for a in $a^n - b^n$, the result is $b^n - b^n$, or 0. Then by § 140, $a^n - b^n$ has $a - b$ as a factor.

Proof of II.

If $- b$ be substituted for a in $a^n - b^n$, the result is $(- b)^n - b^n$; or, since n is even, $b^n - b^n$, or 0.

Then by § 141, $a^n - b^n$ has $a + b$ as a factor.

Proof of III.

If $-b$ be substituted for a in $a^n + b^n$, the result is $(-b)^n + b^n$; or, since n is odd, $-b^n + b^n$, or 0.

Then, $a^n + b^n$ has $a + b$ as a factor.

Proof of IV.

If $-b$ or $+b$ be substituted for a in $a^n + b^n$, the results are $(-b)^n + b^n$ or $b^n + b^n$, respectively.

Since n is even, neither of these is zero.

Then, neither $a + b$ nor $a - b$ is a factor of $a^n + b^n$.

143. We find by actual division

$$\frac{a^4 - b^4}{a + b} = a^3 - a^2b + ab^2 - b^3,$$

$$\frac{a^4 - b^4}{a - b} = a^3 + a^2b + ab^2 + b^3,$$

$$\frac{a^5 + b^5}{a + b} = a^4 - a^3b + a^2b^2 - ab^3 + b^4,$$

$$\frac{a^5 - b^5}{a - b} = a^4 + a^3b + a^2b^2 + ab^3 + b^4; \text{ etc.}$$

In these results, we observe the following laws:

I. *The exponent of a in the first term of the quotient is less by 1 than its exponent in the dividend, and decreases by 1 in each succeeding term.*

II. *The exponent of b in the second term of the quotient is 1, and increases by 1 in each succeeding term.*

III. *If the divisor is $a - b$, all the terms of the quotient are positive; if the divisor is $a + b$, the terms of the quotient are alternately positive and negative.*

144. We will now prove, by *Mathematical Induction*, that the laws of § 143 hold universally.

Assume the laws to hold for $\dfrac{a^n - b^n}{a - b}$, where n is any positive integer.

Then, $\dfrac{a^n - b^n}{a - b} = a^{n-1} + a^{n-2}b + a^{n-3}b^2 + \cdots + b^{n-1}.$ (1)

Now, $\dfrac{a^{n+1} - b^{n+1}}{a - b} = \dfrac{a^{n+1} - a^n b + a^n b - b^{n+1}}{a - b}$

$$= \dfrac{a^n(a - b) + b(a^n - b^n)}{a - b}$$

$$= a^n + b(a^{n-1} + a^{n-2}b + a^{n-3}b^2 + \cdots + b^{n-1}), \text{ by (1)}$$

$$= a^n + a^{n-1}b + a^{n-2}b^2 + \cdots + b^n.$$

This result is in accordance with the laws of § 143.

Hence, if the laws hold for the quotient of the difference of two like powers of a and b divided by $a - b$, they also hold for the quotient of the difference of the next higher powers of a and b divided by $a - b$.

But we know that they hold for $\dfrac{a^5 - b^5}{a - b}$, and therefore they hold for $\dfrac{a^6 - b^6}{a - b}$; and since they hold for $\dfrac{a^6 - b^6}{a - b}$, they hold for $\dfrac{a^7 - b^7}{a - b}$; and so on.

Hence, the laws hold for $\dfrac{a^n - b^n}{a - b}$, where n is any positive integer.

Putting $-b$ for b in (1), we have

$$\dfrac{a^n - (-b)^n}{a - (-b)} = a^{n-1} + a^{n-2}(-b) + \cdots + (-b)^{n-1}.$$

If n is even, $(-b)^n = b^n$, and $(-b)^{n-1} = -b^{n-1}$ (§ 130).

Whence, $\dfrac{a^n - b^n}{a + b} = a^{n-1} - a^{n-2}b + a^{n-3}b^2 - \cdots - b^{n-1}.$ (2)

If n is odd, $(-b)^n = -b^n$, and $(-b)^{n-1} = +b^{n-1}.$

Whence, $\dfrac{a^n + b^n}{a + b} = a^{n-1} - a^{n-2}b + a^{n-3}b^2 - \cdots + b^{n-1}.$ (3)

Equations (2) and (3) are in accordance with the laws of § 143.

Hence, the laws hold for $\dfrac{a^n - b^n}{a + b}$, where n is any even positive integer, and for $\dfrac{a^n + b^n}{a + b}$, where n is any odd positive integer.

145. 1. Divide $a^7 - b^7$ by $a - b$.

By § 143, $\dfrac{a^7 - b^7}{a - b} = a^6 + a^5b + a^4b^2 + a^3b^3 + a^2b^4 + ab^5 + b^6$.

2. Divide $16\,x^4 - 81$ by $2\,x + 3$.

By § 130, $16\,x^4 = (2\,x)^4$.

Then, $\dfrac{16\,x^4 - 81}{2\,x + 3} = (2\,x)^3 - (2\,x)^2 \cdot 3 + (2\,x) \cdot 3^2 - 3^3$

$$= 8\,x^3 - 12\,x^2 + 18\,x - 27.$$

The absolute value of any term after the first, in equations (1), (2), and (3), of § 144, may be obtained by dividing the absolute value of the preceding term by a, and multiplying the result by b.

This would be the shortest method if the numbers involved were large.

EXERCISE 7

Write by inspection the values of the following:

1. $\dfrac{36\,a^2 - 49}{6\,a + 7}$.

2. $\dfrac{121\,x^5 - 64\,y^4z^2}{11\,x^3 - 8\,y^2z}$.

3. $\dfrac{n^3 - 1}{n - 1}$.

4. $\dfrac{8 + m^6}{2 + m^2}$.

5. $\dfrac{125\,a^6 - 27\,x^3}{5\,a^2 - 3\,x}$.

6. $\dfrac{216\,m^3n^6 + 343\,p^9}{6\,mn^2 + 7\,p^3}$.

7. $\dfrac{a^4 - b^4}{a + b}$.

8. $\dfrac{m^5 - n^5}{m - n}$.

9. $\dfrac{1 - x^6}{1 - x}$.

10. $\dfrac{a^7 + x^7}{a + x}$.

11. $\dfrac{n^9 - x^9}{n - x}$.

12. $\dfrac{a^6 - 64\,b^6}{a - 2\,b}$.

13. $\dfrac{625\,m^4 - 256}{5\,m - 4}$.

14. $\dfrac{256\,a^8 - x^8}{2\,a + x}$.

15. $\dfrac{243\,x^5 + 1024\,y^5}{3\,x + 4\,y}$.

146. Symmetry.

An expression containing two or more letters is said to be *symmetrical* with respect to any two of them, when they can be interchanged without altering the value of the expression.

Thus, $a + b + c$ is symmetrical with respect to a and b; for, on interchanging these letters, the expression becomes $b + a + c$.

An expression containing three or more letters is said to be symmetrical with respect to them when it is symmetrical with respect to any two of them.

Thus, $ab + bc + ca$ is symmetrical with respect to the letters a, b, and c; for if a and b be interchanged, the expression becomes $ba + ac + cb$, which is equal to $ab + bc + ca$.

And, in like manner, $ab + bc + ca$ is symmetrical with respect to b and c, and with respect to c and a.

147. Cyclo-symmetry.

An expression containing n letters, a, b, c, $\cdot$, m, n, is said to be *cyclo-symmetrical* with respect to them when, if a is substituted for b, b for c, $\cdot$, m for n, and n for a, the value of the expression is not changed.

The above is called a *cyclical* interchange of letters.

Thus, $(a - b)(b - c)(c - a)$ is cyclo-symmetrical with respect to a, b, and c; for if a is substituted for b, b for c, and c for a, it becomes $(c - a)(a - b)(b - c)$, which by the Commutative Law for Multiplication is equal to $(a - b)(b - c)(c - a)$.

148. Every expression which is symmetrical with respect to a set of letters is also cyclo-symmetrical with respect to them.

For since any two letters can be interchanged without altering the value of the expression, the condition for cyclo-symmetry will be satisfied.

But it is not necessarily true that an expression which is cyclo-symmetrical with respect to a set of letters is also symmetrical with respect to them; for it does not follow that *any* two letters can be interchanged without altering the value of the expression.

149. It follows from §§ 146 and 147 that, if two expressions are symmetrical or cyclo-symmetrical, the results obtained by adding, subtracting, multiplying, or dividing them are, respectively, symmetrical or cyclo-symmetrical.

150. Applications.

The principle of symmetry is often useful in abridging algebraic operations.

1. Expand $(a + b + c)^3$.

We have, $(a + b + c)^3 = (a + b + c)(a + b + c)(a + b + c)$.

This expression is symmetrical with respect to a, b, and c (§ 146), and of the third degree.

There are three possible types of terms of the third degree in a, b, and c; terms like a^3, terms like a^2b, and terms like abc.

It is evident that a^3 has the coefficient **1**; and so, by symmetry, b^3 and c^3 have the coefficient **1**.

It is evident that a^2b has the coefficient **3**; and so, by symmetry, have b^2a, b^2c, c^2b, c^2a, and a^2c.

Let m denote the coefficient of abc.

Then, $(a + b + c)^3$

$$= a^3 + b^3 + c^3 + 3(a^2b + b^2a + b^2c + c^2b + c^2a + a^2c) + mabc.$$

To determine m, we observe that the above equation holds for all values of a, b, and c.

We may therefore let $a = b = c = 1$.

Then, $27 = 3 + 18 + m$; and $m = 6$.

Whence, $(a + b + c)^3$

$$= a^3 + b^3 + c^3 + 3(a^2b + b^2a + b^2c + c^2b + c^2a + a^2c) + 6\ abc.$$

The above result may be written in a more compact form by representing the sum of terms of the same type by the symbol Σ; read *sigma*.

Thus, $(\Sigma a)^3 = \Sigma a^3 + 3\ \Sigma a^2b + 6\ abc$.

2. Expand $(x - y - z)^2 + (y - z - x)^2 + (z - x - y)^2$.

This expression is symmetrical with respect to x, y, and z, and of the second degree.

The possible types of terms of the second degree in x, y, and z are terms like x^2, and terms like xy.

It is evident, by the law of § 134, that x^2 has the coefficient 3; and so, by symmetry, have y^2 and z^2.

Let m denote the coefficient of xy.

Then, $(x - y - z)^2 + (y - z - x)^2 + (z - x - y)^2$

$$= 3(x^2 + y^2 + z^2) + m(xy + yz + zx).$$

To determine m, put $x = y = z = 1$.

Then, $3 = 9 + 3\,m$, or $m = -2$.

Whence, $(x-y-z)^2 + (y-z-x)^2 + (z-x-y)^2$
$$= 3(x^2+y^2+z^2) - 2(xy+yz+zx).$$

3. Expand
$$(a+b+c)^3 + (a+b-c)^3 + (b+c-a)^3 + (c+a-b)^3.$$

The expression is symmetrical with respect to a, b, and c, and of the third degree.

The possible types of terms are terms like a^3, terms like a^2b, and terms like abc.

It is evident, by the law of § 136, that a^3 has the coefficient 2; and so, by symmetry, have b^3 and c^3.

Also, by § 136, a^2b has the coefficient $3+3+3-3$, or 6; and so, by symmetry, have b^2a, b^2c, c^2b, c^2a, and a^2c.

Again, abc has the coefficient $6-6-6-6$, or -12.

Whence,
$$(a+b+c)^3 + (a+b-c)^3 + (b+c-a)^3 + (c+a-b)^3$$
$$= 2(a^3+b^3+c^3) + 6(a^2b+b^2a+b^2c+c^2b+c^2a+a^2c) - 12\,abc.$$

EXERCISE 8

1. In the expansion of an expression which is symmetrical with respect to a, b, and c, what are the possible types of terms of the fourth degree? of the fifth degree? of the sixth degree?

2. If one term of an expression which is symmetrical with respect to a, b, and c, is $(2a-b-c)(2b-c-a)$, what are the others?

3. Is the expression $a(b-c)^2 + b(c-a)^2 + c(a-b)^2$ symmetrical with respect to a, b, and c?

4. Is the expression $(x^2-y^2)^3 + (y^2-z^2)^3 + (z^2-x^2)^3$ symmetrical with respect to x, y, and z?

Expand the following by the symmetrical method :

5. $(a+b+c)^2.$ **6.** $(a+b+c+d)^2.$

7. $(x+y-z)^2 + (y+z-x)^2 + (z+x-y)^2.$

8. $(2a-3b-4c)^2 + (2b-3c-4a)^2 + (2c-3a-4b)^2.$

9. $(a+b+c-d)^2 + (b+c+d-a)^2 + (c+d+a-b)^2$
        $+ (d+a+b-c)^2.$

10. $(a+b+c+d)^3.$

11. $(a+b+c)^3 + (a-b-c)^3 + (b-c-a)^3 + (c-a-b)^3.$

12. $(x+y-z)(y+z-x)(z+x-y).$

13. $[x^2+y^2+z^2 + 2(xy+yz+zx)]^2.$

14. $(a+b+c)(a+b-c)(b+c-a)(a+c-b).$

VIII. FACTORING

151. To **Factor** an algebraic expression is to find two or more expressions which, when multiplied together, shall produce the given expression.

152. In the present chapter we consider only the separation of rational and integral expressions (§ 63), with integral numerical coefficients, into factors of the same form.

153. A **Common Factor** of two or more expressions is an expression which will exactly divide each of them.

FACTORING

154. It is not always possible to factor an expression; there are, however, certain forms which can always be factored; these will be considered in the present treatise.

155. CASE I.   *When the terms of the expression have a common factor.*

1. Factor $14\,ab^4 - 35\,a^3b^2$.
Each term contains the monomial factor $7\,ab^2$.
Dividing the expression by $7\,ab^2$, we have $2\,b^2 - 5\,a^2$.
Then, $14\,ab^4 - 35\,a^3b^2 = 7\,ab^2\,(2\,b^2 - 5\,a^2)$.

2. Factor $(2\,m + 3)\,x^2 + (2\,m + 3)\,y^3$.
The terms have the common binomial factor $2\,m + 3$.
Dividing the expression by $2\,m + 3$, we have $x^2 + y^3$.
Then, $(2\,m + 3)\,x^2 + (2\,m + 3)\,y^3 = (2\,m + 3)\,(x^2 + y^3)$.

3. Factor $(a - b)\,m + (b - a)\,n$.
By § 81, $b - a = -(a - b)$.
Then, $(a - b)\,m + (b - a)\,n = (a - b)\,m - (a - b)\,n$
$$= (a - b)\,(m - n).$$

4. Factor $5\,a\,(x - y) - 3\,a\,(x + y)$.

$$5\,a\,(x-y)-3\,a\,(x+y)=a\,[5\,(x-y)-3\,(x+y)]$$
$$=a\,(5\,x-5\,y-3\,x-3\,y)$$
$$=a\,(2\,x-8\,y)$$
$$=2\,a\,(x-4\,y).$$

We may also solve Ex. 3 by writing the first term in the form
$$-\,(b-a)\,m.$$
Thus, $(a-b)\,m+(b-a)\,n=(b-a)\,n-(b-a)\,m$
$$=(b-a)(n-m).$$

This agrees with § 91; for, by § 91, the signs of *two* factors of a product may be changed without altering the value of the expression. We may thus have more than one form for the factors of an expression.

156. The terms of a polynomial may sometimes be so arranged as to show a common polynomial factor; and the expression can then be factored as in § 155.

1. Factor $ab-ay+bx-xy$.

By § 155, $ab-ay+bx-xy=a\,(b-y)+x(b-y)$.

The terms now have the common factor $b-y$.

Whence, $ab-ay+bx-xy=(a+x)\,(b-y)$.

2. Factor $a^3+2\,a^2-3\,a-6$.

The third term being negative, it is convenient to enclose the last two terms in parentheses preceded by a $-$ sign.

Thus, $a^3+2\,a^2-3\,a-6=(a^3+2\,a^2)-(3\,a+6)$
$$=a^2(a+2)-3(a+2)$$
$$=(a^2-3)(a+2).$$

EXERCISE 9

Factor the following:

1. $(3\,x+5)m+(3\,x+5)$.
2. $(m-n)x+(n-m)(y+z)$.
3. $x^2(5\,y-2\,z)-x^2(2\,y+z)$.
4. $4\,x\,(a-b-c)-5\,y(b+c-a)$.
5. $(a-b)(m^2+xz)-(a-b)(m^2-yz)$.
6. $(m-n)^4-2\,m\,(m-n)^3+m^2(m-n)^2$.
7. $8\,xy+12\,ay+10\,bx+15\,ab$.
8. $m^4+6\,m^3-7\,m-42$.
9. $6-10\,a+27\,a^2-45\,a^3$.
10. $20\,ab-28\,ad-5\,bc+7\,cd$.
11. $ax-ay+az-bx+by-bz$.
12. $3\,am-6\,an+4\,bm-8\,bn+cm-2\,cn$.
13. $ax+ay-az-bx-by+bz+cx+cy-cz$.

157. If an expression when raised to the nth power (n being a positive integer) is equal to another expression, the first expression is said to be an nth **Root** of the second.

Thus, if $a^n = b$, a is an nth root of b.

158. The **Radical Sign**, $\sqrt{}$, when written before an expression, indicates some root of the expression.

Thus, $\sqrt{a^4}$ indicates a *second*, or *square* root of a^4;

$\sqrt[3]{a^9}$ indicates a *third*, or *cube* root of a^9;

$\sqrt[n]{a^{2n}}$ indicates an nth root of a^{2n}; etc.

The *index* of a root is the number written over the radical sign to indicate what root of the expression is taken.

If no index is expressed, the index 2 is understood.

An *even* root is one whose index is an even number; an *odd* root is one whose index is an odd number.

159. A rational and integral expression is said to be a *perfect square*, a *perfect cube*, or, in general, a *perfect nth power*, when it has, respectively, a rational and integral square, cube, or nth root.

160. Since $(2\,a^2b)^3 = 8\,a^6b^3$ (§ 130), a cube root of $8\,a^6b^3$ is $2\,a^2b$.

Again, since $(m^2)^4 = m^8$, a fourth root of m^8 is m^2.

It is evident from this that every *positive* term, which is a perfect nth power, has a *positive* nth root.

We shall call this its *principal nth root*.

We also have $(-m^2)^4 = m^8$; so that another fourth root of m^8 is $-m^2$.

It is evident from the above that every positive term which is a perfect nth power, has, if n is even, in addition to its positive nth root, a *negative* nth root of the same absolute value.

In the present chapter, only the *principal* nth root will be considered.

161. Since $(-3\,x^3)^3 = -27\,x^9$ (§ 130), a cube root of $-27\,x^9$ is $-3\,x^3$.

It is evident from this that every *negative* term, which is a perfect nth power, has a *negative* nth root.

We shall call this its *principal nth root*.

162. It will be shown (§ 756) that a number has *two* different square roots, *three* different cube roots, and, in general, n different nth roots.

It will be understood throughout the remainder of the work, unless the contrary is specified, that when we speak of *the* nth root of a term, we mean the *principal* nth root.

163. Let n be a positive integer, and a and b two equal perfect nth powers; then, by Ax. 5, § 66,

$$\sqrt[n]{a} = \sqrt[n]{b}.$$

That is, *if two perfect nth powers are equal, their principal nth roots are equal.*

164. Any Root of a Power.

Required the value of $\sqrt[n]{a^{mn}}$, where m and n are any positive integers.

By § 128, $\qquad (a^m)^n = a^{mn}.$

Then, by § 157, $\qquad \sqrt[n]{a^{mn}} = a^m.$

165. Any Root of a Product.

Let n be a positive integer, and a, b, c, $\cdots$, numbers which are perfect nth powers.

By § 157, $\qquad (\sqrt[n]{abc\cdots})^n = abc\cdots.$

Also,

$$(\sqrt[n]{a} \times \sqrt[n]{b} \times \sqrt[n]{c} \times \ \cdot\ )^n = (\sqrt[n]{a})^n \times (\sqrt[n]{b})^n \times (\sqrt[n]{c})^n \times \cdots$$
$$= abc\ \cdot\ , \text{ by § 157.}$$

Then, by § 163, $\sqrt[n]{abc\cdots} = \sqrt[n]{a} \times \sqrt[n]{b} \times \sqrt[n]{c} \times \cdots;$

for each of these expressions is the nth root of $abc\cdots$.

This simply means that the principal nth root of a product is equal to the product of the principal nth roots of the factors.

166. Any Root of a Monomial.

From §§ 160, 161, 164, and 165, we have the following rule for finding the principal root of a rational and integral monomial, which is a perfect power of the same degree as the index of the required root:

Extract the required root of the absolute value of the numerical coefficient, and divide the exponent of each letter by the index of the required root.

Give to every even root of a positive term the positive sign, and to every odd root of any term the sign of the term itself.

1. Required the cube root of $64\ x^6$.

By the rule, $\sqrt[3]{64\ x^6} = 4\ x^2$.

2. Required the fourth root of $81\ m^4n^{12}$.

$$\sqrt[4]{81\ m^4n^{12}} = 3\ mn^3.$$

3. Required the fifth root of $-32\ a^{10}b^5c^{15}$.

$$\sqrt[5]{-32\ a^{10}b^5c^{15}} = -2\ a^2bc^3.$$

167. It follows from § 131 that a rational and integral trinomial is a perfect square when its first and third terms are perfect squares, and positive, and its second term plus or minus twice the product of their square roots.

Thus, $4\ x^2 + 12\ xy^2 + 9\ y^4$ is a perfect square.

168. To find the square root of a trinomial perfect square, we reverse the rules of § 131:

Extract the square roots (§ 166) of the first and third terms, and connect the results by the sign of the second term.

1. Find the square root of $4\ x^2 + 12\ xy^2 + 9\ y^4$.

By the rule, $\sqrt{4\ x^2 + 12\ xy^2 + 9\ y^4} = 2\ x + 3\ y^2$.

The expression may be written in the form

$$(-2\ x)^2 + 2(-2\ x)(-3\ y^2) + (-3\ y^2)^2\,;$$

which shows that $(-2\ x) + (-3\ y^2)$, or $-2\ x - 3\ y^2$, is also a square root.

But the first form is simpler, and will be used in the examples of the present chapter.

2. Find the square root of $m^2 - 2\ mn + n^2$.

By the rule, $\sqrt{m^2 - 2\ mn + n^2} = m - n$.

We may write the expression in the form $n^2 - 2\ mn + m^2$; in which case, by the rule, the square root is $n - m$.

169. Case II. *When the expression is a trinomial perfect square.*

1. Factor $25\,a^2 + 40\,ab^3 + 16\,b^6$.

By § 168, the square root of the expression is $5\,a + 4\,b^3$.

Then, $25\,a^2 + 40\,ab^3 + 16\,b^6 = (5\,a + 4\,b^3)^2$.

2. Factor $m^4 - 4\,m^2n^2 + 4\,n^4$.

By § 168, the square root of the expression is either $m^2 - 2\,n^2$, or $2\,n^2 - m^2$.

Then, $m^4 - 4\,m^2n^2 + 4\,n^4 = (m^2 - 2\,n^2)^2$, or $(2\,n^2 - m^2)^2$. (Compare § 91.)

3. Factor $x^2 - 2\,x(y - z) + (y - z)^2$.

We have $x^2 - 2\,x(y - z) + (y - z)^2$

$\qquad = [x - (y - z)]^2 = (x - y + z)^2;$

or, $\qquad = [(y - z) - x]^2 = (y - z - x)^2.$

4. Factor $-9\,a^4 - 6\,a^2 - 1$.

$-9\,a^4 - 6\,a^2 - 1 = -(9\,a^4 + 6\,a^2 + 1) = -(3\,a^2 + 1)^2.$

EXERCISE 10

Find by inspection the values of the following:

1. $\sqrt[3]{-125\,m^9n^3}$. **2.** $\sqrt[4]{16\,x^8y^{16}}$. **3.** $\sqrt[5]{243\,a^5b^{25}c^{20}}$.

Factor the following:

4. $81\,m^2 + 144\,m + 64$.

5. $49\,n^6 - 168\,n^3x^4 + 144\,x^8$.

6. $-25\,a^2 - 60\,ax - 36\,x^2$.

7. $-121\,a^4m^2 + 220\,a^2b^2mn - 100\,b^4n^2$.

8. $9\,x^2 - 6\,x(y + z) + (y + z)^2$.

9. $25(a - b)^2 + 40(a - b)c + 16\,c^2$.

10. $(a + b)^2 + 4(a + b)(a - b) + 4(a - b)^2$.

11. $9(x + y)^2 - 12(x + y)(x - y) + 4(x - y)^2$.

170. Case III. *When the expression is in the form*
$$a^2 + b^2 + c^2 + 2\,ab + 2\,ac + 2\,bc.$$

By § 134, this expression is the square of $a + b + c$.

Ex. Factor $9\,x^2 + y^2 + 4\,z^2 - 6\,xy - 12\,xz + 4\,yz$.

We can write the expression in the form

$$9\,x^2 - 6\,xy + y^2 - 12\,xz + 4\,yz + 4\,z^2.$$

Or, by §§ 155 and 169,

$$(3\,x - y)^2 - 4\,z\,(3\,x - y) + 4\,z^2.$$

This expression is the square of $(3\,x - y) - 2\,z$.

Thus, $9\,x^2 + y^2 + 4\,z^2 - 6\,xy - 12\,xz + 4\,yz = (3\,x - y - 2\,z)^2.$

By § 91, we may put the result in the form $(-3\,x + y + 2\,z)^2.$

EXERCISE II

Factor the following:

1. $a^2 + b^2 + c^2 + 2\,ab - 2\,ac - 2\,bc.$

2. $1 + 25\,m^2 + 36\,n^2 - 10\,m + 12\,n - 60\,mn.$

3. $a^2 + 81\,b^2 + 16 - 18\,ab - 8\,a + 72\,b.$

4. $9\,x^2 + y^2 + 25\,z^2 + 6\,xy + 30\,xz + 10\,yz.$

5. $36\,m^2 + 64\,n^2 + x^2 + 96\,mn - 12\,mx - 16\,nx.$

6. $16\,a^4 + 9\,b^4 + 81\,c^4 - 24\,a^2b^2 - 72\,a^2c^2 + 54\,b^2c^2.$

7. $25\,x^6 + 49\,y^{10} + 36\,z^8 - 70\,x^3y^5 + 60\,x^3z^4 - 84\,y^5z^4.$

171. Case IV. *When the expression is the difference of two perfect squares.*

By § 132, $a^2 - b^2 = (a + b)(a - b).$

Hence, to obtain the factors, we reverse the rule of § 132:

Extract the square root of the first square, and of the second square; add the results for one factor, and subtract the second result from the first for the other.

1. Factor $36\,a^2b^4 - 49\,c^6.$

The square root of $36\,a^2b^4$ is $6\,ab^2$, and of $49\,c^6$ is $7\,c^3.$

Then, $36\,a^2b^4 - 49\,c^6 = (6\,ab^2 + 7\,c^3)(6\,ab^2 - 7\,c^3).$

2. Factor $(2\,x - 3\,y)^2 - (x - y)^2.$

By the rule, $(2\,x - 3\,y)^2 - (x - y)^2$

$$= [(2\,x - 3\,y) + (x - y)][(2\,x - 3\,y) - (x - y)]$$
$$= (2\,x - 3\,y + x - y)(2\,x - 3\,y - x + y)$$
$$= (3\,x - 4\,y)(x - 2\,y).$$

A polynomial of more than two terms may sometimes be expressed as the difference of two perfect squares, and factored by the rule of Case IV.

3. Factor $2\,mn + m^2 - 1 + n^2$.

The first, second, and last terms may be grouped together in the order $m^2 + 2\,mn + n^2$; which expression, by § 168, is the square of $m + n$.

Thus,
$$\begin{aligned} 2\,mn + m^2 - 1 + n^2 &= (m^2 + 2\,mn + n^2) - 1 \\ &= (m + n)^2 - 1 \\ &= (m + n + 1)(m + n - 1). \end{aligned}$$

4. Factor $12\,y + x^2 - 9\,y^2 - 4$.

$$\begin{aligned} 12\,y + x^2 - 9\,y^2 - 4 &= x^2 - 9\,y^2 + 12\,y - 4 \\ &= x^2 - (9\,y^2 - 12\,y + 4) \\ &= x^2 - (3\,y - 2)^2, \text{ by § 168,} \\ &= [x + (3\,y - 2)][x - (3\,y - 2)] \\ &= (x + 3\,y - 2)(x - 3\,y + 2). \end{aligned}$$

EXERCISE 12

Factor the following:

1. $196\,m^4 x^{12} - 289\,n^6 y^{10}$.
2. $36\,a^2 - (2\,a - 3)^2$.
3. $16(2\,m - 7\,x)^2 - 25(3\,n + 4\,y)^2$.
4. $4(8\,a + 3\,b)^2 - 9(4\,a - 5\,b)^2$.
5. $a^2 + b_1^2 - c^2 + 2\,ab$.
6. $x^2 - y^2 - 2\,yz - z^2$.
7. $6\,np + 16\,m^2 - 9\,p^2 - n^2$.
8. $m^2 - 2\,mn + n^2 - x^2 + 2\,xy - y^2$.
9. $16\,a^2 - 8\,ab + b^2 - c^2 - 10\,cd - 25\,d^2$.
10. $28\,xy - 36\,z^2 + 49\,y^2 + 60\,z - 25 + 4\,x^2$.

172. CASE V. *When the expression is in the form*
$$x^4 + ax^2 y^2 + y^4.$$

Certain trinomials of the above form may be factored by expressing them as the difference of two perfect squares, and then employing § 171.

1. Factor $a^4 + a^2 b^2 + b^4$.

By § 167, a trinomial is a perfect square if its first and last terms are perfect squares and positive, and its second term plus or minus twice the product of their square roots.

The given expression can be made a perfect square by adding a^2b^2 to its second term; and this can be done if we subtract a^2b^2 from the result.

Thus,
$$a^4 + a^2b^2 + b^4 = (a^4 + 2\,a^2b^2 + b^4) - a^2b^2$$
$$= (a^2 + b^2)^2 - a^2b^2, \text{ by } § 168,$$
$$= (a^2 + b^2 + ab)(a^2 + b^2 - ab), \text{ by } § 171,$$
$$= (a^2 + ab + b^2)(a^2 - ab + b^2).$$

2. Factor $9\,x^4 - 37\,x^2 + 4$.

The expression will be a perfect square if its second term is $-12\,x^2$.

Thus,
$$9\,x^4 - 37\,x^2 + 4 = (9\,x^4 - 12\,x^2 + 4) - 25\,x^2$$
$$= (3\,x^2 - 2)^2 - (5\,x)^2$$
$$= (3\,x^2 + 5\,x - 2)(3\,x^2 - 5\,x - 2).$$

The expression may also be factored as follows:
$$9\,x^4 - 37\,x^2 + 4 = (9\,x^4 + 12\,x^2 + 4) - 49\,x^2$$
$$= (3\,x^2 + 2)^2 - (7\,x)^2$$
$$= (3\,x^2 + 7\,x + 2)(3\,x^2 - 7\,x + 2).$$

Several expressions in the following set may be factored in two different ways.

The factoring of trinomials of the form $x^4 + ax^2y^2 + y^4$, when the factors involve surds, will be considered in § 459.

EXERCISE 13

Factor the following:

1. $x^4 + 5\,x^2 + 9$.
2. $a^4 - 21\,a^2b^2 + 36\,b^4$.
3. $4 - 33\,x^2 + 4\,x^4$.
4. $25\,m^4 + 6\,m^2n^2 + n^4$.
5. $9\,x^4 + 6\,x^2y^2 + 49\,y^4$.
6. $16\,a^4 - 81\,a^2 + 16$.
7. $64 + 64\,m^2 + 25\,m^4$.
8. $49\,a^4 - 127\,a^2x^2 + 81\,x^4$.

Factor each of the following in two different ways:

9. $x^4 - 17\,x^2 + 16$.
10. $9 - 148\,a^2 + 64\,a^4$.
11. $16\,m^4 - 104\,m^2x^2 + 25\,x^4$.
12. $36\,a^4 - 97\,a^2m^2 + 36\,m^4$.

173. CASE VI. *When the expression is in the form*
$$x^2 + ax + b.$$

By § 133, $x^2 + (m + n)x + mn = (x + m)(x + n)$.

If, then, a trinomial is in the form $x^2 + ax + b$, and a and b are, respectively, the sum and product of two numbers, the factors are x plus one number and x plus the other.

The numbers may be found by inspection.

1. Factor $x^2 + 14x + 45$.

We find two numbers whose sum is 14 and product 45.

By inspection, we determine that these numbers are 9 and 5.

Whence, $x^2 + 14x + 45 = (x + 9)(x + 5)$.

2. Factor $x^2 - 5x + 4$.

We find two numbers whose sum is -5 and product 4.

Since the sum is negative, and the product positive, the numbers must both be negative.

By inspection, we determine that the numbers are -4 and -1.

Whence, $x^2 - 5x + 4 = (x - 4)(x - 1)$.

3. Factor $x^2 + 6x - 16$.

We find two numbers whose sum is 6 and product -16.

Since the sum is positive, and the product negative, the numbers must be of opposite sign; and the positive number must have the greater absolute value.

By inspection, we determine that the numbers are $+8$ and -2.

Whence, $x^2 + 6x - 16 = (x + 8)(x - 2)$.

4. Factor $x^4 - abx^2 - 42\,a^2b^2$.

We find two numbers whose sum is -1 and product -42.

The numbers must be of opposite sign, and the negative number must have the greater absolute value.

By inspection, we determine that the numbers are -7 and $+6$.

Whence, $x^4 - abx^2 - 42\,a^2b^2 = (x^2 - 7\,ab)(x^2 + 6\,ab)$.

5. Factor $1 + 2a - 99a^2$.

We find two numbers whose sum is $+2$ and product -99.

By inspection, we determine that the numbers are $+11$ and -9.

Whence, $1 + 2a - 99a^2 = (1 + 11a)(1 - 9a)$.

If the x^2 term is negative, the entire expression should be enclosed in parentheses preceded by a $-$ sign.

6. Factor $24 + 5x - x^2$.

We have, $24 + 5x - x^2 = -(x^2 - 5x - 24)$
$$= -(x - 8)(x + 3)$$
$$= (8 - x)(3 + x).$$

In case the numbers are large, we may proceed as follows:

Required the numbers whose sum is -26 and product -192.

One of the numbers must be $+$, and the other $-$.

Taking in order, beginning with the factors $+1 \times -192$, all possible pairs of factors of -192, of which one is $+$ and the other $-$, we have:

$$+ 1 \times - 192.$$
$$+ 2 \times - 96.$$
$$+ 3 \times - 64.$$
$$+ 4 \times - 48.$$
$$+ 6 \times - 32.$$

Since the sum of $+6$ and -32 is -26, they are the numbers required.

EXERCISE 14

Factor the following:

1. $x^2 + 18x + 56$.
2. $x^2 + 16x - 57$.
3. $a^2 - 10a - 75$.
4. $y^4 - 21y^2 + 104$.
5. $77 - 4x - x^2$.
6. $84 + 5n - n^2$.
7. $1 + 17m + 70m^2$.
8. $1 + 5ab - 14a^2b^2$.
9. $(x - y)^2 - 15(x - y) - 16$.
10. $(m - n)^2 + 21(m - n) - 130$.

11. $(a + x)^2 - 28(a + x) + 192$.
12. $95 - 14x^4 - x^8$.
13. $105 + 8m^3 - m^6$.
14. $1 + 36xy^2 + 68x^2y^4$.
15. $x^6 - 17x^3yz^2 + 72y^2z^4$.
16. $a^2 - 6ab - 91b^2$.
17. $a^2 + 32amn + 112m^2n^2$.
18. $x^4y^4 + 7x^2y^2z - 170z^2$.
19. $x^2 - (2m + 3n)x + 6mn$.
20. $x^2 - (a - b)x - ab$.

174. Case VII. *When the expression is in the form*
$$ax^2 + bx + c.$$

If a is a perfect square, and b is divisible by $\sqrt{a}$, we may factor the expression directly by the method of § 173.

1. Factor $9x^2 - 18x + 5$.

We have, $\quad 9x^2 - 18x + 5 = (3x)^2 - 6(3x) + 5.$

We find two numbers whose sum is -6, and product 5. The numbers are -5 and -1.

Then, $\quad 9x^2 - 18x + 5 = (3x - 5)(3x - 1).$

If b is not divisible by $\sqrt{a}$, or if a is not a perfect square, we multiply and divide the expression by a, which, by § 96, does not change its value.

2. Factor $6x^2 + 5x - 4$.

Multiplying and dividing the expression by 6, we have

$$6x^2 + 5x - 4 = \frac{36x^2 + 30x - 24}{6} = \frac{(6x)^2 + 5(6x) - 24}{6}.$$

The numbers are 8 and -3.

Then, $\quad 6x^2 + 5x - 4 = \frac{(6x + 8)(6x - 3)}{2 \times 3}.$

Dividing the first factor by 2, and the second by 3, we have
$$6x^2 + 5x - 4 = (3x + 4)(2x - 1).$$

In certain cases, the coefficient of x^2 may be made a perfect square by multiplying by a number less than itself.

3. Factor $8x^2 + 26xy + 15y^2$.

Multiplying and dividing by 2, we have

$$8x^2 + 26xy + 15y^2 = \frac{16x^2 + 52xy + 30y^2}{2}$$
$$= \frac{(4x)^2 + 13y(4x) + 30y^2}{2}$$
$$= \frac{(4x + 10y)(4x + 3y)}{2}$$
$$= (2x + 5y)(4x + 3y).$$

4. Factor $2 + 5x - 3x^2$.

$$2 + 5x - 3x^2 = -(3x^2 - 5x - 2)$$
$$= \frac{(3x)^2 - 5(3x) - 6}{-3}$$
$$= \frac{(3x - 6)(3x + 1)}{-3}$$
$$= (2 - x)(1 + 3x).$$

EXERCISE 15

Factor the following:

1. $4x^2 + 28x + 45$.
2. $6x^2 + x - 2$.
3. $25x^2 - 25mx - 6m^2$.
4. $10x^2 - 39x + 14$.
5. $12x^2 + 11x + 2$.
6. $20a^2x^2 - 23ax + 6$.
7. $36x^2 + 12x - 35$.

8. $72 + 7x - 49x^2$.
9. $6 - x - 15x^2$.
10. $5 + 9n^2 - 18n^4$.
11. $21x^2 + 23xy + 6y^2$.
12. $18x^2 - 27abx - 35a^2b^2$.
13. $7(a - b)^2 - 30(a - b) + 8$.
14. $12(x + y)^2 + 17(x + y) - 7$.
15. $14(m - n)^2 + 39a(m - n) + 10a^2$.
16. $acx^2 - (ad + bc)x + bd$.

175. It is not possible to factor every expression of the form $x^2 + ax + b$ by the method of § 173.

Thus, let it be required to factor $x^2 + 18x + 35$.

We have to find two numbers whose sum is 18, and product 35.

The only pairs of positive integral factors of 35 are 7 and 5, and 35 and 1; and in neither case is the sum 18.

In Chap. XIX will be given a *general* method for factoring any expression of the form $ax^2 + bx + c$.

176. CASE VIII. *When the expression is the cube of a binomial.*

Ex. Factor $8a^3 - 36a^2b^2 + 54ab^4 - 27b^6$.

We must show that the expression is in the form of the cube of a binomial, as obtained by the rule of § 135, and find its cube root.

We can write the expression as follows:

$$(2\,a)^3 - 3(2\,a)^2(3\,b^2) + 3(2\,a)(3\,b^2)^2 - (3\,b^2)^3.$$

This shows that it is a perfect cube, and that its cube root is $2\,a - 3\,b^2$.

Then, $8\,a^3 - 36\,a^2b^2 + 54\,ab^4 - 27\,b^6 = (2\,a - 3\,b^2)^3.$

Factor the following:

EXERCISE 16

1. $x^3 + 3\,x^2 + 3\,x + 1.$
2. $8 - 12\,a + 6\,a^2 - a^3.$
3. $1 + 9\,m + 27\,m^2 + 27\,m^3.$
4. $64\,n^3 - 48\,n^2 + 12\,n - 1.$
5. $8\,a^3 + 36\,a^2b + 54\,ab^2 + 27\,b^3.$
6. $27\,a^3b^3 - 108\,a^2b^2c + 144\,abc^2 - 64\,c^3.$
7. $125\,x^3 - 600\,x^2y + 960\,xy^2 - 512\,y^3.$
8. $216\,m^6 + 756\,m^4x^3 + 882\,m^2x^6 + 343\,x^9.$

177. Case IX. *When the expression is the sum or difference of two perfect cubes.*

By § 138, the sum or difference of two perfect cubes is divisible by the sum or difference, respectively, of their cube roots.

In either case the quotient may be obtained by the rules of § 138.

1. Factor $x^6 - 27\,y^9z^3.$

By § 166, the cube root of x^6 is x^2, and of $27\,y^9z^3$ is $3\,y^3z$. Then one factor is $x^2 - 3\,y^3z$.

Dividing $x^6 - 27\,y^9z^3$ by $x^2 - 3\,y^3z$, the quotient is

$$x^4 + 3\,x^2y^3z + 9\,y^6z^2 \ (\S 138).$$

Then, $x^6 - 27\,y^9z^3 = (x^2 - 3\,y^3z)(x^4 + 3\,x^2y^3z + 9\,y^6z^2).$

2. Factor $a^6 + b^6.$

One factor is $a^2 + b^2$.

Dividing $a^6 + b^6$ by $a^2 + b^2$, the quotient is $a^4 - a^2b^2 + b^4.$

Then, $a^6 + b^6 = (a^2 + b^2)(a^4 - a^2b^2 + b^4).$

3. Factor $(x+a)^3 - (x-a)^3$.

$(x+a)^3 - (x-a)^3$
$$= [(x+a) - (x-a)][(x+a)^2 + (x+a)(x-a) + (x-a)^2]$$
$$= (x+a-x+a)(x^2 + 2ax + a^2 + x^2 - a^2 + x^2 - 2ax + a^2)$$
$$= 2a(3x^2 + a^2).$$

178. CASE X. *When the expression is the sum or difference of two equal odd powers of two numbers.*

By § 142, the sum or difference of two equal odd powers of two numbers is divisible by the sum or difference, respectively, of the numbers.

The quotient may be obtained by laws of § 143.

Ex. Factor $a^5 + 32\,b^5$.

By § 130, $\qquad\qquad 32\,b^5 = (2\,b)^5$.

Then, by § 142, one factor is $a + 2\,b$.

Dividing $a^5 + 32\,b^5$ by $a + 2\,b$, the quotient is

$$a^4 - a^3(2\,b) + a^2(2\,b)^2 - a(2\,b)^3 + (2\,b)^4 \quad (\text{§ 143}).$$

Whence,

$$a^5 + 32\,b^5 = (a + 2\,b)(a^4 - 2\,a^3b + 4\,a^2b^2 - 8\,ab^3 + 16\,b^4).$$

EXERCISE 17

Factor the following :

1. $8\,m^3 - n^3$.
2. $x^3y^3 + 125\,z^3$.
3. $a^6 + 64$.
4. $216\,a^3m^6 - 343\,n^9$.
5. $729\,a^3b^3 + 512\,c^3d^3$.
6. $m^3 - (m+n)^3$.
7. $(x+y)^3 + (x-y)^3$.
8. $27(a-b)^3 - 8\,b^3$.
9. $(2a+x)^3 - (a+2x)^3$.
10. $(5x - 2y)^3 + (3x - 4y)^3$.
11. $x^5 + y^5$.
12. $a^5 - 1$.
13. $a^7 - b^7$.
14. $1 + x^7$.
15. $m^9 + n^9$.
16. $a^9 - 1$.
17. $32\,a^5 - b^5$.
18. $243\,x^5 + y^5$.
19. $m^{14} + 128\,n^7$.
20. $1024\,a^5b^5 - 243\,c^{10}$.

179. By application of the rules already given, an expression may often be resolved into more than two factors.

If the terms of the expression have a common factor, the method of § 155 should always be applied first.

1. Factor $2\,ax^3y^2 - 8\,axy^4$.

By § 155, $2\,ax^3y^2 - 8\,axy^4 = 2\,axy^2(x^2 - 4\,y^2)$

$$= 2\,axy^2(x + 2\,y)(x - 2\,y), \text{ by § 171.}$$

2. Factor $a^6 - b^6$.

By § 171, $\qquad a^6 - b^6 = (a^3 + b^3)(a^3 - b^3)$.

Whence, by § 177,

$$a^6 - b^6 = (a + b)(a^2 - ab + b^2)(a - b)(a^2 + ab + b^2).$$

3. Factor $x^8 - y^8$.

By § 171, $\qquad x^8 - y^8 = (x^4 + y^4)(x^4 - y^4)$

$$= (x^4 + y^4)(x^2 + y^2)(x^2 - y^2)$$

$$= (x^4 + y^4)(x^2 + y^2)(x + y)(x - y).$$

4. Factor $3\,(m + n)^2 - 2\,(m^2 - n^2)$.

$3\,(m + n)^2 - 2\,(m^2 - n^2) = 3\,(m + n)^2 - 2\,(m + n)(m - n)$

$$= (m + n)[3\,(m + n) - 2\,(m - n)]$$

$$= (m + n)(3\,m + 3\,n - 2\,m + 2\,n)$$

$$= (m + n)(m + 5\,n).$$

5. Factor $a(a - 1) - b(b - 1)$.

$a(a - 1) - b(b - 1) = a^2 - a - b^2 + b$

$$= a^2 - b^2 - a + b$$

$$= (a + b)(a - b) - (a - b)$$

$$= (a - b)(a + b - 1).$$

EXERCISE 18

Factor the following :

1. $x^4 - 625$.

2. $a^{12} - 1$.

3. $m^{16} - 1$.

4. $x^6 - 26\,x^3 - 27$.

5. $(a^2 + 4\,ab + b^2)^2 - (a^2 + b^2)^2$.

6. $12\,x^6 - 18\,x^5 - 6\,x^4 + 9\,x^3$.

7. $81\,m^4 - 256\,n^8$.

8. $a^{14} - x^{14}$.

9. $x^6 - 16\,x^3y^3 + 64\,y^6$.

10. $(16\,m^2 + n^2)^2 - 64\,m^2n^2$.

11. $2\,a^7x - 8\,a^5x^3 + 2\,a^3x^5 - 8\,ax^7$.

12. $9\,a^2c^2 - 16\,a^2d^2 - 36\,b^2c^2 + 64\,b^2d^2$.

13. $x^{14} - 2\,x^7 + 1$.

14. $729 - n^6$.

15. $a^2b^3 + a^2y^3 - b^3x^2 - x^2y^3$.

16. $48\,x^3y - 52\,x^2y^2 - 140\,xy^3$.

17. $16\,a^7 - 72\,a^6 + 108\,a^5 - 54\,a^4$.

18. $(m + n)^4 - 2(m + n)^3 + (m + n)^2$.

19. Resolve $a^9 + 512$ into three factors by the method of § 177.

20. $a^2 - m^2 + a + m$.　　**22.** $n^{10} - 1024$.

21. $(x^2 + 4x)^2 - 37(x^2 + 4x) + 160$.　**23.** $m^3 + m + x^3 + x$.

24. $a^2c^2 - 4b^2c^2 - 9a^2d^2 + 36b^2d^2$.

25. $(m - n)(x^2 - y^2) + (x + y)(m^2 - n^2)$.

26. $(x - 1)^3 + 6(x - 1)^2 + 9(x - 1)$.

27. $a^2 - 4b^2 - a - 2b$.

28. $(m + n)(m^2 - x^2) - (m + x)(m^2 - n^2)$.

29. $(x^2 + 4y^2 - z^2)^2 - 16x^2y^2$.　　**31.** $a^3b^3 + 27a^3y^3 - 8b^3x^3 - 216x^3y^3$.

30. $(x^2 - 9x)^2 + 4(x^2 - 9x) - 140$.　**32.** $(2x^2 - 3)^2 - x^2$.

33. $(m^2 + m)^2 + 2(m^2 + m)(m + 1) + (m + 1)^2$.

34. $64a^3x^3 + 8a^3 - 8x^3 - 1$.　　**36.** $(x + 2y)^3 - x(x^2 - 4y^2)$.

35. $(4a^2 - b^2 - 9)^2 - 36b^2$.　　**37.** $(1 + x^3) + (1 + x)^3$.

38. $(a^2 + 6a + 8)^2 - 14(a^2 + 6a + 8) - 15$.

39. $a^4 - 9 + 2a(a^2 + 3)$.　　**43.** $m^8 - m^5 + 32m^3 - 32$.

40. $(x^3 + y^3) - xy(x + y)$.　　**44.** $a(a - c) - b(b - c)$.

41. $(a^3 - 8m^3) - a(a - 2m)^2$.　**45.** $m^2(m + p) + n^2(n - p)$.

42. $18a^5b + 22a^3b^3 + 8ab^5$.　**46.** $x^9 + 8x^5 + x^3 + 8$.

47. $(27m^3 - x^3) + (3m + x)(9m^2 - 12mx + x^2)$.

48. $(4a^2 + 9)^2 - 24a(4a^2 + 9) + 144a^2$.

49. $m^9 + m^6 - 64m^3 - 64$.

50. $(x^2 + y^2)^3 - 4x^2y^2(x^2 + y^2)$.

51. $a^5 + a^4b + a^3b^2 + a^2b^3 + ab^4 + b^5$.

52. $(8n^3 - 27) + (2n - 3)(4n^2 + 4n - 6)$.

180. Factoring by Substitution.

1. Factor $x^3 - 7x^2 + 10x + 6$.

By § 140, if the expression becomes 0 when x is put equal to a, then $x - a$ is a factor.

The positive and negative integral factors of 6 are 1, 2, 3, 6, $-1, -2, -3$, and -6.

It is best to try the numbers in their order of absolute magnitude.

If $x = 1$, the expression becomes $1 - 7 + 10 + 6$.

If $x = -1$, the expression becomes $-1 - 7 - 10 + 6$.

If $x = 2$, the expression becomes $8 - 28 + 20 + 6$.

If $x = -2$, the expression becomes $-8 - 28 - 20 + 6$.

If $x = 3$, the expression becomes $27 - 63 + 30 + 6$, or 0.

This shows that $x - 3$ is a factor.

Dividing the expression by $x - 3$, the quotient is $x^2 - 4x - 2$.
Then, $x^3 - 7x^2 + 10x + 6 = (x - 3)(x^2 - 4x - 2)$.

2. Prove that a is a factor of

$$(a + b + c)(ab + bc + ca) - (a + b)(b + c)(c + a).$$

Putting $a = 0$, the expression becomes

$$(b + c)bc - b(b + c)c, \text{ or } 0.$$

Then, by § 140, a is a factor of the expression.

3. Prove that $m + n$ is a factor of

$$m^4 - 4m^3n + 2m^2n^2 + 5mn^3 - 2n^4.$$

Putting $m = -n$, we have

$$n^4 + 4n^4 + 2n^4 - 5n^4 - 2n^4, \text{ or } 0.$$

Then, $m + n$ is a factor.

EXERCISE 19

Factor the following :

1. $x^3 + 4x^2 + 7x - 12$.

2. $x^4 - x^3 + 6x^2 + 14x + 6$.

3. $x^3 - x^2 - 11x - 10$.

4. $x^3 - 9x^2 + 15x + 9$.

5. $x^3 - 18x + 8$.

6. $x^3 - 5x^2 - 8x + 48$.

7. $x^4 + 8x^3 + 13x^2 - 13x - 4$.

8. $2x^4 - 7x^3 + 10x^2 - 14x + 12$.

Find, without actual division,

9. Whether $x - 3$ is a factor of $x^3 - 6x^2 + 13x - 12$.

10. Whether $x + 2$ is a factor of $x^3 + 7x^2 - 6$.

11. Whether x is a factor of $x(y + z)^2 + y(z + x)^2 + z(x + y)^2$.

12. Whether a is a factor of $a^3(b - c)^3 + b^3(c - a)^3 + c^3(a - b)^3$.

13. Whether $x - y$ is a factor of $(x - y)^3 + (y - z)^3 + (z - x)^3$.

14. Whether $m + n$ is a factor of $m(m + 2n)^3 - n(2m + n)^3$.

15. Whether $a + b + c$ is a factor of

$$a(b + c) + b(c + a) + c(a + b) + a^2 + b^2 + c^2.$$

181. Factoring of Symmetrical Expressions.

The method of § 180 is advantageous in the factoring of symmetrical expressions.   (§§ 146, 147.)

1. Factor

$$a(b+c)^2 + b(c+a)^2 + c(a+b)^2 - a^2(b+c) - b^2(c+a) - c^2(a+b).$$

The expression is symmetrical with respect to a, b, and c.

Being of the third degree, the only literal factors which it can have are three of the type a; three of the type $a+b$; or $a+b+c$, and a factor of the second degree.

Putting $a=0$, the expression becomes

$$bc^2 + cb^2 - b^2c - c^2b, \text{ or } 0.$$

Then, by § 140, a is a factor; and, by symmetry, b and c are factors.

The expression, being of the third degree, can have no other literal factor; but it may have a *numerical* factor.

Let the given expression $= mabc$.

To determine m, let $a = b = c = 1$.

Then, $4 + 4 + 4 - 2 - 2 - 2 = m$, or $m = 6$.

Whence, the given expression $= 6\,abc$.

2. Factor $x^2(y+z) + y^2(z+x) + z^2(x+y) + 3\,xyz$.

The expression is symmetrical with respect to x, y, and z.

The only literal factors which it can have are three of the type x; three of the type $x+y$; or $x+y+z$, and a factor of the second degree.

It is evident that neither x, y, nor z is a factor.

Putting x equal to $-y$, the expression becomes

$$y^2(y+z) + y^2(z-y) - 3\,y^2z,$$

which is not 0.

Then, $x+y$ is not a factor; and, by symmetry, neither $y+z$ nor $z+x$ is a factor.

Putting x equal to $-y-z$, the expression becomes

$$(y+z)^2(y+z) - y^3 - z^3 - 3\,yz(y+z)$$
$$= y^3 + 3\,y^2z + 3\,yz^2 + z^3 - y^3 - z^3 - 3\,y^2z - 3\,yz^2 = 0.$$

Then, $x+y+z$ is a factor.

The other factor must be of the second degree; and, as it is symmetrical with respect to x, y, and z, it must be of the form

$$m(x^2 + y^2 + z^2), \text{ or } n(xy + yz + zx).$$

The first of these cannot be a factor; for, if it were, there would be terms involving x^3, y^3, and z^3 in the given expression.

Then, the given expression $= n(x + y + z)(xy + yz + zx)$.

To determine n, let $x = 1$, $y = 1$, and $z = 0$.

Then, $1 + 1 = 2n$, and $n = 1$.

Then, the given expression $= (x + y + z)(xy + yz + zx)$.

3. Factor $ab(a - b) + bc(b - c) + ca(c - a)$.

The expression is cyclo-symmetrical with respect to a, b, and c.

It is evident that neither a, b, nor c is a factor.

The expression becomes 0 when a is put equal to b.

Then, $a - b$ is a factor; and, by symmetry, $b - c$ and $c - a$ are factors.

The expression can have no other literal factor, but may have a numerical one.

Let the given expression $= m(a - b)(b - c)(c - a)$.

To determine m, let $a = 2$, $b = 1$, and $c = 0$.

Then, $2 = -2m$, and $m = -1$.

Then, the given expression $= -(a - b)(b - c)(c - a)$.

EXERCISE 20

Factor the following:

1. $m^3 + 2m^2n + 2mn^2 + n^3$.
2. $(ab + bc + ca)(a + b + c) - a^2(b + c) - b^2(c + a) - c^2(a + b)$.
3. $x^2(y + z) + y^2(z + x) + z^2(x + y) + 2xyz$.
4. $a(b + c)^2 + b(c + a)^2 + c(a + b)^2 - 4abc$.
5. $a^2(b - c) + b^2(c - a) + c^2(a - b)$.
6. $(x + y + z)(xy + yz + zx) - (x + y)(y + z)(z + x)$.
7. $ab(a + b) + bc(b + c) + ca(c + a) + 2abc$.
8. $(x + y + z)^3 - (x^3 + y^3 + z^3)$.
9. $(x + y + z)(xy + yz + zx) - xyz$.
10. $(x - y)^3 + (y - z)^3 + (z - x)^3$.
11. $a^3(b - c) + b^3(c - a) + c^3(a - b)$.

SOLUTION OF EQUATIONS BY FACTORING

182. Consider the equation

$$A \times B \times C \times \cdots = 0; \tag{1}$$

where A, B, C, $\cdot$, are integral expressions which involve the unknown numbers.

By § 49, if $A \times B \times C \times \cdots = 0$, some one of the factors A, B, C, $\cdot$, must equal 0.

We obtain in this way a series of equations

$$A = 0, \; B = 0, \; C = 0, \cdots. \tag{2}$$

We will now show that these are equivalent (§ 114) to (1).

Any solution of (1) makes $A \times B \times C \times \cdots$ identically equal to 0.

It then makes at least one of the factors A, B, C, $\cdots$, identically equal to 0; and hence satisfies at least one of the equations (2).

Again, any solution of any of the equations (2) makes $A \times B \times C \times \cdots$ identically equal to 0; and hence satisfies (1).

Then, (1) and (2) are equivalent.

It follows from the above that the equation

$$A \times B \times C \times \cdots = 0$$

may be solved by placing the factors of the first member separately equal to zero, and solving the resulting equations.

1. Solve the equation $2 x^2 - x = 0$.

Factoring the first member, the equation becomes

$$x(2x - 1) = 0 \; (§ 155).$$

Placing the factors separately equal to 0,

$$x = 0;$$

and $\qquad\qquad 2x - 1 = 0, \text{ or } x = \dfrac{1}{2}.$

2. Solve the equation $x^3 + 4 x^2 - x - 4 = 0$.

Factoring the first member (§§ 156, 171),

$$(x + 4)(x^2 - 1) = 0, \text{ or } (x + 4)(x + 1)(x - 1) = 0.$$

Then,
$$x + 4 = 0, \text{ or } x = -4;$$
$$x + 1 = 0, \text{ or } x = -1;$$
and
$$x - 1 = 0, \text{ or } x = 1.$$

3. Solve the equation $(2x - 3)^3 = (x - 1)^3 + (x - 2)^3$.

Factoring the second member, we have

$$[(x-1) + (x-2)][(x-1)^2 - (x-1)(x-2) + (x-2)^2]$$
$$= (2x - 3)(x^2 - 2x + 1 - x^2 + 3x - 2 + x^2 - 4x + 4)$$
$$= (2x - 3)(x^2 - 3x + 3).$$

Then the given equation can be written

$$(2x - 3)[(2x - 3)^2 - (x^2 - 3x + 3)] = 0.$$

Or, $(2x - 3)(4x^2 - 12x + 9 - x^2 + 3x - 3) = 0.$

Or, $(2x - 3)(3x^2 - 9x + 6) = 0.$

Dividing both members by 3,

$(2x - 3)(x^2 - 3x + 2) = 0, \text{ or } (2x - 3)(x - 1)(x - 2) = 0.$

Then,
$$2x - 3 = 0, \text{ or } x = \frac{3}{2};$$
$$x - 1 = 0, \text{ or } x = 1;$$
and
$$x - 2 = 0, \text{ or } x = 2.$$

The above examples illustrate the principle (§ 715) that the degree (§ 113) of an equation involving one unknown number indicates the number of its roots; thus, an equation of the third degree has three roots; of the fourth degree, four roots; etc. It should be observed that the roots are not necessarily *unequal*; thus, the equation $x^2 - 2x + 1 = 0$ may be written $(x - 1)(x - 1) = 0$, and therefore the two roots are 1 and 1.

EXERCISE 21

Solve the following equations:

1. $5x^4 + 35x^3 = 0.$

2. $3x^3 - 108x = 0.$

3. $(4x - 3)(4x^2 - 25) = 0.$

4. $x^2 + 23x + 102 = 0.$

5. $x^2 + 4x - 96 = 0.$

6. $x^2 - 17x - 110 = 0.$

7. $(5x + 1)(x^2 + 22x + 121) = 0.$

8. $x^4 - 18x^3 + 32x^2 = 0.$

9. $6x^2 + 7x + 2 = 0.$

10. $10x^2 - 7x - 12 = 0.$

11. $15x^2 + x - 2 = 0.$

12. $12x^3 - 29x^2 + 15x = 0.$

13. $x^2 - ax + bx - ab = 0.$

14. $x^2 + mx + nx + mn = 0.$

15. $x^2 - 2cx - 8x + 16c = 0.$ 16. $x^2 + 3m^2x - 5m^3x - 15m^5 = 0.$

17. $(4x^2 - 28x + 49)(x^2 - 3x - 10)(8x^2 + 14x - 15) = 0.$

18. $27x^3 + 18x^2 - 3x - 2 = 0.$

19. $x^3 + 6x^2 - x - 30 = 0$ (§ 180).

20. $x^4 + 2x^3 - 13x^2 - 14x + 24 = 0.$

21. $(x-2)^2 - 4(x-2) + 3 = 0.$ 22. $(x-2)^3 + 8x^3 = (3x-2)^3.$

23. $x^2 - 4 - (x-2)(3x^2 + 4x - 4) = 0.$

24. $(x^2-1)(x^2-9) = -3(x-1)(x+3).$

25. $(2x+1)^3 - (x+2)^3 = (x-1)^3.$

26. $(x^2-1)(x^3-8) - 19(x+1)(x^2-3x+2) = 0.$

183. It follows from §§ 140 and 182 that

If the first member of the equation

$$A = 0$$

is a rational and integral polynomial involving the unknown number x, and divisible by x − a, the equation has a as a root.

For by § 140, the first member has $x - a$ as a factor.

If A is divisible by $ax - b$, the equation has $\dfrac{b}{a}$ as a root.

Ex. Find whether $-\dfrac{2}{3}$ is a root of the equation

$$3x^4 + 8x^3 + 13x^2 + 9x + 2 = 0.$$

Dividing the first member by $3x + 2$, the quotient is $x^3 + 2x^2 + 3x + 1$; then, $-\dfrac{2}{3}$ is a root.

EXERCISE 22

Find whether :

1. 4 is a root of $x^3 - x^2 - 19x + 28 = 0.$

2. $-\dfrac{5}{2}$ is a root of $6x^3 + 13x^2 + 5x + 25 = 0.$

3. $\dfrac{3}{4}$ is a root of $4x^3 - 11x^2 - 14x - 15 = 0.$

4. -5 is a root of $4x^4 + 22x^3 + 9x^2 - 8x - 15 = 0.$

5. $\dfrac{1}{3}$ is a root of $15x^4 - 17x^3 + 7x^2 - 19x + 6 = 0.$

6. -3 is a root of $9x^4 + 26x^3 - 8x^2 - 11x - 3 = 0.$

IX. HIGHEST COMMON FACTOR. LOWEST COMMON MULTIPLE

HIGHEST COMMON FACTOR

In the present chapter, we consider only rational and integral expressions (§ 63), with integral numerical coefficients.

184. The **Highest Common Factor** (H. C. F.) of two or more expressions is their common factor of *highest degree* (§ 64); or if several common factors are of equally high degree, it is the one having the numerical coefficient of greatest absolute value in its term of highest degree.

There are always two forms of the highest common factor, one of which is the *negative* of the other.

Thus, in the expressions $a^2 - ab$ and $b^2 - ab$, either $a - b$ or $b - a$ will exactly divide each expression.

185. Two expressions are said to be *prime to each other* when unity is their highest common factor.

In determining the highest common factor of expressions, it is convenient to distinguish two cases.

186. CASE I. *When the expressions are monomials, or polynomials which can be readily factored by inspection.*

1. Required the H. C. F. of $42\ a^3b^2$, $70\ a^2bc$, and $98\ a^4b^3d^2$.

The H. C. F. of 42, 70, and 98 is 14.

It is evident by inspection that the expression of highest degree which will exactly divide a^3b^2, a^2bc, and $a^4b^3d^2$, is a^2b.

Then, the H. C. F. of the given expressions is $14\ a^2b$.

It will be observed, in the above result, that *the exponent of each letter is the lowest exponent with which it occurs in any of the given expressions.*

2. Required the H. C. F. of

$$5\,x^4y - 45\,x^2y \text{ and } 10\,x^3y^2 + 40\,x^2y^2 - 210\,xy^2.$$

By §§ 155, 171, and 173,

$$5\,x^4y - 45\,x^2y = 5\,x^2y\,(x^2 - 9)$$
$$= 5\,x^2y\,(x + 3)(x - 3),$$
$$\text{and } 10\,x^3y^2 + 40\,x^2y^2 - 210\,xy^2 = 10\,xy^2\,(x^2 + 4\,x - 21)$$
$$= 10\,xy^2\,(x + 7)(x - 3).$$

The H. C. F. of the numerical coefficients 5 and 10 is 5.

It is evident by inspection that the H. C. F. of the literal portions of the expressions is $xy\,(x - 3)$.

Then, the H. C. F. of the given expressions is $5\,xy\,(x - 3)$.

EXERCISE 23

Find the highest common factor of :

1. $64\,x^3 + 27y^3,\ 16\,x^2 - 9\,y^2,$ and $16\,x^2 + 24\,xy + 9\,y^2.$

2. $2\,x^3 - 12\,x^2 + 16\,x,\ 3\,x^4 - 3\,x^3 - 36\,x^2,$ and $5\,x^5 + 5\,x^4 - 100\,x^3.$

3. $125\,m^3 - 8,\ 10\,m^2 + m - 2,$ and $25\,m^2 - 20\,m + 4.$

4. $a^4 - 3\,a^2 - 28,\ a^4 - 16,$ and $a^3 + a^2 + 4\,a + 4.$

5. $2\,x^3 + x^2 - 6\,x - 3,\ 6\,x^2 + 19\,x + 8,$ and $8\,x^3 + 12\,x^2 + 6\,x + 1.$

6. $27\,x^3 - y^3,\ 243\,x^5 - y^5,$ and $12\,x^2 - 25\,xy + 7\,y^2.$

7. $a^2 + b^2 + c^2 - 2\,ab + 2\,ac - 2\,bc,\ a^2 + b^2 - c^2 - 2\,ab,$ and $a^2 - b^2 - c^2 + 2\,bc.$

8. $27\,a^3 + 135\,a^2b + 225\,ab^2 + 125\,b^3,\ 3\,a^2 + 2\,ab - 5\,b^2,$ and $3\,ac - 6\,ad + 5\,bc - 10\,bd.$

9. $4\,x^4 + 11\,x^2 + 25,\ 2\,x^3 - 9\,x^2 + 14\,x - 15,$ and $2\,x^3 + x^2 - x + 10.$

187. CASE II. *When the expressions are polynomials which cannot be readily factored by inspection.*

Let A and B be two polynomials, arranged according to the descending powers of some common letter, and let the exponent of that letter in the first term of A be not lower than its exponent in the first term of B.

Suppose that, when A is divided by B, the quotient is p, and the remainder C.

We will prove that the H. C. F. of B and C is the same as the H. C. F. of A and B.

The operation of division is shown as follows :

$$B) \ A \ (p$$
$$\frac{pB}{C}$$

We will first prove that every common factor of B and C is a common factor of A and B.

Let F be any common factor of B and C; and let

$$B = bF, \text{ and } C = cF. \tag{1}$$

Since the dividend is equal to the product of the quotient and the divisor, plus the remainder, we have

$$A = pB + C. \tag{2}$$

Substituting in (2) the values of B and C from (1),

$$A = pbF + cF = F (pb + c). \tag{3}$$

It is evident from (1) and (3) that F is a common factor of A and B.

We will next prove that every common factor of A and B is a common factor of B and C.

Let F' be any common factor of A and B; and let

$$A = mF', \text{ and } B = nF'. \tag{4}$$

From (2), $C = A - pB$

$$= mF' - pnF' = F' (m - pn). \tag{5}$$

From (4) and (5), F' is a common factor of B and C.

It follows from the above that the H. C. F. of B and C is the same as the H. C. F. of A and B.

188. Let A, B, and C have the same meanings as in § 187.

Suppose that when B is divided by C, the quotient is q, and the remainder D; that when C is divided by D, the quotient is r, and the remainder E, and so on; and that we finally arrive at a remainder H, which exactly divides the preceding divisor G.

By § 187, the H. C. F. of C and D is the same as the H. C. F. of B and C; the H. C. F. of D and E is the same as the H. C. F. of C and D; and so on.

Hence the H. C. F. of G and H is the same as the H. C. F. of A and B.

But since H exactly divides G, H is itself the H. C. F. of G and H.

Therefore, H is the H. C. F. of A and B.

We derive from the above the following rule for the H. C. F. of two polynomials, A and B, arranged according to the descending powers of some common letter, the exponent of that letter in the first term of A being not lower than its exponent in the first term of B:

Divide A by B.

If there be a remainder, divide the divisor by it; and continue thus to make the remainder the divisor, and the preceding divisor the dividend, until there is no remainder.

The last divisor is the H. C. F. *required.*

Note 1. It is important to keep the work throughout in descending powers of some common letter; and each division should be continued until the exponent of this letter in the first term of the remainder is less than its exponent in the first term of the divisor.

Note 2. If the terms of one of the expressions have a common factor which is not a common factor of the terms of the other, it may be removed; for it can evidently form no part of the highest common factor. In like manner, we may divide any remainder by a factor which is not a factor of the preceding divisor.

Note 3. If the first term of the dividend, or of any remainder, is not divisible by the first term of the divisor, it may be made so by multiplying the dividend or remainder by any term which is not a factor of the divisor.

Note 4. If the first term of any remainder is negative, the sign of each term of the remainder may be changed. (See note to § 184.)

Note 5. If the given expressions have a common factor which can be seen by inspection, remove it, and find the H. C. F. of the resulting expressions.

The result, multiplied by the common factor, will be the H. C. F. of the given expressions.

Note 6. The operation of division may usually be abridged by the use of detached coefficients (§ 104).

1. Required the H.C.F. of

$$6\,a^3 + 7\,a^2b - 3\,ab^2 \text{ and } 4\,a^3b + 8\,a^2b^2 - 3\,ab^3 - 9\,b^4.$$

We remove the factor a from the first expression, and the factor b from the second (Note 2).

We then find the H. C. F. of

$$6\,a^2 + 7\,ab - 3\,b^2 \text{ and } 4\,a^3 + 8\,a^2b - 3\,ab^2 - 9\,b^3.$$

Since $4\,a^3$ is not divisible by $6\,a^2$, we multiply the second expression by 3 (Note 3).

$$
\begin{array}{r}
4\,a^3 + 8\,a^2b - 3\,ab^2 - 9\,b^3 \\
3 \\
\hline
\end{array}
$$

$$6\,a^2 + 7\,ab - 3\,b^2)\overline{12\,a^3 + 24\,a^2b - 9\,ab^2 - 27\,b^3}(2\,a$$
$$\underline{12\,a^3 + 14\,a^2b - 6\,ab^2}$$
$$10\,a^2b - 3\,ab^2 - 27b^3$$

Since $10\,a^2b$ is not divisible by $6\,a^2$, we multiply this remainder by 3.

$$6\,a^2 + 7\,ab - 3\,b^2)30\,a^2b - 9\,ab^2 - 81\,b^3(5\,b$$
$$\underline{30\,a^2b + 35\,ab^2 - 15\,b^3}$$
$$-44\,ab^2 - 66\,b^3$$

Dividing the remainder by $-22\,b^2$ (Notes 2, 4),

$$2\,a + 3\,b)6\,a^2 + 7\,ab - 3\,b^2(3\,a - b$$
$$\underline{6\,a^2 + 9\,ab}$$
$$-2\,ab$$
$$\underline{-2\,ab - 3\,b^2}$$

Then, $2\,a + 3\,b$ is the H. C. F. required.

2. Required the H. C. F. of

$$2\,x^4 - 3\,x^3 - x^2 + x, \text{ and } 6\,x^4 - x^3 + 3\,x^2 - 2\,x.$$

Removing the common factor x (Note 5), and using Detached Coefficients,

$$2 - 3 - 1 + 1)6 - 1 + 3 - 2(3$$
$$\underline{6 - 9 - 3 + 3}$$
$$8 + 6 - 5$$

$$\begin{array}{r} 2 - 3 - 1 + 1 \\ 4 \end{array}$$

$$8 + 6 - 5)\overline{8 - 12 - 4 + 4}(1$$
$$\underline{8 + 6 - 5}$$
$$-18 + 1 + 4$$
$$\underline{4}$$
$$-72 + 4 + 16(-9$$
$$\underline{-72 - 54 + 45}$$
$$29)\underline{58 - 29}$$
$$2 - 1$$

$$2 - 1)8 + 6 - 5(4 + 5$$
$$\underline{8 - 4}$$
$$10 - 5$$
$$\underline{10 - 5}$$

The last divisor is $2x - 1$.

Multiplying this by x, the H. C. F. of the given expressions is $x(2x - 1)$.

189. The H. C. F. of three expressions may be found as follows :

Let A, B, and C be the expressions.

Let G be the H. C. F. of A and B; then, every common factor of G and C is a common factor of A, B, and C.

But since every common factor of two expressions exactly divides their H. C. F. (§ 188), every common factor of A, B, and C is also a common factor of G and C.

Whence, the H. C. F. of G and C is the H. C. F. of A, B, and C.

Hence, *to find the* H. C. F. *of three expressions, find the* H. C. F. *of two of them, and then of this result and the third expression.*

We proceed in a similar manner to find the H. C. F. of any number of expressions.

EXERCISE 24

Find the highest common factor of :

1. $4x^2 + 4x - 3$ and $6x^3 + 11x^2 - x - 6$.

2. $6\,a^3 - 17\,a^2b - 7\,ab^2 + 4\,b^3$ and $12\,a^3 - 13\,a^2b + 21\,ab^2 - 6\,b^3$.

3. $9\,x^4 - 21\,x^3 + 48\,x^2 - 24\,x$ and $15\,x^4 - 25\,x^3 + 25\,x^2 - 55\,x + 30$.

4. $6\,a^4 + a^3 + 5\,a^2 + 7\,a - 3$ and $8\,a^4 - 6\,a^3 + 7\,a^2 - 9$.

5. $6\,x^5 + x^4 + 3\,x^3 - 6\,x^2 - 4\,x$ and $12\,x^5 + 8\,x^4 - 3\,x^3 - 10\,x^2 - 4\,x$.

6. $8\,x^2 - 6\,x - 35$, $10\,x^3 - 27\,x^2 - x + 15$, and $6\,x^3 - 13\,x^2 - 13\,x + 20$.

7. $6\,a^3 - 19\,a^2b + ab^2 + 6\,b^3$, $8\,a^3 - 18\,a^2b - 17\,ab^2 - 3\,b^3$, and $6\,a^3 + 23\,a^2b - 6\,ab^2 - 8\,b^3$.

LOWEST COMMON MULTIPLE

190. A **Common Multiple** of two or more expressions is an expression which is exactly divisible by each of them.

191. The **Lowest Common Multiple** (L. C. M.) of two or more expressions is their common multiple of *lowest degree;* or if several common multiples are of equally low degree, it is the one having the numerical coefficient of least absolute value in its term of highest degree.

There are always two forms of the lowest common multiple, one of which is the *negative* of the other; thus, in the expressions $a^2 - ab$ and $b^2 - ab$, either $ab(a - b)$ or $ab(b - a)$ is exactly divisible by each expression.

In determining the lowest common multiple of expressions, it is convenient to distinguish two cases.

192. CASE I.   *When the expressions are monomials, or polynomials which can be readily factored by inspection.*

1. Required the L. C. M. of $36\,a^3x$, $60\,a^2y^2$, and $84\,cx^3$.

The L. C. M. of 36, 60, and 84 is 1260.

It is evident by inspection that the expression of lowest degree which is exactly divisible by a^3x, a^2y^2, and cx^3, is $a^3cx^3y^2$.

Then, the L. C. M. of the given expressions is $1260\,a^3cx^3y^2$.

It will be observed, in the above result, that *the exponent of each letter is the highest exponent with which it occurs in any of the given expressions.*

2. Required the L. C. M. of

$$x^2 + x - 6,\ x^2 - 4\,x + 4,\ \text{and}\ x^3 - 9\,x.$$

By § 173, $x^2 + x - 6 = (x + 3)(x - 2)$.

By § 169, $x^2 - 4x + 4 = (x - 2)^2$.

By § 171, $x^3 - 9x = x(x + 3)(x - 3)$.

It is evident by inspection that the L. C. M. of these expressions is $x(x - 2)^2(x + 3)(x - 3)$.

EXERCISE 25

Find the lowest common multiple of:

1. $x^2 - 15x + 50$, $x^2 + 2x - 35$, and $x^2 - 3x - 70$.

2. $27a^4 + 64a$, $18a^4 - 32a^2$, and $3a^2 + 7a + 4$.

3. $6x^2 + 7x - 5$, $10x^2 - 9x + 2$, and $8x^3 - 12x^2 + 6x - 1$.

4. $3ac + ad - 6bc - 2bd$, $ac - 4ad - 2bc + 8bd$, and $3c^2 - 11cd - 4d^2$.

5. $a^2 + 4b^2 - 9c^2 - 4ab$, $a^2 - 4b^2 - 9c^2 + 12bc$, and $a^2 + 4b^2 + 9c^2 - 4ab - 6ac + 12bc$.

6. $8m^3 - n^3$, $4m^2 - 4mn + n^2$, and $16m^4 + 4m^2n^2 + n^4$.

7. $x^2 + 5x + 6$, $x^3 - 19x - 30$, and $x^3 - 7x^2 + 2x + 40$.

193. CASE II. *When the expressions are polynomials which cannot be readily factored by inspection.*

Let A and B be any two expressions.

Let F be their H. C. F., and M their L. C. M.; and suppose that $A = aF$, and $B = bF$.

Then, $A \times B = abF^2$.   (1)

Since F is the H. C. F. of A and B, a and b have no common factors; whence, the L. C. M. of aF and bF is abF.

That is, $M = abF$.

Multiplying each of these equals by F, we have

$$F \times M = abF^2.$$ (2)

From (1) and (2), $A \times B = F \times M$.   (Ax. 4, § 66)

That is, *the product of two expressions is equal to the product of their H. C. F. and L. C. M.*

194. It follows from § 193 that, to find the L. C. M. of two expressions,

Divide their product by their highest common factor.

Or, *divide one of the expressions by their highest common factor, and multiply the quotient by the other expression.*

Ex. Required the L. C. M. of

$$x^2 - 8\,xy + 7\,y^2 \text{ and } x^3 - 9\,x^2y + 23\,xy^2 - 15\,y^3.$$

By the rule of § 188, the H. C. F. of the given expressions is $x - y$.

Dividing $x^2 - 8\,xy + 7\,y^2$ by $x - y$, the quotient is $x - 7\,y$.

Then, the L. C. M. of the given expressions is

$$(x - 7\,y)\,(x^3 - 9\,x^2y + 23\,xy^2 - 15\,y^3).$$

195. It follows from § 193 that, if two expressions are prime to each other (§ 185), their product is their L. C. M.

196. The L. C. M. of three expressions may be found as follows:

Let A, B, and C be the expressions.

Let M be the L. C. M. of A and B; then every common multiple of M and C is a common multiple of A, B, and C.

But since every common multiple of two expressions is exactly divisible by their L. C. M., every common multiple of A, B, and C is also a common multiple of M and C.

Whence, the L. C. M. of M and C is the L. C. M. of A, B, and C.

Hence, *to find the* L. C. M. *of three expressions, find the* L. C. M. *of two of them, and then of this result and the third expression.*

We proceed in a similar manner to find the L. C. M. of any number of expressions.

EXERCISE 26

Find the lowest common multiple of :

1. $8\,x^2 - 6\,x - 9$ and $6\,x^3 - 7\,x^2 - 7\,x + 6$.

2. $6\,a^3 + a^2b - 11\,ab^2 - 6\,b^3$ and $6\,a^3 - 5\,a^2b - 8\,ab^2 + 3\,b^3$.

3. $8\,x^3 - 22\,x^2 - 6\,x$ and $8\,x^6 + 6\,x^5 - 11\,x^4 - 23\,x^3 - 5\,x^2$.

4. $x^4 - 2\,x^3 - 2\,x^2 + 7\,x - 6$ and $x^4 - 4\,x^3 + x^2 + 7\,x - 2$.

5. $4\,a^3 + 4\,a^2 - 43\,a + 20$, $\ 4\,a^3 + 20\,a^2 + 13\,a - 12$, and $4\,a^3 + 12\,a^2 - 31\,a - 60$.

6. $6\,x^2 - 7\,x - 3$, $4\,x^3 - 4\,x^2 + 3\,x - 9$, and $4\,x^3 - 12\,x^2 - x + 15$.

X. FRACTIONS

197. In the fraction $\frac{a}{b}$, the dividend a is called the *numerator*, and the divisor b the *denominator*.

The symbol / is often used to represent a fraction; thus, a/b signifies $\frac{a}{b}$.

The numerator and denominator are called the *terms* of the fraction.

198. A *rational fraction* is a fraction whose terms are rational and integral (§ 63).

A monomial is said to be *rational* when it is a rational and integral expression, or a rational fraction.·

A polynomial is said to be rational when each of its terms is rational.

199. By § 96, (1), $\dfrac{a}{b} = \dfrac{ac}{bc}$.

That is, *if the terms of a fraction be both multiplied by the same expression, the value of the fraction is not changed.*

200. By § 30, (2), $\dfrac{\frac{a}{c}}{\frac{b}{c}} = \dfrac{ac}{bc} = \dfrac{a}{b}$.

That is, *if the terms of a fraction be both divided by the same expression, the value of the fraction is not changed.*

201. By § 48, $\dfrac{+a}{+b} = \dfrac{-a}{-b} = -\dfrac{+a}{-b} = -\dfrac{-a}{+b}$.

That is, *if the signs of both terms of a fraction be changed, the sign before the fraction is not changed; but if the sign of either one be changed, the sign before the fraction is changed.*

If either term is a polynomial, care must be taken, on changing its sign, to change the sign of *each of its terms.*

Thus, the fraction $\dfrac{a-b}{c-d}$, by changing the signs of both numerator and denominator, can be written $\dfrac{b-a}{d-c}$ (§ 81).

202. It follows from §§ 91 and 201 that

If either term of a fraction is the indicated product of two or more expressions, the signs of any **even** *number of them may be changed without changing the sign before the fraction; but if the signs of any* **odd** *number of them be changed, the sign before the fraction is changed.*

Thus, the fraction $\dfrac{a-b}{(c-d)(e-f)}$ may be written

$$\dfrac{a-b}{(d-c)(f-e)}, \quad \dfrac{b-a}{(d-c)(e-f)}, \quad -\dfrac{b-a}{(d-c)(f-e)}, \quad \text{etc.}$$

REDUCTION OF FRACTIONS

203. Reduction of a Fraction to its Lowest Terms.

A rational fraction (§ 198) is said to be *in its lowest terms* when its numerator and denominator are prime to each other (§ 185).

204. CASE I. *When the numerator and denominator can be readily factored by inspection.*

By § 200, dividing both terms of a fraction by the same expression, or cancelling common factors in the numerator and denominator, does not alter the value of the fraction.

We then have the following rule:

Resolve both numerator and denominator into their factors, and cancel all that are common to both.

1. Reduce $\dfrac{24\ a^4b^2cx}{40\ a^2b^2c^2d^3}$ to its lowest terms.

We have, $\dfrac{24\ a^4b^2cx}{40\ a^2b^2c^2d^3} = \dfrac{2^3 \times 3 \times a^4b^2cx}{2^3 \times 5 \times a^2b^2c^2d^3}.$

Cancelling the common factor $2^3 \times a^2 b^2 c$, we have

$$\frac{24\, a^4 b^2 c x}{40\, a^2 b^2 c^2 d^3} = \frac{3\, a^2 x}{5\, c d^3}.$$

2. Reduce $\dfrac{x^3 - 27}{x^2 - 2\, x - 3}$ to its lowest terms.

By §§ 177 and 173,

$$\frac{x^3 - 27}{x^2 - 2\, x - 3} = \frac{(x - 3)(x^2 + 3\, x + 9)}{(x - 3)(x + 1)} = \frac{x^2 + 3\, x + 9}{x + 1}.$$

3. Reduce $\dfrac{ax - bx - ay + by}{b^2 - a^2}$ to its lowest terms.

By §§ 156 and 171, $\dfrac{ax - bx - ay + by}{b^2 - a^2} = \dfrac{(a - b)(x - y)}{(b + a)(b - a)}.$

By § 202, the signs of the terms of the factors of the numerator can be changed without altering the value of the fraction; and in this way the first factor of the numerator becomes the same as the second factor of the denominator.

Then, $\dfrac{ax - bx - ay + by}{b^2 - a^2} = \dfrac{(b - a)(y - x)}{(b + a)(b - a)} = \dfrac{y - x}{b + a}.$

If all the factors of the numerator are cancelled, 1 remains to form a numerator.

If all the factors of the denominator are cancelled, it is a case of exact division.

205. CASE II. *When the numerator and denominator cannot be readily factored by inspection.*

By § 184, the H. C. F. of two expressions is their common factor of highest degree, having the numerical coefficient of greatest absolute value in its term of highest degree.

We then have the following rule:

Divide both numerator and denominator by their H. C. F.

Ex. Reduce $\dfrac{6\, a^3 - 11\, a^2 + 7\, a - 6}{2\, a^2 - a - 3}$ to its lowest terms.

By the rule of § 188, the H. C. F. of $6\, a^3 - 11\, a^2 + 7\, a - 6$ and $2\, a^2 - a - 3$ is $2\, a - 3$.

Dividing $6\,a^3 - 11\,a^2 + 7\,a - 6$ by $2\,a - 3$, the quotient is $3\,a^2 - a + 2$.

Dividing $2\,a^2 - a - 3$ by $2\,a - 3$, the quotient is $a + 1$.

Then, $\dfrac{6\,a^3 - 11\,a^2 + 7\,a - 6}{2\,a^2 - a - 3} = \dfrac{3\,a^2 - a + 2}{a + 1}.$

206. Reduction of a Fraction to an Integral or Mixed Expression.

· A **Mixed Expression** is a polynomial consisting of a rational and integral expression (§ 63), together with one or more rational fractions (§ 198), each of which has letters in its denominator when in its lowest terms (§ 203).

Thus, $a + \dfrac{b}{c}$, and $\dfrac{x}{3} + \dfrac{2\,x - y}{x - y}$ are mixed expressions.

1. Reduce $\dfrac{6\,x^2 + 15\,x - 2}{3\,x}$ to a mixed expression.

By the Distributive Law for Division (§ 100),

$$\frac{6\,x^2 + 15\,x - 2}{3\,x} = \frac{6\,x^2}{3\,x} + \frac{15\,x}{3\,x} - \frac{2}{3\,x} = 2\,x + 5 - \frac{2}{3\,x}.$$

A fraction whose denominator is a polynomial may be reduced to an integral or mixed expression by the operation of division, if the degree (§ 64) of the numerator is not less than that of the denominator.

2. Reduce $\dfrac{12\,x^3 - 8\,x^2 + 4\,x - 5}{4\,x^2 + 3}$ to a mixed expression.

$$4\,x^2 + 3\,)\,12\,x^3 - 8\,x^2 + 4\,x - 5\,(3\,x - 2$$
$$\underline{12\,x^3 \qquad\quad + 9\,x}$$
$$-8\,x^2 - 5\,x$$
$$\underline{-8\,x^2 \qquad\quad -6}$$
$$-5\,x + 1$$

Since the dividend is equal to the product of the divisor and quotient, plus the remainder, we have

$$12\,x^3 - 8\,x^2 + 4\,x - 5 = (4\,x^2 + 3)(3\,x - 2) + (-5\,x + 1).$$

Then, by the Distributive Law for Division,

$$\frac{12\,x^3 - 8\,x^2 + 4\,x - 5}{4\,x^2 + 3} = \frac{(4\,x^2 + 3)(3\,x - 2)}{4\,x^2 + 3} + \frac{-5\,x + 1}{4\,x^2 + 3}$$

$$= 3\,x - 2 + \frac{-5\,x + 1}{4\,x^2 + 3}.$$

Then, a remainder of lower degree than the divisor may be written over the divisor in the form of a fraction, and the result added to the quotient.

If the first term of the numerator is negative, as in Ex. 2, it is usual to *change the sign of each term of the numerator*, changing the sign before the fraction (§ 201).

Thus, $\dfrac{12\,x^3 - 8\,x^2 + 4\,x - 5}{4\,x^2 + 3} = 3\,x - 2 - \dfrac{5\,x - 1}{4\,x^2 + 3}.$

207. Reduction of Fractions to their Lowest Common Denominator.

To reduce fractions to their **Lowest Common Denominator** (L. C. D.) is to express them as equivalent fractions, having for their common denominator the L. C. M. of the given denominators.

Ex. Reduce $\dfrac{4\,cd}{3\,a^2b^3}$, $\dfrac{3\,m}{2\,ab^2}$, and $\dfrac{5\,n}{4\,a^3b}$ to their lowest common denominator.

The L. C. M. of $3\,a^2b^3$, $2\,ab^2$, and $4\,a^3b$ is $12\,a^3b^3$ (§ 192).

By § 199, if the terms of a fraction be both multiplied by the same expression, the value of the fraction is not changed.

Multiplying both terms of $\dfrac{4\,cd}{3\,a^2b^3}$ by $4\,a$, both terms of $\dfrac{3\,m}{2\,ab^2}$ by $6\,a^2b$, and both terms of $\dfrac{5\,n}{4\,a^3b}$ by $3\,b^2$, we have

$$\frac{16\,acd}{12\,a^3b^3}, \quad \frac{18\,a^2bm}{12\,a^3b^3}, \quad \text{and} \quad \frac{15\,b^2n}{12\,a^3b^3}.$$

It will be seen that the terms of each fraction are multiplied by an expression, which is obtained by dividing the L. C. D. by the denominator of this fraction.

Whence the following rule.

Find the L. C. M. *of the given denominators.*

Multiply both terms of each fraction by the quotient obtained by dividing the L. C. D. *by the denominator of this fraction.*

Before applying the rule, each fraction should be reduced to its lowest terms.

ADDITION AND SUBTRACTION OF FRACTIONS

208. By § 100, $\dfrac{b}{a}+\dfrac{c}{a}=\dfrac{b+c}{a}$, and $\dfrac{b}{a}-\dfrac{c}{a}=\dfrac{b-c}{a}$.

We then have the following rules:

To add two rational fractions which have a common denominator, add their numerators, and make the result the numerator of a fraction whose denominator is the common denominator.

To subtract two rational fractions which have a common denominator, subtract the numerator of the subtrahend from the numerator of the minuend, and make the result the numerator of a fraction whose denominator is the common denominator.

If the fractions have not a common denominator, it follows from § 30, (3) and (4), that they may be added, or subtracted, by reducing them to equivalent fractions having their lowest common denominator (§ 207), and then using the above rules.

The final result should be reduced to its lowest terms.

209. 1. Simplify $\dfrac{3c}{4a^2b}+\dfrac{5d}{6ab^3}$.

The L. C. D. is $12\,a^2b^3$.

Multiplying the terms of the first fraction by $3\,b^2$, and the terms of the second by $2\,a$, we have

$$\frac{3c}{4a^2b}+\frac{5d}{6ab^3}=\frac{9\,b^2c}{12\,a^2b^3}+\frac{10\,ad}{12\,a^2b^3}=\frac{9\,b^2c+10\,ad}{12\,a^2b^3}.$$

If a fraction whose numerator is a polynomial is preceded by a − sign, it is convenient to enclose the numerator in parentheses preceded by a − sign, as shown in the last term of the numerator in equation (A), of Ex. 2; if this is not done, care must be taken to *change the sign of each term of the numerator* before combining it with the other numerators.

2. Simplify $\dfrac{x+1}{x+5} + \dfrac{x-2}{x-3} - \dfrac{2\,x^2+x-13}{x^2+2\,x-15}$.

Since $x^2 + 2\,x - 15 = (x+5)(x-3)$, the L. C. D. is

$$x^2 + 2\,x - 15.$$

Multiplying the terms of the first fraction by $x-3$, and the terms of the second by $x+5$, we have

$$\dfrac{(x+1)(x-3)}{x^2+2\,x-15} + \dfrac{(x-2)(x+5)}{x^2+2\,x-15} - \dfrac{2\,x^2+x-13}{x^2+2\,x-15}$$

$$= \dfrac{(x+1)(x-3)+(x-2)(x+5)-(2\,x^2+x-13)}{x^2+2\,x-15} \quad \text{(A)}$$

$$= \dfrac{x^2-2\,x-3+x^2+3\,x-10-2\,x^2-x+13}{x^2+2\,x-15}$$

$$= \dfrac{0}{x^2+2\,x-15} = 0 \ (\S\ 105).$$

In certain cases, the principles of §§ 201 and 202 enable us to change the form of a fraction to one which is more convenient for the purposes of addition or subtraction.

3. Simplify $\dfrac{3}{a-b} + \dfrac{2\,b+a}{b^2-a^2}$.

Changing the signs of the terms in the second denominator, at the same time changing the sign before the fraction (§ 201), we have,

$$\dfrac{3}{a-b} - \dfrac{2\,b+a}{a^2-b^2}.$$

The L. C. D. is now $a^2 - b^2$.

Then, $\dfrac{3}{a-b} - \dfrac{2\,b+a}{a^2-b^2} = \dfrac{3(a+b)-(2\,b+a)}{a^2-b^2}$

$$= \dfrac{3\,a+3\,b-2\,b-a}{a^2-b^2} = \dfrac{2\,a+b}{a^2-b^2}.$$

4. Simplify $\dfrac{1}{(x-y)(x-z)} - \dfrac{1}{(y-x)(y-z)} - \dfrac{1}{(z-x)(z-y)}$.

By § 202, we change the sign of the factor $y-x$ in the second denominator, at the same time changing the sign before the fraction; and we change the signs of both factors of the third denominator.

The expression then becomes

$$\frac{1}{(x-y)(x-z)} + \frac{1}{(x-y)(y-z)} - \frac{1}{(x-z)(y-z)}.$$

The L. C. D. is now $(x-y)(x-z)(y-z)$; then the result

$$= \frac{(y-z)+(x-z)-(x-y)}{(x-y)(x-z)(y-z)} = \frac{y-z+x-z-x+y}{(x-y)(x-z)(y-z)}$$

$$= \frac{2y-2z}{(x-y)(x-z)(y-z)} = \frac{2(y-z)}{(x-y)(x-z)(y-z)} = \frac{2}{(x-y)(x-z)}.$$

5. Simplify $2x-3-\dfrac{3x-5}{x+1}$.

$$2x-3-\frac{3x-5}{x+1} = \frac{(2x-3)(x+1)-(3x-5)}{x+1}$$

$$= \frac{2x^2-x-3-3x+5}{x+1} = \frac{2x^2-4x+2}{x+1}.$$

6. Simplify $\dfrac{1}{1-x} + \dfrac{1}{1+x} + \dfrac{2}{1+x^2} + \dfrac{4}{1+x^4}$.

We first add the first two fractions; to the result we add the third fraction, and to this result the fourth fraction.

$$\frac{1}{(1-x)} + \frac{1}{1+x} = \frac{1+x+1-x}{(1+x)(1-x)} = \frac{2}{1-x^2}.$$

$$\frac{2}{1-x^2} + \frac{2}{1+x^2} = \frac{2(1+x^2)+2(1-x^2)}{(1+x^2)(1-x^2)} = \frac{4}{1-x^4}.$$

$$\frac{4}{1-x^4} + \frac{4}{1+x^4} = \frac{4(1+x^4)+4(1-x^4)}{(1+x^4)(1-x^4)} = \frac{8}{1-x^8}.$$

7. Simplify $\dfrac{1}{a-1} - \dfrac{1}{a+1} + \dfrac{1}{a-2} - \dfrac{1}{a+2}$.

We first combine the first two fractions, then the last two, and then add these results.

$$\frac{1}{a-1} - \frac{1}{a+1} = \frac{a+1-(a-1)}{(a+1)(a-1)} = \frac{2}{a^2-1}.$$

$$\frac{1}{a-2} - \frac{1}{a+2} = \frac{a+2-(a-2)}{(a+2)(a-2)} = \frac{4}{a^2-4}.$$

$$\frac{2}{a^2-1} + \frac{4}{a^2-4} = \frac{2\,a^2-8+4\,a^2-4}{(a^2-1)(a^2-4)} = \frac{6\,a^2-12}{a^4-5\,a^2+4}.$$

MULTIPLICATION OF FRACTIONS

210. By § 30, (1), we have the following rule for the product of two fractions:

Multiply the numerators together for the numerator of the product, and the denominators for its denominator.

211. By § 210, $\dfrac{a}{b} \times c = \dfrac{a}{b} \times \dfrac{c}{1} = \dfrac{ac}{b}.$ (1)

Dividing both numerator and denominator by c (§ 200),

$$\frac{a}{b} \times c = \frac{a}{b \div c}.$$ (2)

From (1) and (2), we have the following rule for multiplying a fraction by a rational and integral expression:

If possible, divide the denominator of the fraction by the expression; otherwise, multiply the numerator by the expression.

212. Common factors in the numerators and denominators should be cancelled before performing the multiplication.

Mixed expressions should be expressed in a fractional form (§ 209) before applying the rules.

1. Multiply $\dfrac{10\,a^3y}{9\,bx^2}$ by $\dfrac{3\,b^4x^3}{4\,a^3y^2}$.

$$\frac{10\,a^3y}{9\,bx^2} \times \frac{3\,b^4x^3}{4\,a^3y^2} = \frac{2 \times 5 \times 3 \times a^3b^4x^3y}{3^2 \times 2^2 \times a^3bx^2y^2} = \frac{5\,b^3x}{6\,y}.$$

The factors cancelled are 2, 3, a^3, b, x^2, and y.

2. Multiply together $\dfrac{x^2+2\,x}{x^2+x-6}$, $2-\dfrac{x-4}{x-3}$, and $\dfrac{x^2-9}{x^2-4}$.

$$\frac{x^2+2\,x}{x^2+x-6} \times \left(2-\frac{x-4}{x-3}\right) \times \frac{x^2-9}{x^2-4}$$

$$= \frac{x^2+2\,x}{x^2+x-6} \times \frac{2\,x-6-x+4}{x-3} \times \frac{x^2-9}{x^2-4}$$

$$= \frac{x(x+2)}{(x+3)(x-2)} \times \frac{x-2}{x-3} \times \frac{(x+3)(x-3)}{(x+2)(x-2)} = \frac{x}{x-2}.$$

The factors cancelled are $x+2$, $x-2$, $x+3$, and $x-3$.

3. Multiply $\dfrac{a^2+b^2}{a^2-b^2}$ by $a-b$.

Dividing the denominator by $a-b$, we have

$$\frac{a^2+b^2}{a^2-b^2}\times(a-b)=\frac{a^2+b^2}{a+b}.$$

4. Multiply $\dfrac{m}{m-n}$ by $m+n$.

Multiplying the numerator by $m+n$, we have

$$\frac{m}{m-n}\times(m+n)=\frac{m^2+mn}{m-n}.$$

DIVISION OF FRACTIONS

213. By § 30, (2), we have the following rule:

To divide one fraction by another, multiply the dividend by the divisor inverted.

214. By § 213, $\qquad \dfrac{a}{b}\div c=\dfrac{a}{b}\times\dfrac{1}{c}=\dfrac{a}{bc}.$ $\qquad$ (1)

Dividing both numerator and denominator by c (§ 200),

$$\frac{a}{b}\div c=\frac{a\div c}{b}. \qquad (2)$$

From (1) and (2), we have the following rule for dividing a fraction by a rational and integral expression:

If possible, divide the numerator of the fraction by the expression; otherwise, multiply the numerator by the expression.

215. 1. Divide $\dfrac{6\,a^2b}{5\,x^3y^4}$ by $\dfrac{9\,a^2b^3}{10\,x^2y^7}$.

We have, $\dfrac{6\,a^2b}{5\,x^3y^4}\div\dfrac{9\,a^2b^3}{10\,x^2y^7}=\dfrac{6\,a^2b}{5\,x^3y^4}\times\dfrac{10\,x^2y^7}{9\,a^2b^3}=\dfrac{4\,y^3}{3\,b^2x}.$

Mixed expressions should be expressed in a fractional form (§ 209) before applying the rules.

2. Divide $2-\dfrac{2\,x-3}{x+1}$ by $3-\dfrac{3\,x^2-13}{x^2-1}$.

$$\left(2 - \frac{2x-3}{x+1}\right) \div \left(3 - \frac{3x^2 - 13}{x^2 - 1}\right)$$

$$= \frac{2x + 2 - 2x + 3}{x + 1} \div \frac{3x^2 - 3 - 3x^2 + 13}{x^2 - 1}$$

$$= \frac{5}{x+1} \times \frac{x^2 - 1}{10} = \frac{5(x+1)(x-1)}{2 \times 5 \times (x+1)} = \frac{x-1}{2}.$$

3. Divide $\dfrac{m^3 - n^3}{m^2 + n^2}$ by $m - n$.

Dividing the numerator by $m - n$, we have

$$\frac{m^3 - n^3}{m^2 + n^2} \div (m - n) = \frac{m^2 + mn + n^2}{m^2 + n^2}.$$

4. Divide $\dfrac{a^2 + b^2}{a - b}$ by $a + b$.

Multiplying the denominator by $a + b$, we have

$$\frac{a^2 + b^2}{a - b} \div (a + b) = \frac{a^2 + b^2}{a^2 - b^2}.$$

If the numerator and denominator of the divisor are exactly contained in the numerator and denominator, respectively, of the dividend, it follows from § 210 that *the numerator of the quotient may be obtained by dividing the numerator of the dividend by the numerator of the divisor ; and the denominator of the quotient by dividing the denominator of the dividend by the denominator of the divisor.*

5. Divide $\qquad \dfrac{9x^2 - 4y^2}{x^2 - y^2}$ by $\dfrac{3x + 2y}{x - y}$.

We have, $\quad \dfrac{9x^2 - 4y^2}{x^2 - y^2} \div \dfrac{3x + 2y}{x - y} = \dfrac{3x - 2y}{x + y}.$

216. By § 213, $\qquad \dfrac{1}{\dfrac{a}{b}} = 1 \times \dfrac{b}{a} = \dfrac{b}{a}.$

Hence, *the reciprocal of a fraction is the fraction inverted.*

COMPLEX FRACTIONS

217. A **Complex Fraction** is a fraction having one or more fractions in either or both of its terms.

It is simply a case in division of fractions; its numerator being the dividend, and its denominator the divisor.

218. 1. Simplify $\dfrac{a}{b-\dfrac{c}{d}}$.

$$\frac{a}{b-\dfrac{c}{d}}=\frac{a}{\dfrac{bd-c}{d}}=a\times\frac{d}{bd-c}\,(\S\,213)=\frac{ad}{bd-c}.$$

It is often advantageous to simplify a complex fraction by multiplying its numerator and denominator by the L. C. M. of their denominators (§ 199).

2. Simplify $\dfrac{\dfrac{a}{a-b}-\dfrac{a}{a+b}}{\dfrac{b}{a-b}+\dfrac{a}{a+b}}$.

The L. C. M. of $a+b$ and $a-b$ is $(a+b)(a-b)$.

Multiplying both terms by $(a+b)(a-b)$, we have

$$\frac{a\,(a+b)-a\,(a-b)}{b\,(a+b)+a\,(a-b)}=\frac{a^2+ab-a^2+ab}{ab+b^2+a^2-ab}=\frac{2\,ab}{a^2+b^2}.$$

3. Simplify $\dfrac{1}{1+\dfrac{1}{1+\dfrac{1}{x}}}$.

In examples like the above, it is best to begin by simplifying the *lowest* complex fraction; thus,

$$\frac{1}{1+\dfrac{1}{1+\dfrac{1}{x}}}=\frac{1}{1+\dfrac{x}{x+1}}=\frac{x+1}{x+1+x}=\frac{x+1}{2\,x+1}.$$

EXERCISE 27

Reduce to their lowest terms by factoring :

1. $\dfrac{8\,x^3-125}{2\,x^3+x^2-15\,x}$.

2. $\dfrac{(x^2-49)(x^2-16\,x+63)}{(x^2-14\,x+49)(x^2-2\,x-63)}$.

3. $\dfrac{x^2-9\,y^2-z^2+6\,yz}{x^2-9\,y^2+z^2-2\,xz}$.

4. $\dfrac{21-x-10\,x^2}{15\,xy-20\,x-21\,y+28}$.

5. $\dfrac{a^6 + 28\,a^3b^3 + 27\,b^6}{a^4 + 9\,a^2b^2 + 81\,b^6}$.

6. $\dfrac{2\,x^3 - 5\,x^2 - x + 6}{27 - 36\,x + 54\,x^2 - 8\,x^3}$.

Reduce to their lowest terms by finding the H. C. F. :

7. $\dfrac{10\,x^2 - 7\,x - 6}{4\,x^3 - 4\,x^2 - 5\,x - 1}$.

9. $\dfrac{6\,x^3 - x^2 - 11\,x + 6}{9\,x^3 - 18\,x^2 + 11\,x - 2}$.

8. $\dfrac{4\,a^3 + 13\,a^2b - 4\,ab^2 - 6\,b^3}{8\,a^2 + 14\,ab - 15\,b^2}$.

10. $\dfrac{2\,x^3 - 9\,x^2y - 2\,xy^2 - 15\,y^3}{2\,x^3 - 7\,x^2y - 16\,xy^2 + 5\,y^3}$.

Reduce each of the following to a mixed expression :

11. $\dfrac{9\,x^4 - 2\,x^3 - 20}{12\,x^3}$.

12. $\dfrac{m^5 + n^5}{m - n}$.

13. $\dfrac{12\,x^3 - 3\,x^2 - 22\,x + 8}{3\,x^2 - 5}$.

Simplify the following :

14. $\dfrac{3\,x - y}{x^2 - 2\,y^2} \times (2\,x + y)$.

19. $\dfrac{a^2 + b^2}{a - b} - a + b$.

15. $\dfrac{a^3 + 64\,b^3}{a^3 - 64\,b^3} \times (a - 4\,b)$.

20. $\dfrac{3}{5\,x^2} - \dfrac{2}{15\,xy} + \dfrac{1}{6\,y^2}$.

16. $\dfrac{a^4 - n^4}{a^4 + n^4} \div (a + n)$.

21. $\dfrac{2\,a + 3}{6\,a} - \dfrac{3\,a^2 + 1}{12\,a^2} - \dfrac{3\,a^3 - 2}{36\,a^3}$.

17. $\dfrac{2\,mx}{4\,x + 5\,m} \div (2\,m - 3\,x)$.

22. $\dfrac{5}{2\,m - n} + \dfrac{2\,(4\,m + 3\,n)}{n^2 - 4\,m^2}$.

18. $3\,x + 4 - \dfrac{5\,x + 7}{2\,x - 3}$.

23. $\dfrac{27\,x^3 + 1}{25\,x^2 - 4} - \dfrac{15\,x^2 - x - 2}{25\,x^2 - 20\,x + 4}$.

24. $\dfrac{2\,ac - 6\,ad - bc + 3\,bd}{3\,ac + ad - 6\,bc - 2\,bd} \times \dfrac{a^2 - 7\,ab + 10\,b^2}{10\,a^2 - 3\,ab - b^2}$.

25. $\dfrac{2}{5\,a - \dfrac{4\,a - 1}{1 - \dfrac{2\,a + 5}{3\,a - 2}}}$

26. $\dfrac{\dfrac{1}{1 - x} - \dfrac{1}{1 + x}}{\dfrac{1}{1 - x^2} - \dfrac{1}{1 + x^2}}$

27. $\dfrac{3\,m + 1}{3\,m - 1} + \dfrac{m - 4}{5 - 2\,m} - \dfrac{3\,m^2 - 2\,m - 4}{6\,m^2 - 17\,m + 5}$.

28. $\dfrac{\dfrac{1}{2\,x} + \dfrac{1}{3\,y}}{4\,x^2 - 9\,y^2} + \dfrac{\dfrac{1}{3\,x} - \dfrac{1}{2\,y}}{9\,x^2 - 4\,y^2}$

29. $\dfrac{2}{x + 3} - \dfrac{3}{x - 3} - \dfrac{4}{x + 4} + \dfrac{5}{x - 4}$.

30. $\left(2\,x - 1 + \dfrac{6\,x - 11}{x + 4}\right) \div \left(x + 3 - \dfrac{3\,x + 17}{x + 4}\right)$.

31. $\dfrac{3\,a}{a + b} + \dfrac{3\,a}{a - b} + \dfrac{6\,a^2}{a^2 + b^2} + \dfrac{12\,a^4}{a^4 + b^4}$.

32. $\dfrac{m^2}{m^2 - mn + n^2} - \dfrac{m^2}{m^2 + mn + n^2} - \dfrac{2\,m^3n}{m^4 + m^2n^2 + n^4}$.

33. $\dfrac{\dfrac{a-x}{a+x}-\dfrac{a^3-x^3}{a^3+x^3}}{\dfrac{a-x}{a+x}+\dfrac{a^3-x^3}{a^3+x^3}}.$

34. $\dfrac{4x-1}{6x^2-17x+12}-\dfrac{3x+1}{10x^2-9x-9}.$

35. $\dfrac{b-c}{(a-b)(a-c)}+\dfrac{c-a}{(b-c)(b-a)}-\dfrac{a-b}{(c-a)(c-b)}.$

36. $\dfrac{3}{2n+1}+\dfrac{3}{1-2n}-\dfrac{5n^2}{8n^3+1}-\dfrac{5n^2}{1-8n^3}.$

37. $\dfrac{\dfrac{x}{(x+1)^2}+\dfrac{y}{(y-1)^2}-\dfrac{1}{x+1}-\dfrac{1}{y-1}}{\dfrac{1}{(x+1)(y-1)^2}-\dfrac{1}{(x+1)^2(y-1)}}.$

38. $\dfrac{6a^2-a-2}{8a^2-26a+15}\times\dfrac{8a^2-18a-5}{9a^2+6a-8}\times\dfrac{12a^2+7a-12}{8a^2+6a+1}.$

39. $\left[\left(\dfrac{1}{y-z}-\dfrac{1}{x}\right)\div\left(\dfrac{1}{y+z}-\dfrac{1}{x}\right)\right]\div\dfrac{x^2-y^2-z^2+2yz}{x^2-y^2-z^2-2yz}.$

40. $\dfrac{x^3-2x^2-4x+8}{x^4+3x^3-27x-81}\div\left[\left(1+\dfrac{3x+5}{x^2+6x+9}\right)\times\left(1-\dfrac{4x-13}{x^2-9}\right)\right].$

41. $\dfrac{2a-1}{a-2}-\dfrac{2a+1}{a+2}+\dfrac{6a-1}{a(2-a)}-\dfrac{11}{4-a^2}-\dfrac{8}{a(a^4-16)}.$

42. $\dfrac{y-z}{x^2-(y-z)^2}-\dfrac{x-z}{y^2-(z-x)^2}.$

43. $\dfrac{\left(\dfrac{x+1}{x-1}\right)^2-2+\left(\dfrac{x-1}{x+1}\right)^2}{\left(\dfrac{x+1}{x-1}\right)^2-\left(\dfrac{x-1}{x+1}\right)^2}.$

44. $\dfrac{a^2\left(\dfrac{1}{b}-\dfrac{1}{c}\right)+b^2\left(\dfrac{1}{c}-\dfrac{1}{a}\right)+c^2\left(\dfrac{1}{a}-\dfrac{1}{b}\right)}{a\left(\dfrac{1}{b}-\dfrac{1}{c}\right)+b\left(\dfrac{1}{c}-\dfrac{1}{a}\right)+c\left(\dfrac{1}{a}-\dfrac{1}{b}\right)}$ (§ 181).

45. $\dfrac{1}{a^2-(b+c)^2}+\dfrac{1}{b^2-(c+a)^2}+\dfrac{1}{c^2-(a+b)^2}.$

46. $\dfrac{\left(\dfrac{x+y}{x-y}\right)^3-\left(\dfrac{x-y}{x+y}\right)^3}{\left(\dfrac{x+y}{x-y}\right)^2+1+\left(\dfrac{x-y}{x+y}\right)^2}.$

47. $\dfrac{\dfrac{1-x^2}{1+x^2}+\dfrac{1+x^3}{1-x^3}}{\dfrac{1+x^2}{1-x^2}-\dfrac{1-x^3}{1+x^3}}.$

48. $\dfrac{bc}{(a-b)(a-c)}+\dfrac{ca}{(b-c)(b-a)}+\dfrac{ab}{(c-a)(c-b)}.$

49. $\dfrac{2+x}{2-x}+\dfrac{3+x}{3-x}+\dfrac{4+x}{4-x}+\dfrac{2(x^3-x^2-19x+36)}{(x-2)(x-3)(x-4)}.$

XI. FRACTIONAL AND LITERAL EQUATIONS

INVOLVING LINEAR EQUATIONS

219. Suppose that an equation, with one unknown number, x, has fractional terms.

Transpose all terms to the first member.

Let the terms in the first member be then added, using for a common denominator the L. C. M. of the given denominators; and let the resulting fraction be reduced to its lowest terms.

The equation will then be in the form

$$\frac{A}{B} = 0; \tag{1}$$

where A and B are rational and integral expressions which have no common factor.

If B contains x, the given equation is called a **Fractional Equation**.

By § 117, (1) is equivalent (§ 114) to the given equation.

(The principles demonstrated in §§ 116 to 119, inclusive, and § 122, hold for fractional equations.)

Equation (1) may be *cleared of fractions* (§ 121) by multiplying both members by B, giving the equation

$$A = 0. \tag{2}$$

We will now prove equation (2) equivalent to (1).

Any solution of (1), when substituted for x, makes $\frac{A}{B}$ identically equal to 0.

Then, it must make A identically equal to 0 (§ 105).

Then, it is a solution of (2).

Again, any solution of (2), when substituted for x, makes A identically equal to 0.

Now B cannot equal 0 for this value of x; for if A and B became 0 for the same value of x, say $x = a$, they would have $x - a$ as a common factor (§ 141), which is impossible by § 219.

Hence, any solution of (2), when substituted for x, makes $\dfrac{A}{B}$ identically equal to 0 (§ 105).

Then, it is a solution of (1).

Therefore, (1) and (2) are equivalent.

220. A fractional equation may be cleared of fractions by multiplying both members· by *any* common multiple of the denominators; but in this way additional solutions are introduced, and the resulting equation is not equivalent to the first.

Consider, for example, the equation

$$\frac{1}{1+x}-\frac{x}{1-x^2}=1.$$

Multiplying both members by $1-x^2$, the L. C. M. of the given denominators, we have

$$1-x-x=1-x^2,\text{ or }x^2-2\,x=0.$$

Factoring the first member,

$$x(x-2)=0;\text{ and }x=0\text{ or }2\ (§\ 182).$$

If, however, we multiply both members of the given equation by $(1+x)(1-x^2)$, we have

$$1-x^2-x(1+x)=(1+x)(1-x^2).$$

Then, $1-x^2-x-x^2=1+x-x^2-x^3$, or $x^3-x^2-2\,x=0$. Factoring the first member,

$$x(x+1)(x-2)=0,\text{ and }x=0,-1,\text{ or }2$$

This gives the additional solution $x=-1$; and it may be verified by substitution that this does not satisfy the given equation.

221. If both members of a fractional equation be multiplied by any common multiple of the denominators, the additional roots, if any, introduced must satisfy the equation formed by equating this common multiple to 0.

Thus, in § 220, the additional solution -1 satisfies the equation

$$(1+x)(1-x^2)=0.$$

If, then, we reject all solutions which satisfy the equation formed by equating the common multiple to 0, we shall retain the correct solutions.

222. It follows from § 219 that, if all the terms of a fractional equation with one unknown number be transposed to the first member; and all terms in the first member be added, and the resulting fraction reduced to its lowest terms; and the numerator of this fraction be equated to 0, the resulting equation is equivalent to the first.

But in most cases the above is not the shortest method of solution.

By §§ 220 and 221, we may multiply the members of the given equation by the L. C. M. of the given denominators; and if we reject all solutions which satisfy the equation formed by equating the L. C. M. to 0, only the correct solutions will be retained.

223. We may now give a rule for solving any fractional equation, leading to a linear equation with one unknown number:

Clear the equation of fractions by multiplying each term by the L. C. M. of the given denominators.

Transpose the unknown terms to the first member, and the known terms to the second.

Unite the similar terms, and divide both members by the coefficient of the unknown number.

1. Solve the equation $\dfrac{2}{x-2} - \dfrac{5}{x+2} = \dfrac{2}{x^2-4}$.

Multiplying each term by $x^2 - 4$, the L. C. M. of the given denominators, we have

$$2(x+2) - 5(x-2) = 2.$$

Or, $\qquad 2x + 4 - 5x + 10 = 2.$

Transposing, and uniting terms,

$$-3x = -12, \text{ and } x = 4.$$

Since 4 does not satisfy the equation $x^2 - 4 = 0$, it is the correct solution (§ 222).

If the denominators are partly monomial and partly poly-nomial, it is often advantageous to clear of fractions at first partially; multiplying each term of the equation by the L. C. M. of the *monomial* denominators.

2. Solve the equation

$$\frac{6x+1}{15} - \frac{2x-4}{7x-16} = \frac{2x-1}{5}.$$

Multiplying each term by 15, the L. C. M. of 15 and 5,

$$6x+1 - \frac{30x-60}{7x-16} = 6x-3.$$

Transposing, and uniting terms,

$$4 = \frac{30x-60}{7x-16}.$$

Clearing of fractions, $28x - 64 = 30x - 60.$

Then, $-2x = 4$, and $x = -2.$

-2 does not satisfy the equation $7x - 16 = 0$, and is there-fore the correct root.

If any fractional terms in the equation have the same de-nominator, they should be combined before clearing of frac-tions.

3. Solve the equation $\frac{x}{x^2-1} - 1 = \frac{1}{x^2-1}.$

Transposing the term $\frac{1}{x^2-1}$ to the first member, and com-bining it with the term $\frac{x}{x^2-1}$, we have

$$\frac{x-1}{x^2-1} - 1 = 0, \text{ or } \frac{1}{x+1} - 1 = 0.$$

Clearing of fractions, $1 - x - 1 = 0$, or $x = 0.$

0 does not satisfy the equation $x + 1 = 0$, and is the correct root.

If we solve the given equation by multiplying both members by $x^2 - 1$, we have $x - (x^2 - 1) = 1$, or $x - x^2 + 1 = 1$, or $x - x^2 = 0.$

Factoring the first member,
$$x(1 - x) = 0; \text{ and } x = 0 \text{ or } 1.$$

Now the value $x = 1$ satisfies the equation $x^2 - 1 = 0$; then it must be rejected, and the only solution is $x = 0$.

4. Solve the equation $\dfrac{2}{x + 8} + \dfrac{5}{x + 9} = \dfrac{3}{x + 10} + \dfrac{4}{x + 6}.$

Adding the fractions in each member, we have
$$\frac{7x + 58}{(x + 8)(x + 9)} = \frac{7x + 58}{(x + 10)(x + 6)}.$$

Since $7x + 58$ is a factor of each member, we may place it equal to zero (§ 182).

Then, $7x + 58 = 0$, or $x = -\dfrac{58}{7}.$

The remaining root is given by
$$\frac{1}{(x + 8)(x + 9)} = \frac{1}{(x + 10)(x + 6)},$$
or, $(x + 8)(x + 9) = (x + 10)(x + 6),$
or, $x^2 + 17x + 72 = x^2 + 16x + 60.$

Whence, $x = -12.$

Neither $-\dfrac{58}{7}$ nor -12 satisfies the equation
$$(x + 8)(x + 9)(x + 10)(x + 6) = 0.$$

5. Solve the equation $\dfrac{2x - 1}{2x - 3} + \dfrac{x^2 - x}{x^2 + 4} = 2.$

Dividing each numerator by its corresponding denominator, we can write the equation in the form
$$1 + \frac{2}{2x - 3} + 1 - \frac{x + 4}{x^2 + 4} = 2, \text{ or } \frac{2}{2x - 3} - \frac{x + 4}{x^2 + 4} = 0.$$

Clearing of fractions,
$$2x^2 + 8 - 2x^2 - 5x + 12 = 0;$$
whence, $x = 4.$

EXERCISE 28
Solve the following :

1. $\dfrac{8x - 11}{9} - \dfrac{7x + 4}{12} - \dfrac{3x - 8}{8} = 0.$ **2.** $\dfrac{12x - 5}{21} - \dfrac{3x + 4}{9x + 3} = \dfrac{4x - 5}{7}.$

3. $\dfrac{2x}{4x^2 - 9} = -\dfrac{2}{5} - \dfrac{3}{4x^2 - 9}.$

5. $\dfrac{x + 4}{2x + 3} - \dfrac{2x - 1}{3x - 2} = -\dfrac{1}{6}.$

4. $\dfrac{3x - 1}{x - 5} - \dfrac{5x + 4}{x + 8} = -2.$

6. $\dfrac{5x}{1 - x} - \dfrac{7x}{3 + x} = \dfrac{12(1 - x^2)}{x^2 + 2x - 3}.$

7. $\dfrac{2x - 1}{3x + 5} + \dfrac{5x + 6}{7 - 2x} = 2 - \dfrac{23x^2 - 10}{6x^2 - 11x - 35}.$

8. $\dfrac{3}{x^2 - 9} - \dfrac{5}{x^2 + 7x + 12} = \dfrac{2}{x^2 - 16} - \dfrac{4}{x^2 - 7x + 12}.$

9. $\dfrac{x^2 + 3}{2x^3 - 16} - \dfrac{2x - 1}{3x^2 + 6x + 12} + \dfrac{1}{6x - 12} = 0.$

10. $\dfrac{x - 3}{x + 1} + \dfrac{x + 4}{x - 2} = \dfrac{8x + 2}{x^2 - x - 2} + 1.$

11. $\dfrac{2}{2x - 1} - \dfrac{1}{3x + 2} = \dfrac{7}{6x^2 + x - 2} - \dfrac{1}{2}.$

12. $\dfrac{8}{x - 3} - \dfrac{3}{x + 7} = \dfrac{10}{x - 9} - \dfrac{5}{x + 2}.$

13. $\dfrac{5}{2x - 1} - \dfrac{1}{6x + 5} = \dfrac{10}{3x - 4} - \dfrac{4}{4x + 1}.$

14. $\dfrac{x + 1}{x - 1} + \dfrac{x + 4}{x - 4} = \dfrac{x + 2}{x - 2} + \dfrac{x + 3}{x - 3}.$

15. $\dfrac{x + 2}{x - 3} + \dfrac{x - 3}{x + 4} + \dfrac{x + 4}{x + 2} = 3.$

16. $\dfrac{7x + 10}{x^2 + x - 6} - \dfrac{x^2 - 3}{x^2 - 6x + 8} - \dfrac{x^2 + 2}{x^2 - x - 12} = -2.$

17. $\dfrac{x^2 - 2x + 5}{x^2 - 2x - 3} + \dfrac{x^2 + 3x - 7}{x^2 + 3x + 1} = 2.$

18. $\dfrac{x - 1}{x - 2} + \dfrac{x - 5}{x - 4} + \dfrac{x - 7}{x - 6} + \dfrac{x - 7}{x - 8} = 4.$

224. Problems involving Fractional Equations, leading to Linear Equations with one Unknown Number.

1. A can do a piece of work in 8 days, which B can perform in 10 days. In how many days can it be done by both working together ?

Let x = number of days required.

Then, $\dfrac{1}{x}$ = the part both can do in one day.

Also, $\dfrac{1}{8}$ = the part A can do in one day,

and $\dfrac{1}{10}$ = the part B can do in one day.

By the conditions, $\dfrac{1}{8} + \dfrac{1}{10} = \dfrac{1}{x}$.

$$5x + 4x = 40.$$
$$9x = 40.$$

Whence, $x = 4\frac{4}{9}$, number of days required.

2. The second digit of a number exceeds the first by 2; and if the number be divided by the sum of its digits, the quotient is $4\frac{6}{7}$. Find the number.

Let x = the first digit.

Then, $x + 2$ = the second digit,

and $2x + 2$ = the sum of the digits.

The number itself equals 10 times the first digit, plus the second; then, $10x + (x + 2)$, or $11x + 2$ = the number.

By the conditions, $\dfrac{11x + 2}{2x + 2} = \dfrac{34}{7}$.

$$77x + 14 = 68x + 68.$$
$$9x = 54.$$

Whence, $x = 6$.

Then, the number is 68.

EXERCISE 29

1. The denominator of a fraction exceeds twice the numerator by 4; and if the numerator be increased by 14, and the denominator decreased by 9, the value of the fraction is $\dfrac{7}{3}$. Find the fraction.

2. A can do a piece of work in $3\frac{1}{4}$ hours, B in $3\frac{3}{4}$ hours, and C in $3\frac{1}{3}$ hours. In how many hours can it be done by all working together?

3. The second digit of a number of two figures exceeds the first by 5; and if the number, increased by 1, be divided by the sum of the digits increased by 2, the quotient is 3. Find the number.

4. The numerator of a fraction exceeds the denominator by 5. If the numerator be decreased by 9, and the denominator increased by 6, the sum of the resulting fraction and the given fraction is 2. Find the fraction.

5. A tank has three taps. By the first it can be filled in 3 hours 10 minutes, by the second it can be filled in 4 hours 45 minutes, and by the third it can be emptied in 3 hours 48 minutes. How many hours will it take to fill it if all the taps are open?

6. A freight train runs 6 miles an hour less than a passenger train. It runs 80 miles in the same time that the passenger train runs 112 miles. Find the rate of each train.

7. The digits of a number are three consecutive numbers, of which the middle digit is the greatest, and the first digit the least. If the number be divided by the sum of its digits, the quotient is $\frac{229}{7}$. Find the number.

8. A man walks $13\frac{1}{4}$ miles, and returns in an hour less time by a carriage, whose rate is $1\frac{1}{2}$ times as great as his rate of walking. Find his rate of walking.

9. A vessel runs at the rate of $11\frac{3}{4}$ miles an hour. It takes just as long to run 23 miles up stream as 47 miles down stream. Find the rate of the stream.

10. A can do a piece of work in two-thirds as many days as B, and B can do it in four-fifths as many days as C. Together they can do the work in $3\frac{7}{11}$ days. In how many days can each alone do the work?

11. The first digit of a number of three figures is three-fourths the second, and exceeds the third digit by 2. If the number be divided by the sum of its digits, the quotient is 38. Find the number.

12. A and B together can do a piece of work in $5\frac{1}{4}$ days, B and C together in $6\frac{2}{3}$ days, and C and A together in $5\frac{5}{6}$ days. In how many days can it be done by each working alone?

225. Literal Equations, leading to Linear Equations with one Unknown Number.

Ex. Solve the equation $\dfrac{x}{x-a} - \dfrac{x+2b}{x+a} = \dfrac{a^2+b^2}{x^2-a^2}$.

Multiplying each term by x^2-a^2,

$$x(x+a) - (x+2b)(x-a) = a^2+b^2,$$
$$x^2 + ax - (x^2 + 2bx - ax - 2ab) = a^2 + b^2,$$
$$x^2 + ax - x^2 - 2bx + ax + 2ab = a^2 + b^2,$$
$$2ax - 2bx = a^2 - 2ab + b^2.$$

Factoring both members, $2x(a-b) = (a-b)^2$.

Dividing by $2(a-b)$, $\qquad x = \dfrac{(a-b)^2}{2(a-b)} = \dfrac{a-b}{2}$.

Since $\dfrac{a-b}{2}$ does not satisfy the equation $x^2 - a^2 = 0$, it is the correct solution.

EXERCISE 30

Solve the following:

1. $(x - 2\,a - b)^2 - (x + a + 2\,b)^2 = 0.$

2. $\dfrac{bx}{a} - \dfrac{a^2 + b^2}{a^2} = \dfrac{a^2}{b^2} - \dfrac{x(a - b)}{b}.$

3. $\dfrac{5}{5\,x + 2\,m} - \dfrac{2}{4\,x - 3\,m} = \dfrac{6\,m}{20\,x^2 - 7\,mx - 6\,m^2}.$

4. $\dfrac{4\,x + 3\,n}{x + 2\,n} + \dfrac{4\,x - 5\,n}{3\,n - x} = \dfrac{10\,n^2}{x^2 - nx - 6\,n^2}.$

5. $(x + a - b)^3 - (x - a + b)^3 = 2(a - b)(3\,x^2 + x).$

6. $\dfrac{ax - a^2}{x - b} + \dfrac{bx - b^2}{x - a} = a + b.$

7. $\dfrac{x - a}{b} + \dfrac{x - b}{c} + \dfrac{x - c}{a} = \dfrac{bc(x + b) - ab^2 - a^2c}{abc}.$

8. $\dfrac{a}{x - a} - \dfrac{b}{x - b} = \dfrac{a - b}{x - c}.$

9. $\dfrac{x}{x^2 - 4\,a^2} - \dfrac{1}{2\,a} = 1 - \dfrac{x^2 - 2\,a - 4\,a^2}{x^2 - 4\,a^2}.$

10. $\dfrac{x - a}{x + 2\,a} - \dfrac{x + a}{x - 3\,a} = \dfrac{2\,ax + 19\,a^2}{x^2 - ax - 6\,a^2} - 1.$

11. $\dfrac{1}{x - 2\,a} - \dfrac{1}{6\,x + a} = \dfrac{7}{3\,x - 8\,a} - \dfrac{3}{2\,x - 3\,a}.$

12. $\dfrac{4\,x}{x - 4\,n} - \dfrac{x}{x + n} = \dfrac{4\,x}{x + 4\,n} - \dfrac{x}{x + 3\,n}.$

13. $(x + a)^3 + (x + b)^3 + (x + c)^3 = 3(x + a)(x + b)(x + c).$

14. $\dfrac{m + n}{x + m - n} - \dfrac{2\,m}{x - m + n} + \dfrac{m - n}{x - m - n} = 0.$

15. $\dfrac{a}{x - 2\,b} - \dfrac{b}{x - 2\,a} = \dfrac{a - b}{x - a - b}.$

16. $\dfrac{x^2 - 2\,ax + 5\,a^2}{x^2 - 2\,ax - 3\,a^2} + \dfrac{3\,x^2 + 3\,ax - 2\,a^2}{x^2 + ax + 2\,a^2} = 4.$

17. $\dfrac{x + a}{x - a} + \dfrac{x + b}{x - b} + \dfrac{x - a - b}{x + a + b} = 3.$

18. $\dfrac{x + n}{x - n} - \dfrac{x - 2\,n}{x + 2\,n} = \dfrac{x + 6\,n}{x - 6\,n} - \dfrac{x + 3\,n}{x - 3\,n}.$

19. $(x + 2\,a)^3 + (x + b)^3 = (2\,x + 2\,a + b)^3.$

226. Problems involving Literal Equations, leading to Linear Equations with one Unknown Number.

Prob. Divide a into two parts such that m times the first shall exceed n times the second by b.

Let $\qquad\qquad\qquad\qquad x =$ the first part.

Then, $\qquad\qquad\qquad a - x =$ the second part.

By the conditions, $\qquad mx = n(a - x) + b$.

$$mx = an - nx + b.$$

$$mx + nx = an + b.$$

$$x(m + n) = an + b.$$

Whence, $\qquad\qquad\qquad x = \dfrac{an + b}{m + n}$, the first part. $\qquad\qquad$ (1)

Also, $\qquad\qquad a - x = a - \dfrac{an + b}{m + n} = \dfrac{am + an - an - b}{m + n}$

$$= \dfrac{am - b}{m + n}, \text{ the other part.} \qquad\qquad (2)$$

The results can be used as *formulæ* for solving any problem of the above form.

Thus, let it be required to divide 25 into two parts such that 4 times the first shall exceed 3 times the second by 37.

Here, $a = 25$, $m = 4$, $n = 3$, and $b = 37$.

Substituting these values in (1) and (2),

the first part $\qquad = \dfrac{25 \times 3 + 37}{7} = \dfrac{75 + 37}{7} = \dfrac{112}{7} = 16$,

and the second part $= \dfrac{25 \times 4 - 37}{7} = \dfrac{100 - 37}{7} = \dfrac{63}{7} = 9$.

EXERCISE 31

1. Divide a into two parts whose quotient shall be m.

2. Two men, A and B, a miles apart, set out at the same time, and travel towards each other. A travels at the rate of m miles an hour, and B at the rate of n miles an hour. How far will each have travelled when they meet?

3. Divide a into three parts such that the first shall be one-mth the second, and one-nth the third.

4. If A can do a piece of work in a hours, B in b hours, C in c hours, and D in d hours, how many hours will it take to do the work if all work together?

5. What principal at r per cent interest will amount to a dollars in t years?

6. In how many years will p dollars amount to a dollars at r per cent interest?

7. Divide a into two parts such that one shall be m times as much above b as the other lacks of c.

8. A grocer mixes a pounds of coffee worth m cents a pound, b pounds worth n cents a pound, and c pounds worth p cents a pound. Find the cost per pound of the mixture.

9. A was m times as old as B a years ago, and will be n times as old as B in b years. Find their ages at present.

10. If A and B can do a piece of work in a days, B and C in b days, and A and C in c days, how many days will it take each working alone?

227. *A linear equation containing but one unknown number cannot have more than one root.*

Every linear equation containing but one unknown number, can be reduced to the form

$$x = a.$$

If possible, let this equation have two different roots, r_1 and r_2.

Then, by § 110, $r_1 = a,$

and $r_2 = a.$

Whence, $r_1 = r_2$ (Ax. 4, § 66).

But this is impossible, since by hypothesis, r_1 and r_2 are different; hence, a linear equation containing but one unknown number cannot have more than one root.

XII. SIMULTANEOUS LINEAR EQUATIONS

CONTAINING TWO OR MORE UNKNOWN NUMBERS

228. An equation containing two or more unknown numbers is satisfied by an indefinitely great number of sets of values of these numbers.

Consider, for example, the equation $x + y = 5$.

Putting $x = 1$, we have $1 + y = 5$, or $y = 4$.

Putting $x = 2$, we have $2 + y = 5$, or $y = 3$; etc.

Thus the equation is satisfied by the sets of values

$$x = 1, y = 4,$$

and $$x = 2, y = 3;$$

and this could be extended indefinitely, for we may give to x any numerical value whatever.

An equation which has an indefinitely great number of solutions is called an **Indeterminate Equation.**

229. Consider the equations

$$\begin{cases} x + y = 5, & (1) \\ 2x + 2y = 10. & (2) \end{cases}$$

By § 119, equation (2) is equivalent to (1).

Hence, every solution of (1) is a solution of (2), and every solution of (2) is a solution of (1).

Again, consider the equations

$$\begin{cases} x + y = 5, & (3) \\ x - y = 3. & (4) \end{cases}$$

Equation (3) is satisfied by the set of values $x = 4$, $y = 1$; as also is equation (4).

But (4) is not satisfied by *every* solution of (3), nor is (3) satisfied by every solution of (4).

Thus, (3) and (4) are not equivalent.

If two equations, containing two or more unknown numbers, are not equivalent, they are called **Independent.**

230. Consider the equations

$$\begin{cases} x + y = 5, & (1) \\ x + y = 6. & (2) \end{cases}$$

It is evidently impossible to find a set of values of x and y which shall satisfy both (1) and (2).

Two equations which express incompatible relations between the unknown numbers involved are called **Inconsistent**.

If they express possible relations between the unknown numbers, they are called **Consistent**.

231. A system of equations is called **Simultaneous** when each contains two or more unknown numbers, and every equation of the system is satisfied by the same set or sets of values of the unknown numbers.

A **Solution** of a system of simultaneous equations is a set of values of the unknown numbers which satisfies every equation of the system.

232. Two systems of equations, involving two or more unknown numbers, are said to be *equivalent* when every solution of either system is a solution of the other.

PRINCIPLES USED IN SOLVING SIMULTANEOUS EQUATIONS

233. *If for any equation of a system an equivalent equation be put, the resulting system is equivalent to the first.*

Let

$$\begin{cases} A = B, \\ C = D, \end{cases} \quad (1)$$

be equations involving two or more unknown numbers; and $E = F$ an equation equivalent to (1).

To prove the system of equations

$$\begin{cases} A = B, \\ E = F, \end{cases} \quad (2)$$

equivalent to the first system.

Since every solution of (1) is also a solution of (2), every solution of the first system is a solution of the second.

And since every solution of (2) is a solution of (1), every solution of the second system is a solution of the first.

Therefore, the two systems are equivalent (§ 232).

In like manner, the theorem may be proved for a system of any number of equations.

234. *If for either equation, in a system of two, we put an equation whose first and second members are the sums, or differences, respectively, of the given first and second members, the resulting system will be equivalent to the first.* ·

Let
$$\begin{cases} A = B, \\ C = D, \end{cases}$$

be equations involving two or more unknown numbers.

To prove the system of equations
$$\begin{cases} A = B, \\ A + C = B + D, \end{cases}$$

equivalent to the first system.

Any solution of the first system, when substituted for the unknown numbers, makes A equal to B, and C equal to D.

It then makes $A + C$ equal to $B + D$ (§ 115, 1).

Then it is a solution of the second system.

Again, any solution of the second system makes A equal to B, and $A + C$ equal to $B + D$.

It then makes C equal to D (§ 115, 2).

Then it is a solution of the first system.

Therefore, the two systems are equivalent.

In like manner, the first system is equivalent to the system
$$\begin{cases} A = B, \\ A - C = B - D. \end{cases}$$

235. It may be proved, as in § 234, that if the equations
$$A = B, \ C = D, \ E = F, \text{ etc.,} \tag{1}$$

involve two or more unknown numbers, and any equation be replaced by an equation whose first member is the sum of any of the given first members, and second member the sum of the corresponding second members, the resulting system will be equivalent to the first.

The above is also the case if the signs of both members, in any of the equations (1), be changed from + to −.

For example, any equation may be replaced by the equation

$$A + C - E = B + D - F.$$

236. *If any equation of a system be solved for one of the unknown numbers, and the value found be substituted for this unknown number in each of the other equations, the resulting system will be equivalent to the first.*

Let
$$\begin{cases} A = B, & (1) \\ C = D, & (2) \end{cases}$$

be equations involving two unknown numbers, x and y.

Let E be the value of x obtained by solving (1); and let $F = G$ be the equation obtained by substituting E for x in (2).

To prove the system of equations

$$\begin{cases} x = E, & (3) \\ F = G, \end{cases}$$

equivalent to the first system.

We know that (3) is equivalent to (1); hence, any solution of the first system is a solution of (3) (§ 233).

Again, any solution of the first system makes E identically equal to x; and also makes C equal to D.

Then it must make the expression obtained by putting E for x, in C, equal to the expression obtained by putting E for x, in D; that is, it makes F equal to G.

Then, any solution of the first system is also a solution of the second.

Again, since (3) is equivalent to (1), any solution of the second system is a solution of (1).

Also, any solution of the second system makes x identically equal to E, and also makes F equal to G.

Then it must make the expression obtained by putting x for E, in F, equal to the expression obtained by putting x for E, in G; that is, it makes C equal to D.

Then, any solution of the second system is also a solution of the first.

Therefore, the two systems are equivalent.

In like manner, the theorem may be proved for a system of any number of equations, involving any number of unknown numbers.

237. Any equation involving two unknown numbers, x and y, can be reduced to the form $ax + by = c$.

If we have two independent simultaneous equations of the form $ax + by = c$, they may be combined in such a way as to form a single equation involving but one unknown number.

This operation is called **Elimination**.

There are three principal methods of elimination.

I. ELIMINATION BY ADDITION OR SUBTRACTION.

238. 1. Solve the equations $\begin{cases} 5x - 3y = 19. & (1) \\ 7x + 4y = 2. & (2) \end{cases}$

Multiplying (1) by 4, $\qquad 20x - 12y = 76.$ $\qquad$ (3)

Multiplying (2) by 3, $\qquad 21x + 12y = 6.$ $\qquad$ (4)

Adding (3) and (4), $\qquad\qquad 41x = 82.$ $\qquad$ (5)

Whence, $\qquad\qquad\qquad\qquad x = 2.$ $\qquad$ (6)

Substituting $x = 2$ in (1), $\qquad 10 - 3y = 19.$ $\qquad$ (7)

Whence, $\qquad\qquad\qquad -3y = 9,$ or $y = -3.$ (8)

The above is an example of elimination by *addition*.

(The principles demonstrated in §§ 116 to 119, inclusive, and § 122, hold for equations with more than one unknown number.)

By § 119, equation (1) is equivalent to (3), and (2) to (4).

Then, by two applications of § 233, the given system is equivalent to the system (3) and (4).

By § 234, the system (3) and (4) is equivalent to the system (3) and (5).

By § 122, equation (6) is equivalent to (5); and then by § 233, the system (3) and (5) is equivalent to the system (3) and (6), or to the system (1) and (6).

By § 236, the system (1) and (6) is equivalent to the system (6) and (7); which by § 233 is equivalent to the system (6) and (8).

Thus, the given system is equivalent to the system (6) and (8); and since no solutions are introduced nor lost, (6) and (8) form the correct solution.

2. Solve the equations $\begin{cases} 15\,x + 8\,y = \quad 1. & (1) \\ 10\,x - 7\,y = -24. & (2) \end{cases}$

Multiplying (1) by 2, $30\,x + 16\,y = \quad 2.$ (3)

Multiplying (2) by 3, $30\,x - 21\,y = -72.$ (4)

Subtracting (4) from (3), $37\,y = 74$, and $y = 2.$

Substituting $y = 2$ in (1), $15\,x + 16 = 1.$

Whence, $15\,x = -15$, and $x = -1.$

The above is an example of elimination by *subtraction*.

We speak of *adding* a system of equations when we mean placing the sum of the first members equal to the sum of the second members.

Abbreviations of this kind are frequent in Algebra ; thus we speak of *multiplying* an equation when we mean multiplying each of its terms.

From the above examples, we have the following rule:

If necessary, multiply the given equations by such numbers as will make the coefficients of one of the unknown numbers in the resulting equations of equal absolute value.

Add or subtract the resulting equations according as the coefficients of equal absolute value are of unlike or like sign.

If the coefficients which are to be made of equal absolute value are prime to each other, each may be used as the multiplier for the other equation ; but if they are not prime to each other, such multipliers should be used as will produce their lowest common multiple.

Thus, in Ex. 1, to make the coefficients of y of equal absolute value, we multiply (1) by 4 and (2) by 3; but in Ex. 2, to make the coefficients of x of equal absolute value, since the L.C.M. of 10 and 15 is 30, we multiply (1) by 2 and (2) by 3.

II. ELIMINATION BY SUBSTITUTION

239. *Ex.* Solve the equations $\begin{cases} 7\,x - 9\,y = \quad 15. & (1) \\ 8\,y - 5\,x = -17. & (2) \end{cases}$

Transposing $-5\,x$ in (2), $8\,y = 5\,x - 17.$

Whence, $y = \dfrac{5\,x - 17}{8}.$ (3)

Substituting in (1), $7\,x - 9\left(\dfrac{5\,x - 17}{8}\right) = 15.$ (4)

Clearing of fractions, $56\,x - 9\,(5\,x-17) = 120.$
Or, $56\,x - 45\,x + 153 = 120.$
Uniting terms, $11\,x = -33.$
Whence, $x = -3.$ (5)

Substituting $x = -3$ in (3), $y = \dfrac{-15-17}{8} = -4.$ (6)

By § 236, the given system of equations is equivalent to the system (3) and (4); or, since (4) is equivalent to (5), to the system (3) and (5).

By § 236, the system (3) and (5) is equivalent to the system (5) and (6); whence, the given system is equivalent to the system (5) and (6).

From the above example, we have the following rule:

From one of the given equations find the value of one of the unknown numbers in terms of the other, and substitute this value in place of that number in the other equation.

III. ELIMINATION BY COMPARISON

240. *Ex.* Solve the equations $\begin{cases} 2\,x - 5\,y = -16. & (1) \\ 3\,x + 7\,y = 5. & (2) \end{cases}$

Transposing $-5\,y$ in (1), $2\,x = 5\,y - 16.$

Whence, $x = \dfrac{5\,y - 16}{2}.$ (3)

Transposing $7\,y$ in (2), $3\,x = 5 - 7\,y.$

Whence, $x = \dfrac{5 - 7\,y}{3}.$ (4)

Equating values of x, $\dfrac{5\,y - 16}{2} = \dfrac{5 - 7\,y}{3}.$ (5)

Clearing of fractions, $15\,y - 48 = 10 - 14\,y.$
Transposing, $29\,y = 58.$
Whence, $y = 2.$ (6)

Substituting $y = 2$ in (3), $x = \dfrac{10 - 16}{2} = -3.$ (7)

By § 233, the given system of equations is equivalent to the system (3) and (4); or, since, by Ax. 4, § 66, (4) is equivalent to (5), to the system (3) and (5).

But (5) is equivalent to (6) ; so that the given system is equivalent to the system (3) and (6).

By § 236, the system (3) and (6) is equivalent to the system (6) and (7).

From the above example, we have the following rule:

From each of the given equations, find the value of the same unknown number in terms of the other, and place these values equal to each other.

241. If the given equations are not in the form $ax + by = c$, they should first be reduced to this form, when they may be solved by either method of elimination.

In solving fractional simultaneous equations, we are liable to get results which do not satisfy the given equations.

By § 221, we must reject any solution which satisfies the equation obtained by equating to zero the L. C. M. of the given denominators.

242. 1. Solve the equations

$$\begin{cases} \dfrac{7}{x+3} - \dfrac{3}{y+4} = 0. & (1) \\ x(y-2) - y(x-5) = -13. & (2) \end{cases}$$

Multiplying each term of (1) by $(x+3)(y+4)$,
$$7y + 28 - 3x - 9 = 0, \text{ or } 7y - 3x = -19. \qquad (3)$$
From (2),
$$xy - 2x - xy + 5y = -13, \text{ or } 5y - 2x = -13. \qquad (4)$$

Multiplying (3) by 2, $14y - 6x = -38.$ (5)

Multiplying (4) by 3, $15y - 6x = -39.$ (6)

Subtracting (5) from (6), $y = -1.$

Substituting in (4), $-5 - 2x = -13.$

Whence, $-2x = -8, \text{ or } x = 4.$

Since $x = 4$ and $y = -1$ do not satisfy the equation $(x+3)(y+4) = 0$, the solution $x = 4$, $y = -1$ is correct (§ 241).

2. Solve the equations $\begin{cases} 2x + 3y = 13. & (1) \\ \dfrac{1}{x-2} + \dfrac{1}{y-3} = 0. & (2) \end{cases}$

Multiplying each term of (2) by $(x-2)(y-3)$,

$$y - 3 + x - 2 = 0, \text{ or } y = -x + 5. \tag{3}$$

Substituting in (1), $2x - 3x + 15 = 13, \text{ or } x = 2.$

Substituting in (3), $y = -2 + 5 = 3.$

Since $x = 2$ and $y = 3$ satisfy the equation $(x-2)(y-3) = 0$, the solution must be rejected.

The above solution satisfies the first given equation, but not the second ; it is impossible to find a solution which will satisfy both given equations.

In solving *literal* simultaneous linear equations, the method of elimination by addition or subtraction is usually to be preferred.

3. Solve the equations $\begin{cases} ax + by = c. & (1) \\ a'x + b'y = c'. & (2) \end{cases}$

Multiplying (1) by b', $ab'x + bb'y = b'c.$

Multiplying (2) by b, $a'bx + bb'y = bc'.$

Subtracting, $\overline{(ab' - a'b)x = b'c - bc'.}$

Whence, $x = \dfrac{b'c - bc'}{ab' - a'b}.$

Multiplying (1) by a', $aa'x + a'by = ca'. \tag{3}$

Multiplying (2) by a, $aa'x + ab'y = c'a. \tag{4}$

Subtracting (3) from (4), $(ab' - a'b)y = c'a - ca'.$

Whence, $y = \dfrac{c'a - ca'}{ab' - a'b}.$

Certain equations in which the unknown numbers occur in the denominators of fractions may be readily solved without previously clearing of fractions.

4. Solve the equations $\begin{cases} \dfrac{10}{x} - \dfrac{9}{y} = 8. & (1) \\[2mm] \dfrac{8}{x} + \dfrac{15}{y} = -1. & (2) \end{cases}$

Multiplying (1) by 5, $\dfrac{50}{x} - \dfrac{45}{y} = 40.$

Multiplying (2) by 3, $\dfrac{24}{x} + \dfrac{45}{y} = -3.$

Adding,
$$\frac{74}{x} = 37.$$

Whence,
$$74 = 37\,x, \text{ and } x = 2.$$

Substituting in (1),
$$5 - \frac{9}{y} = 8.$$

Whence,
$$-\frac{9}{y} = 3, \text{ and } y = -3.$$

EXERCISE 32

Solve the following:

1. $\begin{cases} .08\,x + .9\,y = .048. \\ .3\,x - .35\,y = .478. \end{cases}$

2. $\begin{cases} \dfrac{5}{3\,x} - \dfrac{7}{y} = -\dfrac{29}{9}. \\ \dfrac{3}{x} + \dfrac{5}{4\,y} = \dfrac{9}{8}. \end{cases}$

3. $\begin{cases} \dfrac{2\,x - 3\,y}{4} + \dfrac{4\,x + 6\,y}{3} = -\dfrac{1}{2}. \\ \dfrac{5\,x + 2\,y}{2} + \dfrac{7\,y - 3\,x}{5} = \dfrac{39}{10}. \end{cases}$

4. $\begin{cases} m(x + y) + n(x - y) = 2. \\ m^2(x + y) - n^2(x - y) = m - n. \end{cases}$

5. $\begin{cases} \dfrac{x + y}{x - y} = -\dfrac{1}{10}. \\ \dfrac{3\,x + 8}{y - 4} = \dfrac{6\,x - 1}{2\,y + 3}. \end{cases}$

6. $\begin{cases} 3\,x - 4\,y = -11. \\ \dfrac{2}{x + 5} - \dfrac{5}{y + 1} = 0. \end{cases}$

7. $\begin{cases} ax + \dfrac{b}{y} = m. \\ cx + \dfrac{d}{y} = n. \end{cases}$

8. $\begin{cases} (a + b)x + (a - b)y = 2\,(a^2 + b^2). \\ \dfrac{b}{x - a - b} = \dfrac{a}{y - a + b}. \end{cases}$

9. $\begin{cases} \dfrac{m}{x - a} + \dfrac{n}{y + b} = 1. \\ \dfrac{n}{x - a} + \dfrac{m}{y + b} = 1. \end{cases}$

10. $\begin{cases} \dfrac{3}{2\,x + y} - \dfrac{24}{x - 4\,y} = -2. \\ \dfrac{7}{2\,x + y} - \dfrac{16}{x - 4\,y} = -3. \end{cases}$

11. $\begin{cases} \dfrac{2\,xy + 3}{x - 2} - \dfrac{4\,y + 5}{x + 3} = 2\,y. \\ \dfrac{2\,x + 3\,y - 1}{2\,x + y} - \dfrac{3\,x - 8\,y}{3\,x - 11\,y} = -\dfrac{25\,y^2}{(2\,x + y)(3\,x - 11\,y)}. \end{cases}$

12. $\begin{cases} (a + b)x + (a - b)y = 2\,a^2 - 2\,b^2. \\ \dfrac{y}{a - b} - \dfrac{x}{a + b} = \dfrac{4\,ab}{a^2 - b^2}. \end{cases}$

SIMULTANEOUS LINEAR EQUATIONS CONTAINING MORE THAN TWO UNKNOWN NUMBERS

243. If we have *three* independent simultaneous equations, containing *three* unknown numbers, we may combine any two of them by one of the methods of elimination explained in §§ 238 to 240, so as to obtain a single equation containing only two unknown numbers.

We may then combine the remaining equation with either of the other two, and obtain another equation containing the same two unknown numbers.

By solving the two equations containing two unknown numbers, we may obtain their values; and substituting them in either of the given equations, the value of the remaining unknown number may be found.

We proceed in a similar manner when the number of equations and of unknown numbers is greater than three.

The method of elimination by addition or subtraction is usually the most convenient.

If any equation is fractional, we should reject any solution which satisfies the equation obtained by equating to zero the L. C. M. of the given denominators (§ 241).

1. Solve the equations
$$\begin{cases} 6x - 4y - 7z = 17. & (1) \\ 9x - 7y - 16z = 29. & (2) \\ 10x - 5y - 3z = 23. & (3) \end{cases}$$

Multiplying (1) by 3,	$18x - 12y - 21z = 51.$	(4)
Multiplying (2) by 2,	$18x - 14y - 32z = 58.$	(5)
Subtracting,	$2y + 11z = -7.$	(6)
Multiplying (1) by 5,	$30x - 20y - 35z = 85.$	(7)
Multiplying (3) by 3,	$30x - 15y - 9z = 69.$	(8)
Subtracting (7) from (8),	$5y + 26z = -16.$	(9)
Multiplying (6) by 5,	$10y + 55z = -35.$	(10)
Multiplying (9) by 2,	$10y + 52z = -32.$	(11)
Subtracting,	$3z = -3,$ or $z = -1.$	(12)
Substituting in (6),	$2y - 11 = -7,$ or $y = 2.$	(13)
Substituting in (1),	$6x - 8 + 7 = 17,$ or $x = 3.$	(14)

By §§ 119 and 233, the given system of equations is equivalent to the system (3), (4), and (5) ; which, by ·§ 235, is equivalent to the system (3), (4), and (6), or to the system (1), (3), and (6).

But (1) is equivalent to (7), and (3) to (8) ; so that the given system is equivalent to the system (6), (7), and (8) ; this, by § 235, is equivalent to the system (6), (7), and (9), or to the system (1), (6), and (9).

But the system (1), (6), and (9) is equivalent to the system (1), (10), and (11) ; which, by § 235, is equivalent to the system (1), (10), and (12).

The system (1), (10), and (12) is equivalent to the system (1), (6), and (12) ; which, by two applications of § 236, is equivalent to the system (12), (13), and (14).

In certain cases the solution may be abridged by aid of the artifice which is employed in the following example.

2. Solve the equations

$$\begin{cases} u + x + y = 6. & (1) \\ x + y + z = 7. & (2) \\ y + z + u = 8. & (3) \\ z + u + x = 9. & (4) \end{cases}$$

Adding, $3u + 3x + 3y + 3z = 30.$

Whence, $u + x + y + z = 10.$ (5)

Subtracting (2) from (5), $u = 3.$

Subtracting (3) from (5), $x = 2.$

Subtracting (4) from (5), $y = 1.$

Subtracting (1) from (5), $z = 4.$

EXERCISE 33

Solve the following :

1. $\begin{cases} 5x + y - 4z = -5. \\ 3x - 5y - 6z = -20. \\ x - 3y + 8z = -27. \end{cases}$

2. $\begin{cases} \dfrac{x-y}{3} - \dfrac{y-z}{4} = \dfrac{7}{3}. \\ \dfrac{y-z}{3} + \dfrac{z+x}{5} = -\dfrac{13}{15}. \\ \dfrac{z+x}{2} - \dfrac{x-y}{5} = \dfrac{43}{10}. \end{cases}$

3. $\begin{cases} ax + by = (a+b)c. \\ by + cz = (c+a)b. \\ cz + ax = (b+c)a. \end{cases}$

4. $\begin{cases} 2x - 5y = -26. \\ 7x + 6z = -33. \\ \dfrac{3}{y-4} = \dfrac{4}{z+2}. \end{cases}$

5.
$$\begin{cases} u + 3x - 2y - z = -3. \\ 2u - x - y + 3z = 23. \\ u + x + 3y - 2z = -12. \\ 3u - 2x + y + z = 22. \end{cases}$$

6.
$$\begin{cases} \dfrac{1}{x} + \dfrac{1}{y} + \dfrac{1}{z} = a. \\ \dfrac{1}{y} + \dfrac{1}{z} + \dfrac{1}{u} = b. \\ \dfrac{1}{z} + \dfrac{1}{u} + \dfrac{1}{x} = c. \\ \dfrac{1}{x} + \dfrac{1}{y} + \dfrac{1}{z} = d. \end{cases}$$

7.
$$\begin{cases} \dfrac{3x - y}{5} - \dfrac{4z - 5y}{2} = \dfrac{19}{2}. \\ \dfrac{2x - 3z}{6} - \dfrac{x - 4y}{4} = \dfrac{7}{4}. \\ \dfrac{4x + z}{3} - \dfrac{3y + 5z}{2} = \dfrac{49}{3}. \end{cases}$$

8.
$$\begin{cases} \dfrac{3}{x + y} + \dfrac{4}{x - z} = 2. \\ \dfrac{6}{x + y} - \dfrac{5}{y - z} = 1. \\ \dfrac{4}{x - z} + \dfrac{5}{y - z} = 2. \end{cases}$$

9.
$$\begin{cases} x + y + z = 0. \\ (b + c)x + (c + a)y + (a + b)z = 0. \\ bcx + cay + abz = 1. \end{cases}$$

10.
$$\begin{cases} \dfrac{x}{a + b} - \dfrac{y + b}{c} = 0. \\ \dfrac{y}{b + c} - \dfrac{z + c}{a} = 0. \\ \dfrac{z}{c + a} - \dfrac{x + a}{b} = 0. \end{cases}$$

PROBLEMS INVOLVING SIMULTANEOUS LINEAR EQUATIONS WITH TWO OR MORE UNKNOWN NUMBERS

244. In solving problems where two or more letters are used to represent unknown numbers, we must obtain from the conditions of the problem *as many independent equations* (§ 229) *as there are unknown numbers to be determined.*

1. If 3 be added to both numerator and denominator of a fraction, its value is $\frac{2}{3}$; and if 2 be subtracted from both numerator and denominator, its value is $\frac{1}{2}$; find the fraction.

Let $x =$ the numerator,

and $y =$ the denominator.

By the conditions, $\dfrac{x + 3}{y + 3} = \dfrac{2}{3}$,

and $\dfrac{x - 2}{y - 2} = \dfrac{1}{2}$.

Solving these equations, $x = 7$, $y = 12$; whence, the fraction is $\dfrac{7}{12}$.

2. A crew can row 10 miles in 50 minutes down stream, and 12 miles in an hour and a half against the stream. Find the rate in miles per hour of the current, and of the crew in still water.

Let $x =$ number of miles an hour of the crew in still water,
and $y =$ number of miles an hour of the current.

Then, $x + y =$ number of miles an hour of the crew down stream,
and $x - y =$ number of miles an hour of the crew up stream.

The number of miles an hour rowed by the crew is equal to the distance in miles divided by the time in hours.

Then, $$x + y = 10 \div \frac{5}{6} = 12,$$

and $$x - y = 12 \div \frac{3}{2} = 8.$$

Solving these equations, $x = 10$, $y = 2$.

3. The sum of the three digits of a number is 13. If the number, decreased by 8, be divided by the sum of its second and third digits, the quotient is 25; and if 99 be added to the number, the digits will be inverted. Find the number.

Let $x =$ the first digit,
        $y =$ the second,
and $z =$ the third.

Then, $100 x + 10 y + z =$ the number,
and $100 z + 10 y + x =$ the number with its digits inverted.

By the conditions of the problem,
$$x + y + z = 13,$$
$$\frac{100 x + 10 y + z - 8}{y + z} = 25,$$
and $100 x + 10 y + z + 99 = 100 z + 10 y + x.$

Solving these equations, $x = 2$, $y = 8$, $z = 3$; and the number is 283.

EXERCISE 34

1. If 3 be added to the numerator of a certain fraction, and 7 subtracted from the denominator, its value is $\frac{6}{7}$; and if 1 be subtracted from the numerator, and 7 added to the denominator, its value is $\frac{2}{5}$. Find the fraction.

2. Find two numbers such that one shall be n times as much greater than a as the other is less than a; and the quotient of their sum by their difference equal to b.

3. If the greater of two numbers be divided by the less, the quotient is 1, and the remainder 6. And if the greater, increased by 14, be divided by the less, diminished by 4, the quotient is 5, and the remainder 4. Find the numbers.

4. A sum of money at simple interest amounted to $1868.40 in 7 years, and to $2174.40 in 12 years. Find the principal and the rate.

5. A certain number of two digits exceeds three times the sum of its digits by 4. If the digits be inverted, the sum of the resulting number and the given number exceeds three times the given number by 2. Find the number.

6. A man invests a certain sum of money at a certain rate of interest. If the principal had been $1200 greater, and the rate one per cent greater, his income would have been increased by $118. If the principal had been $3200 greater, and the rate two per cent greater, his income would have been increased by $312. What sum did he invest, and at what rate?

7. The middle digit of a number of three figures is one-half the sum of the other two digits. If the number be divided by the sum of its digits, the quotient is 20, and the remainder 9; and if 594 be added to the number, the digits will be inverted. Find the number.

8. A crew row $16\frac{1}{2}$ miles up stream and 18 miles down stream in 9 hours. They then row 21 miles up stream and $19\frac{1}{4}$ miles down stream in 11 hours. Find the rate in miles an hour of the stream, and of the crew in still water.

9. A and B can do a piece of work in $\frac{35}{12}$ hours, A and C in $\frac{14}{9}$ hours, A and D in $\frac{21}{10}$ hours, and B and C in $\frac{10}{7}$ hours. How many hours will it take each alone to do the work?

10. A and B run a race of 280 feet. The first heat, A gives B a start of 70 feet, and neither wins the race. The second heat, A gives B a start of 35 feet, and beats him by $6\frac{2}{3}$ seconds. How many feet can each run in a second?

11. A, B, C, and D play at cards. After B has won one-half of A's money, C one-third of B's, D one-fourth of C's, and A one-fifth of D's, they have each $10, except B who has $16. How much had each at first?

12. The fore-wheel of a carriage makes a revolutions more than the hind-wheel in travelling b feet. If the circumference of the fore-wheel were increased by one-mth, and the circumference of the hind-wheel by one-nth, the fore-wheel would make c revolutions more than the hind-wheel in travelling d feet. Find the circumference of each wheel.

13. The sum of the four digits of a number is 14. The sum of the last three digits exceeds twice the first by 2. Twice the sum of the second and third digits exceeds three times the sum of the first and fourth by 3. And if 2727 be subtracted from the number, the digits will be inverted. Find the number.

14. A and B run a race from P to Q and back; the distance from P to Q being 108 yards. The first heat, A reaches Q first, and meets B on his return at a point 12 yards from Q. The second heat, A increases his speed by 2 yards a second, and B by 1 yard a second; and now A meets B 18 yards from Q. How many yards can each run in a second?

15. A train running from A to B, meets with an accident which delays it a hours. It then proceeds at a rate one-nth less than its former rate, and arrives at B b hours late. Had the accident occurred c miles nearer B, the train would have been d hours late. Find the rate of the train before the accident, and the distance to B from the point of detention.

16. A man buys 60 shares of stock, part paying dividends at the rate of $3\frac{3}{4}$ per cent, and the remainder at the rate of $4\frac{1}{2}$ per cent. If the first part had paid dividends at the rate of $4\frac{1}{2}$ per cent, and the other at the rate of $3\frac{3}{4}$ per cent, the total annual income would have been $12 less. How many shares of each kind did he buy?

XIII.   DISCUSSION OF LINEAR EQUATIONS

VARIABLES AND LIMITS

245. A *variable number*, or simply a *variable*, is a number which may assume, under the conditions imposed upon it, an indefinitely great number of different values.

A *constant* is a number which remains unchanged throughout the same discussion.

A *limit* of a variable is a constant number, the difference between which and the variable may be made less than any assigned number, however small, without ever becoming zero.

In other words, a limit of a variable is a fixed number which the variable approaches indefinitely near, but never actually reaches.

246. It is evident that the difference between a variable and its limit is a variable which approaches the limit zero.

247. Interpretation of $\dfrac{a}{0}$**.**

Consider the series of fractions

$$\frac{a}{3}, \frac{a}{\cdot 3}, \frac{a}{\cdot 03}, \frac{a}{\cdot 003} \ldots;$$

where each denominator after the first is one-tenth of the preceding denominator.

It is evident that, by sufficiently continuing the series, the denominator may be made less than any assigned number, however small, and the value of the fraction greater than any assigned number, however great.

In other words, *if the numerator of a fraction remains constant, while the denominator approaches the limit 0, the value of the fraction increases without limit.*

It is customary to express this principle as follows:

$$\frac{a}{0} = \infty .$$

The symbol ∞ is called *Infinity;* it simply stands for that which is greater than any number, however great.

248. Interpretation of $\frac{a}{0}$.

Consider the series of fractions

$$\frac{a}{3}, \frac{a}{30}, \frac{a}{300}, \frac{a}{3000}, \ldots;$$

where each denominator after the first is ten times the preceding denominator.

It is evident that, by sufficiently continuing the series, the denominator may be made greater than any assigned number, however great, and the value of the fraction less than any assigned number, however small.

In other words,

If the numerator of a fraction remains constant, while the denominator increases without limit, the value of the fraction approaches the limit 0.

It is customary to express this principle as follows:

$$\frac{a}{\infty} = 0.$$

It must be clearly understood that no *literal meaning* can be attached to such results as

$$\frac{a}{0} = \infty, \text{ and } \frac{a}{\infty} = 0;$$

for there can be no such thing as division, unless the divisor is a *finite number.*

If such forms occur in mathematical investigations, they must be interpreted as in §§ 247 and 248.

249. Interpretation of $\frac{0}{0}$.

By § 44, $\frac{0}{0}$ signifies a number which, when multiplied by 0, gives 0.

But by §§ 37 and 40, if *any* number be multiplied by 0, the result is 0.

Hence, $\frac{0}{0}$ may be any number whatever.

For this reason the fraction $\dfrac{0}{0}$ is called **Indeterminate**.

250. A **Function** of a number is any expression which contains the number.

Thus, the expression $2\,x^2 - 3\,ax + 5\,a^2$ is a function of x.

251. Function Notation.

A function of x is often represented by the symbol $f(x)$; read "f-function of x," or simply "f-x."

If, in any investigation, $f(x)$ stands for a certain function of x, then, whatever value a may have, $f(a)$ represents the result obtained by substituting a for x in the given function.

Thus, if $\quad f(x) = x^2 + 3\,x - 2,$ then

$$f(3) = 3^2 + 3 \cdot 3 - 2 = 16;$$
$$f(-3) = (-3)^2 + 3(-3) - 2 = -2; \text{ etc.}$$

Functions of x are also represented by the symbols $F(x)$, $\phi(x)$, etc.

THE THEOREM OF LIMITS

252. *If two functions of the same variable are so related that, as the variable changes its value, they are equal for every value which the variable can assume, and each approaches a certain limit, then the two limits are equal.*

Let y and z be functions of a certain variable, x; and let them be equal for every value which the variable x can assume, and approach the limits y' and z', respectively.

To prove that $\qquad y' = z'.$

Let $y' - y = m,$ and $z' - z = n.$

Then, m and n are variables which can be made less than any assigned number, however small (§ 246).

Then, $m - n$ is either zero, or else a variable which can be made less than any assigned number, however small.

But $m - n = y' - y - z' + z = y' - z';$ for, by hypothesis, y and z are equal.

Since $y' - z'$ is not a variable, $m - n$ is not a variable.

Then, $m - n$ is 0; and hence its equal, $y' - z'$ is 0, or $y' = z'.$

PROPOSITIONS IN REGARD TO LIMITS

253. *The limit of the sum of a constant and a variable is the sum of the constant and the limit of the variable.*

Let a be a constant, and x a variable whose limit is x'.

Then, $x' - x$ can be made less than any assigned number, however small (§ 245).

Whence, $(x' + a) - (x + a)$, which equals $x' - x$, can be made less than any assigned number, however small.

Then, $x' + a$ is the limit of $x + a$.

254. *The limit of the sum of any finite number of variables is the sum of their limits.*

Let x, y, z, $\cdots$, be variables whose limits are x', y', z', $\cdots$, respectively.

Then, $x' - x$, $y' - y$, $z' - z$, $\cdot$, can be made less than any assigned number, however small.

Whence, $(x' - x) + (y' - y) + (z' - z) + \cdots$,

or, $(x' + y' + z' + \cdots) - (x + y + z + \cdots)$,

can be made less than any assigned number, however small.

Then, $x' + y' + z' + \cdots$ is the limit of $x + y + z + \cdots$.   (1)

255. Any two corresponding positive signs, in (1), § 254, may be changed to negative.

Thus, $x' - y' + z' + \cdots$ is the limit of $x - y + z + \cdots$.

256. *The limit of the product of a constant and a variable is the constant multiplied by the limit of the variable.*

Let a, x, and x' have the same meaning as in § 253.

Then, $a(x' - x)$, or $ax' - ax$, can be made less than any assigned number, however small.

Whence, ax' is the limit of ax.

257. *The limit of the product of any number of variables is the product of their limits.*

Let x, y, z, $\cdot$, be variables having the limits x', y', z', $\cdot$, respectively; and let $x' - x = l$, $y' - y = m$, $z' - z = n$, $\cdots$.

Then, l, m, n, $\cdots$, can be made less than any assigned number, however small.

Now, $x'y'z' \cdots = (x+l)(y+m)(z+n) \cdots$

$\qquad = xyz \cdots + $ terms involving $l, m, n, \cdots$.

Then, $x'y'z' \cdots - xyz \cdots = $ terms involving $l, m, n, \cdots$. (1)

The second member of (1) can be made less than any assigned number, however small.

Then, $x'y'z' \cdots$ is the limit of $xyz \cdots$.

258. Let n be a positive integer, and x a variable having the limit x'; then,

$\qquad$ limit of $x^n = $ limit of $x \times x \times x \times \cdots$ to n factors

$\qquad\qquad = x' \times x' \times x' \times \cdots$ to n factors, by § 257,

$\qquad\qquad = (x')^n = ($ limit of $x)^n$.

259. *The limit of the quotient of two variables is the quotient of their limits, if the divisor be not zero.*

Let x and y be variables having the limits x' and y', respectively; and suppose that y' is not zero.

Let $x' - x = l$, and $y' - y = m$; then, $x = x' - l$ and $y = y' - m$.

Now,

$$\frac{x'}{y'} - \frac{x}{y} = \frac{x'}{y'} - \frac{x'-l}{y'-m} = \frac{x'y' - mx' - (x'y' - ly')}{y'(y'-m)} = \frac{ly' - mx'}{y'^2 - my'}. \quad (1)$$

Since l and m can be made less than any assigned number, however small (§ 245), the numerator of this fraction can be made less than any assigned number, however small.

Also, the denominator can be made to differ from y'^2 by less than any assigned number, however small.

Then, the fraction (1) can be made less than any assigned number, however small.

Whence, $\frac{x'}{y'}$ is the limit of $\frac{x}{y}$.

INTERPRETATION OF NEGATIVE RESULTS

260. A problem is said to be **Impossible** when its conditions cannot be satisfied.

It is said to be **Indeterminate** when the number of its solutions is indefinitely great.

261. 1. The length of a field is 10 rods, and its breadth 8 rods; how many rods must be added to the breadth so that the area may be 60 square rods ?

Let $x =$ number of rods to be added.

By the conditions, $10 (8 + x) = 60.$

Then, $80 + 10 x = 60$, or $x = - 2.$

By § 78, adding $- 2$ rods is the same thing as *subtracting* 2 rods. Hence, 2 rods must be subtracted from the breadth in 'order that the area may be 60 square rods.

The above problem is impossible arithmetically ; for the area of the field is at present 80 square rods ; and it is impossible to make it 60 square rods by adding anything to the breadth.

If we should modify the problem so as to read :

"The length of a field is 10 rods, and its breadth 8 rods ; how many rods must be *subtracted* from the breadth so that the area may be 60 square rods ? "

and let x denote the number of rods to be subtracted, we should find $x = 2.$

Also, if we had solved the given problem by letting x denote the number of rods to be *subtracted*, we should have found $x = 2.$

2. A is 35 years of age, and B 20 ; it is required to determine the epoch at which A's age is twice as great as B's.

Let us suppose that the required epoch is x years *after* the present date.

By the conditions, $35 + x = 2 (20 + x).$

Then, $35 + x = 40 + 2 x$, or $x = - 5.$

By § 56, $- 5$ years *after* is the same thing as 5 years *before* the present date.

Therefore, the required epoch is 5 years before the present date.

If we had supposed the required epoch to be x years *before* the present date, we should have found $x = 5.$

From the discussion of the above problems, we infer that **a** negative result may be obtained :

1. In consequence of·the fact that the problem is arithmetically impossible.

2. In consequence of a wrong choice between two possible hypotheses as to the nature of the unknown number.

In the first case, it is usually possible to form an analogous problem, whose conditions are satisfied by the absolute value of the negative result, by attributing to the unknown number a quality the opposite of that which had been attributed to it.

In either case, a positive result may be obtained by attributing to the unknown number a quality the opposite of that which had been attributed to it; and the *equations* answering to the new conditions may be derived from the old equations by changing the sign of the unknown number wherever it occurs.

Similar considerations hold in problems involving two or more unknown numbers.

A negative result sometimes indicates that the problem is impossible.

3. If 11 times the number of persons in a certain house, increased by 18, be divided by 4, the result equals twice the number increased by 3; find the number.

Let $x =$ the number.

By the conditions, $\dfrac{11\,x + 18}{4} = 2\,x + 3.$

Whence, $11\,x + 18 = 8\,x + 12$, and $x = -2.$

The negative result shows that the problem is impossible.

262. A problem may also be impossible when the solution is fractional, or zero.

1. A man has two kinds of money; dimes and cents. The total number of coins is 23, and their value 37 cents. How many has he of each?

Let $x =$ number of dimes.

Then, $23 - x =$ number of cents.

The x dimes are worth 10 x cents ; then, by the conditions,

$$10\,x + 23 - x = 37 ; \text{ and } x = \frac{14}{9}.$$

The fractional result shows that the problem is impossible.

2. The denominator of a fraction exceeds the numerator by 6; and if 2 be added to the numerator, the value of the fraction is $\frac{1}{2}$. Find the fraction.

Let $x =$ the numerator.

Then, $x + 6 =$ the denominator.

By the conditions, $\dfrac{x+2}{x+6} = \dfrac{1}{3}.$

Whence, $3x + 6 = x + 6$; and $x = 0.$

The result shows that the problem is impossible.

THE PROBLEM OF THE COURIERS

263. The discussion of the following problem serves to further illustrate the interpretation of negative and zero results, besides furnishing an interpretation of infinite and indeterminate results.

The Problem of the Couriers. Two couriers, A and B, are travelling along the same road in the same direction, RR', at the rates of m and n miles an hour, respectively. If at any time, say 12 o'clock, A is at P, and B is a miles beyond him at Q, after how many hours, and how many miles beyond P, are they together?

Let A and B meet x hours after 12 o'clock, and y miles beyond P.

They will then meet $y - a$ miles beyond Q.

Since A travels mx miles, and B nx miles, in x hours, we have
$$\begin{cases} y = mx, \\ y - a = nx. \end{cases}$$

Solving these equations, we obtain

$$x = \frac{a}{m-n}, \text{ and } y = \frac{am}{m-n}.$$

We will now discuss these results under different hypotheses.

1. $m > n$.

In this case, the values of x and y are *positive*.

This means that the couriers meet at some time *after* 12, at some point to the *right* of P.

This agrees with the hypothesis made; for if m is greater than n, A is travelling faster than B; and he must overtake him at some point beyond their positions at 12 o'clock.

2. $m < n$.

In this case, the values of x and y are *negative*.

This means that the couriers met at some time *before* 12, at some point to the *left* of P.

This agrees with the hypothesis made; for if m is less than n, A is travelling more slowly than B; and they must have been together before 12 o'clock, and before they could have advanced as far as P.

3. $a = 0$, and $m > n$ or $m < n$.

In this case, $x = 0$ and $y = 0$.

This means that the travellers are together at 12 o'clock, at the point P.

This agrees with the hypothesis made; for if $a = 0$, and m and n are unequal, the couriers are together at 12 o'clock, and are travelling at unequal rates; and they could not have been together before 12, and will not be together afterwards.

4. $m = n$, and a not equal to 0.

In this case, the values of x and y take the form $\frac{a}{0}$, and are *infinite* (§ 247).

No definite values can be assigned to x and y, and the problem is impossible.

This agrees with the hypothesis made; for if $m = n$, and a is not zero, the couriers are a miles apart at 12 o'clock, and are travelling at the same rate; and they never could have been, and never will be together.

Therefore, *an infinite result indicates that the problem is impossible.*

In this case, as $m - n$ approaches the limit 0, the values of x and y increase without limit.

That is, as the difference of the rates of the couriers approaches the limit 0, both the number of hours after 12 o'clock, and the number of miles beyond P, when A and B are together, increase without limit.

5. $m = n$, and $a = 0$.

In this case, the values of x and y take the form $\dfrac{0}{0}$, and are *indeterminate* (§ 249).

This means that any value of x whatever, with the corresponding value of y, is a solution of the problem.

This agrees with the hypothesis made; for if $m = n$, and $a = 0$, the couriers are together at 12 o'clock, and travelling at the same rate; and they always have been, and always will be together.

Thus, *an indeterminate result indicates that the number of solutions is indefinitely great.*

EXERCISE 35

Interpret the negative results, and modify the enunciation accordingly, in the following :

1. If the length of a field is 12 rods, and its width 9 rods, how many rods must be subtracted from the width so that the area may be 144 square rods ?

2. A is 44 years of age, and B 12 years; how many years ago was A three times as old as B ?

3. A's assets are double those of B.   When A has gained $250, and B $170, A's assets are five times those of B.   Find the assets of each.

4. A cistern has two pipes.   When both are open, it is filled in $7\frac{1}{2}$ hours ; and the first pipe alone can fill it in 3 hours.   How many hours does the second pipe take to fill it ?

5. A and B are travelling due east at the rates of $4\frac{1}{2}$ and $3\frac{1}{2}$ miles an hour, respectively.   At noon, A is 5 miles due east of B.   How many miles to the east of A's position at noon will he overtake B ?

6. A has $720, and B $300.   After A has gained a certain sum, and B has gained two-thirds this sum, A has three times as much money as B. How much did each gain ?

In each of the following, interpret the solution :

7. The number of apple and pear trees in an orchard is 23 ; and seven times the number of apple trees plus twice the number of pear trees equals 82.   How many are there of each kind ?

8. The number of silver coins in a purse exceeds the number of gold coins by 3.   And five times the number of silver coins exceeds three times the number of gold coins by 3.   How many are there of each kind ?

9. The numerator of a fraction is four times the denominator; and if the numerator be diminished by 9, and the denominator by 15, the value of the fraction is $\frac{3}{5}$. Find the fraction.

10. A is a years old, and B b years. After how many years will A be n times as old as B?

Discuss the solution in the cases when $n = 1$ and a is not equal to b, and when $n = 1$ and $a = b$.

11. What number must be added to both terms of the fraction $\frac{a}{b}$ to make it equal $\frac{c}{d}$?

Discuss the solution in the cases when $\frac{a}{b} = \frac{c}{d}$ and c is not equal to d, when $c = d$ and $\frac{a}{b}$ is not equal to $\frac{c}{d}$, and when $c = d$ and $\frac{a}{b} = \frac{c}{d}$.

12. Two couriers, A and B, are travelling along the same road, in the in the same direction, at the rates of m' and m'' miles an hour, respectively. B passes a certain point n hours after A. How many hours after B passes this point will he overtake A?

Determine for what values of the letters the solution is positive, negative, zero, impossible, and indeterminate, and discuss the solution in each case.

13. The circumference of the fore-wheel of a carriage is a feet, and of the hind-wheel b feet. How far will the carriage have travelled when the fore-wheel has made n revolutions more than the hind-wheel?

Discuss the solution in the following cases :

1. $n = 0$, a and b unequal. 2. $a = b$, n not equal to zero. 3. $a = b, n = 0$.

INDETERMINATE FORMS

264. The indeterminate form $\frac{0}{0}$ does not always represent a fraction which may have any value whatever.

Take, for example, the fraction $\frac{x^2 - a^2}{x^2 - ax}$.

If $x = a$, the fraction takes the form $\frac{0}{0}$.

Dividing both numerator and denominator by $x - a$,

$$\frac{x^2 - a^2}{x^2 - ax} = \frac{x + a}{x} ; \tag{1}$$

which holds so long as x does not equal a (§ 115, 4).

The second member of (1) approaches the limit 2 when x approaches the limit a.

Then, $\dfrac{x^2 - a^2}{x^2 - ax}$ approaches the limit 2 when x approaches the limit a.

We call the limit approached by the fraction $\dfrac{x^2 - a^2}{x^2 - ax}$, when x approaches the limit a, the *value of the fraction when* $x = a$.

In any similar case, we divide both terms of the fraction by the expression which makes each term vanish, and find the limit approached by the result.

In the problem of § 264, the result $\dfrac{0}{0}$ was obtained in consequence of two *independent hypotheses*, one causing the numerator to vanish, and the other the denominator ; and in any similar case we should find the result $\dfrac{0}{0}$ susceptible of the same interpretation.

But in the above example, the result $\dfrac{0}{0}$ is obtained in consequence of the *same hypothesis* causing both numerator and denominator to vanish.

265. The Indeterminate Forms $\dfrac{\infty}{\infty}$, $0 \times \infty$, and $\infty - \infty$.

1. To find the limit approached by the fraction $\dfrac{1 + 2x}{3 + 5x}$, when x is indefinitely increased.

Dividing each term of the fraction by x, we have

$$\lim_{x \doteq \infty} \frac{1 + 2x}{3 + 5x} = \lim_{x \doteq \infty} \frac{\dfrac{1}{x} + 2}{\dfrac{3}{x} + 5} = \frac{0 + 2}{0 + 5} \ (\S\ 248) = \frac{2}{5}.$$

We use the notation $\lim\limits_{x \doteq \infty}$ for the words "the limit when x is indefinitely increased of," and the notation $\lim\limits_{x \doteq a}$ for the words "the limit as x approaches a of."

In the above example, the fraction takes the indeterminate form $\dfrac{\infty}{\infty}$ when x is indefinitely increased.

In any similar case, we divide both numerator and denominator of the fraction by the highest power of x.

2. Find the value of the expression $(x^3 + 8)\left(1 + \dfrac{1}{x+2}\right)$, when $x = -2$.

The expression takes the indeterminate form $0 \times \infty$ when $x = -2$.

We have

$$\lim_{x \doteq -2}\left[(x^3 + 8)\left(1 + \frac{1}{x+2}\right)\right] = \lim_{x \doteq -2}(x^3 + 8 + x^2 - 2x + 4)$$

$$= \lim_{x \doteq -2}(x^3 + x^2 - 2x + 12) = -8 + 4 + 4 + 12 = 12.$$

In any similar case, we simplify the expression as much as possible before finding the limit.

3. Find the value of $\dfrac{1}{1-x} - \dfrac{2x}{1-x^2}$ when $x = 1$.

The expression takes the indeterminate form $\infty - \infty$ when $x = 1$.

Now, $$\lim_{x \doteq 1}\left(\frac{1}{1-x} - \frac{2x}{1-x^2}\right) = \lim_{x \doteq 1}\frac{1 + x - 2x}{1 - x^2}$$

$$= \lim_{x \doteq 1}\frac{1-x}{1-x^2} = \lim_{x \doteq 1}\frac{1}{1+x} = \frac{1}{2}.$$

EXERCISE 36

Find the values of the following:

1. $\dfrac{x^2 - 16}{x^2 - 2x - 8}$ when $x = 4$.

2. $\dfrac{4 + 5x - 3x^2}{7 - x + 4x^2}$ when x is indefinitely increased.

3. $\dfrac{8x^2 - 2x - 3}{12x^2 - 25x + 12}$ when $x = \frac{3}{4}$.

6. $\dfrac{1 + \dfrac{1}{x+1}}{1 + \dfrac{1}{x^2 - 1}}$ when $x = -1$.

4. $\dfrac{x^3 + 9x^2 + 27x + 27}{x^4 - 18x^2 + 81}$ when $x = -3$.

7. $\dfrac{1}{x-2} - \dfrac{12}{x^3 - 8}$ when $x = 2$.

5. $\dfrac{4x^3 + 2x^2 + 2x + 1}{8x^3 + 1}$ when $x = -\frac{1}{2}$.

8. $\dfrac{x^3 - 3x^2 + 3x - 2}{x^3 - 7x + 6}$ when $x = 2$.

9. $(2x^2 - 5x - 3)\left(2 + \dfrac{1}{x-3}\right)$ when $x = 3$.

DISCUSSION OF THE SOLUTION OF A SYSTEM OF SIMULTANEOUS LINEAR EQUATIONS

266. A system of simultaneous equations is said to be **Indeterminate** when the number of solutions is indefinitely great.

267. Any system of two simultaneous linear equations, involving two unknown numbers, can be reduced to the form

$$\begin{cases} a_1x + b_1y = c_1, & (1) \\ a_2x + b_2y = c_2; & (2) \end{cases}$$

where a_1, b_1, c_1, a_2, b_2, and c_2, may have any numerical values whatever, except that a_1, b_1, a_2, and b_2 cannot be zero.

By Ex. 3, § 242, the solution of the above system is

$$x = \frac{b_2c_1 - b_1c_2}{a_1b_2 - a_2b_1}, \text{ and } y = \frac{c_2a_1 - c_1a_2}{a_1b_2 - a_2b_1}.$$

These fractions have definite values as long as a_1b_2 does not equal a_2b_1.

We will now discuss the values of x and y when

$$a_1b_2 = a_2b_1. \qquad (A)$$

(1) If $b_2c_1 - b_1c_2$ is not zero, x is infinite (§ 247).

From (A), $$a_2 = \frac{a_1b_2}{b_1}. \qquad (B)$$

Then, $$c_2a_1 - c_1a_2 = c_2a_1 - \frac{c_1a_1b_2}{b_1} = \frac{a_1}{b_1}(b_1c_2 - b_2c_1). \qquad (C)$$

Since neither a_1, b_1, nor $b_1c_2 - b_2c_1$ is zero, $c_2a_1 - c_1a_2$ is not zero.

Whence, y is also infinite.

By aid of equation (B), the given equation (2) can be written

$$\frac{a_1b_2}{b_1}x + b_2y = c_2, \text{ or } a_1x + b_1y = \frac{b_1c_2}{b_2};$$

by multiplying each term by $\frac{b_1}{b_2}$.

Thus, the given equations are *inconsistent*; for, by (1), we have $a_1x + b_1y = c_1$.

Hence, *infinite results show that the given equations are inconsistent.*

(2) If $b_2c_1 - b_1c_2$ is zero, x takes the form $\frac{0}{0}$, and may have any value whatever (§ 249); for in this case we have two independent hypotheses, one causing the numerator to become zero, and the other the denominator.   (Compare § 264.)

In this case, by (C), $c_2a_1 - c_1a_2$ is also zero; so that y is indeterminate.

From the equations $b_2c_1 - b_1c_2 = 0$ and $c_2a_1 - c_1a_2 = 0$, we have

$$b_2 = \frac{b_1c_2}{c_1}, \text{ and } a_2 = \frac{c_2a_1}{c_1}.$$

Then the given equation (2) can be written

$$\frac{a_1c_2}{c_1}x + \frac{b_1c_2}{c_1}y = c_2, \text{ or } a_1x + b_1y = c_1;$$

which is the same as (1).

We thus have a single equation to determine two unknown numbers.

Hence, *indeterminate results show that the given equations are not independent.*

Similar considerations hold for any system of simultaneous linear equations, involving more than two unknown numbers.

268. We will illustrate the principles of § 267 by an example.

Consider the system of equations

$$\begin{cases} a_1x + b_1y + c_1z = d_1, \\ a_2x + b_2y + c_2z = d_2, \\ a_3x + b_3y + c_3z = d_3. \end{cases}$$

Solving, we find

$$x = \frac{d_1b_2c_3 - d_1b_3c_2 + d_2b_3c_1 - d_2b_1c_3 + d_3b_1c_2 - d_3b_2c_1}{a_1b_2c_3 - a_1b_3c_2 + a_2b_3c_1 - a_2b_1c_3 + a_3b_1c_2 - a_3b_2c_1}; \quad (1)$$

with results of similar form for y and z.

We will now use equation (1) as a *formula* for finding the value of x in the following system of equations.

$$\begin{cases} 3\,x - 2\,x + z = 5, \\ 2\,x + 3\,y - 2\,z = -1, \\ x - 5\,y + 3\,z = 6. \end{cases}$$

Here, $a_1 = 3$, $b_1 = -2$, $c_1 = 1$, $d_1 = 5$, $a_2 = 2$, $b_2 = 3$, $c_2 = -2$, $d_2 = -1$, $a_3 = 1$, $b_3 = -5$, $c_3 = 3$, $d_3 = 6$.

Substituting these values in (1), we have

$$x = \frac{45 - 50 + 5 - 6 + 24 - 18}{27 - 30 - 10 + 12 + 4 - 3} = \frac{0}{0};$$

and the same result will be found for y and z.

The indeterminate results show that the given equations are not independent (§ 267); this may be seen by observing that the first equation is the sum of the second and third.

In this case, x may have any value whatever.

We will now apply formula (1) to the following system:

$$\begin{cases} 2\,x + 5\,y - 3\,z = 8, \\ x - 4\,y + 2\,z = 3, \\ 3\,x + y - z = -2. \end{cases}$$

Here, $a_1 = 2$, $b_1 = 5$, $c_1 = -3$, $d_1 = 8$, $a_2 = 1$, $b_2 = -4$, $c_2 = 2$, $d_2 = 3$, $a_3 = 3$, $b_3 = 1$, $c_3 = -1$, $d_3 = -2$.

Substituting these values in (1), we have

$$x = \frac{32 - 16 - 9 + 15 - 20 + 24}{8 - 4 - 3 + 5 + 30 - 36} = \frac{26}{0} = \infty;$$

and the same result will be found for y and z.

The infinite results show that the given equations are inconsistent (§ 267); this may be seen by observing that the sum of the first two equations gives $3\,x + y - z = 11$, while the third requires that $3\,x + y - z$ should equal -2.

269. Number of Solutions of a System of Simultaneous Linear Equations.

If we have a system of m independent and consistent simultaneous linear equations, involving m unknown numbers, we may eliminate $m - 1$ of the unknown numbers, and obtain a single linear equation involving one unknown number.

By § 227, the latter has one solution.

Whence, the given system of equations has one solution.

And, in general, *a system of independent and consistent linear equations has a single solution when the number of equations is the same as the number of unknown numbers.*

If we have a system of m independent linear equations, involving $m + n$ unknown numbers, we may eliminate $m - 1$ of the unknown numbers, and obtain a single linear equation involving the remaining $n + 1$ unknown numbers.

By § 228, the latter has an indefinitely great number of solutions; and hence the given system has an indefinitely great number of solutions.

And, in general, *a system of independent linear equations has an indefinitely great number of solutions when the number of equations is less than the number of unknown numbers.*

If we have a system of $m + n$ independent linear equations, involving m unknown numbers, we may find a set of values of the unknown numbers which will satisfy any m of the equations.

But this set of values will not satisfy the remaining n equations; and hence the given system has no solution.

And, in general, *a system of independent linear equations has no solution when the number of equations is greater than the number of unknown numbers.*

XIV. GRAPHICAL REPRESENTATION

270. Rectangular Co-ordinates of a Point.

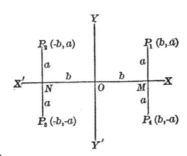

Let XX' and YY' be straight lines, intersecting at right angles at O; OY being above, and OY' below, XX', when OX is horizontal and extends to the right, and OX' to the left, of O.

Let P_1 be any point in the plane of XX' and YY', and draw line P_1M perpendicular to XX'.

Then, OM and MP_1 are called the *rectangular co-ordinates* of P_1; OM is called the *abscissa*, and MP_1 the *ordinate*.

The lines XX' and YY' are called the *axis* of X and *axis* of Y, respectively; and O the *origin*.

We express the fact that the abscissa of a point is b, and its ordinate a, by saying that, for the point in question, $x = b$ and $y = a$; or, more concisely, we speak of the point as the point (b, a); where the first term in parentheses is understood to be the abscissa, and the second term the ordinate.

271. Let M and N be points on OX and OX', respectively, such that $OM = ON = b$; and draw lines P_1P_4 and P_2P_3 through M and N, respectively, perpendicular to XX', making

$$MP_1 = MP_4 = NP_2 = NP_3 = a.$$

Then, each of the points P_1, P_2, P_3, and P_4 will have its abscissa equal to b, and its ordinate equal to a.

To avoid this ambiguity, abscissas measured to the *right* of O are considered $+$, and to the *left*, $-$; and ordinates measured *above* XX' are considered $+$, and *below*, $-$.

Then the co-ordinates of the points will be as follows:

$$P_1, (b, a); \quad P_2, (-b, a); \quad P_3, (-b, -a); \quad P_4, (b, -a).$$

It is understood, in the above convention respecting signs, that *the figure is so placed that OX is horizontal, and extends to the right of O.*

If a point lies upon XX', its ordinate is zero; and if it lies upon YY', its abscissa is zero.

The co-ordinates of the origin are $(0, 0)$.

272. Plotting Points.

To *plot* a point when its co-ordinates are given, lay off the abscissa to the right or left of O, according as it is $+$ or $-$, and then draw a perpendicular, equal in length to the ordinate, above or below XX' according as the ordinate is $+$ or $-$.

Thus, to plot the point $(-3, 2)$, lay off 3 units to the left of O upon XX', and then erect a perpendicular 2 units in length above XX'.

GRAPH OF A LINEAR EQUATION INVOLVING TWO UNKNOWN NUMBERS

273. Consider the equation $y = x + 2$.

If we give any numerical value to x, we may, by aid of the relation $y = x + 2$, calculate a corresponding value for y.

If $x = 0$, $y = 2$. (A)
If $x = 1$, $y = 3$. (B)
If $x = 2$, $y = 4$. (C)
If $x = 3$, $y = 5$. (D)
If $x = -1$, $y = 1$. (E)
If $x = -2$, $y = 0$. (F)
If $x = -3$, $y = -1$; etc. (G)

Now let these be regarded as the co-ordinates of points; and let the points be plotted, as explained in § 272.

They will be found to lie on a certain line, GD, which is called the **Graph** of the given equation.

By assuming fractional values for x, we may obtain intermediate points of the graph.

274. We shall always find that a linear equation, involving two unknown numbers, has a straight line for a graph; this may be proved as follows:

Every such equation can be put in the form $y = ax + b$.

We will first show that the graph of $y = ax$ is a straight line.

The equation $y = ax$ is satisfied if $x = 0$ and $y = 0$; hence, the graph of $y = ax$ passes through O.

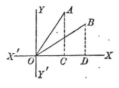

Let A and B be any other two points on the graph; draw lines OA and OB; also, lines AC and BD perpendicular to OX.

Since A and B are on the graph,

$$AC = a \times OC, \text{ and } BD = a \times OD.$$

Then, $\dfrac{AC}{OC} = \dfrac{BD}{OD}$, since each of these equals a.

Then, triangles OAC and OBD are similar; and OB coincides with OA.

Therefore, all points in the graph of $y = ax$ are in a straight line passing through O.

Now the graph of $y = ax + b$ can be obtained from that of $y = ax$ by increasing the ordinate of each point of the graph of $y = ax$ by b.

Hence, the graph of $y = ax + b$ is a straight line *parallel to* the graph of $y = ax$.

It follows from the above that the graphs of $y = ax + b$ and $y = ax + c$ are parallel.

275. A straight line is determined by any two of its points.

Then, it is sufficient, when finding the graph of a linear equation involving two unknown numbers, to find two of its points, and draw a straight line through them.

The points most easily determined are those in which the graph intersects the axes.

For all points on OX, $y = 0$; hence, to find where the graph cuts OX, put $y = 0$, and calculate the value of x.

To find where the graph cuts OY, put $x = 0$, and calculate the value of y.

Let it be required, for example, to plot the graph of $2x + 3y = -7$.

Put $y=0$; then $2x = -7$, and $x = -\dfrac{7}{2}$.

Then plot A on OX', $\dfrac{7}{2}$ units to the left of O.

Put $x=0$; then $3y = -7$, and $y = -\dfrac{7}{3}$.

Then plot B on OY', $\dfrac{7}{3}$ units below O.

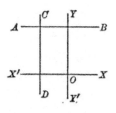

Draw the straight line AB; this is the required graph.

The above method cannot, of course, be used for a straight line passing through the origin, nor for the equations of § 276.

276. Consider the equation $y = 5$.

This means that every point in the graph has its ordinate equal to 5.

Then the graph is the straight line AB, parallel to XX', and 5 units above it.

In like manner, the graph of $x = -3$ is the straight line CD, parallel to YY', and 3 units to the left of it.

The graph of $y = 0$ is the axis of X, and the graph of $x = 0$ is the axis of Y.

EXERCISE 37

Plot the graphs of the following:

1. $3x + 2y = 6$.
2. $x - 4y = 4$.
3. $x = 2$.
4. $y = -4$.
5. $2x = 3y$.
6. $x + y = 0$.
7. $16x - 27y = -72$.
8. $8x + 15y = -6$.

INTERSECTIONS OF GRAPHS

277. Consider the equations

$$\begin{cases} 3\,x - y = -\,9. & (AB) \\ x + 2\,y = \quad 4. & (CD) \end{cases}$$

Let AB be the graph of $3\,x - y = -\,9$, and CD the graph of $x + 2\,y = 4$.

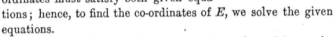

Let AB and CD intersect at E.

Since E lies on each graph, its co-ordinates must satisfy both given equations; hence, to find the co-ordinates of E, we solve the given equations.

In this case, the solution is $x = -\,2$, $y = 3$; and it may be verified in the figure that these are the co-ordinates of E.

Hence, *if the graphs of any two linear equations, with two unknown numbers, intersect, the co-ordinates of the point of intersection form a solution of the system of equations represented by the graphs.*

EXERCISE 38

Verify the principle of § 277 in the following systems :

1. $\begin{cases} 4\,x + 5\,y = 24. \\ 3\,x - 2\,y = -\,5. \end{cases}$

2. $\begin{cases} 3\,x + 7\,y = 5. \\ 8\,x + 3\,y = -\,18. \end{cases}$

3. $\begin{cases} 5\,x - 4\,y = 0. \\ 7\,x + 6\,y = -\,29. \end{cases}$

4. $\begin{cases} 9\,x + 14\,y = -\,25. \\ 3\,x - 4\,y = 22. \end{cases}$

278. Graphs of Inconsistent and Indeterminate Linear Equations, with two Unknown Numbers.

Consider the equations

$$\begin{cases} 3\,x - 2\,y = \quad 5. & (AB) \\ 6\,x - 4\,y = -\,7. & (CD) \end{cases}$$

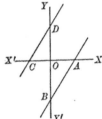

The equations can be written,

$$y = \frac{3}{2}x - \frac{5}{2}, \text{ and } y = \frac{3}{2}x + \frac{7}{4};$$

and it was shown in § 274 that the graphs of two equations of this form are parallel.

The given equations are *inconsistent;* and we shall always find that two inconsistent equations, with two unknown numbers, are represented by parallel graphs.

Again, consider the equations

$$\begin{cases} 3\,x - 2\,y = 5. \\ 6\,x - 4\,y = 10. \end{cases}$$

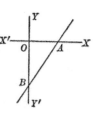

In this case, the graphs coincide.

The given equations are not *independent;* and in any similar case, we should find that the graphs were coincident.

279. Graphical Representation of Linear Expressions involving one Unknown Number.

Consider the expression $3\,x + 5$.

Put $y = 3\,x + 5$; and let the graph of this equation be found as in § 275.

Putting $y = 0$, $x = -\dfrac{5}{3}$; then the graph cuts XX' $\dfrac{5}{3}$ units to the left of O.

Putting $x = 0$, $y = 5$; then the graph cuts YY' 5 units above O.

The graph is the straight line AB.

It was shown in § 274 that the graph of a linear equation, with two unknown numbers, is a straight line.

280. Graphical Representation of Roots (§ 110).

Consider the equation $ax + b = 0$. (1)

To find the graph of the first member, put $y = ax + b$. (2)

The abscissa of the point in which this graph intersects OX, must, when substituted for x in (2), make $y = 0$.

Then, it makes the first member of (1) equal to zero, and is therefore a root of the given equation.

Hence, *the abscissa of the point in which the graph of the first member of any linear equation, with one unknown number, intersects XX', is the root of the equation.*

Consider, for example, the equation $3x + 5 = 0$.

The graph of the first member was found in § 279.

This intersects XX' at the point A, whose abscissa is $-\dfrac{5}{3}$; and the root of the equation is $-\dfrac{5}{3}$.

EXERCISE 39

Verify the principles of § 278 in the four following systems :

1. $\begin{cases} 3x + 4y = 16. \\ 3x + 4y = -16. \end{cases}$
   3. $\begin{cases} 2x - 7y = 14. \\ 4x - 14y = 28. \end{cases}$

2. $\begin{cases} 2x - 5y = 0. \\ 6x - 15y = 30. \end{cases}$
   4. $\begin{cases} 5x + 6y = 15. \\ 15x + 18y = 45. \end{cases}$

Plot the graphs of the first members of the following equations, and in each case verify the principle of § 280 :

5. $2x + 7 = 0.$ 6. $5x - 4 = 0.$

XV. INVOLUTION AND EVOLUTION

INVOLUTION

281. Involution is the process of raising an expression to any power whose exponent is a positive integer.

We have already given (§ 130) a rule for raising a rational and integral monomial to any power whose exponent is a positive integer.

282. Any Power of a Fraction.

We have $\qquad \left(\dfrac{a}{b}\right)^n = \dfrac{a}{b} \times \dfrac{a}{b} \times \cdots$ to n factors

$$= \frac{a \times a \times \cdots \text{ to } n \text{ factors}}{b \times b \times \cdots \text{ to } n \text{ factors}} = \frac{a^n}{b^n}.$$

Then, *a fraction may be raised to any power whose exponent is a positive integer by raising both numerator and denominator to the required power, and dividing the first result by the second.*

Ex. $\left(-\dfrac{2\,x^4}{3\,y^3}\right)^5 = -\dfrac{(2\,x^4)^5}{(3\,y^3)^5} = -\dfrac{32\,x^{20}}{243\,y^{15}}$ (§ 130).

THE BINOMIAL THEOREM

283. A **Series** is a succession of terms.

A **Finite Series** is one having a limited number of terms.

An **Infinite Series** is one having an unlimited number of terms.

284. In §§ 131 and 135, we gave rules for finding the square or cube of any binomial.

The **Binomial Theorem** is a formula by means of which any power of a binomial may be expanded into a series.

In the present chapter, we shall consider those cases only in which the exponent is a *positive integer.*

285. Proof of the Theorem for a Positive Integral Exponent.

The following are obtained by actual multiplication.

$$(a+x)^2 = a^2 + 2\,ax + x^2;$$
$$(a+x)^3 = a^3 + 3\,a^2x + 3\,ax^2 + x^3;$$
$$(a+x)^4 = a^4 + 4\,a^3x + 6\,a^2x^2 + 4\,ax^3 + x^4;\ \text{etc.}$$

In these results, we observe the following laws:

1. The number of terms is greater by 1 than the exponent of the binomial.

2. The exponent of a in the first term is the same as the exponent of the binomial, and decreases by 1 in each succeeding term.

3. The exponent of x in the second term is 1, and increases by 1 in each succeeding term.

4. The coefficient of the first term is 1, and the coefficient of the second term is the exponent of the binomial.

5. If the coefficient of any term be multiplied by the exponent of a in that term, and the result divided by the exponent of x in the term increased by 1, the quotient will be the coefficient of the next following term.

We will now prove by Mathematical Induction (Note, § 134) that these laws hold for any positive integral power of $a+x$.

Assume the laws to hold for $(a+x)^n$, where n is any positive integer.

Then,
$$(a+x)^n = a^n + na^{n-1}x + \frac{n(n-1)}{2}a^{n-2}x^2 + \cdots. \qquad (1)$$

Let P, Q, and R denote the coefficients of the terms involving $a^{n-r}x^r$, $a^{n-r-1}x^{r+1}$, and $a^{n-r-2}x^{r+2}$, respectively, in the second member of (1); thus,

$$(a+x)^n = a^n + na^{n-1}x + \cdots$$
$$+ Pa^{n-r}x^r + Qa^{n-r-1}x^{r+1} + Ra^{n-r-2}x^{r+2} + \cdots. \quad (2)$$

Multiplying both members by $a+x$, we have
$$(a+x)^{n+1} = a^{n+1} + na^nx + \cdots + Qa^{n-r}x^{r+1} + Ra^{n-r-1}x^{r+2} + \cdots$$
$$+ a^nx + \cdots + Pa^{n-r}x^{r+1} + Qa^{n-r-1}x^{r+2} + \cdots$$
$$= a^{n+1} + (n+1)a^nx + \cdots$$
$$+ (P+Q)a^{n-r}x^{r+1} + (Q+R)a^{n-r-1}x^{r+2} + \cdots. \ (3)$$

This result is in accordance with the *second, third,* and *fourth* laws.

Since the fifth law is assumed to hold with respect to the second member of (2), we shall have

$$Q = \frac{P(n-r)}{r+1}, \text{ and } R = \frac{Q(n-r-1)}{r+2}.$$

Therefore,

$$\frac{Q+R}{P+Q} = \frac{Q + \dfrac{Q(n-r-1)}{r+2}}{\dfrac{Q(r+1)}{n-r} + Q} = \frac{\dfrac{Q(n+1)}{r+2}}{\dfrac{Q(n+1)}{n-r}} = \frac{n-r}{r+2}.$$

Whence,
$$Q + R = (P+Q)\frac{n-r}{r+2}.$$

But $n - r$ is the exponent of a in that term of (3) whose coefficient is $P + Q$, and $r + 2$ is the exponent of x increased by 1.

Therefore, the *fifth* law holds with respect to (3).

Hence, if the laws hold for any power of $a + x$ whose exponent is a positive integer, they also hold for a power whose exponent is greater by 1.

But the laws have been shown to hold for $(a + x)^4$, and hence they hold for $(a + x)^5$; and since they hold for $(a + x)^5$, they hold for $(a + x)^6$; and so on.

Hence, they hold when the exponent is any positive integer.

By aid of the fifth law, the coefficients of the successive terms after the second, in the second member of (2), may be readily found; thus,

$$(a+x)^n = a^n + na^{n-1}x + \frac{n(n-1)}{1 \cdot 2}a^{n-2}x^2$$

$$+ \frac{n(n-1)(n-2)}{1 \cdot 2 \cdot 3}a^{n-3}x^3 + \cdots. \quad (4)$$

This result is called the *Binomial Theorem.*

In place of the denominators $1 \cdot 2$, $1 \cdot 2 \cdot 3$, etc., it is customary to write $\lfloor 2, \lfloor 3,$ etc. The symbol $\lfloor n$, read "*factorial n*," signifies the product of the natural numbers from 1 to n inclusive.

286. In expanding expressions by the Binomial Theorem, it is convenient to obtain the exponents and coefficients of the terms by aid of the laws of § 285, which have been proved to hold for any positive integral exponent.

1. Expand $(a + x)^5$.

The exponent of a in the first term is 5, and decreases by 1 in each succeeding term.

The exponent of x in the second term is 1, and increases by 1 in each succeeding term.

The coefficient of the first term is 1; of the second, 5.

Multiplying 5, the coefficient of the second term, by 4, the exponent of a in that term, and dividing the result by the exponent of x increased by 1, or 2, we have 10 as the coefficient of the third term; and so on.

Then, $(a + x)^5 = a^5 + 5\,a^4x + 10\,a^3x^2 + 10\,a^2x^3 + 5\,ax^4 + x^5.$

It will be observed that the coefficients of terms equally distant from the ends of the expansion are equal; this law will be proved in § 288.

Thus the coefficients of the latter half of an expansion may be written out from the first half.

If the second term of the binomial is *negative*, it should be enclosed, negative sign and all, in parentheses before applying the laws; in reducing, care must be taken to apply the principles of § 130.

2. Expand $(1 - x)^6$.

$$(1 - x)^6 = [1 + (- x)]^6$$
$$= 1^6 + 6 \cdot 1^5 \cdot (- x) + 15 \cdot 1^4 \cdot (- x)^2 + 20 \cdot 1^3 \cdot (- x)^3$$
$$+ 15 \cdot 1^2 \cdot (- x)^4 + 6 \cdot 1 \cdot (- x)^5 + (- x)^6$$
$$= 1 - 6\,x + 15\,x^2 - 20\,x^3 + 15\,x^4 - 6\,x^5 + x^6.$$

If the first term of the binomial is a number expressed in Arabic numerals, it is convenient to write the exponents at first without reduction; the result should afterwards be reduced to its simplest form.

If either term of the binomial has a coefficient or exponent other than unity, it should be enclosed in parentheses before applying the laws.

3. Expand $(3\,m^2 + 2\,n^3)^4$.

$$(3\,m^2 + 2\,n^3)^4 = [(3\,m^2) + (2\,n^3)]^4$$
$$= (3\,m^2)^4 + 4\,(3\,m^2)^3(2\,n^3) + 6\,(3\,m^2)^2(2\,n^3)^2$$
$$+ 4\,(3\,m^2)\,(2\,n^3)^3 + (2\,n^3)^4$$
$$= 81\,m^8 + 216\,m^6n^3 + 216\,m^4n^6 + 96\,m^2n^9 + 16\,n^{12}.$$

A polynomial may be expressed as a binomial, and raised to any positive integral power by successive applications of the Binomial Theorem.

But for second or third powers, the methods of §§ 134 and 136 are shorter.

4. Expand $(x^2 - 2\,x - 2)^4$.

$$(x^2 - 2\,x - 2)^4 = [(x^2 - 2\,x) + (-2)]^4$$
$$= (x^2 - 2\,x)^4 + 4(x^2 - 2\,x)^3(-2) + 6(x^2 - 2\,x)^2(-2)^2$$
$$+ 4(x^2 - 2\,x)\,(-2)^3 + (-2)^4$$
$$= x^8 - 8\,x^7 + 24\,x^6 - 32\,x^5 + 16\,x^4$$
$$- 8(x^6 - 6\,x^5 + 12\,x^4 - 8\,x^3)$$
$$+ 24(x^4 - 4\,x^3 + 4\,x^2) - 32(x^2 - 2\,x) + 16$$
$$= x^8 - 8\,x^7 + 16\,x^6 + 16\,x^5 - 56\,x^4 - 32\,x^3 + 64\,x^2 + 64\,x + 16.$$

287. *To find the rth or general term in the expansion of* $(a+x)^n$.

The following laws hold for any term in the expansion of $(a+x)^n$, in equation (4), § 285:

1. The exponent of x is less by 1 than the number of the term.

2. The exponent of a is n minus the exponent of x.

3. The last factor of the numerator is greater by 1 than the exponent of a.

4. The last factor of the denominator is the same as the exponent of x.

Therefore, in the rth term, the exponent of x will be $r - 1$.

The exponent of a will be $n - (r - 1)$, or $n - r + 1$.

The last factor of the numerator will be $n - r + 2$.

The last factor of the denominator will be $r - 1$.

Hence, the rth term

$$= \frac{n(n-1)(n-2)\cdots(n-r+2)}{1\cdot2\cdot3\cdots(r-1)}\,a^{n-r+1}x^{r-1}. \qquad (1)$$

In finding any term of an expansion, it is convenient to obtain the coefficient and exponents of the terms by the above laws.

Ex. Find the 8th term of $(3\,a - b^5)^{11}$.

We have, $(3\,a - b^5)^{11} = [(3\,a) + (-b^5)]^{11}$.

The exponent of $(-b^5)$ is $8-1$, or 7.

The exponent of $(3\,a)$ is $11-7$, or 4.

The first factor of the numerator is 11, and the last factor $4+1$, or 5.

The last factor of the denominator is 7.

Then, the 8th term $= \dfrac{11\cdot10\cdot9\cdot8\cdot7\cdot6\cdot5}{1\cdot2\cdot3\cdot4\cdot5\cdot6\cdot7}(3\,a)^4(-b^5)^7$

$$= 330\,(81\,a^4)\,(-b^{35}) = -\,26730\,a^4b^{35}.$$

If the second term of the binomial is negative, it should be enclosed, sign and all, in parentheses before applying the laws.

If either term of the binomial has a coefficient or exponent other than unity, it should be enclosed in parentheses before applying the laws.

288. Multiplying both terms of the coefficient, in (1), § 287, by the product of the natural numbers from 1 to $n-r+1$, inclusive, the coefficient of the rth term becomes

$$\frac{n(n-1)\cdots(n-r+2)\cdot(n-r+1)\cdots2\cdot1}{\underline{|r-1}\times1\cdot2\cdots(n-r+1)} = \frac{\underline{|n}}{\underline{|r-1}\,\underline{|n-r+1}}.$$

To find the coefficient of the rth term *from the end*, which since the number of terms is $n+1$, is the $[n-(r-2)]$th from the beginning, we put in the above formula $n-r+2$ for r.

Then, the coefficient of the rth term from the end is

$$\frac{\underline{|n}}{\underline{|n-r+2-1}\,\underline{|n-(n-r+2)+1}},\text{ or } \frac{\underline{|n}}{\underline{|n-r+1}\,\underline{|r-1}}.$$

Hence, *in the expansion of* $(a+x)^n$, *the coefficients of terms equidistant from the ends of the expansion are equal.*

289. Properties of Coefficients in the Expansion of $(a+x)^n$.

I. Putting in (4), § 285, $a=1$ and $x=1$, we have

$$2^n = 1 + n + \frac{n(n-1)}{\lfloor 2} + \cdots + 1.$$

That is, *the sum of the coefficients, in the expansion of $(a+x)^n$, is equal to 2^n.*

II. Putting in (4), $a=1$ and $x=-1$, we have

$$0 = 1 - n + \frac{n(n-1)}{\lfloor 2} - \frac{n(n-1)(n-2)}{\lfloor 3} + \cdots.$$

Or, $$1 + \frac{n(n-1)}{\lfloor 2} + \cdots = n + \frac{n(n-1)(n-2)}{\lfloor 3} + \cdots.$$

That is, *the sum of the coefficients of the odd terms is equal to the sum of the coefficients of the even terms.*

290. The Greatest Coefficient in the Expansion of $(a+x)^n$.

By § 287, the coefficient of the $(r+1)$th term, in the expansion of $(a+x)^n$, is

$$\frac{n(n-1)\cdots(n-r+1)}{\lfloor r}.$$

This is obtained by multiplying the coefficient of the rth term by $\dfrac{n-r+1}{r}$, or $\dfrac{n+1}{r} - 1$.

The latter expression decreases as r increases.

· It is evident that the successive coefficients, commencing with the first term, will increase numerically so long as

$$\frac{n-r+1}{r} \text{ is } > 1.$$

I. Suppose n even; and let $n = 2m$, where m is a positive integer.

Then, $\dfrac{n-r+1}{r}$ becomes $\dfrac{2m-r+1}{r}$.

If $r = m$, $\dfrac{2m-r+1}{r}$ becomes $\dfrac{m+1}{m}$, and is > 1.

If $r = m + 1$, $\dfrac{2\,m - r + 1}{r}$ becomes $\dfrac{m}{m + 1}$, and is < 1.

Then, the greatest coefficient will be when $r = m + 1$.

As the number of terms in the expansion is $2\,m + 1$, it follows that the middle term has the greatest coefficient.

II. Suppose n odd; and let $n = 2\,m + 1$, where m is a positive integer.

Then, $\dfrac{n - r + 1}{r}$ becomes $\dfrac{2\,m - r + 2}{r}$.

If $r = m$, $\quad\dfrac{2\,m - r + 2}{r}$ becomes $\dfrac{m + 2}{m}$, and is > 1.

If $r = m + 1$, $\dfrac{2\,m - r + 2}{r}$ becomes $\dfrac{m + 1}{m + 1}$, and equals 1.

If $r = m + 2$, $\dfrac{2\,m - r + 2}{r}$ becomes $\dfrac{m}{m + 2}$, and is < 1.

There will then be *two* terms having the greatest coefficient; those where $r = m + 1$ and $r = m + 2$.

EXERCISE 40

Expand the following:

1. $\left(-\dfrac{5\,a^2b}{2\,c^3}\right)^3$. 4. $(a + b)^6$. 7. $(2\,a^2 - b^3)^6$.

2. $\left(-\dfrac{3\,m^4x^2}{ny^3}\right)^6$. 5. $(x - y)^7$. 8. $\left(x^6 - \dfrac{y^4z}{3}\right)^5$.

3. $\left(\dfrac{a^5x^2y^6}{4\,b^3c^4}\right)^5$. 6. $(1 + x^2)^8$. 9. $\left(\dfrac{2\,m^2}{n} + \dfrac{5\,n^2}{m}\right)^4$.

Expand the following to five terms:

10. $(x + y)^9$.   11. $(ab - 1)^{10}$.   12. $(m^2 - 2\,n^3)^{11}$.

Expand the following:

13. $(2\,x^2 + x + 3)^3$.   16. $(2\,x^2 + x - 4)^4$.
14. $(4\,a^2 - 3\,ab - b^2)^3$.   17. $(1 + 2\,x + x^2)^5$.
15. $(1 - 3\,x + 2\,x^2)^4$.   18. $(x^2 - 3\,x - 2)^5$.

Find the
19. 8th term of $(a + x)^{11}$.   20. 10th term of $(1 - n)^{14}$.

21. 9th term of $(a^2 + 1)^{15}$.   23. 7th term of $(x^2 - 2\,y^3)^{12}$.

22. 5th term of $\left(\dfrac{3\,a}{b} - \dfrac{b}{2\,a}\right)^{9}$.   24. Middle term of $\left(m^2 + \dfrac{n^3}{3}\right)^{10}$.

25. Term involving x^{14} in $\left(x^4 + \dfrac{n}{2\,x}\right)^{16}$.

26. Term involving x^{11} in $\left(2\,x^2 - \dfrac{1}{3\,x^3}\right)^{13}$.

EVOLUTION

291. Evolution is the process of finding any root (§ 157) of an expression.

We shall consider in the present chapter those cases only in which both the expression and its root are rational (§ 198).

We have already given (§ 166) a rule for finding the principal root of a rational and integral monomial, which is a perfect power of the same degree as the index of the required root.

292. If m and n are positive integers, we have, by § 164,

$$\sqrt[n]{a^{mn}} = a^m.$$

Whence, by § 157, $\sqrt[n]{(a^n)^m} = (\sqrt[n]{a_n})^m.$

This method is preferable to that of § 166, if the expression whose root is to be found is a power of a number which is a perfect power of the same degree as the index of the root.

Ex. $\sqrt[5]{(32\,a^{10})^3} = (\sqrt[5]{32\,a^{10}})^3 = (2\,a^2)^3 = 8\,a^6.$

293. Any Root of a Fraction.

Let n be a positive integer, and a and b numbers which are perfect nth powers.

By § 165, $\sqrt[n]{\dfrac{a}{b}} \times \sqrt[n]{b} = \sqrt[n]{\dfrac{a}{b} \times b} = \sqrt[n]{a}.$

Dividing both members by $\sqrt[n]{b}$,

$$\sqrt[n]{\dfrac{a}{b}} = \dfrac{\sqrt[n]{a}}{\sqrt[n]{b}}.$$

Then, to find any root of a fraction, each of whose terms is a perfect power of the same degree as the index of the required root, *extract the required root of both numerator and denominator, and divide the first result by the second.*

$$Ex. \quad \sqrt[3]{-\frac{27\,a^3b^6}{64\,c^9}} = -\frac{\sqrt[3]{27\,a^3b^6}}{\sqrt[3]{64\,c^9}} = -\frac{3\,ab^2}{4\,c^3}.$$

SQUARE ROOT OF A POLYNOMIAL

294. In § 168, we gave a rule for finding the square root of a trinomial perfect square; and, in § 170, of an expression of the form
$$a^2 + b^2 + c^2 + 2\,ab + 2\,ac + 2\,bc,$$

which could be seen, by inspection, to be a perfect square.

We will now consider the method of finding the square root of any polynomial perfect square.

Let A and B be rational and integral expressions (§ 63); and suppose them to be arranged in the same order of powers of some common letter, x.

Let the exponent of x in the last term of A be greater, or less, than its exponent in the first term of B, according as A and B are arranged in descending, or ascending, powers of x.

By § 131, $(A+B)^2 = A^2 + 2\,AB + B^2.$

Whence, $(A+B)^2 - A^2 = 2\,AB + B^2.$

If the expression $2\,AB + B^2$ be arranged in the same order of powers of x as A and B, its first term must be twice the product of the first term of A and the first term of B.

Hence, the first term of B may be obtained by dividing the first term of $2\,AB + B^2$ by twice the first term of A.

By the expression "first term of A," in the above discussion, we mean the *sum* of all the terms of A containing the highest, or lowest, power of x, according as A is arranged in descending, or ascending, powers of x.

Thus, if $A = ax^4 + bx^4 + cx^3$, the first term of A is $(a+b)x^4$.

A similar meaning is attached to the expressions "last term of A," and "first term of B."

295. We will now consider an example.

Required the square root of

$$24\,x - 12\,x^3 - 7\,x^2 + 4\,x^4 + 16.$$

Arranging the expression according to the descending powers of x, we are to find an expression which, when squared, will produce

$$4\,x^4 - 12\,x^3 - 7\,x^2 + 24\,x + 16.$$

It is evident from § 134 that the first term of the expression is the square of the term containing the highest power of x in the square root.

Hence, the term containing the highest power of x in the square root must be the square root of $4\,x^4$, or $2\,x^2$.

Denoting the term of the root already found by A, and the remainder of the root, arranged in descending powers of x, by B, we have

$$(A + B)^2 - A^2 = 4\,x^4 - 12\,x^3 - 7\,x^2 + 24\,x + 16 - (2\,x^2)^2$$
$$= -12\,x^3 - 7\,x^2 + 24\,x + 16. \tag{1}$$

By § 294, the first term of B may be obtained by dividing the first term of (1), $-12\,x^3$, by twice A, or $4\,x^2$; that is, the first term of B is $-3\,x$.

Hence, the first two terms of the root are $2\,x^2 - 3\,x$.

Denoting this expression by A', and the remainder of the root, arranged in descending powers of x, by B', we have

$$(A' + B')^2 - A'^2$$
$$= 4\,x^4 - 12\,x^3 - 7\,x^2 + 24\,x + 16 - (2\,x^2 - 3\,x)^2$$
$$= 4\,x^4 - 12\,x^3 - 7\,x^2 + 24\,x + 16 - (4\,x^4 - 12\,x^3 + 9\,x^2)$$
$$= -16\,x^2 + 24\,x + 16. \tag{2}$$

By § 294, the first term of B' may be obtained by dividing the first term of (2), $-16\,x^2$, by twice the first term of A', or $4\,x^2$; that is, the first term of B' is -4.

Hence, the first three terms of the root are $2\,x^2 - 3\,x - 4$.

Denoting this expression by A'', and the remainder of the root, arranged in descending powers of x, by B'', we have

$(A'' + B'')^2 - A''^2$

$\quad = 4\,x^4 - 12\,x^3 - 7\,x^2 + 24\,x + 16 - (2\,x^2 - 3\,x - 4)^2$

$\quad = 4\,x^4 - 12\,x^3 - 7\,x^2 + 24\,x + 16 - (4\,x^4 - 12\,x^3 - 7\,x^2 + 24\,x + 16)$

$\quad = 0.$

Hence, the required square root is $2\,x^2 - 3\,x - 4$.

296. Let the last term of A' be C.

Then, $A' = A + C$, and $A'^2 = A^2 + 2\,AC + C^2.$

Therefore,

$$(A' + B')^2 - A'^2 = (A + B)^2 - A^2 - 2\,AC - C^2$$
$$= [(A + B)^2 - A^2] - (2\,A + C)C.$$

In like manner, if C' denotes the last term of A'',

$$(A'' + B'')^2 - A''^2 = [(A' + B')^2 - A'^2] - (2\,A' + C')C';$$

and so on.

That is, any remainder after the first may be obtained by subtracting from the preceding remainder an expression which is formed by doubling the part of the root already found, adding to it the next term of the root, and multiplying the result by this term.

The expressions $2\,A$, $2\,A'$, etc., are called *trial-divisors*, and $2\,A + C$, $2\,A' + C'$, etc., *complete divisors*.

297. It is customary to arrange the work as follows, the complete divisors and remainders being formed by the rule of § 296 :

$$
\begin{array}{l}
4\,x^4 - 12\,x^3 - 7\,x^2 + 24\,x + 16 \underline{\lfloor 2\,x^2 - 3\,x - 4} \\
4\,x^4
\end{array}
$$

$$
\begin{array}{l|l}
\hline
4\,x^2 - 3\,x & -12\,x^3 - 7\,x^2 + 24\,x + 16, \text{ 1st Rem.} \\
 -3\,x & -12\,x^3 + 9\,x^2 \\
\hline
4\,x^2 - 6\,x - 4 & -16\,x^2 + 24\,x + 16, \text{ 2d Rem.} \\
\phantom{4\,x^2 - 6\,x} - 4 & -16\,x^2 + 24\,x + 16
\end{array}
$$

To avoid needless repetition, the last three terms of the first remainder, and the last two terms of the second, may be omitted.

We then have the following rule for extracting the square root of a polynomial perfect square:

Arrange the expression according to the powers of some letter.

Extract the square root of the first term (§ 294), write the result as the first term of the root, and subtract its square from the given expression, arranging the remainder in the same order of powers as the given expression.

Divide the first term of the remainder by twice the first term of the root, and add the quotient to the part of the root already found, and also to the trial-divisor.

Multiply the complete divisor by the term of the root last obtained, and subtract the product from the remainder.

If other terms remain, proceed as before, doubling the part of the root already found for the next trial-divisor.

If the expression had been written

$$16 + 24\,x - 7\,x^2 - 12\,x^3 + 4\,x^4,$$

the square root would have been obtained in the form $4 + 3\,x - 2\,x^2$, which is the negative of $2\,x^2 - 3\,x - 4$.

298. With the notation of § 296,

$$2\,A' = 2\,A + 2\,C.$$

In like manner, $2\,A'' = 2\,A' + 2\,C'$; and so on.

That is, *any trial-divisor, after the first, is equal to the preceding complete divisor with its last term doubled.*

SQUARE ROOT OF AN ARITHMETICAL NUMBER

The term "*number*," in the following discussion, signifies an integral or decimal perfect square, expressed in Arabic numerals.

299. The square root of 100 is 10; of 10000 is 100; etc.

Hence, the square root of a number between 1 and 100 is between 1 and 10; the square root of a number between 100 and 10000 is between 10 and 100; etc.

That is, the square root of an integer of one or two digits contains one digit; the square root of an integer of three or four digits contains two digits; etc.

Hence, *if a point be placed over every second digit of an integer, beginning at the units' place, the number of points shows the number of digits in its square root.*

300. If a is an integral perfect square, then $\dfrac{a}{10^{2n}}$, where n is any positive integer, is also a perfect square.

But $\dfrac{a}{10^{2n}}$ is a number whose decimal part contains an *even* number of digits, and which differs from a only in the position of its decimal point.

Hence, *if a point be placed over every second digit of any number, beginning at the units' place, and extending in either direction, the number of points shows the number of digits in its square root.*

301. Let a, b, and c represent positive integers.

We have,

$$\frac{(a+b+c)^2 - a^2}{2\,a} = \frac{2\,a(b+c) + (b+c)^2}{2\,a} = b + c + \frac{(b+c)^2}{2\,a}.$$

That is, if the remainder obtained by subtracting a^2 from $(a+b+c)^2$ be divided by $2\,a$, the quotient is greater than b.

In like manner, if the remainder obtained by subtracting a^2 from $(a+b)^2$ be divided by $2\,a$, the quotient is greater than b.

302. We will now consider an example.

Required the square root of $10\dot{7}19\dot{0}7\dot{6}$.

Pointing the number in accordance with the rule of § 299, we find that there are four digits in its square root.

Since the number is between 9000000 and 16000000, the square root is between 3000 and 4000.

That is, the first digit of the root is 3.

Let a represent the number 3000; b the second digit of the root, multiplied by 100; and c the number consisting of the last two digits of the root in their order.

Then, $a + b + c$ represents the root; now,

$$\frac{(a+b+c)^2 - a^2}{2\,a} = \frac{10719076 - 9000000}{6000} = \frac{1719076}{6000} = 286.+.$$

By § 301, this is greater than b.

Hence, b is a multiple of 100 less than 286.+.

Assume, then, $b = 200$.

Then, the first two digits of the root would be 32.

Let a' represent the number 3200; b' the third digit of **the** root, multiplied by 10; and c' the last digit of the root.

Then, $a' + b' + c'$ represents the root; now,

$$\frac{(a' + b' + c')^2 - a'^2}{2\,a'} = \frac{10719076 - 10240000}{6400} = \frac{479076}{6400} = 74.+.$$

By § 301, this is greater than b'.

Hence, b' is a multiple of 10 less than 74.+.

Assume, then, $b' = 70$.

Then, the first three digits of the root would be 327.

Let a'' represent the number 3270, and b'' the last digit of the root.

Then, $a'' + b''$ represents the root; now,

$$\frac{(a'' + b'')^2 - a''^2}{2\,a''} = \frac{10719076 - 10692900}{6540} = \frac{26176}{6540} = 4.+.$$

By § 301, this is greater than b''; assume, then, $b'' = 4$.

Since $(3274)^2 = 10719076$, the required square root is 3274.

303. We have with the notation of § 302,

$$
\begin{aligned}
(a' + b' + c')^2 - a'^2 &= (a + b + c)^2 - (a + b)^2 \\
&= (a + b + c)^2 - a^2 - 2\,ab - b^2 \\
&= [(a + b + c)^2 - a^2] - (2\,a + b)b.
\end{aligned}
$$

Similarly,

$$(a'' + b'')^2 - a''^2 = [(a' + b' + c')^2 - a'^2] - (2\,a' + b')b'.$$

That is, any remainder after the first may be obtained by subtracting from the preceding remainder a number which is formed by doubling the part of the root already obtained, adding to it the next root digit followed by as many ciphers as there are digits in the remainder of the root, and multiplying the result by the latter number.

The numbers represented by $2\,a$, $2\,a'$, etc., are called *trial-divisors*, and those represented by $2\,a + b$, $2\,a' + b'$, etc., *complete divisors.*

304. The work of the example of § 302 may be arranged as follows, the complete divisors and remainders being formed by the rule of § 303 :

$$10719076 \mid 3000 + 200 + 70 + 4$$

	$a^2 = 9000000$	
1st Comp. Div.,	$6000 + 200$	1719076
	200	1240000
2d Comp. Div.,	$6400 + 70$	479076
	70	452900
3d Comp. Div.,	$6540 + 4$	26176
	4	26176

Omitting the ciphers for the sake of brevity, and condensing the operation, it will stand as follows :

$$10719076 \mid 3274$$

	9
62	171
	124
647	4790
	4529
6544	26176
	26176

We then have the following rule for extracting the square root of an integral perfect square :

Separate the number into periods by pointing every second digit, beginning with the units' place.

Find the greatest square in the left-hand period, and write its square root as the first digit of the root; subtract the square of the first root-digit from the left-hand period, and to the result annex the next period.

Divide this remainder, omitting the last digit, by twice the part of the root already found, and annex the quotient to the root, and also to the trial-divisor.

Multiply the complete divisor by the root-digit last obtained, and subtract the product from the remainder.

*If other periods remain, proceed as before, doubling the part
of the root already found for the next trial-divisor.*

Note 1. It sometimes happens that, on multiplying a complete divisor
by the digit of the root last obtained, the product is greater than the
remainder. In such a case, the digit of the root last obtained is too great,
and one less must be substituted for it.

Note 2. If any root-digit is 0, annex 0 to the trial-divisor, and annex
to the remainder the next period.

305. We will now show how to obtain the square root of a
number which is not integral.

Required the square root of 49.449024.

We have, $\sqrt{49.449024} = \sqrt{\dfrac{49449024}{1000000}} = \dfrac{7032}{1000}$ (§ 293) $= 7.032$.

The work may be arranged as follows :

$$
\begin{array}{r|l}
\multicolumn{2}{l}{49.449024\,\lfloor 7.032} \\
49 & \\
\hline
1403 & 4490 \\
 & 4209 \\
\hline
14062 & 28124 \\
 & 28124 \\
\hline
\end{array}
$$

Since 14 is not contained in 4, we write 0 as the second root-digit, in
the above example ; we then annex 0 to the trial-divisor 14, and annex to
the remainder the next period, 90.

Hence, if any number be pointed in accordance with the rule
of § 300, the rule of § 304 may be applied to the result, and
the decimal point inserted in its proper position in the root.

306. After $n+1$ digits of the square root of an integral
perfect square have been found by the rule of § 304, n more
may be obtained by simple division only, supposing $2n+1$ to
be the whole number.

For let a represent the integer whose first $n+1$ digits are
the first $n+1$ digits of the root in their order, and whose last
n digits are ciphers; and let b represent the integer consisting
of the last n digits of the root in their order.

Then, $a+b$ represents the root.

We have, $(a + b)^2 - a^2 = 2\,ab + b^2.$

Whence, $\dfrac{(a + b)^2 - a^2}{2\,a} = b + \dfrac{b^2}{2\,a}.$

That is, $(a + b)^2 - a^2$, divided by $2\,a$, will give the last n digits of the root, increased by $\dfrac{b^2}{2\,a}.$

We will now prove that $\dfrac{b^2}{2\,a}$ is less than $\dfrac{1}{2}$; so that, by neglecting the remainder arising from the division, we obtain the part of the root required.

By hypothesis, b contains n digits.

Then, b^2 cannot contain more than $2\,n$ digits.

But a contains $2\,n + 1$ digits.

Hence, $\dfrac{b^2}{a}$ is less than 1; and therefore $\dfrac{b^2}{2\,a}$ is less than $\dfrac{1}{2}.$

If, then, the $(n + 1)$th remainder be divided by twice the part of the root already found, the remaining n digits of the root may be obtained.

The method applies to the square root of any number.

Ex. Required the square root of 638.876176.

$$
\begin{array}{r}
63\dot{8}.8\dot{7}61\dot{7}6\,\lfloor 25.2 \\
4 \\
\hline
45 \mid 238 \\
\mid 225 \\
\hline
502 \mid 1387 \\
\mid 1004 \\
\hline
50.4)\,3.836176\,(.076 \\
3528 \\
\hline
3081
\end{array}
$$

We obtain the first three digits of the root by the ordinary method, and the other two by the method of § 306; that is, by dividing the third remainder, 3.836176, by twice the part of the root already obtained, or 50.4.

The required root is 25.2 + .076, or 25.276.

CUBE ROOT OF A POLYNOMIAL

307. In § 176, we gave a method for finding the cube root of any expression of the form

$$a^3 + 3\,a^2b + 3\,ab^2 + b^3, \text{ or } a^3 - 3\,a^2b + 3\,ab^2 - b^3.$$

We will now consider the method of finding the cube root of any polynomial perfect cube.

Let A and B have the same meanings as in § 294.

By § 135, $\qquad (A + B)^3 = A^3 + 3\,A^2B + 3\,AB^2 + B^3.$

Whence, $\qquad (A + B)^3 - A^3 = 3\,A^2B + 3\,AB^2 + B^3.$

If the expression $3\,A^2B + 3\,AB^2 + B^3$ be arranged in the same order of powers of x as A and B, its first term must be three times the product of the square of the first term of A and the first term of B.

Hence, the first term of B may be obtained by dividing the first term of $3\,A^2B + 3\,AB^2 + B^3$ by three times the square of the first term of A.

308. We will now consider an example.

Required the cube root of

$$40\,x^3 - 6\,x^5 - 64 + x^6 - 96\,x.$$

Arranging the expression according to the descending powers of x, we are to find an expression which, when cubed, will produce $\qquad x^6 - 6\,x^5 + 40\,x^3 - 96\,x - 64.$

It is evident from § 136 that the first term of the expression is the cube of the term containing the highest power of x in the cube root.

Hence, the term containing the highest power of x in the cube root must be the cube root of x^6, or x^2.

Denoting the term of the root already found by A, and the remainder of the root, arranged in descending powers of x, by B, we have

$$(A + B)^3 - A^3 = x^6 - 6\,x^5 + 40\,x^3 - 96\,x - 64 - (x^2)^3$$
$$= -6\,x^5 + 40\,x^3 - 96\,x - 64. \qquad (1)$$

By § 307, the first term of B may be obtained by dividing the first term of (1), $-6\,x^5$, by three times the square of A, or $3\,x^4$; that is, the first term of B is $-2\,x$.

Hence, the first two terms of the root are $x^2 - 2\,x$.

Denoting this expression by A', and the remainder of the root, arranged in descending powers of x, by B', we have

$(A' + B')^3 - A'^3$

$= x^6 - 6\,x^5 + 40\,x^3 - 96\,x - 64 - (x^2 - 2\,x)^3$

$= x^6 - 6\,x^5 + 40\,x^3 - 96\,x - 64 - (x^6 - 6\,x^5 + 12\,x^4 - 8\,x^3)$

$= -12\,x^4 + 48\,x^3 - 96\,x - 64.$ (2)

Then, the first term of B' may be obtained by dividing the first term of (2), $-12\,x^4$, by three times the square of the first term of A', or $3\,x^4$; that is, the first term of B' is -4.

Hence, the first three terms of the root are $x^2 - 2\,x - 4$.

Denoting this expression by A'', and the remainder of the root, arranged in descending powers of x, by B'', we have

$(A'' + B'')^3 - A''^3$

$= x^6 - 6\,x^5 + 40\,x^3 - 96\,x - 64 - (x^2 - 2\,x - 4)^3 = 0.$

Hence, the required cube root is $x^2 - 2\,x - 4$.

309. Let the last term of A' be C.

Then, $A' = A + C$; whence,

$(A' + B')^3 - A'^3 = (A + B)^3 - A^3 - 3\,A^2C - 3\,AC^2 - C^3$

$= [(A + B)^3 - A^3] - (3\,A^2 + 3\,AC + C^2)C.$

In like manner, if C' denotes the last term of A'',

$(A'' + B'')^3 - A''^3 = [(A' + B')^3 - A'^3] - (3\,A'^2 + 3\,A'C' + C'^2)C';$

and so on.

That is, any remainder after the first may be obtained by subtracting from the preceding remainder an expression which is formed by adding together three times the square of the part of the root already found, three times the product of the part of the root already found by the next term of the root, and the square of the next term of the root, and multiplying the sum by the latter term.

The expressions $3\,A^2$, $3\,A'^2$, etc., are called *trial-divisors*, and $3\,A^2 + 3\,AC + C^2$, $3\,A'^2 + 3\,A'C' + C'^2$, etc., *complete divisors*.

310. We arrange the work as follows, the complete divisors and the remainders being formed by the rule of § 309:

$$
\begin{array}{l}
x^6 - 6\,x^5 + 40\,x^3 - 96\,x - 64 \,\big|\, x^2 - 2\,x - 4 \\
\underline{x^6} \\
\hline
3\,x^4 - 6\,x^3 + 4\,x^2 \,\big|\, -6\,x^5 + 40\,x^3 - 96\,x - 64 \\
\qquad\qquad\qquad\; -6\,x^5 + 12\,x^4 - 8\,x^3 \\
\hline
3\,x^4 - 12\,x^3 + 12\,x^2 \qquad\quad -12\,x^4 + 48\,x^3 - 96\,x - 64 \\
\qquad\quad -12\,x^2 + 24\,x + 16 \,\big| \\
\hline
3\,x^4 - 12\,x^3 \qquad\quad +24\,x + 16 \,\big|\, -12\,x^4 + 48\,x^3 - 96\,x - 64 \\
\hline
\end{array}
$$

The last three terms of the first remainder, and the last two terms of the second, may be omitted.

We then have the following rule for extracting the cube root of a polynomial perfect cube:

Arrange the expression according to the powers of some letter.

Extract the cube root of the first term, write the result as the first term of the root, and subtract its cube from the given expression; arranging the remainder in the same order of powers as the given expression.

Divide the first term of the remainder by three times the square of the first term of the root, and write the result as the next term of the root.

Add to the trial-divisor three times the product of the term of the root last obtained by the part of the root previously found, and the square of the term of the root last obtained.

Multiply the complete divisor by the term of the root last obtained, and subtract the result from the remainder.

If other terms remain, proceed as before, taking three times the square of the part of the root already found for the next trial-divisor.

311. With the notation of § 309,

$$3\,A'^2 = 3\,(A + C)^2 = 3\,A^2 + 6\,AC + 3\,C^2$$
$$= 3\,A^2 + 3\,AC + C^2 + (3\,AC + 2\,C^2).$$

In like manner,

$$3\,A''^2 = 3\,A'^2 + 3\,A'C' + C'^2 + (3\,A'C' + 2\,C'^2)\,;\ \text{etc.}$$

That is, if the last term of the expression which is added to any trial-divisor be doubled, the result, added to the corresponding complete divisor, will give the next trial-divisor.

Thus, in the example of § 310, if we add to the first complete divisor $3\,x^4 - 6\,x^3 + 4\,x^2$, the expression $-6\,x^3 + 8\,x^2$, the result, $3\,x^4 - 12\,x^3 + 12\,x^2$, is the next trial-divisor.

CUBE ROOT OF AN ARITHMETICAL NUMBER

The term "*number*," in the following discussion, signifies a positive integral or decimal perfect cube, expressed in Arabic numerals.

312. The cube root of 1000 is 10; of 1000000 is 100; etc.

Hence, the cube root of a number between 1 and 1000 is between 1 and 10; the cube root of a number between 1000 and 1000000 is between 10 and 100; etc.

That is, the cube root of an integer of one, two, or three digits contains one digit; the cube root of an integer of four, five, or six digits contains two digits; etc.

Hence, *if a point be placed over every third digit of an integer, beginning at the units' place, the number of points shows the number of digits in its cube root.*

313. If a is an integral perfect cube, then $\dfrac{a}{10^{3n}}$, where n is any positive integer, is also a perfect cube.

But $\dfrac{a}{10^{3n}}$ is a number, the number of digits in whose decimal part is divisible by 3, and which differs from a only in the position of its decimal point.

Therefore, *if a point be placed over every third digit of any number, beginning at the units' place and extending in either direction, the number of points shows the number of digits in its cube root.*

314. Let a, b, and c represent positive integers.

Then, $\dfrac{(a+b+c)^3 - a^3}{3\,a^2} = \dfrac{3\,a^2(b+c) + 3\,a(b+c)^2 + (b+c)^3}{3\,a^2}$

$$= b + c + \dfrac{3\,a\,(b+c)^2 + (b+c)^3}{3\,a^2}.$$

That is, if the remainder obtained by subtracting a^3 from $(a+b+c)^3$ be divided by $3\,a^2$, the quotient is greater than b.

Similarly, if the remainder obtained by subtracting a^3 from $(a+b)^3$ be divided by $3\,a^2$, the quotient is greater than b.

315. We will now consider an example.

Required the cube root of 9745491456.

Pointing the number in accordance with the rule of § 312, we find that there are four digits in its cube root.

Since the number is between 8000000000 and 27000000000, the cube root is between 2000 and 3000.

That is, the first digit of the root is 2.

Let a represent the number 2000; b the second digit of the root, multiplied by 100; and c the number consisting of the last two digits of the root in their order.

Then, $a+b+c$ represents the root; now,

$$\dfrac{(a+b+c)^3 - a^3}{3\,a^2} = \dfrac{9745491456 - 8000000000}{12000000}$$

$$= \dfrac{1745491456}{12000000} = 145.+.$$

By § 314, this is greater than b.

Hence, b is a multiple of 100 less than $145.+$.

Assume, then, $b = 100$.

Then, the first two digits of the root would be 21.

Let a' represent the number 2100; b' the third digit of the root multiplied by 10; and c' the last digit of the root.

Then, $a' + b' + c'$ represents the root; now,

$$\dfrac{(a'+b'+c')^3 - a'^3}{3\,a'^2} = \dfrac{9745491456 - 9261000000}{13230000}$$

$$= \dfrac{484491456}{13230000} = 36.+.$$

By § 314, this is greater than b'.

Hence, b' is a multiple of 10 less than 36.+.

Assume, then, $b' = 30$.

Then, the first three digits of the root would be 213.

Let a'' represent the number 2130, and b'' the last digit of the root.

Then, $a'' + b''$ represents the root; now,

$$\frac{(a'' + b'')^3 - a''^3}{3\, a''^2} = \frac{9745491456 - 9663597000}{13610700}$$

$$= \frac{81894456}{13610700} = 6.+.$$

By § 314, this is greater than b''; assume, then, $b'' = 6$.

Then, since $(2136)^3 = 9745491456$, the required cube root is 2136.

316. We have with the notation of § 315,

$$(a' + b' + c')^3 - a'^3 = (a + b + c)^3 - (a + b)^3$$
$$= (a + b + c)^3 - a^3 - 3\,a^2b - 3\,ab^2 - b^3$$
$$= [(a + b + c)^3 - a^3] - (3\,a^2 + 3\,ab + b^2)\,b.$$

Similarly,

$$(a'' + b'')^3 - a''^3 = [(a' + b' + c')^3 - a'^3] - (3\,a'^2 + 3\,a'b' + b'^2)\,b'.$$

That is, any remainder after the first may be obtained by subtracting from the preceding remainder a number which is formed by taking three times the square of the part of the root already obtained, adding to it three times the product of the part of the root already obtained by the next root-digit followed by as many ciphers as there are digits in the remainder of the root, plus the square of the latter number, and multiplying the result by the latter number.

The numbers represented by $3\,a^2$, $3\,a'^2$, etc., are called *trial-divisors*, and those represented by $3\,a^2 + 3\,ab + b^2$, $3\,a'^2 + 3\,a'b' + b'^2$, etc., *complete divisors*.

317. The work of the example of § 315 may be arranged as follows, the complete divisors and remainders being formed by the rule of § 316.

$$\dot{9}7454914\dot{5}\dot{6}\ \underline{\big|\ 2000+100+30+6}$$
$$a^3 = 8000000000$$

	12000000	1745491456
	600000	
	10000	
1st. Comp. Div.,	12610000	1261000000
	13230000	484491456
	189000	
	900	
2d Comp. Div.,	13419900	402597000
	13610700	81894456
	38340	
	36	
3d Comp. Div.,	13649076	81894456

Condensing the operation, it will stand as follows:

$$\dot{9}7454914\dot{5}\dot{6}\ \underline{\big|\ 2136}$$
$$8$$

1200	1745
60	
1	
1261	1261
132300	484491
1890	
9	
134199	402597
13610700	81894456
38340	
36	
13649076	81894456

We then have the following rule for extracting the cube root of an integral perfect cube:

Separate the number into periods by pointing every third digit, beginning with the units' place.

Find the greatest cube in the left-hand period, and write its cube root as the first digit of the root; subtract the cube of the first root-digit from the left-hand period, and to the result annex the next period.

Divide this remainder by three times the square of the part of the root already found, with two ciphers annexed, and write the quotient as the next digit of the root.

Add to the trial-divisor three times the product of the last root-digit by the part of the root previously found, with one cipher annexed, and the square of the last root-digit.

Multiply the complete divisor by the digit of the root last obtained, and subtract the product from the remainder.

If other periods remain, proceed as before, taking three times the square of the part of the root already found, with two ciphers annexed, for the next trial-divisor.

Note 1, § 304, applies with equal force to the above rule.

If any root-digit is 0, annex two ciphers to the trial-divisor, and annex to the remainder the next period.

318. With the notation of § 315,
$$3\,a'^2 = 3\,(a+b)^2 = 3\,a^2 + 6\,ab + 3\,b^2$$
$$= 3\,a^2 + 3\,ab + b^2 + (3\,ab + 2\,b^2).$$

In like manner,
$$3\,a''^2 = 3\,a'^2 + 3\,a'b' + b'^2 + (3\,a'b' + 2\,b'^2)\,;\ \text{etc.}$$

That is, *if the first number and the double of the second number required to complete any trial-divisor be added to the complete divisor, the result, with two ciphers annexed, will give the next trial-divisor.*

319. We will now show how to obtain the cube root of a number which is not integral.

Required the cube root of 1073.741824.

We have, $\sqrt[3]{1073.741824} = \sqrt[3]{\dfrac{1073741824}{1000000}}$
$$= \frac{1024}{100}\ (\S\,29\grave{3}) = 10.24.$$

The work may be arranged as follows:

$$\begin{array}{r|l}
\overset{\cdot}{1}07\overset{\cdot}{3}.7\overset{\cdot}{4}1824 & \overline{10.24} \\
\hline
1 & \\
\hline
30000 & 73741 \\
600 & \\
4 & \\
\hline
30604 & 61208 \\
600 & \overline{12533824} \\
8 & \\
\hline
3121200 & \\
12240 & \\
16 & \\
\hline
3133456 & 12533824
\end{array}$$

Here the second root-digit is 0; we then annex two ciphers to the trial-divisor 300, and annex to the remainder the next period, 741.

The second trial-divisor is formed by the rule of § 318.

Adding to the complete divisor 30604 the first number, 600, and twice the second number, 8, required to complete the trial-divisor 30000, we have 31212 ; annexing two ciphers to this, the result is 3121200.

Hence, if any number be pointed in accordance with the rule of § 313, the rule of § 317 may be applied to the result, and the decimal point inserted in its proper position in the root.

320. After $n + 2$ digits of the cube root of an integral perfect cube have been found by the rule of § 317, n more may be obtained by division, supposing $2n + 2$ to be the whole number.

For let a represent the integer whose first $n + 2$ digits are the first $n + 2$ digits of the root in their order, and whose last n digits are ciphers, and b the integer consisting of the last n digits of the root in their order; then, $a+b$ represents the root.

We have, $\qquad (a + b)^3 - a^3 = 3\,a^2b + 3\,ab^2 + b^3.$

Whence, $\qquad \dfrac{(a + b)^3 - a^3}{3\,a^2} = b + \dfrac{b^2}{a} + \dfrac{b^3}{3\,a^2}.$

That is, $(a + b)^3 - a^3$, divided by $3\,a^2$, will give the last n digits of the root, increased by $\dfrac{b^2}{a} + \dfrac{b^3}{3\,a^2}.$

By hypothesis, b contains n digits.

Then, b^2 cannot contain more than $2n$ digits.

But a contains $2n+2$ digits; and hence $\dfrac{b^2}{a}$ is less than $\dfrac{1}{10}$.

Again, $\dfrac{b^3}{3\,a^2} = \dfrac{b^2}{a} \times \dfrac{b}{3\,a}$; and since $\dfrac{b^2}{a}$ is less than $\dfrac{1}{10}$, and $\dfrac{b}{3\,a}$ less than 1, $\dfrac{b^3}{3\,a^2}$ is also less than $\dfrac{1}{10}$.

Therefore, $\dfrac{b^2}{a} + \dfrac{b^3}{3\,a^2}$ is less than $\dfrac{1}{5}$.

If, then, the $(n+2)$th remainder be divided by three times the square of the part of the root already found, the remaining n digits of the root may be obtained.

The method applies to the cube root of any number.

Ex. Required the cube root of 1452648.865311064.

$$1452648.865311064 \,|\, \underline{113.2}$$

```
          1452648.865311064 | 113.2
              1
        ─────────
  300  |  452
   30  |
 ·  1  |
 ─────   ─────────
  331  |  331
   30  |  121648
    2  |
 ─────
 36300 |
   990 |
     9 |
 ─────   ─────────
 37299 | 111897
   990 |  9751865
    18 |
 ───────
3830700 |
   6780 |
      4 |
 ───────  ─────────
3837484 | 7674968
   6780 |
      8 |
 ──────────
38442.72)2076.897311064(.054
          19221360
         ─────────
          15476131
```

We obtain the first four digits of the root by the ordinary method, and the other two by § 320; that is, by dividing the fourth remainder, 2076.897311064, by three times the square of the part of the root already found, or 38442.72.

The required root is $113.2 + .054$, or 113.254.

ANY ROOT OF A POLYNOMIAL

321. Let A and B have the same meaning as in § 294.

By § 285, if n is any positive integer,

$$(A + B)^n = A^n + nA^{n-1}B + \cdots.$$

Whence, $\quad (A + B)^n - A^n = nA^{n-1}B + \cdots.$

If the expression $nA^{n-1}B + \cdots$ be arranged in the same order of powers of x as A and B, its first term must be n times the product of the $(n-1)$th power of the first term of A by the first term of B.

Hence, the first term of B may be obtained by dividing the first term of the expression $nA^{n-1}B + \cdots$ by n times the $(n-1)$th power of the first term of A.

322. It follows from § 321, exactly as in §§ 295 and 308, that the nth root of a polynomial, which is a perfect power of the nth degree, may be found by the following rule:

Arrange the expression according to the powers of some letter.

Extract the nth root of the first term, and write the result as the first term of the root; subtract from the polynomial its first term, and arrange the remainder in the same order of powers as the given expression.

Divide the first term of the remainder by n times the $(n-1)$th power of the first term of the root, and write the result as the second term of the root.

Subtract from the given polynomial the nth power of the part of the root already found, and arrange the remainder in the same order of powers as the given expression.

If other terms remain, proceed as before, dividing the first term of the remainder by n times the $(n-1)$th power of the first term of the root; and continue in this manner until there is no remainder.

ANY ROOT OF AN ARITHMETICAL NUMBER

The term " *number*," in the following discussion, signifies a positive, integral or decimal, perfect power of the degree denoted by the index of the required root, expressed in Arabic numerals.

323. It may be proved, as in §§ 299, 300, 312, and 313, that:

If a point be placed over every nth digit of any number, beginning at the units' place and extending in either direction, the number of points shows the number of digits in its nth root.

324. Let a, b, c, and n represent positive integers.

By § 285, $\dfrac{(a+b+c)^n - a^n}{na^{n-1}} = \dfrac{[a+(b+c)]^n - a^n}{na^{n-1}}$

$$= \frac{na^{n-1}(b+c) + \cdots}{na^{n-1}} = b + c + \cdots.$$

That is, if the remainder obtained by subtracting a^n from $(a+b+c)^n$ be divided by na^{n-1}, the quotient is greater than b.

In like manner, if the remainder obtained by subtracting a^n from $(a+b)^n$ be divided by na^{n-1}, the quotient is greater than b.

325. It is evident, from §§ 323 and 324, that the *n*th root of a positive integral perfect *n*th power may be found by a process similar to that employed in §§ 302 and 315.

The general rule will be as follows:

Point the number in accordance with the rule of § 323, and let the number of digits in the root be m.

Find the greatest perfect nth power in the left-hand period, and write its nth root as the first digit of the root.

Raise the part of the root already found, with $m-1$ ciphers annexed, to the nth power, and subtract the result from the given number.

Raise the part of the root already found, with $m-1$ ciphers annexed, to the $(n-1)th$ power, and multiply the result by n.

Divide the remainder by this number.

If the quotient is a number whose integral part contains $m-1$ digits, write its first digit as the next digit of the root; otherwise, write 0 as the next root-digit.

Raise the part of the root already found, with $m - 2$ ciphers annexed, to the nth power, and subtract the result from the given number.

The above process is to be repeated until there is no remainder; the only change being that, in the successive applications of the rule, $m - 2$, $m - 3$, etc., are written in place of $m - 1$ in the fourth, sixth, and seventh paragraphs.

The rule may be used to find the nth root of any number.

Ex. Find the cube root of 34550.415593.

In this case, $n = 3$ and $m = 4$.

$$34550.415593 \underline{\lfloor 32.57}$$
$$3000^3 = 27000000000$$
$$3 \times 3000^2 = 27000000)\overline{7550415593}(200 +$$
$$3200^3 = \overline{32768000000}$$
$$3 \times 3200^2 = 30720000)\overline{1782415593}(50 +$$
$$3250^3 = \overline{34328125000}$$
$$3 \times 3250^2 = 31687500)\overline{222290593}(7 +$$
$$3257^3 = \overline{34550415593}$$

Hence, the required root is 32.57.

Some of the ciphers may be omitted in practice.

It sometimes happens that, on raising the part of the root already found to the nth power, the result is greater than the given number; in such a case, the digit of the root last obtained is too great, and one less must be substituted for it.

326. Let m and n be positive integers, and a a perfect power of the degree mn.

By § 157, $$(\sqrt[mn]{a})^{mn} = a, \tag{1}$$

and $$(\sqrt[m]{\sqrt[n]{a}})^m = \sqrt[n]{a}. \tag{2}$$

Raising both members of (2) to the nth power,

$$(\sqrt[m]{\sqrt[n]{a}})^{mn} = a. \tag{3}$$

From (1) and (3), by § 163,

$$\sqrt[mn]{a} = \sqrt[m]{\sqrt[n]{a}};$$

for each of these expressions is the mnth root of a.

That is, *the mnth root of a* (§ 162) *equals the mth root of the nth root of a.*

The above is only true of *principal* roots.

It follows from the above that the fourth root of a perfect power of the fourth degree equals the square root of the square root of the expression.

The sixth root of a perfect power of the sixth degree equals the cube root of the square root of the expression; etc.

In like manner, if *m*, *n*, and *p* are positive integers, and *a* a perfect power of the degree *mnp*,

$$\sqrt[mnp]{a} = \sqrt[m]{(\sqrt[n]{\sqrt[p]{a}})};$$

and so on.

327. Let *m*, *n*, and *r* be positive integers, and *a* a rational number whose *m*th power is positive if *n* is even.

By § 157, $(\sqrt[n]{a^m})^n = a^m.$

Raising both members to the *r*th power, we have

$$(\sqrt[n]{a^m})^{nr} = a^{mr}. \tag{1}$$

Also, $(\sqrt[nr]{a^{mr}})^{nr} = a^{mr}. \tag{2}$

From (1) and (2), $(\sqrt[n]{a^m})^{nr} = (\sqrt[nr]{a^{mr}})^{nr}.$

Taking the *nr*th root of both members (§ 163),

$$\sqrt[n]{a^m} = \sqrt[nr]{a^{mr}}, \text{ and } \sqrt[nr]{a^{mr}} = \sqrt[n]{a^m}.$$

This means that the principal *n*th root of a^m is equal to the principal *nr*th root of a^{mr}.

(The general theorems of evolution, in §§ 163, 164, 165, 292, 293, 326, and 327, were there proved only for *principal* roots.

That of § 326 is only true for such roots.

The others are true for certain values of the roots which are not principal roots; take, for example, the equation

$$\sqrt[n]{ab} = \sqrt[n]{a} \times \sqrt[n]{b} \text{ (§ 165)}.$$

If $n = 2$, $a = 4$, $b = 9$, it becomes $\sqrt{4 \times 9} = \sqrt{4} \times \sqrt{9}.$

The last equation is true when the value $+6$ is taken for $\sqrt{4 \times 9}$, -2 for $\sqrt{4}$, and -3 for $\sqrt{9}$; also, when the value -6 is taken for $\sqrt{4 \times 9}$, $+2$ for $\sqrt{4}$, and -3 for $\sqrt{9}$.)

EXERCISE 41

Find the values of the following:

1. $\sqrt[3]{(125\,a^3)^2}$.   2. $\sqrt[4]{(16\,x^8y^{12})^5}$.   3. $\sqrt[5]{(-243\,a^5b^{25}c^{10})^3}$.

Find by inspection the values of the following:

4. $\sqrt[3]{-\dfrac{8\,a^{18}}{343\,b^6}}$.   5. $\sqrt[4]{\dfrac{625\,x^{16}}{81\,y^8}}$.   6. $\sqrt[5]{\dfrac{m^{15}n^{20}}{32\,p^{30}}}$.

Find the square roots of:

7. $49\,a^4 + 16\,b^4 + 14\,a^3b - 8\,ab^3 - 55\,a^2b^2$.

8. $16\,x^2 + 9\,y^2 + 25\,z^2 - 24\,xy - 40\,xz + 30\,yz$.

9. $\dfrac{x^4}{9\,y^8} - \dfrac{x^3}{3\,y^6} + \dfrac{31\,x^2}{60\,y^4} - \dfrac{2\,x}{5\,y^2} + \dfrac{4}{25}$.

10. $4\,x^2 - 31\,x^4 + 4 - 30\,x^5 + 44\,x^3 + 25\,x^6 - 16\,x$.

11. 99729.64.   12. 64.91041489.   13. $.0063138916$.

Find the cube roots of:

14. $27\,x^5 - 27\,x^5y - 99\,x^4y^2 + 71\,x^3y^3 + 132\,x^2y^4 - 48\,xy^5 - 64\,y^6$.

15. $\dfrac{8\,a^3}{b^3} - \dfrac{12\,a^2}{b^2} + \dfrac{10\,a}{b} - 5 + \dfrac{5\,b}{3\,a} - \dfrac{b^2}{3\,a^2} + \dfrac{b^3}{27\,a^3}$.

16. $12\,x^4 - 6\,x^8 - 27\,x + x^9 + 62\,x^3 + 9\,x^7 + 27 - 45\,x^2 + 13\,x^6 - 45\,x^5$.

17. 201.230056.   18. 8831234.763.   19. $.537764475968$.

20. Find the fourth root of

$16\,x^8 + 32\,x^7 - 72\,x^6 - 136\,x^5 + 145\,x^4 + 204\,x^3 - 162\,x^2 - 108\,x + 81$.

21. Find the sixth root of

$1 + 12\,x + 54\,x^2 + 100\,x^3 + 15\,x^4 - 168\,x^5 - 76\,x^6 + 168\,x^7$
$+ 15\,x^8 - 100\,x^9 + 54\,x^{10} - 12\,x^{11} + x^{12}$.

22. Find the fifth root of

$32\,x^{10} - 80\,x^9 + 240\,x^8 - 360\,x^7 + 570\,x^6 - 561\,x^5 + 570\,x^4$
$- 360\,x^3 + 240\,x^2 - 80\,x + 32$.

23. Find the fourth root of 888.73149456.

24. Find the sixth root of $.009229812275335744$.

25. Find the fifth root of 8472886.09443.

XVI. INEQUALITIES

328. An **Inequality** is a statement that one of two expressions is greater or less than another.

The *First Member* of an inequality is the expression to the left of the sign of inequality, and the *Second Member* is the expression to the right of that sign.

Any term of either member of an inequality is called a *term* of the inequality.

Two or more inequalities are said to *subsist in the same sense* when the first member is the greater or the less in both.

Thus, $a > b$ and $c > d$ subsist in the same sense.

PROPERTIES OF INEQUALITIES

329. *An inequality will continue in the same sense after the same number has been added to, or subtracted from, both members.*

This follows from § 23, which is supposed to hold for all values of the letters involved.

330. It follows from § 329, that *a term may be transposed from one member of an inequality to the other by changing its sign.*

If the same term appears in both members of an inequality affected with the same sign, it may be cancelled.

331. *If the signs of all the terms of an inequality be changed, the sign of inequality must be reversed.*

For consider the inequality $a - b > c - d$.

Transposing every term, $d - c > b - a$.   (§ 330)

That is, $b - a < d - c$.

332. Let $a - b$ be a positive number.

Then, $(a - b) + b > b$; that is, $a > b$.

Again, let $a - b$ be a negative number.

Then, $(a - b) + b < b$; that is, $a < b$.

333. *An inequality will continue in the same sense after both members have been multiplied or divided by the same positive number.*

For consider the inequality $a > b$.

By § 332, $a - b$ is a positive number.

Hence, if m is a positive number, each of the numbers

$$m(a - b) \quad \text{and} \quad \frac{a - b}{m},$$

or, $\qquad ma - mb \quad \text{and} \quad \dfrac{a}{m} - \dfrac{b}{m}$, is positive.

Therefore, $\qquad ma > mb$, and $\dfrac{a}{m} > \dfrac{b}{m}$.

334. It follows from §§ 331 and 333 that *if both members of an inequality be multiplied or divided by the same negative number, the sign of inequality must be reversed.*

335. *If any number of inequalities, subsisting in the same sense, be added member to member, the resulting inequality will also subsist in the same sense.*

For consider the inequalities $a > b,\ a' > b',\ a'' > b'',\ \cdots$.

Then each of the numbers, $a - b,\ a' - b',\ a'' - b'',\ \cdots$, is positive.

Therefore, their sum

$$a - b + a' - b' + a'' - b'' + \cdots,$$

or, $\qquad a + a' + a'' + \cdots - (b + b' + b'' + \cdots),$

is a positive number.

Whence, $\quad a + a' + a'' + \cdots > b + b' + b'' + \cdots$.

336. If two inequalities, subsisting in the same sense, be *subtracted* member from member, the resulting inequality does not necessarily subsist in the same sense.

Thus, if $a > b$ and $a' > b'$, the numbers $a - b$ and $a' - b'$ are positive.

But $(a - b) - (a' - b')$, or its equal $(a - a') - (b - b')$, may be positive, negative, or zero; and hence $a - a'$ may be greater than, less than, or equal to $b - b'$.

337. If $a > b$ and $a' > b'$, and each of the numbers a, a', b, b', is positive, then $\qquad aa' > bb'$.

For since $a - b$, $a' - b'$, a, and b' are positive numbers, each of the numbers $\qquad a\,(a' - b')$ and $b'\,(a - b)$ is positive.

Then, $\qquad\qquad aa' > ab'$, and $ab' > bb'$.

Then by § 335, $\qquad aa' + ab' > ab' + bb'$.

Whence, $\qquad\qquad aa' > bb'$.

338. If we have any number of inequalities subsisting in the same sense, as $a > b$, $a' > b'$, $a'' > b''$, $\cdots$, and each of the numbers a, a', a'', $\cdot$, b, b', b'', $\cdot$, is positive, then

$$aa'a'' \cdots > bb'b'' \cdots .$$

For by § 337, $\qquad aa' > bb'$.

Also, $\qquad\qquad a'' > b''$.

Whence, $\qquad\qquad aa'a'' > bb'b''$ (§ 337).

Continuing the process with the remaining inequalities, we obtain finally $\qquad aa'a'' \cdots > bb'b'' \cdots .$

339. It follows from § 338 that, if a is $> b$, and a and b are positive numbers, and n a positive integer, then

$$a^n > b^n.$$

340. If n is a positive integer, and a and b perfect nth powers such that a is $> b$, then

$$\sqrt[n]{a} > \sqrt[n]{b}.$$

For, if $\sqrt[n]{a}$ were $< \sqrt[n]{b}$, raising both members to the nth power, we should have $a < b$. $\qquad$ (§ 339)

And, if $\sqrt[n]{a} = \sqrt[n]{b}$, a would be equal to b.

Both of these conclusions are contrary to the hypothesis that a is $> b$.

Hence, $\qquad\qquad \sqrt[n]{a} > \sqrt[n]{b}.$

341. Examples.

1. Find the limit of x in the inequality

$$7x - \frac{23}{3} < \frac{2x}{3} + 5.$$

Multiplying both members by 3 (§ 333), we have

$$21x - 23 < 2x + 15.$$

Transposing (§ 330), and uniting terms,

$$19x < 38.$$

Dividing both members by 19 (§ 333),

$$x < 2.$$

2. Find the limits of x and y in the following:

$$\begin{cases} 3x + 2y > 37. & (1) \\ 2x + 3y = 33. & (2) \end{cases}$$

Multiply (1) by 3, $9x + 6y > 111.$
Multiply (2) by 2, $4x + 6y = 66.$
Subtracting (§ 329), $5x > 45$, and $x > 9.$
Multiply (1) by 2, $6x + 4y > 74.$
Multiply (2) by 3, $6x + 9y = 99.$
Subtracting, $-5y > -25.$
Divide both members by -5, $y < 5$ (§ 334).

3. Between what limiting values of x is $x^2 - 4x < 21$?

$x^2 - 4x$ is < 21 if $x^2 - 4x - 21$ is < 0.

That is, if $(x+3)(x-7)$ is negative.

Now $(x+3)(x-7)$ is negative if x is between -3 and 7.

Hence, $x^2 - 4x$ is < 21 if x is > -3, and < 7.

4. Prove that if a and b are positive numbers,

$$\frac{a}{b} + \frac{b}{a} \not< 2.$$

We have $(a-b)^2 \not< 0$; or, $a^2 - 2ab + b^2 \not< 0$.

Transposing $-2ab$, $a^2 + b^2 \not< 2ab$.

Dividing each term by ab,

$$\frac{a}{b} + \frac{b}{a} \not< 2.$$

5. Prove that, if a and b are unequal positive numbers,
$$a^3 + b^3 > a^2 b + b^2 a.$$

We have $(a - b)^2 > 0$; or, $a^2 - 2ab + b^2 > 0$.

Transposing $-ab$, $a^2 - ab + b^2 > ab$.

Multiplying both members by the positive number $a + b$,
$$a^3 + b^3 > a^2 b + b^2 a.$$

6. Prove that, if $a, b,$ and c are unequal positive numbers,
$$2(a^3 + b^3 + c^3) > a^2 b + b^2 a + b^2 c + c^2 b + c^2 a + a^2 c.$$

By Ex. 5, $a^3 + b^3 > a^2 b + b^2 a,$

$b^3 + c^3 > b^2 c + c^2 b,$

and $c^3 + a^3 > c^2 a + a^2 c.$

Adding, $2(a^3 + b^3 + c^3) > a^2 b + b^2 a + b^2 c + c^2 b + c^2 a + a^2 c.$

EXERCISE 42

Find the limits of x in the following:

1. $(2x - 3)^3 - 71 > 4x(2x - 5)(x - 2)$.

2. $(2 - 3x)(3 - x) + 4x + 39 > 3 + (2 + 3x)(x + 3)$.

3. $(x - 1)(x - 2)(x' - 3) < (x - 5)(x + 6)(x - 7)$.

4. $a^2(x - 1) < 2b^2(2x - 1) - ab$, if $a - 2b$ is positive.

5. $\dfrac{x - m}{n} + 2 > \dfrac{x + n}{m}$, if m and n are positive and $m < n$.

Find the limits of x and y in the following:

6. $\begin{cases} 5x + 6y < 45. \\ 3x - 4y = -11. \end{cases}$ **7.** $\begin{cases} 7x - 4y > 41. \\ 3x + 7y = 35. \end{cases}$

8. Find the limits of x when
$$3x - 11 < 24 - 11x, \text{ and } 5x + 23 < 20x + 3.$$

9. If 6 times a certain positive integer, plus 14, is greater than 13 times the integer, minus 63, and 17 times the integer, minus 23, is greater than 8 times the integer, plus 31, what is the integer?

10. If 7 times the number of houses in a certain village, plus 33, is less than 12 times the number, minus 82, and 9 times the number, minus 43, is less than 5 times the number, plus 61, how many houses are there?

11. A farmer has a number of cows such that 10 times their number, plus 3, is less than 4 times the number, plus 79 ; and 14 times their number, minus 97, is greater than 6 times the number, minus 5.   How many cows has he ?

12. Between what limiting values of x is $x^2 + 3x < 4$?

13. Between what limiting values of x is $2x^2 + 13x > 24$?

14. Between what limiting values of x is $6x^2 < 19x - 10$?

Prove that, for any values of x,

15. $9x^2 + 25 \not< 30x$.   **16.** $x(x-3) \not< \dfrac{x}{2} - \dfrac{49}{16}$.

Prove that, for any values of a and b,

17. $(4a + 3b)(4a - 3b) \not< 6b(4a - 3b)$.

18. $a^4 + b^4 \not< 2ab(a^2 - ab + b^2)$.

Prove that, if all the letters represent unequal positive numbers,

19. $a^3 + a^2b + ab^2 + b^3 > 2ab(a + b)$.

20. $a^2 + b^2 + c^2 > ab + bc + ca$.

21. $a^2b^2 + b^2c^2 + c^2a^2 > a^2bc + b^2ca + c^2ab$.

22. $(a + b - c)^2 + (b + c - a)^2 + (c + a - b)^2 > ab + bc + ca$.

23. $a^2b + ab^2 + b^2c + bc^2 + c^2a + ca^2 > 6abc$.

24. $(a^2 + b^2 + c^2)(x^2 + y^2 + z^2) \not< (ax + by + cz)^2$.

XVII. SURDS. THEORY OF EXPONENTS

342. Meaning of $\sqrt{2}$.

It is impossible to find a rational number (§ 51) whose square shall equal 2; but we can find two rational numbers, which shall differ from each other by less than any assigned number, however small, whose squares shall be less, and greater than 2, respectively.

For, writing the squares of the consecutive integers 1, 2, etc., we have $1^2 = 1$, $2^2 = 4$, etc.

Hence, 1 and 2 are two numbers which differ by 1, and whose squares are less and greater than 2, respectively.

Again, $1.1^2 = 1.21$, $1.2^2 = 1.44$, $1.3^2 = 1.69$, $1.4^2 = 1.96$, $1.5^2 = 2.25$, etc.

Hence, 1.4 and 1.5 are two numbers which differ by .1, and whose squares are less and greater than 2, respectively.

Again, $1.41^2 = 1.9881$, $1.42^2 = 2.0164$, etc.

Hence, 1.41 and 1.42 are two numbers which differ by .01, and whose squares are less and greater than 2, respectively.

By sufficiently continuing the above process, we can find two numbers which shall differ from each other by less than any assigned number, however small, whose squares shall be less and greater than 2, respectively.

343. The successive numbers,. in the illustration of § 342, whose squares are less than 2, are 1, 1.4, 1.41, etc.; and the numbers whose squares are greater than 2, are 2, 1.5, 1.42, etc.

If each series be continued to r terms, the difference between the rth terms of the two series is

$$\frac{1}{10^{r-1}};$$

which can be made less than any assigned number, however small, by sufficiently increasing r.

Therefore, the rth terms of the two series approach the same limit (§ 245), when r is indefinitely increased.

This limit is taken as the definition of $\sqrt{2}$.

344. In general, if n is any positive integer, and a a rational number (§ 51), which is not a perfect power of the nth degree, and which is positive if n is even, it is impossible to find a number whose nth power shall equal a.

We can find, however, two rational numbers which shall differ from each other by less than any assigned number, however small, whose nth powers shall be less and greater than a, respectively.

345. If n and a have the same meaning as in § 344, and a_1, a_2, a_3, etc., is a series of rational numbers whose nth powers are less than a, and a'_1, a'_2, a'_3, etc., a series of rational numbers whose nth powers are greater than a, such that $a'_1 \sim a_1 = 1$, $a'_2 \sim a_2 = .1$, $a'_3 \sim a_3 = .01$, etc., we may show, as in § 343, that the rth terms of the two series approach the same limit, when r is indefinitely increased.

This limit is taken as the definition of $\sqrt[n]{a}$.

The expression $\sqrt[n]{a}$ is called a **Surd**.

The symbol $\sim$ signifies the *difference* of the numbers between which it is placed.

346. In the illustration of § 342, we also have $(-1)^2 = 1$, $(-2)^2 = 4$, etc.

It is therefore possible to find two *negative* rational numbers, which shall differ from each other by less than any assigned number, however small, whose squares shall be less and greater than 2, respectively.

This is also the case with every surd of the form $\sqrt[n]{a}$, when n is even.

347. If a is *positive*, and a_1, a_2, etc., and a'_1, a'_2, etc., be taken with positive signs, we shall call the limit approached by the rth terms of the two series of § 345, when r is indefinitely increased, the *principal* nth root of a.

If a is *negative*, we shall call the negative limit approached by the rth terms of the series, when r is indefinitely increased, the principal nth root of a.

OPERATIONS INVOLVING SURDS

348. It is necessary to define Addition and Multiplication, when any or all of the numbers involved are *surds*.

Let n and p be positive integers.

Let a be a rational number which is not a perfect power of the nth degree, and is positive if n is even.

Let b be a rational number which is not a perfect power of the pth degree, and is positive if p is even.

Let $a_1, a_2, \cdots, a_r, \cdot$, be a series of rational numbers whose nth powers are less than a, and $a'_1, a'_2, \cdot, a'_r, \cdots$, a series whose nth powers are greater than a, such that

$$a'_1 \sim a_1 = 1, a'_2 \sim a_2 = .1, \cdots, a'_r \sim a_r = (.1)^{r-1}, \cdots.$$

Let $b_1, b_2, \cdot, b_r, \cdot$, be a series of rational numbers whose pth powers are less than b, and $b'_1, b'_2, \cdot, b'_r, \cdots$, a series whose pth powers are greater than b, such that

$$b'_1 \sim b_1 = 1, b'_2 \sim b_2 = .1, \cdots, b'_r \sim b_r = (.1)^{r-1}, \cdots.$$

Then to *add* $\sqrt[p]{b}$ to $\sqrt[n]{a}$, is to find the limit, when r is indefinitely increased, of $a_r + b_r$.

To *multiply* $\sqrt[n]{a}$ by $\sqrt[p]{b}$ is to find the limit, when r is indefinitely increased, of $a_r \times b_r$.

349. A meaning similar to the above is attached to any expression, which is not a rational number, and which is the result of any finite number of the following operations performed upon one or more rational numbers, provided that, in any indicated root, the number under the radical sign is positive if the index of the root is even:

Addition; Subtraction; Multiplication; Division; raising to any positive integral power; extracting any root.

350. We will now show how to prove the laws of §§ 12 and 14, when any or all of the letters involved represent *surds*.

Let it be required, for example, to prove the Commutative Law for Multiplication (§ 14) with respect to the product of two surds, $\sqrt[n]{a}$ and $\sqrt[p]{b}$, where n, p, a, and b have the same meanings as in § 348.

Or, to prove $\sqrt[n]{a} \times \sqrt[p]{b} = \sqrt[p]{b} \times \sqrt[n]{a}.$

With the notation of § 348, $\sqrt[n]{a} \times \sqrt[p]{b}$ is the limit, when r is indefinitely increased, of $a_r \times b_r$.

Also, $\sqrt[p]{b} \times \sqrt[n]{a}$ is the limit, when r is indefinitely increased, of $b_r \times a_r$.

By § 14, since a_r and b_r are rational numbers,

$$a_r \times b_r = b_r \times a_r.$$

Then, $a_r \times b_r$ and $b_r \times a_r$ are functions of r which are equal for every positive integral value of r; and, by § 252, their limits when r is indefinitely increased are equal.

Hence, $\qquad \sqrt[n]{a} \times \sqrt[p]{b} = \sqrt[p]{b} \times \sqrt[n]{a}.$

This simply means that the product of the principal nth root of a (§ 347) by the principal pth root of b is equal to the product of the principal pth root of b by the principal nth root of a. (Compare § 162.)

A similar interpretation must be given to every result involving surds.

In like manner, the remaining laws of §§ 12 and 14 may be proved to hold, when any or all of the letters involved represent surds.

351. Since the remaining results of Chap. I, and the results in Chaps. II to XVI, inclusive, are formal consequences of the laws of §§ 12 and 14, it follows that every statement or rule, in these chapters, in regard to expressions where any letter involved represents any rational number, holds equally when the letter represents a surd.

This is also the case when the letter represents any number of the form described in § 349.

APPROXIMATE ROOTS

352. Any one of the successive numbers, in the example of § 342, is called an *approximate square root* of 2.

In general, any one of the numbers a_1, a_2, etc., or a'_1, a'_2, etc., in § 345, is called an *approximate nth root* of a.

353. The successive numbers, in the example of § 342, whose squares are less than 2, may be obtained by regarding 2 as a perfect square, and applying the rule of § 304.

$$
\begin{array}{r|l}
\multicolumn{2}{l}{\quad\quad\dot{2}.\dot{0}\dot{0}\dot{0}\dot{0}\dot{0}\dot{0} \mid 1.414} \\
\multicolumn{2}{l}{\quad\quad\; 1} \\
\hline
24 & 1\;00 \\
& \quad 96 \\
\hline
281 & 400 \\
& 281 \\
\hline
2824 & 11900 \\
& 11296 \\
\hline
& \quad 604
\end{array}
$$

The process may be continued to any desired extent.

In like manner the rule of § 317 may be used to find an approximate cube root of a number (Note, § 312) which is not a perfect cube; and the rule of § 325 may be used to find an approximate *n*th root of a number (Note, § 323) which is not a perfect power of the *n*th degree.

The considerations in §§ 306 and 320 apply equally to approximate square and cube roots.

354. To find an approximate root of a fraction whose terms are positive integers expressed in Arabic numerals, whose denominator is, and whose numerator is not, a perfect power of the degree denoted by the index of the required root, we may divide the required approximate root of the numerator by the required root of the denominator (§ 293).

If the denominator is not a perfect power of the degree denoted by the index of the required root, the fraction should be reduced to an equivalent fraction whose denominator is a perfect power of this degree.

Thus, let it be required to find the square root of $\frac{3}{8}$ approximately, to four decimal places.

$$\sqrt{\frac{3}{8}} = \sqrt{\frac{6}{16}} = \frac{\sqrt{6}}{4}\,(\S\ 293) = \frac{2.4494}{4} = .6123\ \cdots.$$

EXERCISE 43

Find the approximate value of each of the following to five decimal places:

1. $\sqrt{5}$. 2. $\sqrt{13}$. 3. $\sqrt{.851}$. 4. $\sqrt{.003}$.

5. $\sqrt{\frac{11}{16}}$.   **8.** $\sqrt{\frac{5}{28}}$.   **11.** $\sqrt[3]{.7}$ **14.** $\sqrt[3]{\frac{1}{3}}$.

6. $\sqrt{\frac{1}{7}}$.   **9.** $\sqrt[3]{4}$.   **12.** $\sqrt[3]{.02}$.   **15.** $\sqrt[3]{\frac{5}{9}}$.

7. $\sqrt{\frac{7}{32}}$.   **10.** $\sqrt[3]{11}$.   **13.** $\sqrt[3]{\frac{5}{8}}$.   **16.** $\sqrt[3]{\frac{7}{16}}$.

THE THEORY OF EXPONENTS

355. In the preceding portions of the work, an exponent has been considered only as a *positive integer*.

Thus, if m is a positive integer,

$$a^m = a \times a \times a \times \cdots \text{ to } m \text{ factors.} \qquad (\S\ 60)$$

356. We have proved the following results to hold when m and n represent positive integers, and a any rational number:

$$a^m \times a^n = a^{m+n} \ (\S\ 85). \qquad (1)$$
$$(a^m)^n = a^{mn} \ (\S\ 128). \qquad (2)$$

357. It is necessary to employ exponents which are not positive integers; and we now proceed to define those forms of exponent which are rational numbers, but not positive integers.

In determining what meanings to assign to the new forms, it will be convenient to have them such that the above law for multiplication shall hold with respect to them.

We shall therefore *assume* equation (1), § 356, to hold, whatever number is represented by a, for all *rational* values of m and n, including the case where either m or n is zero; and find what meanings must be attached in consequence to *fractional*, *negative*, and *zero* exponents.

358. Meaning of a Fractional Exponent.

Required the meaning of $a^{\frac{p}{q}}$, where p and q represent positive integers.

If (1), § 356, is to hold for all rational values of m and n, we have

$$a^{\frac{p}{q}} \times a^{\frac{p}{q}} \times \cdots \text{ to } q \text{ factors} = a^{\frac{p}{q}+\frac{p}{q}+\cdots \text{ to } q \text{ terms}} = a^{\frac{p}{q} \times q} = a^p.$$

That is, $$(a^{\frac{p}{q}})^q = a^p.$$

Whence, by § 157, $$a^{\frac{p}{q}} = \sqrt[q]{a^p}.$$

We shall then define $a^{\frac{p}{q}}$ as being the qth root of a^p.

For example, $a^{\frac{3}{4}} = \sqrt[4]{a^3}$; $a^{\frac{5}{2}} = \sqrt{a^5}$; $a^{\frac{1}{3}} = \sqrt[3]{a}$; etc.

We shall throughout the remainder of the work regard $a^{\frac{p}{q}}$ as being the *principal* qth root of a^p.

359. Meaning of a Zero Exponent.

Required the meaning of a^0.

By § 356, (1), if m is any rational number

$$a^m \times a^0 = a^{m+0} = a^m.$$

Whence, $$a^0 = \frac{a^m}{a^m} = 1.$$

We shall then define a^0 as being equal to **1**.

360. Meaning of a Negative Exponent.

Required the meaning of a^{-s}, where s represents a positive integer or a positive fraction.

By § 356, (1), $a^{-s} \times a^s = a^{-s+s} = a^0 = 1$ (§ 359).

Whence, $$a^{-s} = \frac{1}{a^s}.$$

We shall then define a^{-s} as being equal to 1 divided by a^s.

For example, $a^{-2} = \frac{1}{a^2}$; $a^{-\frac{2}{3}} = \frac{1}{a^{\frac{2}{3}}}$; $3\,x^{-1}y^{-\frac{1}{2}} = \frac{3}{xy^{\frac{1}{2}}}$; etc.

361. It follows from § 360 that

Any factor of the numerator of a fraction may be transferred to the denominator, or any factor of the denominator to the numerator, if the sign of its exponent be changed.

Thus, $\dfrac{a^2b^3}{cd^4}$ may be written in the forms

$$\frac{b^3}{a^{-2}cd^4}, \quad \frac{a^2b^3c^{-1}}{d^4}, \quad \frac{a^2d^{-4}}{b^{-3}c}, \text{ etc.}$$

362. We will now prove that, with the definitions of §§ 358 and 360, equation (1), § 356, holds for all rational values of m, n, and a, provided that a^m and a^n are rational numbers or surds.

It will be understood that, in all fractional exponents, the results are limited to *principal* roots.

· I. Let m and n be fractions of the form $\dfrac{p}{q}$ and $\dfrac{r}{s}$, respectively, where p, q, r, and s represent positive integers.

By § 358,
$$a^{\frac{p}{q}} \times a^{\frac{r}{s}} = \sqrt[q]{a^p} \times \sqrt[s]{a^r}$$

$$= \sqrt[qs]{a^{ps}} \times \sqrt[qs]{a^{qr}} \qquad (\text{§ 327})$$

$$= \sqrt[qs]{a^{ps} \times a^{qr}} \qquad (\text{§ 165})$$

$$= \sqrt[qs]{a^{ps+qr}} \qquad (\text{§ 85})$$

$$= a^{\frac{ps+qr}{qs}} = a^{\frac{p}{q}+\frac{r}{s}}.$$

We have now proved that (1), § 356, holds when m and n represent any positive rational numbers.

II. Let m be rational and positive, and let $n = -q$, where q is rational, positive, and less than m.

By §§ 85, or 362, I, $a^{m-q} \times a^q = a^{m-q+q} = a^m$.

Whence,
$$a^{m-q} = \frac{a^m}{a^q} = a^m \times a^{-q} \ (\text{§ 360}).$$

That is,
$$a^m \times a^{-q} = a^{m-q}.$$

In like manner, the law may be proved to hold when n is rational and positive, and $m = -p$, where p is rational, positive, and less than n.

III. Let m be rational and positive, and let $n = q$, where q is rational, positive, and greater than m.

By § 361, $a^m \times a^{-q} = \dfrac{1}{a^{-m}a^q} = \dfrac{1}{a^{-m+q}} \ (\text{§ 362, II}) = a^{m-q}$.

In like manner, the law may be proved to hold when n is rational and positive, and $m = -p$, where p is rational, positive, and greater than n.

IV. Let $m = -p$, and $n = -q$, where p and q are rational and positive.

Then, $a^{-p} \times a^{-q} = \dfrac{1}{a^p a^q} = \dfrac{1}{a^{p+q}}$ (§§ 85, or 362, I) $= a^{-p-q}$.

Hence, $a^m \times a^n = a^{m+n}$ for all rational values of m and n.

For example, $\qquad a^2 \times a^{-5} = a^{2-5} = a^{-3}$;

$$a \times a^{\frac{5}{2}} = a^{1+\frac{5}{2}} = a^{\frac{7}{2}}; \text{ etc.}$$

363. We have for all rational values of a, m, and n, provided that a^m and a^n are rational numbers or surds,

$$a^{m-n} \times a^n = a^{m-n+n} \text{ (§§ 85, 362)} = a^m.$$

Whence, $\qquad\qquad \dfrac{a^m}{a^n} = a^{m-n}$.

For example, $\qquad\qquad \dfrac{a^{-\frac{3}{4}}}{a} = a^{-\frac{3}{4}-1} = a^{-\frac{7}{4}}$;

$$\dfrac{a^{\frac{1}{2}}}{a^{-2}} = a^{\frac{1}{2}+2} = a^{\frac{5}{2}}; \text{ etc.}$$

364. We will now prove that equation (2), § 356, holds for all rational values of a, m, and n, provided that a^m and a^{mn} are rational numbers or surds.

In all fractional exponents, the results are limited to principal roots.

I. Let n be a positive integer.

Then, $(a^m)^n = a^m \times a^m \times a^m \times \cdots$ to n factors

$\qquad = a^{m+m+m+\cdots \text{ to } n \text{ terms}}$ (§§ 85, 362) $= a^{mn}$.

II. Let $n = \dfrac{p}{q}$, where p and q are positive integers.

Then, $(a^m)^{\frac{p}{q}} = \sqrt[q]{(a^m)^p} = \sqrt[q]{a^{mp}}$ (§ 364, I) $= a^{\frac{mp}{q}}$.

III. Let $n = -s$, where s is rational and positive.

Then, $(a^m)^{-s} = \dfrac{1}{(a^m)^s} = \dfrac{1}{a^{ms}}$ (§ 364, I or II) $= a^{-ms}$.

Hence, $(a^m)^n = a^{mn}$ for all rational values of m and n.

For example, $\qquad (a^{\frac{1}{2}})^{\frac{2}{3}} = a^{\frac{1}{2} \times \frac{2}{3}} = a^{\frac{1}{3}}$;

$$(a^{-2})^{-\frac{1}{5}} = a^{-2 \times -\frac{1}{5}} = a^{\frac{2}{5}};$$

$$(a^4)^{-1} = a^{4 \times -1} = a^{-4}; \text{ etc.}$$

SURDS. THEORY OF EXPONENTS 221

365. *To prove* $(abc \cdots)^n = a^n b^n c^n \cdots$ *for all rational values of* $a, b, c, \cdot$, *and* n, *provided that* $a^n, b^n, c^n, \cdot$, *are rational numbers or surds.*

The theorem was proved in § 129 for any positive integral value of n, and in § 165 for any value of n of the form $\dfrac{1}{m}$, where m is a positive integer.

I. Let $n = \dfrac{p}{q}$, where p and q are positive integers.

By § 364, $[(abc \cdots)^{\frac{p}{q}}]^q = (abc \cdots)^p = a^p b^p c^p \cdots$ (§ 129). $\qquad$ (1)

By § 129, $(a^{\frac{p}{q}} b^{\frac{p}{q}} c^{\frac{p}{q}} \cdots)^q = (a^{\frac{p}{q}})^q (b^{\frac{p}{q}})^q (c^{\frac{p}{q}})^q \cdots = a^p b^p c^p \cdots$. $\qquad$ (2)

From (1) and (2),

$$[(abc \cdots)^{\frac{p}{q}}]^q = (a^{\frac{p}{q}} b^{\frac{p}{q}} c^{\frac{p}{q}} \cdots)^q.$$

Whence, $\qquad (abc \cdots)^{\frac{p}{q}} = a^{\frac{p}{q}} b^{\frac{p}{q}} c^{\frac{p}{q}} \cdots$ (§ 163).

This means that the principal qth root of $(abc \cdots)^p$ is equal to the product of the principal qth roots of $a^p, b^p, c^p, \cdots$.

II. Let $n = -s$, where s is rational and positive.

Then, $\qquad (abc \cdot)^{-s} = \dfrac{1}{(abc \cdots)^s}$

$$= \dfrac{1}{a^s b^s c^s \cdots} \quad \text{(§§ 129, or 365, I)}$$

$$= a^{-s} b^{-s} c^{-s} \cdots.$$

Hence, $(abc \cdot)^n = a^n b^n c^n \cdots$ for all rational values of m and n.

366. Examples.

In the following examples, every letter is supposed to represent a rational number such that every expression of the form a^n is a rational number or surd.

The value of a number affected with a fractional exponent may be found by first, if possible, extracting the root indicated by the denominator, and then raising the result to the power indicated by the numerator.

1. Find the value of $(-8)^{\frac{2}{3}}$.

$$(-8)^{\frac{2}{3}} = \sqrt[3]{(-8)^2} = (\sqrt[3]{-8})^2 \text{ (§ 292)} = (-2)^2 = 4.$$

2. Multiply $a + 2\,a^{\frac{2}{3}} - 3\,a^{\frac{1}{3}}$ by $2 - 4\,a^{-\frac{1}{3}} - 6\,a^{-\frac{2}{3}}$.

$$
\begin{array}{l}
\quad a + 2\,a^{\frac{2}{3}} \;-\; 3\,a^{\frac{1}{3}} \\[2pt]
\quad 2 - 4\,a^{-\frac{1}{3}} -\; 6\,a^{-\frac{2}{3}} \\[2pt]
\hline
2\,a + 4\,a^{\frac{2}{3}} \;-\; 6\,a^{\frac{1}{3}} \\[2pt]
\qquad\; -4\,a^{\frac{2}{3}} \;-\; 8\,a^{\frac{1}{3}} + 12 \\[2pt]
\qquad\qquad\quad -\;6\,a^{\frac{1}{3}} - 12 + 18\,a^{-\frac{1}{3}} \\[2pt]
\hline
2\,a \qquad\quad -\,20\,a^{\frac{1}{3}} \qquad +\,18\,a^{-\frac{1}{3}}.
\end{array}
$$

3. Divide $18\,xy^{-2} - 23 + x^{-\frac{1}{2}}y + 6\,x^{-1}y^{2}$

$$\text{by } 3\,x^{\frac{1}{4}}y^{-1} + x^{\frac{1}{4}} - 2\,x^{-\frac{1}{4}}y.$$

$$
\begin{array}{l|l}
18\,xy^{-2} - 23 + x^{-\frac{1}{2}}y + 6\,x^{-1}y^{2} & \;3\,x^{\frac{1}{4}}y^{-1} + x^{\frac{1}{4}} - 2\,x^{-\frac{1}{4}}y \\[2pt]
\underline{18\,xy^{-2} + 6\,x^{\frac{1}{2}}y^{-1} - 12\qquad\qquad} & \;6\,x^{\frac{1}{4}}y^{-1} - 2\,x^{-\frac{1}{4}} - 3\,x^{-\frac{3}{4}}y \\[2pt]
\quad -6\,x^{\frac{1}{2}}y^{-1} - 11 + \;\; x^{-\frac{1}{2}}y + 6\,x^{-1}y^{2} & \\[2pt]
\quad \underline{-6\,x^{\frac{1}{2}}y^{-1} - \;\; 2 + 4\,x^{-\frac{1}{2}}y\qquad} & \\[2pt]
\qquad\qquad\quad -\;9 - 3\,x^{-\frac{1}{2}}y + 6\,x^{-1}y^{2} & \\[2pt]
\qquad\qquad\quad \underline{-\;9 - 3\,x^{-\frac{1}{2}}y + 6\,x^{-1}y^{2}} &
\end{array}
$$

It is important to arrange the dividend, divisor, and each remainder in the same order of powers of some common letter.

4. Expand $\left(\dfrac{1}{m^{\frac{3}{4}}} - \sqrt[3]{m^{4}}\right)^{5}$ by the Binomial Theorem.

$$
\left(\frac{1}{m^{\frac{3}{4}}} - \sqrt[3]{m^{4}}\right)^{5} = [\,m^{-\frac{3}{4}} + (-\,m^{\frac{4}{3}})\,]^{5}
$$

$$
= (m^{-\frac{3}{4}})^{5} + 5\,(m^{-\frac{3}{4}})^{4}(-\,m^{\frac{4}{3}}) + 10\,(m^{-\frac{3}{4}})^{3}(-\,m^{\frac{4}{3}})^{2}
$$

$$
+\, 10\,(m^{-\frac{3}{4}})^{2}(-\,m^{\frac{4}{3}})^{3} + 5\,(m^{-\frac{3}{4}})(-\,m^{\frac{4}{3}})^{4}
$$

$$
+\,(-\,m^{\frac{4}{3}})^{5}
$$

$$
= m^{-\frac{15}{4}} - 5\,m^{-3} \cdot m^{\frac{4}{3}} + 10\,m^{-\frac{9}{4}} \cdot m^{\frac{8}{3}} - 10\,m^{-\frac{3}{2}} \cdot m^{4}
$$

$$
+\, 5\,m^{-\frac{3}{4}} \cdot m^{\frac{16}{3}} - m^{\frac{20}{3}}
$$

$$
= m^{-\frac{15}{4}} - 5\,m^{-\frac{5}{3}} + 10\,m^{\frac{5}{12}} - 10\,m^{\frac{5}{2}} + 5\,m^{\frac{55}{12}} - m^{\frac{20}{3}}.
$$

EXERCISE 44

It will be understood, in the following set of examples, that every letter used as the index of a root represents a positive integer, and every other letter a rational number, such that every expression of the form a^n or $\sqrt[n]{a}$ is a rational number or surd.

Express with radical signs:

1. $a^{\frac{2}{3}}b^{\frac{1}{5}}$. **2.** $x^{\frac{2}{3}}y^{\frac{5}{6}}z^{\frac{1}{4}}$. **3.** $6\,m^{\frac{4}{7}}n^{\frac{7}{8}}$. **4.** $\dfrac{p}{a^2}\dfrac{1}{x^3}\dfrac{m}{y^n}$.

Express with fractional exponents:

5. $\sqrt{m^7}\sqrt[4]{n}$. **6.** $5\sqrt[3]{a^5}\sqrt[9]{b^8}$. **7.** $\sqrt[5]{a^4}\sqrt[7]{b^6}\sqrt[9]{c}$. **8.** $\sqrt[m]{x^p}\sqrt{y^n}$.

Express with positive exponents:

9. x^7y^{-4}. **10.** $4\,a^{-\frac{3}{4}}b^{\frac{4}{3}}$. **11.** $m^{-\frac{1}{5}}n^{-\frac{3}{2}}$. **12.** $a^{-m}b^nc^{-\frac{p}{q}}$.

In each of the following, transfer all literal factors from the denominator to the numerator:

13. $\dfrac{ax^3}{b^2y^{\frac{3}{2}}}$. **14.** $\dfrac{2\,m^{\frac{1}{2}}}{3\,n^4p^{-3}}$. **15.** $\dfrac{5\,x^{-\frac{2}{3}}}{4\,y^{\frac{3}{2}}z^{-\frac{1}{4}}}$. **16.** $\dfrac{1}{a^mb^{-n}c^{-\frac{p}{q}}}$.

In each of the following, transfer all literal factors from the numerator to the denominator:

17. $\dfrac{x^3y^{\frac{2}{3}}}{z^{\frac{1}{4}}}$. **18.** $\dfrac{a^{-5}b^{-\frac{3}{4}}}{1}$. **19.** $\dfrac{2\,m^{-\frac{4}{5}}x^{\frac{5}{6}}}{5\,n^2y^{-\frac{2}{3}}}$. **20.** $\dfrac{a^{-p}b^qc^{\frac{m}{n}}}{6}$.

Find the values of the following:

21. $(a^{\frac{3}{10}})^5$. **23.** $(x^4)^{-\frac{7}{12}}$. **25.** $125^{\frac{2}{3}}$. **27.** $(-1024)^{\frac{3}{5}}$.

22. $(a^{-3})^{-9}$. **24.** $(a^{-\frac{7}{6}})^{\frac{9}{14}}$. **26.** $16^{\frac{7}{4}}$. **28.** $729^{\frac{5}{6}}$.

Multiply the following:

29. $x^{\frac{3}{2}} - 4\,x^{\frac{3}{4}} - 5 + 6\,x^{-\frac{3}{4}}$ by $2\,x^{-\frac{3}{4}} + x^{-\frac{3}{2}} - 3\,x^{-\frac{9}{4}}$.

30. $m^{-\frac{2}{3}} + 2\,m^{-1}n^{-1} + 3\,m^{-\frac{2}{3}}n^{-2}$ by $2\,m^{-\frac{2}{3}}n^{-1} - 4\,m^{-\frac{1}{3}}n^{-2} + 6\,n^{-3}$.

31. $3\,a^{\frac{3}{2}}b^{\frac{1}{3}} + 4\,ab^{\frac{2}{3}} - a^{\frac{1}{2}}b$ by $6\,a^{\frac{1}{4}}b^{-\frac{2}{3}} - 8\,a^{-\frac{1}{4}}b^{-\frac{1}{3}} - 2\,a^{-\frac{3}{4}}$.

Divide the following:

32. $m^{-2}n - 5\,n^{-1} + 4\,m^2n^{-3}$ by $m^{-4}n^2 - m^{-3}n - 2\,m^{-2}$.

33. $x^2y^{-\frac{4}{3}} - 10\,xy^{-\frac{2}{3}} + 9$ by $x^{\frac{3}{2}}y^{\frac{1}{3}} + 2\,xy^{\frac{2}{3}} - 3\,x^{\frac{1}{2}}y$.

34. $a^{\frac{4}{3}}b^{\frac{1}{2}} - 2\,b^2 + a^{-\frac{4}{3}}b^{\frac{7}{2}}$ by $a^{\frac{2}{3}}b^{\frac{1}{4}} - 2\,b^{\frac{3}{2}} + a^{-\frac{2}{3}}b^{\frac{4}{4}}$.

(In the following ten examples, use the rules of Chap. VII.)

Find the value of :

35. $(2\,a^{\frac{3}{4}} + 3\,b^{-\frac{1}{2}})^2.$

36. $(5\,m^{-2}n^3 - 8\,m^2n^{-3})^2.$

37. $(4\,x^{\frac{1}{3}}y^{-\frac{3}{4}} + 7\,z^{-2})(4\,x^{\frac{1}{3}}y^{-\frac{3}{4}} - 7\,z^{-2}).$

38. $(3\,x^{\frac{2}{3}} - 4\,y^{-\frac{5}{2}})^3.$

40. $(a^2b^{-\frac{1}{3}} - 2\,a^{\frac{1}{2}} - a^{-1}b^{\frac{2}{3}})^2.$

39. $(a^{-2}b^3 + 2\,a^3b^{-2})^3.$

41. $(x^{\frac{1}{3}} - 3\,x^{\frac{1}{6}} + 2\,x^{-\frac{1}{6}})^3.$

42. $\dfrac{25\,a^{-6} - 49\,m^{\frac{3}{2}}}{5\,a^{-3} - 7\,m^{\frac{3}{4}}}.$

43. $\dfrac{8\,x^2 + 27\,y^{-\frac{2}{5}}}{2\,x^{\frac{2}{3}} + 3\,y^{-\frac{2}{15}}}.$

44. $\dfrac{a^{\frac{1}{5}\cdot 2} - b^{-\frac{3}{2}}}{a^{\frac{2}{5}} + b^{-\frac{1}{4}}}.$

45. Factor $a^2 - 8\,b^{-9}$ by the rule of § 177.

46. Factor $a^{\frac{4}{3}} + a^{\frac{2}{3}}b^{-\frac{3}{4}} + b^{-\frac{3}{2}}$ by the rule of § 172.

Expand the following by the Binomial Theorem :

47. $(a^{3p} + 3\,b^{-\frac{m}{n}})^4.$

49. $(a^{-\frac{2}{3}}\sqrt[4]{b^3} - b^{-\frac{3}{4}}\sqrt[3]{a^2})^6.$

48. $\left(x^{\frac{3}{2}}y^{-\frac{1}{4}} - \dfrac{1}{z^3}\right)^7.$

50. $\left(\dfrac{2\sqrt{m^5}}{\sqrt[3]{n}} + \dfrac{n^{-\frac{1}{6}}}{m^{-\frac{3}{4}}}\right)^5.$

Find the

51. 6th term of $(\sqrt[n]{a^m} + \sqrt[n]{a})^{17}.$

52. 7th term of $\left(x^{-\frac{2}{3}}y^{\frac{3}{4}} - \dfrac{z^{\frac{1}{2}}}{3}\right)^{14}.$

53. 10th term of $\left(2\sqrt[3]{n} - \dfrac{1}{\sqrt[5]{n^2}}\right)^{13}.$

54. Find the square root of $a^{\frac{4}{3}}b^{-3} - 6\,a^{\frac{2}{3}}b^{-2} + 5\,b^{-1} + 12\,a^{-\frac{2}{3}} + 4\,a^{-\frac{4}{3}}b.$

55. Find the cube root of

$$x^{\frac{1}{2}} - 6\,x^{\frac{1}{3}} + 21\,x^{-\frac{1}{6}} - 44\,x^{-\frac{1}{2}} + 63\,x^{-\frac{5}{6}} - 54\,x^{-\frac{7}{6}} + 27\,x^{-\frac{3}{2}}.$$

Simplify the following :

56. $[\sqrt[3]{(x^{\frac{1}{2}}y^{-2})} \div \sqrt[5]{(x^{-\frac{2}{3}}y^4)}]^{\frac{19}{11}}.$

60. $[\sqrt[q^2]{(\sqrt[p+q]{x^{p-q}})}]^{\frac{p}{p-q}-1}.$

57. $\dfrac{\sqrt[6]{a^9}}{\sqrt[6]{b^5}\sqrt[9]{c}} \times \dfrac{\sqrt[4]{b^3}\sqrt[12]{c^7}}{\sqrt[15]{a^8}}.$

61. $\dfrac{x^{\frac{3m}{2n}} - 1}{x^{\frac{m}{2n}} + 1} + \dfrac{x^{\frac{3m}{2n}} + 1}{x^{\frac{m}{2n}} - 1}.$

58. $\left(\dfrac{a^{m+n}}{a^{m-n}}\right)^{2m}\left(\dfrac{a^{2m}}{a^{2n}}\right)^{m-n}.$

62. $\dfrac{a^{\frac{1}{3}} + b^{\frac{1}{3}}}{a^{-\frac{1}{3}} - b^{-\frac{1}{3}}} \times \dfrac{a^{-\frac{1}{3}} + b^{-\frac{1}{3}}}{a^{\frac{1}{3}} - b^{\frac{1}{3}}} + 1.$

59. $\dfrac{x^{\frac{1}{3}} + y^{\frac{1}{3}}}{x^{\frac{1}{3}} - y^{\frac{1}{3}}} - \dfrac{x + y}{x - y}.$

63. $\dfrac{a^{\frac{1}{3}} + 2\,b^{\frac{1}{3}}}{a^{\frac{1}{3}} - 2\,b^{\frac{1}{3}}} - \dfrac{7\,a^{\frac{1}{3}}b^{\frac{1}{3}} + 6\,b^{\frac{2}{3}}}{a^{\frac{2}{3}} - a^{\frac{1}{3}}b^{\frac{1}{3}} - 6\,b^{\frac{2}{3}}}.$

REDUCTION OF SURDS

It will be understood, in §§ 367 to 398, inclusive, that every letter used as the index of a root, represents a positive integer, and every other letter a rational number such that every expression of the form $\sqrt[n]{a}$ is a surd.

367. If a surd is in the form $b\sqrt[n]{a}$, where a and b are rational expressions (§ 198), b is called the *coefficient*, and n the *index*; and the surd is said to be of the nth degree.

368. A *quadratic surd* is a surd of the second degree.

369. **Similar Surds** are surds which do not differ at all, or differ only in their coefficients; as $2\sqrt[3]{ax^2}$ and $3\sqrt[3]{ax^2}$.

Dissimilar Surds are surds which are not similar.

370. Reduction of a Surd to its Simplest Form.

A surd is said to be in its *simplest form* when the expression under the radical sign is rational and integral (§ 63), is not a perfect power of the degree denoted by any factor of the index of the surd, and has no factor which is a perfect power of the same degree as the surd.

371. CASE I. *When the expression under the radical sign is a perfect power of the degree denoted by a factor of the index.*

Ex. Reduce $\sqrt[6]{8}$ to its simplest form.

We have, $\qquad \sqrt[6]{8} = \sqrt[6]{2^3} = \sqrt{2}$ (§ 327).

372. CASE II. *When the expression under the radical sign is rational and integral, and has a factor which is a perfect power of the same degree as the surd.*

1. Reduce $\sqrt[3]{54}$ to its simplest form.

We have, $\sqrt[3]{54} = \sqrt[3]{27 \times 2} = \sqrt[3]{27} \times \sqrt[3]{2}$ (§ 165) $= 3\sqrt[3]{2}$.

We can use § 165 in the above; for we know by § 351 that it holds when $\sqrt[n]{a}$, $\sqrt[n]{b}$, $\sqrt[n]{c}$, ..., are surds.

2. Reduce $\sqrt{3\,a^3b - 12\,a^2b^2 + 12\,ab^3}$ to its simplest form.

$$\sqrt{3\,a^3b - 12\,a^2b^2 + 12\,ab^3} = \sqrt{(a^2 - 4\,ab + 4\,b^2)3\,ab}$$
$$= \sqrt{a^2 - 4\,ab + 4\,b^2}\,\sqrt{3\,ab} = (a - 2\,b)\sqrt{3\,ab}.$$

We then have the following rule:

Resolve the expression under the radical sign into two factors, the second of which contains no factor which is a perfect power of the same degree as the surd.

Extract the required root of the first factor, and multiply the result by the indicated root of the second.

If the expression under the radical sign has a numerical factor which cannot be readily factored by inspection, it is convenient to resolve it into its prime factors.

3. Reduce $\sqrt[3]{1944}$ to its simplest form.

$$\sqrt[3]{1944} = \sqrt[3]{2^3 \times 3^5} = \sqrt[3]{2^3 \times 3^3} \times \sqrt[3]{3^2} = 2 \times 3 \times \sqrt[3]{9} = 6\sqrt[3]{9}.$$

4. Reduce $\sqrt{125 \times 147}$ to its simplest form.

$$\sqrt{125 \times 147} = \sqrt{5^3 \times 3 \times 7^2} = 5 \times 7 \times \sqrt{5 \times 3} = 35\sqrt{15}.$$

373. CASE III. *When the expression under the radical sign is a fraction.*

In this case, we *multiply both terms of the fraction by such an expression as will make the denominator a perfect power of the same degree as the surd*, and then proceed as in § 372.

Ex. Reduce $\sqrt{\dfrac{9}{8\,a^3}}$ to its simplest form.

Multiplying both terms of the fraction by $2\,a$, we have

$$\sqrt{\frac{9}{8\,a^3}} = \sqrt{\frac{9 \times 2\,a}{16\,a^4}} = \sqrt{\frac{9}{16\,a^4} \times 2\,a} = \sqrt{\frac{9}{16\,a^4}} \times \sqrt{2\,a} = \frac{3}{4\,a^2}\sqrt{2\,a}.$$

374. Reduction of Surds of Different Degrees to Surds of the Same Degree.

Ex. Reduce $\sqrt{2}$, $\sqrt[3]{3}$, and $\sqrt[4]{5}$ to surds of the same degree.

The lowest common multiple of 2, 3, and 4 is 12.

By § 327,
$$\sqrt{2} = \sqrt[12]{2^6} = \sqrt[12]{64}.$$
$$\sqrt[3]{3} = \sqrt[12]{3^4} = \sqrt[12]{81}.$$
$$\sqrt[4]{5} = \sqrt[12]{5^3} = \sqrt[12]{125}.$$

We then have the following rule:

Make the index of each surd the L. C. M. *of the given indices; and raise the expression under each radical sign to a power whose exponent is obtained by dividing this* L. C. M. *by the given index.*

The relative magnitude of surds may be determined by reducing them, if necessary, to surds of the same degree.

Thus, since $\sqrt[12]{64} < \sqrt[12]{81} < \sqrt[12]{125}$, it follows that $\sqrt{2} < \sqrt[3]{3} < \sqrt[4]{5}$.

ADDITION AND SUBTRACTION OF SURDS

375. To add or subtract *similar surds* (§ 369), add or subtract their coefficients, and multiply the result by their common surd part.

1. Required the sum of $\sqrt{20}$ and $\sqrt{45}$.

Reducing each surd to its simplest form (§ 372),

$$\sqrt{20} + \sqrt{45} = \sqrt{4 \times 5} + \sqrt{9 \times 5} = 2\sqrt{5} + 3\sqrt{5} = 5\sqrt{5}.$$

2. Simplify $\sqrt{\dfrac{1}{2}} + \sqrt{\dfrac{2}{3}} - \sqrt{\dfrac{9}{8}}$.

$$\sqrt{\frac{1}{2}} + \sqrt{\frac{2}{3}} - \sqrt{\frac{9}{8}} = \sqrt{\frac{1}{4} \times 2} + \sqrt{\frac{1}{9} \times 6} - \sqrt{\frac{9}{16} \times 2}$$
$$= \frac{1}{2}\sqrt{2} + \frac{1}{3}\sqrt{6} - \frac{3}{4}\sqrt{2} = \frac{1}{3}\sqrt{6} - \frac{1}{4}\sqrt{2}.$$

MULTIPLICATION OF SURDS

376. 1. Multiply $\sqrt{6}$ by $\sqrt{15}$.

By § 165, $\sqrt{6} \times \sqrt{15} = \sqrt{6 \times 15} = \sqrt{90} = 3\sqrt{10}$.

2. Multiply $\sqrt{2a}$ by $\sqrt[3]{4a^2}$.

Reducing to surds of the same degree (§ 374),

$$\sqrt{2a} \times \sqrt[3]{4a^2} = \sqrt[6]{2^3a^3} \times \sqrt[6]{4^2a^4} = \sqrt[6]{2^3a^3 \times 2^4a^4}$$
$$= \sqrt[6]{2^6a^6 \times 2a} = 2a\sqrt[6]{2a}.$$

3. Multiply $\sqrt{5}$ by $\sqrt[6]{5}$.

$$\sqrt{5} \times \sqrt[6]{5} = \sqrt[6]{5^3} \times \sqrt[6]{5} = \sqrt[6]{5^4}$$
$$= \sqrt[3]{5^2} \ (\text{§ 327}) = \sqrt[3]{25}.$$

We then have the following rule:

To multiply together two or more surds, reduce them, if neces-sary, to surds of the same degree.

Multiply together the expressions under the radical signs, and write the result under the common radical sign.

The result should be reduced to its simplest form.

4. Multiply $3\sqrt{1+x}-4\sqrt{x}$ by $\sqrt{1+x}+2\sqrt{x}$.

$$3\sqrt{1+x}-4\sqrt{x}$$
$$\sqrt{1+x}+2\sqrt{x}$$
$$\overline{3(1+x)-4\sqrt{x+x^2}}$$
$$+6\sqrt{x+x^2}-8\,x$$
$$\overline{3(1+x)+2\sqrt{x+x^2}-8\,x=3-5\,x+2\sqrt{x+x^2}.}$$

377. If a surd is in the form $b\sqrt[n]{a}$, where a and b are rational expressions, the coefficient may be introduced under the radical sign by raising it to the nth power, and multiplying the expression under the radical sign by the result.

Ex. Introduce the coefficient of $2\,a\sqrt[3]{3\,x^2}$ under the radical sign.

$$2\,a\sqrt[3]{3\,x^2}=\sqrt[3]{8\,a^3}\,\sqrt[3]{3\,x^2}=\sqrt[3]{8\,a^3\times 3\,x^2}=\sqrt[3]{24\,a^3x^2}.$$

378. A rational expression may be expressed in the form of a surd of any degree by raising it to the power denoted by the index, and writing the result under the corresponding radical sign.

DIVISION OF SURDS

379. 1. Divide $\sqrt[3]{405}$ by $\sqrt[3]{5}$.

By § 293, $\dfrac{\sqrt[3]{405}}{\sqrt[3]{5}}=\sqrt[3]{\dfrac{405}{5}}=\sqrt[3]{81}=3\sqrt[3]{3}.$

We can use § 293 in the above; for we know by § 351 that it holds when $\sqrt[n]{a}$ and $\sqrt[n]{b}$ are surds.

2. Divide $\sqrt[3]{4}$ by $\sqrt{6}$.

Reducing to surds of the same degree (§ 374),

$$\frac{\sqrt[3]{4}}{\sqrt{6}} = \frac{\sqrt[6]{4^2}}{\sqrt[6]{6^3}} = \sqrt[6]{\frac{2^4}{2^3 \times 3^3}} = \sqrt[6]{\frac{2}{3^3}} = \sqrt[6]{\frac{2 \times 3^3}{3^6}} = \frac{1}{3}\sqrt[6]{54}.$$

We then have the following rule:

To divide two surds, reduce them, if necessary, to surds of the same degree.

Divide the expression under the radical sign in the dividend by the expression under the radical sign in the divisor, and write the result under the common radical sign.

The result should be reduced to its simplest form.

3. Divide $\sqrt{10}$ by $\sqrt[6]{40}$.

$$\frac{\sqrt{10}}{\sqrt[6]{40}} = \frac{\sqrt[6]{10^3}}{\sqrt[6]{40}} = \sqrt[6]{\frac{2^3 \times 5^3}{2^3 \times 5}} = \sqrt[6]{5^2} = \sqrt[3]{5} \ (\S 327).$$

4. Divide $\sqrt[4]{6} - 2\sqrt{3}$ by $\sqrt[4]{3}$.

$$\frac{\sqrt[4]{6} - 2\sqrt{3}}{\sqrt[4]{3}} = \frac{\sqrt[4]{6}}{\sqrt[4]{3}} - \frac{2\sqrt[4]{3^2}}{\sqrt[4]{3}} = \sqrt[4]{2} - 2\sqrt[4]{3}.$$

INVOLUTION AND EVOLUTION OF SURDS

380. 1. Raise $\sqrt[6]{12}$ to the third power.

$$(\sqrt[6]{12})^3 = (12^{\frac{1}{6}})^3 = 12^{\frac{3}{6}} \ (\S 364) = 12^{\frac{1}{2}} = \sqrt{12} = 2\sqrt{3}.$$

2. Raise $\sqrt[5]{2}$ to the fourth power.

$$(\sqrt[5]{2})^4 = (2^{\frac{1}{5}})^4 = 2^{\frac{4}{5}} = \sqrt[5]{2^4} = \sqrt[5]{16}.$$

Then, to raise a surd to any power whose exponent is a positive integer,

If possible, divide the index of the surd by the exponent of the required power ; otherwise, raise the expression under the radical sign to the required power.

3. Extract the cube root of $\sqrt[3]{27\,x^3}$.

$$\sqrt[3]{(\sqrt[5]{27\,x^3})} = (\sqrt[5]{(3\,x)^3})^{\frac{1}{3}} = [(3\,x)^{\frac{3}{5}}]^{\frac{1}{3}} = (3\,x)^{\frac{1}{5}} = \sqrt[5]{3\,x}.$$

4. Extract the fifth root of $\sqrt[3]{6}$.

$$\sqrt[5]{(\sqrt[3]{6})} = (6^{\frac{1}{3}})^{\frac{1}{5}} = 6^{\frac{1}{15}} = \sqrt[15]{6}.$$

Then, to extract any root of a surd,

If possible, extract the required root of the expression under the radical sign ; otherwise, multiply the index of the surd by the index of the required root.

If the surd has a coefficient which is not a perfect power of the degree denoted by the index of the required root, it should be introduced under the radical sign (§ 377) before applying the rule.

Thus, $\sqrt[5]{(4\sqrt{2})} = \sqrt[6]{(\sqrt{32})} = \sqrt{2}.$

SPECIAL METHODS IN MULTIPLICATION

381. The rules of Chap. VII should be used to find the value of any product which comes under them.

1. Expand $(\sqrt{6} - \sqrt{3})^2$.

By § 131, $(\sqrt{6} - \sqrt{3})^2 = (\sqrt{6})^2 - 2\sqrt{6} \times \sqrt{3} + (\sqrt{3})^2$

$$= 6 - 2\sqrt{3^2 \times 2} + 3 = 9 - 6\sqrt{2}.$$

2. Expand $(4 + \sqrt[6]{5})(4 - \sqrt[6]{5})$.

By § 132, $(4 + \sqrt[6]{5})(4 - \sqrt[6]{5}) = 4^2 - (\sqrt[6]{5})^2 = 16 - \sqrt[3]{5}$ (§ 380).

SURD FACTORS

382. The methods of Chap. VIII may be employed to separate an expression into surd factors.

1. Factor $2\sqrt{x} - 6x$ by the method of § 155.

$$2\sqrt{x} - 6x = 2\sqrt{x} - 6(\sqrt{x})^2 = 2\sqrt{x}(1 - 3\sqrt{x}).$$

2. Factor $a - b$ by the method of § 171.

$$a - b = (\sqrt{a})^2 - (\sqrt{b})^2 = (\sqrt{a} + \sqrt{b})(\sqrt{a} - \sqrt{b}).$$

We may also factor $a - b$ by the method of § 177 ; thus,

$$a - b = (\sqrt[3]{a})^3 - (\sqrt[3]{b})^3 = (\sqrt[3]{a} - \sqrt[3]{b})[(\sqrt[3]{a})^2 + \sqrt[3]{a}\sqrt[3]{b} + (\sqrt[3]{b})^2]$$
$$= (\sqrt[3]{a} - \sqrt[3]{b})(\sqrt[3]{a^2} + \sqrt[3]{ab} + \sqrt[3]{b^2}).$$

REDUCTION OF A FRACTION WHOSE DENOMINATOR IS NOT A RATIONAL EXPRESSION TO AN EQUIVALENT FRACTION HAVING A RATIONAL DENOMINATOR

383. CASE I. *When the denominator is a monomial.*

The reduction may be effected by multiplying both terms of the fraction by a surd of the same degree as the denominator, having under its radical sign such an expression as will make the denominator of the resulting fraction rational.

Ex. Reduce $\dfrac{5}{\sqrt[3]{3\,a^2}}$ to an equivalent fraction having a rational denominator.

Multiplying both terms by $\sqrt[3]{9\,a}$, we have

$$\frac{5}{\sqrt[3]{3\,a^2}}=\frac{5\sqrt[3]{9\,a}}{\sqrt[3]{3\,a^2}\,\sqrt[3]{9\,a}}=\frac{5\sqrt[3]{9\,a}}{\sqrt[3]{27\,a^3}}=\frac{5\sqrt[3]{9\,a}}{3\,a}.$$

384. CASE II. *When the denominator is the sum of a rational expression and a quadratic surd, or of two quadratic surds.*

1. Reduce $\dfrac{5-\sqrt{2}}{5+\sqrt{2}}$ to an equivalent fraction having a rational denominator.

Multiplying both terms by $5-\sqrt{2}$, we have

$$\frac{5-\sqrt{2}}{5+\sqrt{2}}=\frac{(5-\sqrt{2})^2}{(5+\sqrt{2})(5-\sqrt{2})}$$

$$=\frac{25-10\sqrt{2}+2}{25-2}\ \text{(§§ 131, 132)}=\frac{27-10\sqrt{2}}{23}.$$

2. Reduce $\dfrac{3\sqrt{a}-2\sqrt{a-b}}{2\sqrt{a}-3\sqrt{a-b}}$ to an equivalent fraction having a rational denominator.

Multiplying both terms by $2\sqrt{a}+3\sqrt{a-b}$,

$$\frac{3\sqrt{a}-2\sqrt{a-b}}{2\sqrt{a}-3\sqrt{a-b}}=\frac{(3\sqrt{a}-2\sqrt{a-b})(2\sqrt{a}+3\sqrt{a-b})}{(2\sqrt{a}-3\sqrt{a-b})(2\sqrt{a}+3\sqrt{a-b})}$$

$$=\frac{6\,a+5\sqrt{a}\sqrt{a-b}-6(a-b)}{4\,a-9(a-b)}=\frac{6\,b+5\sqrt{a^2-ab}}{9\,b-5\,a}.$$

We then have the following rule.

Multiply both terms of the fraction by the denominator with the sign between its terms reversed.

If the denominator is the sum of a rational expression and two or more quadratic surds, or the sum of three or more quadratic surds, the fraction may be reduced to an equivalent fraction having a rational denominator by repeated applications of the above rule.

Thus, $\dfrac{4-\sqrt{3}-\sqrt{7}}{4+\sqrt{3}-\sqrt{7}} = \dfrac{(4-\sqrt{3}-\sqrt{7})(4+\sqrt{3}+\sqrt{7})}{(4+\sqrt{3}-\sqrt{7})(4+\sqrt{3}+\sqrt{7})}$

$= \dfrac{4^2-(\sqrt{3}+\sqrt{7})^2}{(4+\sqrt{3})^2-(\sqrt{7})^2}$ (§ 132) $= \dfrac{6-2\sqrt{21}}{12+8\sqrt{3}} = \dfrac{3-\sqrt{21}}{6+4\sqrt{3}}.$

Multiplying both terms of the latter by $6-4\sqrt{3}$,

$\dfrac{4-\sqrt{3}-\sqrt{7}}{4+\sqrt{3}-\sqrt{7}} = \dfrac{(3-\sqrt{21})(6-4\sqrt{3})}{6^2-(4\sqrt{3})^2}$

$= \dfrac{18-6\sqrt{21}-12\sqrt{3}+12\sqrt{7}}{-12}$

$= \dfrac{-9+3\sqrt{21}+6\sqrt{3}-6\sqrt{7}}{6}.$

The example may also be solved by multiplying both terms of the given fraction by $4-\sqrt{3}+\sqrt{7}$, or by $4-\sqrt{3}-\sqrt{7}$.

385. CASE III. *When the denominator is the sum of a rational expression and a surd of the nth degree, or of two surds of the nth degree.*

1. Reduce $\dfrac{1}{2+\sqrt[3]{3}}$ to an equivalent fraction having a rational denominator.

We have, $(a+b)(a^2-ab+b^2)=a^3+b^3.$

Then, $(2+\sqrt[3]{3})[2^2-2\sqrt[3]{3}+(\sqrt[3]{3})^2]=2^3+(\sqrt[3]{3})^3.$

Then, if we multiply both terms of the fraction by

$$2^2-2\sqrt[3]{3}+(\sqrt[3]{3})^2,$$

the denominator will become rational.

Thus, $\dfrac{1}{2+\sqrt[3]{3}}=\dfrac{2^2-2\sqrt[3]{3}+(\sqrt[3]{3})^2}{2^3+(\sqrt[3]{3})^3}=\dfrac{4-2\sqrt[3]{3}+\sqrt[3]{9}}{11}$.

2. Reduce $\dfrac{1}{\sqrt[4]{7}-\sqrt[4]{5}}$ to an equivalent fraction having a rational denominator.

We have, $(a-b)(a^3+a^2b+ab^2+b^3)=a^4-b^4$.

Then, if we multiply both terms of the fraction by
$$(\sqrt[4]{7})^3+(\sqrt[4]{7})^2(\sqrt[4]{5})+(\sqrt[4]{7})(\sqrt[4]{5})^2+(\sqrt[4]{5})^3,$$
the denominator will become rational; thus,

$$\frac{1}{\sqrt[4]{7}-\sqrt[4]{5}}=\frac{(\sqrt[4]{7})^3+(\sqrt[4]{7})^2(\sqrt[4]{5})+(\sqrt[4]{7})(\sqrt[4]{5})^2+(\sqrt[4]{5})^3}{(\sqrt[4]{7})^4-(\sqrt[4]{5})^4}$$

$$=\frac{\sqrt[4]{343}+\sqrt[4]{245}+\sqrt[4]{175}+\sqrt[4]{125}}{2}$$

The method of Case III can be applied to the cases where the denominator is of the form $\sqrt[m]{a}+\sqrt[n]{b}$, or $\sqrt[m]{a}-\sqrt[n]{b}$.

3. Reduce $\dfrac{1}{\sqrt[3]{2}-\sqrt{5}}$ to an equivalent fraction having a rational denominator.

The *lowest common multiple of the indices* 3 *and* 2 *is* 6.

Now, $(a-b)(a^5+a^4b+a^3b^2+a^2b^3+ab^4+b^5)=a^6-b^6$.

Then, if we multiply both terms of the fraction by
$$(\sqrt[3]{2})^5+(\sqrt[3]{2})^4(\sqrt{5})+(\sqrt[3]{2})^3(\sqrt{5})^2+(\sqrt[3]{2})^2(\sqrt{5})^3+(\sqrt[3]{2})(\sqrt{5})^4$$
$$+(\sqrt{5})^5,$$
the denominator will become rational.

Multiplying both terms by the above expression, we have

$$\frac{1}{\sqrt[3]{2}-\sqrt{5}}=\frac{2\sqrt[3]{4}+2\sqrt[3]{2}\sqrt{5}+10+5\sqrt[3]{4}\sqrt{5}+25\sqrt[3]{2}+25\sqrt{5}}{(\sqrt[3]{2})^6-(\sqrt{5})^6}$$

$$=\frac{2\sqrt[3]{4}+2\sqrt[6]{4}\sqrt[6]{125}+10+5\sqrt[6]{16}\sqrt[6]{125}+25\sqrt[3]{2}+25\sqrt{5}}{4-125}$$

$$=-\frac{10+2\sqrt[3]{4}+2\sqrt[6]{500}+5\sqrt[6]{2000}+25\sqrt[3]{2}+25\sqrt{5}}{121}.$$

4. Reduce $\dfrac{\sqrt{2}-\sqrt[4]{3}}{\sqrt{2}+\sqrt[4]{3}}$ to an equivalent fraction having a rational denominator.

The lowest common multiple of the indices is 4.

Now, $(a+b)(a^3-a^2b+ab^2-b^3)=a^4-b^4.$

Multiplying both terms of the fraction by
$$(\sqrt{2})^3-(\sqrt{2})^2(\sqrt[4]{3})+(\sqrt{2})(\sqrt[4]{3})^2-(\sqrt[4]{3})^3,$$
we have

$$\frac{\sqrt{2}-\sqrt[4]{3}}{\sqrt{2}+\sqrt[4]{3}}=\frac{(\sqrt{2}-\sqrt[4]{3})(2\sqrt{2}-2\sqrt[4]{3}+\sqrt{2}\sqrt[4]{9}-\sqrt[4]{27})}{(\sqrt{2})^4-(\sqrt[4]{3})^4}$$

$$=4-2\sqrt{2}\sqrt[4]{3}+2\sqrt[4]{9}-\sqrt{2}\sqrt[4]{27}$$
$$\qquad -2\sqrt{2}\sqrt[4]{3}+2\sqrt[4]{9}-\sqrt{2}\sqrt[4]{27}+3$$
$$=7-4\sqrt[4]{4}\sqrt[4]{3}+4\sqrt[4]{9}-2\sqrt[4]{4}\sqrt[4]{27}$$
$$=7-4\sqrt[4]{12}+4\sqrt{3}-2\sqrt[4]{108}.$$

386. The methods of §§ 383 to 385 are often advantageous in finding the approximate value of a fraction whose denominator is not rational.

Ex. Find the approximate value of $\dfrac{1}{2-\sqrt{2}}$ to three places of decimals.

$$\frac{1}{2-\sqrt{2}}=\frac{2+\sqrt{2}}{(2-\sqrt{2})(2+\sqrt{2})}=\frac{2+\sqrt{2}}{4-2}=\frac{2+1.414\cdots}{2}=1.707\cdots.$$

387. In like manner, a fraction whose numerator is not rational may in certain cases be reduced to an equivalent fraction having a rational numerator.

PROPERTIES OF QUADRATIC SURDS (§ 368)

388. *A quadratic surd cannot equal the sum of a rational expression and a quadratic surd.*

For, if possible, let $\sqrt{a}=b+\sqrt{c}$,
where b is a rational expression, and $\sqrt{a}$ and $\sqrt{c}$ quadratic surds.

Squaring both members, $a = b^2 + 2b\sqrt{c} + c$,

or, $\qquad\qquad 2b\sqrt{c} = a - b^2 - c$.

Whence, $\qquad\qquad \sqrt{c} = \dfrac{a - b^2 - c}{2b}$.

That is, a quadratic surd equal to a rational expression. But this is impossible; whence, $\sqrt{a}$ cannot equal $b + \sqrt{c}$.

389. *If* $a + \sqrt{b} = c + \sqrt{d}$, *where* a *and* c *are rational expressions, and* $\sqrt{b}$ *and* $\sqrt{d}$ *quadratic surds, then*

$$a = c, \text{ and } \sqrt{b} = \sqrt{d}.$$

For, transposing a, $\quad \sqrt{b} = c - a + \sqrt{d}$.

Then, $c - a = 0$; for, by § 388, a quadratic surd cannot equal a rational expression plus a quadratic surd.

Therefore, $a = c$, and consequently $\sqrt{b} = \sqrt{d}$.

390. *If* $\sqrt{a + \sqrt{b}} = \sqrt{x} + \sqrt{y}$, *where* a, b, x, *and* y *are rational expressions, and* a *greater than* $\sqrt{b}$, *then*

$$\sqrt{a - \sqrt{b}} = \sqrt{x} - \sqrt{y}.$$

Squaring both members of the given equation,

$$a + \sqrt{b} = x + 2\sqrt{xy} + y.$$

Whence, by § 389, $\qquad a = x + y$,

and $\qquad\qquad \sqrt{b} = 2\sqrt{xy}$.

Subtracting, $\qquad a - \sqrt{b} = x - 2\sqrt{xy} + y$.

Extracting the square root of both members,

$$\sqrt{a - \sqrt{b}} = \sqrt{x} - \sqrt{y}.$$

391. The preceding principles may be used to find the square root of certain expressions which are in the form of the sum of a rational expression and a quadratic surd.

Ex. Find the square root of $13 - \sqrt{160}$.

Assume, $\qquad \sqrt{13 - \sqrt{160}} = \sqrt{x} - \sqrt{y}$. $\qquad$ (1)

Then by § 390, $\qquad \sqrt{13 + \sqrt{160}} = \sqrt{x} + \sqrt{y}$. $\qquad$ (2)

Multiply (1) by (2), $\sqrt{169 - 160} = x - y.$

Or, $\hspace{3.5cm} x - y = 3.$ $\hspace{2cm}$ (3)

Squaring (1), $\hspace{1cm} 13 - \sqrt{160} = x - 2\sqrt{xy} + y.$

Whence, by § 389, $\hspace{1cm} x + y = 13.$ $\hspace{2cm}$ (4)

Adding (3) and (4), $\hspace{1cm} 2x = 16,$ or $x = 8.$

Subtracting (3) from (4), $\hspace{0.5cm} 2y = 10,$ or $y = 5.$

Substitute in (1), $\hspace{0.3cm} \sqrt{13 - \sqrt{160}} = \sqrt{8} - \sqrt{5} = 2\sqrt{2} - \sqrt{5}.$

392. Examples like that of § 391 may be solved by inspection, by putting the given expression into the form of a trinomial perfect square (§ 167), as follows:

Reduce the surd term so that its coefficient may be 2.

Separate the rational term into two parts whose product shall be the expression under the radical sign of the surd term.

Extract the square root of each part, and connect the results by the sign of the surd term (§ 168).

1. Extract the square root of $8 + \sqrt{48}.$

We have, $\hspace{2cm} \sqrt{48} = 2\sqrt{12}.$

We then separate 8 into two parts whose product is 12. The parts are 6 and 2; whence,

$$\sqrt{8 + \sqrt{48}} = \sqrt{6 + 2\sqrt{12} + 2} = \sqrt{6} + \sqrt{2}.$$

2. Extract the square root of $22 - 3\sqrt{32}.$

We have, $\hspace{1cm} 3\sqrt{32} = \sqrt{9 \times 8 \times 4} = 2\sqrt{72}.$

We then separate 22 into two parts whose product is 72. The parts are 18 and 4; whence,

$$\sqrt{22 - 3\sqrt{32}} = \sqrt{18 - 2\sqrt{72} + 4} = \sqrt{18} - \sqrt{4} = 3\sqrt{2} - 2.$$

393. It is sometimes possible to find, by the methods of §§ 391 and 392, the square root of an expression which is the sum of two quadratic surds.

Ex. Required the square root of $\sqrt{392} + \sqrt{360}.$

$$\sqrt{(\sqrt{392}+\sqrt{360})}=\sqrt{[\sqrt{2}(\sqrt{196}+\sqrt{180})]}$$
$$=\sqrt{(\sqrt{2})}\sqrt{14+2\sqrt{45}}$$
$$=\sqrt[4]{2}\sqrt{9+2\sqrt{45}+5} \ (\S \ 392)$$
$$=\sqrt[4]{2}(3+\sqrt{5}).$$

394. It may be proved, as in § 390, that if $\sqrt[3]{a+\sqrt{b}}=x+\sqrt{y}$, where a and x are rational expressions, and $\sqrt{b}$ and $\sqrt{y}$ quadratic surds, then

$$\sqrt[3]{a-\sqrt{b}}=x-\sqrt{y}.$$

EXERCISE 45

Reduce each of the following to its simplest form :   :

1. $\sqrt[3]{121}$. 3. $\sqrt[14]{128\,a^7b^{21}}$. 5. $\sqrt[5]{480}$. 7. $7\sqrt{112\,x^5y^7z^6}$.

2. $\sqrt[15]{343}$. 4. $\sqrt[12]{625\,x^{12}y^4z^8}$. 6. $\sqrt[3]{4116}$. 8. $\sqrt[4]{80\times108\times120}$.

9. $\sqrt{96\,a^3b+240\,a^2b^2+150\,ab^3}$. 10. $\sqrt{(2\,x^2+x-15)(2\,x^2-19\,x+35)}$.

11. $\sqrt[4]{\dfrac{7}{8}}$. 12. $\sqrt[3]{\dfrac{81\,a^4}{16\,bc^2}}$. 13. $\sqrt{\dfrac{8\,x^2-48\,x+72}{3\,x}}$.

Reduce to surds of the same degree :

14. $\sqrt{3}$, $\sqrt[4]{7}$, and $\sqrt{15}$.   15. $\sqrt[3]{2\,a^2b}$, $\sqrt[6]{6\,b^3c^5}$, and $\sqrt[9]{14\,c^4a^7}$.

16. Arrange in order of magnitude $\sqrt[4]{3}$, $\sqrt[6]{5}$, and $\sqrt[8]{11}$.

Simplify the following :

17. $\sqrt[3]{320}-\sqrt[3]{135}+\sqrt[3]{625}$.   18. $\sqrt{\dfrac{25}{18}}+\sqrt{\dfrac{40}{2^7}}+\sqrt{\dfrac{5}{6}}$.

19. $5\sqrt[3]{294}-9\sqrt{150}+18\sqrt{\dfrac{8}{27}}-24\sqrt{\dfrac{27}{32}}$.

20. $\sqrt{63\,a^9b^5}+\sqrt{175\,a^3b^7}+ab^2\sqrt{63\,a^7b}-210\,a^4b^2+175\,ab^3$.

21. $(m+n)\sqrt{\dfrac{m+n}{m-n}}-(m-n)\sqrt{\dfrac{m-n}{m+n}}-(mn-3\,n^2)\sqrt{\dfrac{1}{m^2-n^2}}$.

Multiply the following :

22. $\sqrt[3]{4\,ab^2}$ and $\sqrt[6]{8\,b^4c^3}$.   23. $\sqrt[3]{24}$, $\sqrt[4]{\dfrac{9}{8}}$, and $\sqrt[2]{\dfrac{8}{27}}$.

24. $5\sqrt{m+n}-8\sqrt{m-n}$ and $6\sqrt{m+n}-7\sqrt{m-n}$.

25. $7\sqrt{8}+3\sqrt{27}-2\sqrt{20}$ and $7\sqrt{2}-3\sqrt{3}-4\sqrt{5}$.

In the following, introduce the coefficients under the radical signs:

26. $2\sqrt[5]{5}$.   **27.** $4\,x^2y^3\sqrt[3]{3\,x^4y^2}$.   **28.** $5\,a^3b^4\sqrt[4]{\dfrac{6\,b^2}{125\,a^6}}$.

29. $\dfrac{a-x}{a+x}\sqrt{\dfrac{a^2-ax-2\,x^2}{a^2+2\,ax-3\,x^2}}$.   **30.** $\dfrac{x^2-1}{x^2-2}\sqrt{2-\dfrac{(x-2)^2}{(x-1)^2}}$.

Divide the following:

31. $\sqrt[3]{144}$ by $\sqrt[6]{12}$.   **32.** $\sqrt[3]{14\,ab^2}$ by $\sqrt[4]{7\,a^3b^2}$.   **33.** $\sqrt[3]{\dfrac{9}{4}}$ by $\sqrt[5]{\dfrac{9}{16}}$.

34. $\sqrt[6]{243}+\sqrt[3]{48}$ by $\sqrt{3}$.   **35.** $\sqrt{x^2+2\,x-3}$ by $\sqrt{x^2-6\,x+5}$.

     36. $\sqrt[3]{a^2-b^2}$ by $\sqrt[3]{a^2b^2+ab^3}$.

Simplify the following:

37. $(\sqrt[9]{54})^3$.   **39.** $(\sqrt[3]{11\,x^2y})^6$.   **41.** $\sqrt[5]{(\sqrt{243\,a^6b^{10}})}$.

38. $(\sqrt[6]{3\,a^4b^3})^4$.   **40.** $\sqrt{(\sqrt[7]{12})}$.   **42.** $\sqrt[4]{(3\,x\sqrt[3]{3\,x^5})}$.

Expand the following by the rules of Chap. VII:

43. $(5\sqrt{2}+2\sqrt{6})^2$.   **47.** $\sqrt[3]{4+2\sqrt{3}}\times\sqrt[3]{4-2\sqrt{3}}$.

44. $(6\sqrt{5}+7\sqrt{3})(6\sqrt{5}-7\sqrt{3})$.   **48.** $\sqrt{3\sqrt{5}-2\sqrt{7}}\times\sqrt{3\sqrt{5}+2\sqrt{7}}$.

45. $(3\sqrt{x+y}-4\sqrt{x-y})^2$.   **49.** $(\sqrt{a}+\sqrt{b}+\sqrt{c})(\sqrt{a}+\sqrt{b}-\sqrt{c})$.

46. $(3\sqrt{5}-2\sqrt{10})^3$.   **50.** $(\sqrt[6]{4}+\sqrt[3]{9})(\sqrt[6]{4}-\sqrt[3]{9})$.

     51. $(2\sqrt{3}+5\sqrt{2}-\sqrt{5})(2\sqrt{3}-5\sqrt{2}+\sqrt{5})$.

52. $(\sqrt{10}-4\sqrt{5}+5\sqrt{2})^2$.   **53.** $(2\sqrt{2}+\sqrt{6}-\sqrt{3})^3$.

Factor the following:

54. $\sqrt{2\,a}+\sqrt{3\,a}$.   **55.** $x-\sqrt{x}-20$.   **56.** $ac+a\sqrt{d}-c\sqrt{b}-\sqrt{bd}$.

57. Factor $\sqrt[6]{9}-\sqrt[3]{4}$ by the rule of § 171.

58. Factor $a-b$ by the method of § 178, taking $\sqrt[5]{a}-\sqrt[5]{b}$ for the first factor.

Reduce each of the following to an equivalent fraction having a rational denominator:

59. $\dfrac{6\,a^2}{\sqrt[5]{27\,ab^4c^3}}$.   **62.** $\dfrac{\sqrt{x^2+y^2}-\sqrt{x^2-y^2}}{\sqrt{x^2+y^2}+\sqrt{x^2-y^2}}$.   **65.** $\dfrac{1}{\sqrt[3]{a}+\sqrt[3]{b}}$.

60. $\dfrac{\sqrt{x}+\sqrt{y}}{\sqrt{x}-\sqrt{y}}$.   **63.** $\dfrac{1}{\sqrt{\sqrt{11}+3}-\sqrt{\sqrt{11}-3}}$.   **66.** $\dfrac{1}{m-\sqrt[4]{n}}$.

61. $\dfrac{3\sqrt{5}-\sqrt{3}}{4\sqrt{5}+5\sqrt{3}}$.   **64.** $\dfrac{\sqrt{6}+\sqrt{3}-3\sqrt{2}}{\sqrt{6}-\sqrt{3}+3\sqrt{2}}$.   **67.** $\dfrac{1}{\sqrt[5]{5}+\sqrt[4]{4}}$.

68. $\dfrac{1}{3 + \sqrt[5]{2}}.$ **69.** $\dfrac{1}{\sqrt[3]{a} - \sqrt[6]{b}}.$ **70.** $\dfrac{\sqrt[3]{4} - \sqrt{3}}{\sqrt[3]{4} + \sqrt{3}}.$

Find the approximate value of each of the following to five places of decimals :

71. $\dfrac{5}{3 - \sqrt{3}}.$ **72.** $\dfrac{\sqrt{6} - \sqrt{5}}{\sqrt{6} + \sqrt{5}}.$ **73.** $\dfrac{4\sqrt{7} + 7\sqrt{3}}{3\sqrt{7} - 5\sqrt{3}}.$

Extract the square root of each of the following :

74. $24 + 2\sqrt{140}.$ **76.** $38 - 5\sqrt{52}.$ **78.** $\sqrt{343} + \sqrt{168}.$

75. $87 - \sqrt{2240}.$ **77.** $61 + 28\sqrt{3}.$ **79.** $\sqrt{1058} - \sqrt{896}.$

80. $2x - 3y - 2\sqrt{x^2 - 3xy}.$ **81.** $4a + 2 + 2\sqrt{3a^2 + 8a - 3}.$

Expand by the Binomial Theorem :

82. $(x + \sqrt{yz})^7.$ **83.** $\left(\sqrt{\dfrac{m}{n}} - \dfrac{1}{2}\sqrt{\dfrac{n}{m}}\right)^5.$ **84.** $\left(\dfrac{3a}{\sqrt{b}} + \dfrac{b}{3\sqrt{a}}\right)^6.$

Find the

85. 5th term of $(2x + 3\sqrt{y})^{12}.$ **86.** 9th term of $\left(\sqrt{\dfrac{a}{x}} - \sqrt{\dfrac{x}{a}}\right)^{16}.$

SOLUTION OF EQUATIONS INVOLVING THE UNKNOWN NUMBERS UNDER RADICAL SIGNS

395. To solve an equation involving the unknown numbers under radical signs, we transpose the terms so that a surd term may stand alone in one member, and then raise both members to a power of the same degree as the surd.

If surd terms still remain, we repeat the operation.

396. We will now prove that

If both members of an equation be raised to the same positive integral power the resulting equation will have all the solutions of the given equation, and, in general, additional ones.

Consider the equation $A = B.$ (1)

Raising both members to the nth power, n being a positive integer, we have
$$A^n = B^n, \text{ or } A^n - B^n = 0. \tag{2}$$

Factoring the first member (§ 178),
$$(A - B)(A^{n-1} + A^{n-2}B + \cdots + B^{n-1}) = 0. \tag{3}$$

By § 182, (3) is equivalent to the equations
$$\begin{cases} A - B = 0, \text{ or } A = B, \text{ and} \\ A^{n-1} + A^{n-2}B + \cdots + B^{n-1} = 0. \end{cases}$$

Thus, equation (2) has not only the solutions of (1), but also the solutions of
$$A^{n-1} + A^{n-2}B + \cdots + B^{n-1} = 0,$$

which, in general, do not satisfy (1).

Take, for example, the equation
$$x = 3. \tag{1}$$

Squaring both members, we have
$$x^2 = 9, \text{ or } x^2 - 9 = 0. \tag{2}$$

Factoring the first member, and placing the factors separately equal to 0 (§ 182), we have

$$x + 3 = 0, \text{ or } x = -3;$$

and
$$x - 3 = 0, \text{ or } x = 3.$$

Thus, equation (2) has the root 3, and, in addition, the root -3.

397. It follows from § 396 that all solutions obtained by raising both members of an equation to any positive integral power should be *verified;* only such as satisfy the given equation should be retained.

In verifying solutions of equations involving the unknown numbers under radical signs, it should be carefully borne in mind that *only principal values of the roots are considered* (§ 162).

398. Examples.

1. Solve the equation $\sqrt{x^2 - 5} - x = -1.$

Transposing $-x$, $\qquad \sqrt{x^2 - 5} = x - 1.$

Squaring both members, $\qquad x^2 - 5 = x^2 - 2x + 1.$

Transposing, $\qquad 2x = 6; \text{ whence, } x = 3.$

Putting $x = 3$, the given first member becomes
$$\sqrt{9 - 5} - 3 = 2 - 3 = -1.$$

Thus, the solution $x = 3$ satisfies the given equation.

2. Solve the equation $\sqrt{2x-1} + \sqrt{2x+6} = 7$.

Transposing $\sqrt{2x-1}$, $\qquad \sqrt{2x+6} = 7 - \sqrt{2x-1}$.

Squaring, $\qquad 2x+6 = 49 - 14\sqrt{2x-1} + 2x - 1$.

Transposing, $\quad 14\sqrt{2x-1} = 42$, or $\sqrt{2x-1} = 3$.

Squaring, $\qquad 2x-1 = 9$; whence, $x = 5$.

Putting $x = 5$, the given first member becomes $\sqrt{9} + \sqrt{16} = 3 + 4 = 7$. Thus, the solution $x = 5$ is correct.

3. Solve the equation $\quad \sqrt{x-6} - \sqrt{x} = \dfrac{3}{\sqrt{x-6}}$.

Clearing of fractions, $x - 6 - \sqrt{x^2-6x} = 3$.

Transposing, $-\sqrt{x^2-6x} = 9 - x$.

Squaring, $\qquad x^2 - 6x = 81 - 18x + x^2$.

Then, $\qquad\qquad 12x = 81$; whence, $x = \dfrac{81}{12} = \dfrac{27}{4}$.

Putting $x = \dfrac{27}{4}$, the given first member becomes

$$\sqrt{\tfrac{3}{4}} - \sqrt{\tfrac{27}{4}} = \tfrac{1}{2}\sqrt{3} - \tfrac{3}{2}\sqrt{3} = -\sqrt{3}.$$

The second member becomes $\dfrac{3}{\sqrt{\tfrac{3}{4}}} = \dfrac{3}{\tfrac{1}{2}\sqrt{3}} = 2\sqrt{3}$.

Thus, the solution $x = \dfrac{27}{4}$ does not satisfy the given equation; in this case there is no solution.

4. Solve the equation $\sqrt{2-3x} + \sqrt{1+4x} = \sqrt{3+x}$.

Squaring both members,

$$2 - 3x + 2\sqrt{2-3x}\sqrt{1+4x} + 1 + 4x = 3 + x.$$

Whence, $\qquad\qquad 2\sqrt{2-3x}\sqrt{1+4x} = 0$;

or, $\qquad\qquad\qquad \sqrt{2-3x}\sqrt{1+4x} = 0$.

Squaring, $\qquad\qquad (2-3x)(1+4x) = 0$.

Solving as in § 182, $\qquad\qquad 2 - 3x = 0$, or $x = \dfrac{2}{3}$;

and, $\qquad\qquad\qquad\qquad 1 + 4x = 0$, or $x = -\dfrac{1}{4}$.

Both values satisfy the given equation.

EXERCISE 46

Solve the following:

1. $\sqrt[3]{8\,x^3 - 36\,x^2} + 3 = 2\,x.$

3. $\dfrac{\sqrt{3\,x+1} + \sqrt{3\,x}}{\sqrt{3\,x+1} - \sqrt{3\,x}} = \dfrac{1}{4}.$

2. $\sqrt{5\,x-19} - \sqrt{5\,x+14} = -3.$

4. $\sqrt{6\,x} - \sqrt{6\,x - 11} = \dfrac{5}{\sqrt{6\,x-11}}.$

5. $\sqrt{ax + bc} + \sqrt{ax - bc} = \sqrt{4\,ax - 2\,bc}.$

6. $\sqrt{x - 2\,a} - \sqrt{x} = \dfrac{a}{\sqrt{x - 2\,a}}.$ **7.** $\sqrt{(x - \sqrt{bx + a^4})} = a.$

8. $\sqrt{x^2 - 5\,x - 2} + \sqrt{x^2 + 3\,x + 6} = 4.$

9. $\sqrt{4\,x + 1} - \sqrt{x - 8} = \sqrt{9\,x - 83}.$

10. $\sqrt{2\,x - 5\,a} + \sqrt{3\,x + 4\,b} = \sqrt{5\,x - 5\,a + 4\,b}.$.

11. $\sqrt{(x + a)(x + b)} + \sqrt{(x - a)(x - b)} = \sqrt{2\,x^2 + 2\,ab}.$

12. $\sqrt{2\,x + 5} + \sqrt{3\,x - 2} = \sqrt{(5\,x + 3 + \sqrt{24\,x^2 + 15})}.$

13. $\dfrac{3\sqrt{2\,x - 1} + 4}{6\sqrt{2\,x - 1} - 1} = \dfrac{\sqrt{2\,x - 1} + 6}{2\sqrt{2\,x - 1} - 5}.$

14. $\sqrt{x^2 + 10\,x - 24} + \sqrt{x^2 + 7x + 12} = \sqrt{4\,x^2 + 17\,x + 4}.$

15. $\sqrt{2\,x + 1} + \sqrt{3\,x + 2} = \sqrt{x + 2} + \sqrt{4\,x + 1}.$

IRRATIONAL NUMBERS

399. Consider the series

$$a'_1,\ a'_2,\ \cdots,\ a'_r,\ \cdots, \tag{1}$$

and
$$a_1,\ a_2,\ \cdots,\ a_r,\ \cdots; \tag{2}$$

in which the terms of (1) continually decrease, and the terms of (2) continually increase; and let $a'_r - a_r$ approach the limit 0, when r is indefinitely increased.

Then, any expression which is not a rational number, and which is greater than the terms of (1), and less than the terms of (2), is called an **Irrational Number**.

The common limit of the rth terms of (1) and (2), when r is indefinitely increased, is considered the value of the above irrational number.

A surd is one form of irrational number.

Rational and irrational numbers are called **Real Numbers**.

400. Consider, for example, the expression $a^{\sqrt{2}}$.

$a^{\sqrt{2}}$ lies between the two series (compare § 343),

$$a^2, a^{1.5}, a^{1.42}, \cdots, \tag{1}$$

and $\qquad\qquad a^1, a^{1.4}, a^{1.41}, \cdots. \tag{2}$

If we represent the rth term of (2) by $a^{\frac{n}{10^{r-1}}}$, the rth term
of (1) will be $a^{\frac{n+1}{10^{r-1}}}$.

Then, the difference between the rth terms will be

$$a^{\frac{n+1}{10^{r-1}}} - a^{\frac{n}{10^{r-1}}} = a^{\frac{n}{10^{r-1}}}(a^{\frac{1}{10^{r-1}}} - 1). \tag{3}$$

Now, $a^{\frac{n}{10^{r-1}}}$ is always less than a^2.

And, by § 343, $a^{\frac{1}{10^{r-1}}}$ approaches the limit a^0, or 1 (§ 359),
when r is indefinitely increased.

Therefore, the expression (3) approaches the limit 0 when r
is indefinitely increased.

Hence, $a^{\sqrt{2}}$ is the limit of the rth term of either (1) or (2),
when r is indefinitely increased.

A meaning similar to the above will be attached to any form
of irrational exponent.

401. The definitions of Addition and Multiplication, given
in § 348, hold when any or all of the numbers involved are
irrational:

402. It may be shown, as in § 350, that the fundamental
laws of §§ 12 and 14 hold when any of the letters involved
represent irrational numbers.

Then, every statement or rule, in the remaining portions of
Chap. I, or in Chaps. II to XVI, inclusive, in regard to
expressions where any letter involved represents any rational
number, holds also when the letter represents any real number.

Also, the theorems of §§ 165 and 293 may be proved to hold
when any or all of the letters a, b, c, etc., represent irrational
numbers which are positive if n is even; and the theorem of
§ 327 may be proved to hold when a is any irrational number
whose mth power is positive if n is even.

403. We will now prove that equation (1), § 356, holds when m is a positive rational number, and n a surd of the form $\sqrt[p]{b}$, where p and b have the same meanings as in § 348.

By § 399, $a^m \times a^{\sqrt[p]{b}}$ is the limit, when r is indefinitely increased, of $a^m \times a^{b_r}$, where b_r has the same meaning as in § 348.

Also, $a^{m+\sqrt[p]{b}}$ is the limit of a^{m+b_r}, when r is indefinitely increased.

But since m and b_r are rational,

$$a^m \times a^{b_r} = a^{m+b_r} \quad (\S\S 85 \text{ or } 362).$$

Then, $a^m \times a^{b_r}$ and a^{m+b_r} are functions of r which are equal for every rational value of r; and, by § 252, their limits when r is indefinitely increased are equal.

Hence, $\qquad a^m \times a^{\sqrt[p]{b}} = a^{m+\sqrt[p]{b}}.$

In like manner, we may prove

$$a^m \times a^n = a^{m+n},$$

in every case, not previously considered, where a, m, and n are any real numbers, provided a^m and a^n are real numbers.

404. It may be proved, as in § 403, that

$$\frac{a^m}{a^n} = a^{m-n},$$

$$(a^m)^n = a^{mn},$$

$$a^{-m} = \frac{1}{a^m},$$

and $\qquad (abc \cdots)^n = a^n b^n c^n \; \cdot,$

in every case, not previously considered, where a, b, c, $\cdots$, m, and n represent any real numbers, provided a^m, a^n, a^{mn}, b^n, c^n, $\cdots$, are real numbers.

405. It follows from §§ 402 to 404 that every result in §§ 367 to 398 inclusive holds when any letter involved, except when the index of a root, represents any irrational number, such that every expression of the form $\sqrt[n]{a}$ is an irrational number.

GRAPHICAL REPRESENTATION OF IRRATIONAL NUMBERS

406. It was shown, in § 343, that $\sqrt{2}$ was intermediate in value between the series

$$2,\ 1.5,\ 1.42,\ \cdots,\ \text{and}\ 1,\ 1.4,\ 1.41,\ \cdots;$$

and that $\sqrt{2}$ is the limit of the rth term of either series when r is indefinitely increased.

Let A, A_1, A_2, $\cdots$, A_r, $\cdots$ be the points in the scale of § 57, corresponding to the numbers 1, 1.4, 1.41, · ; and B, B_1, B_2 · , B_r, $\cdots$ the points corresponding to the numbers 2, 1.5, 1.42, $\cdots$.

The distance between A_r and B_r approaches the limit 0, when r is indefinitely increased; that is, OA_r and OB_r approach the same limit.

If OP is this limit, OP represents $\sqrt{2}$.

In like manner, a point exists whose distance from O represents any irrational number whatever.

XVIII. PURE IMAGINARY AND COMPLEX NUMBERS

It will be understood, in §§ 407 to 414, inclusive, that every letter represents a positive real number (§ 399).

PURE IMAGINARY NUMBERS

407. We define $\sqrt[n]{-a}$, where a is any positive real number, and n an even positive integer, as an expression whose nth power equals $-a$.

That is, $$(\sqrt[n]{-a})^n = -a.$$

The symbol $\sqrt[n]{-a}$ is called a **Pure Imaginary Number.**

It is, of course, impossible to find any real number whose nth power equals $-a$; but there are many advantages in including in the number-system of Algebra the result of any finite number of the operations addition, subtraction, multiplication, division, involution, and evolution, with rational numbers.

The pure imaginary number $\sqrt{-1}$ is called the *imaginary unit;* it is usually represented by the letter i.

OPERATIONS WITH PURE IMAGINARY NUMBERS

408. In deriving the rules for operations with pure imaginary numbers, we shall follow the method employed in Chap. II; that is, *we shall assume that the fundamental laws of §§ 12 and 14 hold for such numbers,* and find what meaning must, in consequence, be attached to the operations.   (Compare § 50.)

It follows from this that every statement or rule in the remaining part of Chap. I, or in Chaps. II to XVI, inclusive, in regard to expressions where any letter involved represents any rational number, holds equally where the letter represents a pure imaginary number.   (Compare § 351.)

409. To prove that, if a is any positive real number,

$$\sqrt{-a} = \sqrt{a}\,\sqrt{-1}.$$

By § 407, $$(\sqrt{-a})^2 = -a. \tag{1}$$

And since the result of § 129 holds when any of the letters $a, b, c, \cdots$ represents a pure imaginary number (§ 408),

$$(\sqrt{a}\sqrt{-1})^2 = (\sqrt{a})^2(\sqrt{-1})^2$$
$$= a \times (-1) = -a. \qquad (2)$$

From (1) and (2), $\quad (\sqrt{-a})^2 = (\sqrt{a}\,\sqrt{-1})^2.$

Then by § 163, $\qquad \sqrt{-a} = \sqrt{a}\,\sqrt{-1}.$

410. By § 409, $\qquad \sqrt{-27} = \sqrt{27}\,\sqrt{-1}$
$$= 3\sqrt{3}\,\sqrt{-1} \quad (\S\ 372)$$
$$= 3\sqrt{-3} \quad (\S\ 409).$$

It is evident from this that the methods of §§ 372, 373, and 377 hold for pure imaginary numbers.

411. Powers of $\sqrt{-1}$.

By § 407, $(\sqrt{-1})^2 = -1.$

Then,

$$(\sqrt{-1})^3 = (\sqrt{-1})^2 \times \sqrt{-1} = (-1) \times \sqrt{-1} = -\sqrt{-1};$$
$$(\sqrt{-1})^4 = (\sqrt{-1})^2 \times (\sqrt{-1})^2 = (-1) \times (-1) = 1; \text{ etc.}$$

In general, if n is any positive integer,

$$(\sqrt{-1})^{4n} = [(\sqrt{-1})^4]^n = 1^n = 1;$$
$$(\sqrt{-1})^{4n+1} = (\sqrt{-1})^{4n} \times \sqrt{-1} = \sqrt{-1};$$
$$(\sqrt{-1})^{4n+2} = (\sqrt{-1})^{4n} \times (\sqrt{-1})^2 = (\sqrt{-1})^2 = -1;$$
$$(\sqrt{-1})^{4n+3} = (\sqrt{-1})^{4n} \times (\sqrt{-1})^3 = (\sqrt{-1})^3 = -\sqrt{-1}.$$

412. Addition and Subtraction.

Two pure imaginary numbers may be added or subtracted by the method of § 375.

Ex. Add $\sqrt{-4}$ and $\sqrt{-36}$.

By § 410,

$$\sqrt{-4} + \sqrt{-36} = 2\sqrt{-1} + 6\sqrt{-1}$$
$$= (2+6)\sqrt{-1} \ (\S\ 14,\ \text{III}) = 8\sqrt{-1}.$$

413. Multiplication.

The product of two or more pure imaginary numbers may be obtained by aid of the principles of §§ 409 and 411.

1. Multiply $\sqrt{-2}$ by $\sqrt{-3}$.

By § 409, $\sqrt{-2} \times \sqrt{-3} = \sqrt{2}\sqrt{-1} \times \sqrt{3}\sqrt{-1}$

$$= \sqrt{2}\sqrt{3}(\sqrt{-1})^2, \text{ by § 14, I and II,}$$

$$= \sqrt{6} \times (-1) \ (\text{§ 411}) = -\sqrt{6}.$$

2. Multiply together $\sqrt{-9}$, $\sqrt{-16}$, and $\sqrt{-25}$.

$$\sqrt{-9} \times \sqrt{-16} \times \sqrt{-25} = 3\sqrt{-1} \times 4\sqrt{-1} \times 5\sqrt{-1}$$

$$= 60\,(\sqrt{-1})^3 = 60\,(-\sqrt{-1}) \ (\text{§ 411}) = -60\sqrt{-1}.$$

3. Multiply $2\sqrt{-2} + \sqrt{-5}$ by $\sqrt{-2} - 3\sqrt{-5}$.

Since all the rules of Chap. IV hold for pure imaginary numbers, we can multiply as in § 88.

$$
\begin{array}{l}
2\sqrt{-2} + \ \sqrt{-5} \\
\underline{\sqrt{-2} - 3\sqrt{-5}} \\
2(-2) + \ \sqrt{2}\sqrt{5}(\sqrt{-1})^2 \\
\quad\quad\quad -6\sqrt{2}\sqrt{5}(\sqrt{-1})^2 - 3(-5) \\
\overline{-4 \ -5\sqrt{10}(-1) \quad\quad\quad +15 = 11 + 5\sqrt{10}.}
\end{array}
$$

414. Division.

1. Divide $\sqrt{-40}$ by $\sqrt{-5}$.

By § 409, $\dfrac{\sqrt{-40}}{\sqrt{-5}} = \dfrac{\sqrt{40}\sqrt{-1}}{\sqrt{5}\sqrt{-1}} = \dfrac{\sqrt{40}}{\sqrt{5}} = \sqrt{8} = 2\sqrt{2}.$

Since the rule of § 96 holds for pure imaginary numbers, $\sqrt{-1}$ is cancelled in the same manner as a real factor.

2. Divide $\sqrt{15}$ by $\sqrt{-3}$.

By § 411,

$$\frac{\sqrt{15}}{\sqrt{-3}} = \frac{-\sqrt{15}(\sqrt{-1})^2}{\sqrt{3}\sqrt{-1}} = -\sqrt{5}(\sqrt{-1}) = -\sqrt{-5}.$$

3. Reduce $\dfrac{2\sqrt{3}-3\sqrt{-2}}{2\sqrt{3}+3\sqrt{-2}}$ to an equivalent fraction having a real denominator.

This may be effected by multiplying both terms of the fraction by the denominator with the sign between its terms changed.

Multiplying both terms by $2\sqrt{3}-3\sqrt{-2}$,

$$\frac{2\sqrt{3}-3\sqrt{-2}}{2\sqrt{3}+3\sqrt{-2}}=\frac{(2\sqrt{3}-3\sqrt{-2})^2}{(2\sqrt{3})^2-(3\sqrt{-2})^2}\quad(\S\ 132)$$

$$=\frac{12-12\sqrt{3}\sqrt{2}\sqrt{-1}+9(-2)}{12-9(-2)}\quad(\S\ 131)$$

$$=\frac{-6-12\sqrt{6}\sqrt{-1}}{30}=-\frac{1+2\sqrt{-6}}{5}.$$

EXERCISE 47

In the following examples, every letter occurring under a radical sign is supposed to represent a positive real number.

1. What is the value of $(\sqrt{-1})^{18}$? of $(\sqrt{-1})^{31}$? of $(\sqrt{-1})^{49}$?

Simplify the following:

2. $(\sqrt{-3})^6$.   **3.** $(\sqrt{-5})^7$.   **4.** $5\sqrt{-9}+2\sqrt{-25}$.

5. $7\sqrt{-80}-3\sqrt{-125}-\sqrt{-245}$.

6. $\sqrt{-\dfrac{1}{3}}+\sqrt{-\dfrac{27}{16}}-\sqrt{-\dfrac{49}{12}}-\sqrt{-\dfrac{16}{27}}$.

Multiply the following:

7. $\sqrt{-5}$ and $\sqrt{-45}$.   **9.** $\sqrt{a-b}$ and $\sqrt{b-a}$.

8. $\sqrt{-7}$, $\sqrt{-14}$, and $\sqrt{-21}$.   **10.** $\sqrt{-6}$, $\sqrt{-8}$, and $\sqrt{10}$.

11. $\sqrt{-18}$, $\sqrt{-27}$, $\sqrt{-32}$, and $\sqrt{-48}$.

12. $8+5\sqrt{-3}$ and $7-6\sqrt{-3}$.

13. $6\sqrt{-7}-5\sqrt{-6}$ and $4\sqrt{-7}+3\sqrt{-6}$.

Divide the following:

14. $\sqrt{-108}$ by $\sqrt{-6}$.   **16.** $\sqrt{120}$ by $\sqrt{-5}$.   **18.** $\sqrt{84}$ by $\sqrt{-7}$.

15. $\sqrt{-441}$ by $\sqrt{-3}$.   **17.** $\sqrt{-224}$ by $\sqrt{-2}$.   **19.** $\sqrt{-160}$ by $\sqrt{8}$.

Expand the following by the rules of Chap. VII:

20. $(4\sqrt{-3} + 5\sqrt{-2})^2$. **22.** $(3\sqrt{-5} + 2\sqrt{-6})(3\sqrt{-5} - 2\sqrt{-6})$.

21. $(\sqrt{-6} - \sqrt{-5})^3$.   **23.** $(3\sqrt{-2} + \sqrt{-3} - 2\sqrt{-5})^2$.

   24. $(\sqrt{-7} - \sqrt{-5} + \sqrt{-3})(\sqrt{-7} + \sqrt{-5} - \sqrt{-3})$.

Reduce each of the following to an equivalent fraction having a real denominator:

25. $\dfrac{3 - \sqrt{-7}}{3 + \sqrt{-7}}$.   **26.** $\dfrac{2\sqrt{-5} + 7\sqrt{-3}}{4\sqrt{-5} - 3\sqrt{-3}}$.   **27.** $\dfrac{1}{2 + 3\sqrt{-2} - \sqrt{-6}}$.

Expand the following by the Binomial Theorem:

28. $(\sqrt{-5} + 3\sqrt{-2})^4$.   **29.** $(\sqrt{a} - \sqrt{-b})^6$.

Simplify the following:

30. $\dfrac{3}{5 - 4\sqrt{-5}} + \dfrac{6}{7 + 2\sqrt{-5}}$.   **31.** $\dfrac{2\sqrt{5} + 3\sqrt{-6}}{2\sqrt{5} - 3\sqrt{-6}} - \dfrac{2\sqrt{5} - 3\sqrt{-6}}{2\sqrt{5} + 3\sqrt{-6}}$.

COMPLEX NUMBERS

It will be understood, throughout the remainder of the present chapter, that every letter represents a real number.

415. The expression $a + bi$ (§ 407), where a and b are any real numbers whatever, is called a **Complex Number**.

In operations with complex numbers, we shall assume the laws of §§ 12 and 14 to hold.

It follows from this that the statement in the last paragraph of § 408 is equally true of complex numbers.

416. Addition, Subtraction, Multiplication, and Division of Complex Numbers.

1. Add $a + bi$ and $c + di$.

Since the laws of § 12 hold for complex numbers,

$$(a + bi) + (c + di) = a + c + bi + di$$
$$= a + c + (b + d)i, \text{ by § 12, II, and § 14, III.}$$

2. Subtract $c + di$ from $a + bi$.

$$(a + bi) - (c + di) = a + bi - c - di \text{ (§ 81)}$$
$$= a - c + (b - d)i, \text{ by § 12, and § 24, (7).}$$

3. Multiply $a + bi$ by $c + di$.

By § 88, $(a + bi)(c + di) = ac + adi + bci + bdi^2$

$$= ac - bd + (ad + bc)i, \text{ by § 411.}$$

4. Express the quotient of $a + bi$ by $c + di$ as a complex number.

Multiplying both numerator and denominator by $c - di$, we have

$$\frac{a + bi}{c + di} = \frac{(a + bi)(c - di)}{(c + di)(c - di)} = \frac{ac - adi + bci - bdi^2}{c^2 - d^2 i^2}$$

$$= \frac{ac + bd + (bc - ad)i}{c^2 + d^2} = \frac{ac + bd}{c^2 + d^2} + \frac{bc - ad}{c^2 + d^2}i.$$

417. It follows from § 416 that the result of any finite number of additions, subtractions, multiplications, and divisions, performed upon complex numbers, is a complex number.

418. By the definition of 0,

$$i \times 0 = i(a - a) = ia - ia(\text{§ 24, (7)}) = 0.$$

It follows from this that the complex number $a + bi$ becomes a real number when b is 0.

It also becomes a pure imaginary number when a is 0.

Hence, $a + bi$ cannot equal 0 unless both

$$a = 0, \text{ and } b = 0.$$

419. *If $a + bi = c + di$, where a, b, c, and d are real numbers, then $a = c$, and $b = d$.*

Transposing the terms of the given equation, we have

$$a - c + (b - d)i = 0.$$

Then, by § 418, $a - c = 0$, and $b - d = 0$.

Whence, $a = c$, and $b = d$.

420. Square Root of a Complex Number.

We will now prove that $\sqrt{a + bi}$, where a and b are real, can be expressed in the form $\sqrt{x} + i\sqrt{y}$, where $\sqrt{x}$ and $\sqrt{y}$ are real.

Squaring both members of the equation

$$\sqrt{a + bi} = \sqrt{x} + i\sqrt{y}, \tag{1}$$

we have $\qquad a + bi = x + 2i\sqrt{xy} - y.$

Then by § 419, $\qquad a = x - y, \tag{2}$

and $\qquad bi = 2i\sqrt{xy}.$

Subtracting, $\qquad a - bi = x - 2i\sqrt{xy} - y.$

Extracting the square roots of both members,

$$\sqrt{a - bi} = \sqrt{x} - i\sqrt{y}. \tag{3}$$

Multiply (1) by (3), $\qquad \sqrt{a^2 + b^2} = x + y. \tag{4}$

Add (2) and (4), $\qquad \sqrt{a^2 + b^2} + a = 2x,\ \text{or}\ x = \dfrac{\sqrt{a^2 + b^2} + a}{2}.$

Subtract (2) from (4), $\sqrt{a^2 + b^2} - a = 2y,\ \text{or}\ y = \dfrac{\sqrt{a^2 + b^2} - a}{2},$

It is evident from this that $\sqrt{x}$ and $\sqrt{y}$ are real.

421. It follows from (1) and (3), § 420, that

If $\sqrt{a + bi} = \sqrt{x} + i\sqrt{y}$, where a, b, x, and y, are real numbers, then $\sqrt{a - bi} = \sqrt{x} - i\sqrt{y}$.

422. The preceding principles may be used to find the square root of a complex number.

1. Find the square root of $7 - 6\sqrt{-2}$.

Assume, $\qquad \sqrt{7 - 6\sqrt{-2}} = \sqrt{x} - \sqrt{y}\sqrt{-1}. \tag{1}$

Then by § 421, $\quad \sqrt{7 + 6\sqrt{-2}} = \sqrt{x} + \sqrt{y}\sqrt{-1}. \tag{2}$

Multiplying (1) by (2), we have

$$\sqrt{49 - 36(-2)} = x + y,$$

or, $\qquad x + y = 11. \tag{3}$

Squaring (1), $\qquad 7 - 6\sqrt{-2} = x - 2\sqrt{xy}\sqrt{-1} - y.$

Whence by § 419, $\qquad x - y = 7. \tag{4}$

Add (3) and (4), $\qquad 2x = 18,\ \text{or}\ x = 9.$

Subtract (4) from (3), $\qquad 2y = 4,\ \text{or}\ y = 2.$

Substitute in (1), $\sqrt{7-6\sqrt{-2}}=\sqrt{9}-\sqrt{2}\sqrt{-1}=3-\sqrt{-2}$.

The example may also be solved by the method of § 392.

We have $6\sqrt{-2}=2\sqrt{9\times(-2)}$.

We then separate 7 into two parts whose product is $9\times(-2)$.

The parts are 9 and -2; then, $\sqrt{7-6\sqrt{-2}}=\sqrt{9}-\sqrt{-2}=3-\sqrt{-2}$.

We may also find by the above methods the square root of an expression of the form $a+\sqrt{b}$, or $a-\sqrt{b}$, when a is negative.

2. Find the square root of $-35+12\sqrt{6}$.

We have $\sqrt{-35+12\sqrt{6}}=\sqrt{-1}\sqrt{35-2\sqrt{216}}$.

Separating 35 into two parts whose product is 216,

$$\sqrt{-35+12\sqrt{6}}=\sqrt{-1}\sqrt{(27-2\sqrt{27\times8}+8)}$$
$$=\sqrt{-1}(\sqrt{27}-\sqrt{8})=3\sqrt{-3}-2\sqrt{-2}.$$

EXERCISE 48

Extract the square roots of the following:

1. $13+\sqrt{-192}$. 3. $-38-8\sqrt{-30}$. 5. $-52-2\sqrt{640}$.

2. $18-5\sqrt{-28}$. 4. $-26+\sqrt{480}$. 6. $2\sqrt{-16}$.

423. Putting $a=0$ and $b=1$, in § 420, we have $x=y=\dfrac{1}{2}$. Substituting these values in (1), we have

$$\sqrt{i}=\frac{1+i}{\sqrt{2}}=\frac{1}{2}(1+i)\sqrt{2}.$$

424. Cube Root of a Complex Number.

We will now prove that if $\sqrt[3]{a+bi}=c+di$, where a, b, c, and d are real, then $\sqrt[3]{a-bi}=c-di$.

Cubing both members of the equation

$$\sqrt[3]{a+bi}=c+di,$$

we have, by § 411, $a+bi=c^3+3c^2di-3cd^2-d^3i$.

Then by § 419, $a=c^3-3cd^2$,

and $bi=3c^2di-d^3i$.

Subtracting, $a-bi=c^3-3c^2di-3cd^2+d^3i$.

Extracting the cube root of both members,

$$\sqrt[3]{a - bi} = c - di.$$

425. The complex numbers $a + bi$ and $a - bi$ are called Conjugate.

We have $(a + bi) \times (a - bi) = a^2 - b^2 i^2 = a^2 + b^2.$

Also, $(a + bi) + (a - bi) = 2\,a.$

Hence, *the sum and product of two conjugate complex numbers are real.*

It will be shown in the Appendix (§ 804), that any even root of a negative number, or any root of a pure imaginary or complex number, can be expressed as a complex number.

GRAPHICAL REPRESENTATION OF PURE IMAGINARY AND COMPLEX NUMBERS

426. Let XX' be a fixed straight line, and O a fixed point in that line.

It was shown in §§ 57 and 406 that any positive real number, $+ a$, could be represented by the dis-

tance from O to A, a units to the right of O in OX; and any negative real number, $- a$, by the distance from O to A', a units to the left of O in OX'.

427. Since $- a$ is the same as $(+ a) \times (- 1)$, it follows from § 426 that the product of $+ a$ by $- 1$ is represented by turning the line OA which represents the number $+ a$, through two right angles, in a direction opposite to the motion of the hands of a clock.

We may then regard $- 1$, in the product of any real number by $- 1$, as an operator which turns the line which represents the first factor through two right angles, in a direction opposite to the motion of the hands of a clock.

428. Graphical Representation of the Imaginary Unit.

By the definition of § 407, $- 1 = i \times i.$

Then, since one multiplication by i, followed by another multiplication by i, turns the line which represents the first factor through *two* right angles, in a direction opposite to the hands of a clock, we may regard multiplication by i as turning the line through *one* right angle, in the same direction.

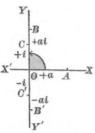

Thus, let XX' and YY' be fixed straight lines, intersecting at right angles at O, the letters being arranged as in the figure of § 270.

Then, if $+a$ be represented by the line OA, where A is a units to the right of O in OX, $+ai$ may be represented by OB, and $-ai$ by OB', where B is a units above, and B' a units below, O, in YY'.

Also, $+i$ may be represented by OC, and $-i$ by OC', where C is one unit above, and C' one unit below, O, in YY'.

It will be understood throughout the remainder of the chapter that, in any figure where the lines XX' and YY' occur, they are fixed straight lines intersecting at right angles at O, the letters being arranged as in the figure of § 270; that all positive or negative real numbers are represented by lines to the right or left of O, respectively, in XX'; and all positive or negative pure imaginary numbers by lines above or below O, respectively, in YY'.

429. Graphical Representation of Complex Numbers.

We will now show how to represent the complex number $a + bi$.

Let a be represented by OA, to the right of O if a is positive, to the left if a is negative.

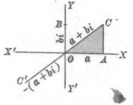

Let bi be represented by OB, above O if b is positive, below if b is negative.

Draw line AC equal and parallel to OB, on the same side of XX' as OB, and line OC.

Then, OC is considered the result of adding bi to a; that is, OC represents $a + bi$.

This agrees with the methods already given for adding a real or pure imaginary number, if either a or b is zero.

The figure represents the case where a and b are both positive; if a is positive and b negative, OC will lie between OX and OY'; if a is negative, OC will lie between OY and OX' if b is positive, and between OX' and OY' if b is negative.

In accordance with §§ 57 and 406, $-(a + bi)$ may be represented by line OC', where OC' is equal in length to OC, and drawn in the opposite direction from O.

430. The *modulus* of a real, pure imaginary, or complex number is the length of the line which represents the number.

The *argument* is the angle between the line which represents the number and OX, measured from OX in a direction opposite to the motion of the hands of a clock.

If, for example, in the figure of § 429, $\angle XOC = 30°$, the argument of the complex number represented by OC is 30°, and the argument of the complex number represented by OC' is 210°.

The modulus is always taken positive, and the argument may have any value from 0° to 360°.

The real numbers $+ a$ and $- a$ have the modulus a, and arguments 0° and 180°, respectively; the pure imaginary numbers $+ ai$ and $- ai$ have the modulus a, and arguments 90° and 270°, respectively.

431. In the figure of § 428, $OC = \sqrt{\overline{OA}^2 + \overline{AC}^2} = \sqrt{a^2 + b^2}$; that is, the modulus of the complex number $a + bi$ is $\sqrt{a^2 + b^2}$; this is also the modulus of the complex numbers $a - bi$, $-a + bi$, and $-a - bi$.

432. Graphical Representation of Addition.

We will now show how to represent the result of adding b to a, where a and b are any two real, pure imaginary, or complex numbers.

Let a be represented by OA, and b by OB.

Draw line AC equal and parallel to OB, on the same side of OA as OB, and line OC.

Then, OC is considered the result of adding b to a; that is, line OC represents $a + b$.

This agrees with the method of § 429, which is a special case of the above.

In like manner, the sum of any number of real, pure imaginary, or complex numbers may be represented by a straight line drawn from O.

433. Graphical Representation of Subtraction.

Let a and b be any two real, pure imaginary, or complex numbers.

Let a be represented by OA, and b by OB; and complete parallelogram $OBAC$.

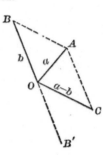

By § 432, OA represents the result of adding the number represented by OB to the number represented by OC.

That is, if b be added to the number represented by OC, the sum is equal to a; hence, $a - b$ is represented by line OC.

434. Graphical Representation of Multiplication.

Since $+ai$ may be written $(+1) \times (+ai)$, the product of $+1$ by $+ai$ is represented by turning the line OA, which represents the number $+1$, through one right angle, in a direction opposite to the motion of the hands of a clock, and multiplying the result by a.

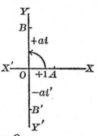

And since $-ai$ may be written $(+1) \times (-ai)$, the product of $+1$ by $-ai$ is represented by a line equal in length to that which represents the product of $+1$ by $+ai$, but drawn in the opposite direction from O.

This suggests the following:

The product of any real, pure imaginary, or complex number by $+ai$ may be represented by turning the line which represents the number through one right angle, in a direction opposite to the motion of the hands of a clock, and multiplying the result by a.

The product of any real, pure imaginary, or complex number by $-ai$ may be represented by a line equal in length to the line which represents its product by $+ai$, but drawn in the opposite direction from O.

435. Since $a + bi$ may be written $(+1) \times (a + bi)$, the product of $+1$ by $a + bi$ is represented by turning the line OA, which represents the number $+1$, through an angle equal to the argument of $a+bi$ (§ 430), in a direction opposite to the motion of the hands of a clock, and multiplying the result by the modulus of $a+bi$.

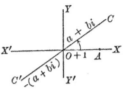

And since $-(a + bi)$ may be written $(+1) \times (-a - bi)$, the product of $+1$ by $-(a + bi)$ is represented by a line equal in length to that which represents the product of $+1$ by $a + bi$, but drawn in the opposite direction from O.

This suggests the following:

If a and b are any real numbers, the product of any real, pure imaginary, or complex number by $a + bi$ may be represented by turning the line which represents the number through an angle equal to the amplitude of $a + bi$, in a direction opposite to the motion of the hands of a clock, and multiplying the result by the modulus of $a + bi$.

The product of any real, pure imaginary, or complex number by $-(a + bi)$ may be represented by a line equal in length to the line which represents its product by $a + bi$, but drawn in the opposite direction from O.

436. Let a and b be any two real, pure imaginary, or complex numbers, represented by the lines OA and OB, respectively.

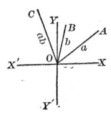

The result of multiplying a by b is represented by line OC, where angle XOC is the sum of angles XOA and XOB, and $OC = OA \times OB$ (§ 435).

That is, ab is represented by OC.

In like manner, the product of any number of real, pure imaginary, or complex numbers may be represented by a straight line drawn from O.

437. Graphical Representation of Division.

Let a and b be any two real, pure imaginary, or complex numbers.

Let a be represented by OA, and b by OB.

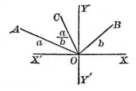

Draw line OC, making $\angle XOC =$ $\angle XOA - \angle XOB$, and $OC = \dfrac{OA}{OB}$.

Then, $\angle XOA = \angle XOC + \angle XOB$, and $OA = OC \times OB$.

Whence, by § 436, OA represents the product of the number represented by OC by the number represented by OB.

Then, OC represents a number which, when multiplied by b, gives a; and hence OC represents $\dfrac{a}{b}$.

Therefore, the quotient of any two real, pure imaginary, or complex numbers can be represented by a straight line drawn from O.

438. Graphical Representation of Roots.

Let a be any real, pure imaginary, or complex number, represented by line OA.

Draw line OB making $\angle XOB = \dfrac{1}{n} \angle XOA$, and having its length equal to the nth root of the modulus of a.

Then, $\angle XOA = n \times \angle XOB$, and the modulus of a is the nth power of the length of OB.

Then, by § 436, OA represents the nth power of the number represented by OB.

Whence, OB represents $\sqrt[n]{a}$.

439. It follows from §§ 432, 433, 436, 437, and 438 that any number which is the result of any finite number of the following operations performed upon one or more real, pure imaginary, or complex numbers, may be represented by a straight line drawn from O:

Addition; Subtraction; Multiplication; Division; raising to any power whose exponent is a rational number (§ 51); extracting any root.

This is a graphical representation of the fact that any such number can be expressed in the form $a + bi$, where a and b are real numbers, either of which may be zero. (Compare §§ 417 and 804.)

We shall limit ourselves in the present work to numbers of the above form.

The discussion of *complex exponents* requires a knowledge of Higher Trigonometry.

XIX. QUADRATIC EQUATIONS

440. A **Quadratic Equation** is an equation of the second degree (§ 113), with one or more unknown numbers.

In the present chapter we consider only quadratic equations involving one unknown number.

The principles demonstrated in §§ 116 to 119, inclusive, and § 122, hold for quadratic equations.

441. By transposing all terms to the first member, any quadratic equation, involving one unknown number, x, may be reduced to the form
$$ax^2 + bx + c = 0.$$

If neither b nor c is zero, this is called a **Complete Quadratic Equation.**

A Complete Quadratic Equation is sometimes called an *Affected Quadratic Equation.*

If either or both of the numbers b and c are zero, the equation is called an *Incomplete Quadratic Equation.*

An incomplete quadratic equation of the form $ax^2 + c = 0$, is called a **Pure Quadratic Equation.**

In § 183, we showed how to solve quadratic equations of the forms

$ax^2 + bx = 0$, $ax^2 + c = 0$, $x^2 + ax + b = 0$, and $ax^2 + bx + c = 0$, when the first members could be resolved into factors.

442. Consider the equation
$$A^2 = B^2,$$

where A is a rational and integral expression involving the unknown numbers.

We may write the equation,
$$A^2 - B^2 = 0, \text{ or } (A + B)(A - B) = 0.$$

By § 182, the latter is equivalent to the set of equations
$$A + B = 0, \text{ and } A - B = 0.$$

Or, to the equations $A = + B$, and $A = - B$, which may be written together in the form

$$A = \pm B.$$

The sign $\pm$, called the *double sign*, when prefixed to a number, indicates that it may be either $+$ or $-$.

Thus, the given equation is equivalent to an equation which is obtained by equating the positive square root of the first member to $\pm$ the square root of the second.

PURE QUADRATIC EQUATIONS

443. A pure quadratic equation may be solved by reducing it, if necessary, to the form $x^2 = a$, and then equating x to $\pm \sqrt{a}$ (§ 442).

1. Solve the equation $\qquad 3x^2 + 7 = \dfrac{5x^2}{4} + 35.$

Clearing of fractions, $\qquad 12x^2 + 28 = 5x^2 + 140.$

Transposing and uniting terms, $\qquad 7x^2 = 112.$

Dividing by 7, $\qquad x^2 = 16.$

Equating x to $\pm$ the square root of 16, $x = \pm 4.$

2. Solve the equation $\qquad 7x^2 - 5 = 5x^2 - 13.$

Transposing and uniting terms, $\qquad 2x^2 = -8.$

Or, $\qquad x^2 = -4.$

Equating x to $\pm$ the square root of -4, $x = \pm \sqrt{-4}$

$$= \pm 2\sqrt{-1} \,(\S\,409).$$

In this case, both values of x are *imaginary* (§ 407); it is impossible to find a real value of x which will satisfy the given equation.

EXERCISE 49

Solve the following

1. $2(3x - 5)^2 + 3(x + 10)^2 = 434.$ $\qquad$ **2.** $(x + 1)^3 - (x - 1)^3 = 20.$

3. $\dfrac{5x^2}{6} + \dfrac{9x^2}{16} + \dfrac{5}{12} = \dfrac{11x^2}{12} - \dfrac{7x^2}{8} - 5.$

4. $(2x + 7)(5x - 6) - (4x - 3)(7x + 5) - 24x + 59 = 0.$

5. $(x + 2a)(x + 3b) + (x - 2a)(x - 3b) = x^2 + 4a^2 + 9b^2.$

6. $\dfrac{3\,x^2+7}{7}-\dfrac{5\,x^2+3}{14}-\dfrac{4\,x^2-10}{35}=0.$

7. $(x+1)(x-2)(x-3)-(x-1)(x+2)(x+3)=-52.$

COMPLETE QUADRATIC EQUATIONS

444. First Method of Completing the Square.

By transposing the terms involving x to the first member, and all other terms to the second, and then dividing both members by the coefficient of x^2, any complete quadratic equation can be reduced to the form

$$x^2 + px = q.$$

A trinomial is a perfect square when its first and third terms are perfect squares and positive, and its second term plus or minus twice the product of their square roots (§ 167).

Then, the square root of the third term is equal to the second term divided by twice the square root of the first.

Hence, the *square root* of the expression which must be added to $x^2 + px$ to make it a perfect square, is $\dfrac{px}{2\,x}$, or $\dfrac{p}{2}.$

Adding to both members the square of $\dfrac{p}{2}$, we have

$$x^2 + px + \frac{p^2}{4} = q + \frac{p^2}{4} = \frac{p^2 + 4\,q}{4}.$$

By § 442, this is equivalent to an equation which is obtained by equating the positive square root of the first member to $\pm$ the square root of the second.

Then, it is equivalent to

$$x + \frac{p}{2} = \pm\,\frac{\sqrt{p^2+4\,q}}{2}, \text{ or to } x = \frac{-p \pm \sqrt{p^2+4\,q}}{2}.$$

Adding to both members such an expression as will make the first member a perfect trinomial square, is called *Completing the Square.*

445. We derive from § 444 the following rule for solving a complete quadratic equation.

Reduce the equation to the form $x^2 + px = q$.

Complete the square, by adding to both members the square of one-half the coefficient of x.

Equate the positive square root of the first member to $\pm$ the square root of the second, and solve the linear equations thus formed.

446. 1. Solve the equation $3\,x^2 - 8\,x = -4$.

Dividing by 3, $\qquad\qquad x^2 - \dfrac{8\,x}{3} = -\dfrac{4}{3}.$

Adding to both members the square of $\dfrac{4}{3}$, we have

$$x^2 - \frac{8\,x}{3} + \left(\frac{4}{3}\right)^2 = -\frac{4}{3} + \frac{16}{9} = \frac{4}{9}.$$

Equating the positive square root of the first member to $\pm$ the square root of $\dfrac{4}{9}$,

$$x - \frac{4}{3} = \pm\frac{2}{3}.$$

Transposing $-\dfrac{4}{3}$, $\qquad x = \dfrac{4}{3} \pm \dfrac{2}{3} = 2 \text{ or } \dfrac{2}{3}.$

If the coefficient of x^2 is negative, the sign of each term must be changed.

2. Solve the equation $\;-9\,x^2 - 21\,x = 10$.

Dividing by -9, $\qquad\qquad x^2 + \dfrac{7\,x}{3} = -\dfrac{10}{9}.$

Adding to both members the square of $\dfrac{7}{6}$,

$$x^2 + \frac{7\,x}{3} + \left(\frac{7}{6}\right)^2 = -\frac{10}{9} + \frac{49}{36} = \frac{9}{36}.$$

Equating the positive square root of the first member to $\pm$ the square root of $\dfrac{9}{36}$,

$$x + \frac{7}{6} = \pm\frac{3}{6}.$$

Whence, $\qquad\qquad x = -\dfrac{7}{6} \pm \dfrac{3}{6} = -\dfrac{2}{3} \text{ or } -\dfrac{5}{3}.$

447. By § 167, $a^2x^2 + bx$ will become a perfect trinomial square by adding to it the square of $\dfrac{bx}{2\,ax}$, or $\dfrac{b}{2\,a}$.

Hence, we may complete the square by *adding to both members the square of the quotient obtained by dividing the coefficient of x by twice the square root of the coefficient of x^2.*

This is usually a more convenient rule than that of § 445, when the coefficient of x^2 is a perfect square.

1. Solve the equation $9\,x^2 - 5\,x = 4$.

Adding to both members the square of $\dfrac{5}{2 \times 3}$,

$$9\,x^2 - 5\,x + \left(\frac{5}{6}\right)^2 = 4 + \frac{25}{36} = \frac{169}{36}.$$

Extracting square roots, $3\,x - \dfrac{5}{6} = \pm\,\dfrac{13}{6}$.

Then, $\qquad\qquad\qquad 3\,x = \dfrac{5}{6} \pm \dfrac{13}{6} = 3 \text{ or } -\dfrac{4}{3}$.

Dividing by 3, $\qquad\qquad\qquad x = 1 \text{ or } -\dfrac{4}{9}$.

If the coefficient of x^2 is not a perfect square, it may be made so by multiplication.

2. Solve the equation $8\,x^2 - 15\,x = 2$.

Multiplying each term by 2, $16\,x^2 - 30\,x = 4$.

Adding to both members the square of $\dfrac{30}{2 \times 4}$, or $\dfrac{15}{4}$,

$$16\,x^2 - 30\,x + \left(\frac{15}{4}\right)^2 = 4 + \frac{225}{16} = \frac{289}{16}.$$

Extracting square roots, $4\,x - \dfrac{15}{4} = \pm\,\dfrac{17}{4}$.

Then, $\qquad\qquad\qquad 4\,x = \dfrac{15}{4} \pm \dfrac{17}{4} = 8 \text{ or } -\dfrac{1}{2}$.

Whence, $x = 2 \text{ or } -\dfrac{1}{8}.$

If the coefficient of x^2 is negative, the sign of each term must be changed.

448. Second Method of completing the Square.

Every complete quadratic equation can be reduced to the form $ax^2 + bx + c = 0$, or $ax^2 + bx = -c$ (§ 441).

Multiplying both members by $4\,a$, we have

$$4\,a^2x^2 + 4\,abx = -4\,ac.$$

Completing the square by adding to both members the square of $\dfrac{4\,ab}{2 \times 2\,a}$ (§ 447), or b, we obtain

$$4\,a^2x^2 + 4\,abx + b^2 = b^2 - 4\,ac.$$

Extracting square roots, $2\,ax + b = \pm \sqrt{b^2 - 4\,ac}.$

Transposing, $2\,ax = -b \pm \sqrt{b^2 - 4\,ac}.$

Whence, $x = \dfrac{-b \pm \sqrt{b^2 - 4\,ac}}{2\,a}.$

We derive from the above the following rule for completing the square:

Reduce the equation to the form $ax^2 + bx + c = 0$.

Multiply both members by four times the coefficient of x^2, and add to each the square of the coefficient of x in the given equation.

The advantage of this method over the preceding is in avoiding fractions in completing the square.

449. 1. Solve the equation $2\,x^2 - 7\,x = -3$.

Multiplying both members by 4×2, or 8,

$$16\,x^2 - 56\,x = -24.$$

Adding to both members the square of 7,

$$16\,x^2 - 56\,x + 7^2 = -24 + 49 = 25.$$

Extracting square roots, $4x - 7 = \pm 5$.

$$4x = 7 \pm 5 = 12 \text{ or } 2.$$

Whence, $\qquad x = 3 \text{ or } \frac{1}{2}.$

If the coefficient of x in the given equation is *even*, fractions may be avoided, and the rule modified, as follows:

Multiply both members by the coefficient of x^2, and add to each the square of half the coefficient of x in the given equation.

2. Solve the equation $15x^2 + 28x = 32$.

Multiplying both members by 15, and adding to each the square of 14, we have

$$15^2x^2 + 15(28x) + 14^2 = 480 + 196 = 676.$$

Extracting square roots, $15x + 14 = \pm 26$.

$$15x = -14 \pm 26 = 12 \text{ or } -40.$$

Whence, $\qquad x = \frac{4}{5} \text{ or } -\frac{8}{3}.$

The method of completing the square exemplified in the present section is called the *Hindoo Method.*

EXERCISE 50

The following may be solved by either of the preceding methods, preference being given to the one best adapted to the example under consideration.

1. $x^2 - x = 12.$

2. $3x^2 - 17x = -10.$

3. $5x^2 + 17x = 12.$

4. $10x^2 + 27x + 14 = 0.$

5. $36x^2 - 24x = 77.$

6. $49x^2 + 21x - 4 = 0.$

7. $6 + 23x - 18x^2 = 0.$

8. $4x^2 - 12x = 23.$

9. $8x^2 + 7x + 2 = 0.$

10. $36x^2 + 3x = 5.$

11. $28x^2 + 29x + 6 = 0.$

12. $10 - 37x = -30x^2.$

13. $x(5x + 22) + 35 = (2x + 5)^2.$

14. $(2x+1)^3 - (2x+3)^3 = -386.$

15. $(3x + 2)(2x - 3) = (4x - 1)^2 - 14.$

16. $(x + 4)(2x - 1) + (2x - 1)(3x + 2) - (3x + 2)(4x - 1) = -49.$

17. $(x + 1)(x + 3) = (x + 7)\sqrt{2} + 12.$

18. $(5 + 2\sqrt{3})x^2 - (4 + 14\sqrt{3})x = 9 - 14\sqrt{3}.$

450. Solution of Complete Quadratic Equations by Formula.
It follows from § 448 that, if

$$ax^2 + bx + c = 0,$$

then
$$x = \frac{-b \pm \sqrt{b^2 - 4ac}}{2a}. \tag{1}$$

This result may be used as a *formula* for the solution of any complete quadratic equation in the form $ax^2 + bx + c = 0$.

1. Solve the equation $2x^2 + 5x - 18 = 0$.

Here, $a = 2$, $b = 5$, and $c = -18$; substituting these values in (1), we have

$$x = \frac{-5 \pm \sqrt{25 + 144}}{4} = \frac{-5 \pm 13}{4} = 2 \text{ or } -\frac{9}{2}.$$

2. Solve the equation $110x^2 - 21x = -1$.

Here, $a = 110$, $b = -21$, $c = 1$.

Then, $\quad x = \dfrac{21 \pm \sqrt{441 - 440}}{220} = \dfrac{21 \pm 1}{220} = \dfrac{1}{10} \text{ or } \dfrac{1}{11}.$

Dividing both terms of the fraction in equation (1) by 2,

$$x = \frac{-\frac{b}{2} \pm \sqrt{\frac{b^2 - 4ac}{4}}}{a} \; (\text{§ 377}) = \frac{-\frac{b}{2} \pm \sqrt{\left(\frac{b}{2}\right)^2 - ac}}{a}. \tag{2}$$

This is a convenient formula in case the coefficient of x in the given equation is *even*.

3. Solve the equation $-5x^2 + 14x + 3 = 0$.

Here, $a = -5$, $b = 14$, $c = 3$; substituting in (2),

$$x = \frac{-7 \pm \sqrt{49 + 15}}{-5} = \frac{-7 \pm 8}{-5} = -\frac{1}{5} \text{ or } 3.$$

Particular attention must be paid to the *signs* of the coefficients in making the substitution.

The student should now work the examples of Exercise 50 by formula.

451. Fractional Equations involving Quadratics.

In solving fractional equations which involve quadratics, we reject any solution which satisfies the equation obtained by equating to zero the L. C. M. of the given denominators (§ 222).

1. Solve the equation $\dfrac{3}{x-6} - \dfrac{2}{x-5} = 1.$

Multiplying each term by $(x-6)(x-5)$, we have

$$3x - 15 - 2x + 12 = x^2 - 11x + 30.$$

Or, $\qquad\qquad\qquad\qquad x^2 - 12x = -33.$

Completing the square, $\quad x^2 - 12x + 6^2 = 3.$

Extracting square roots, $\qquad\quad x - 6 = \pm\sqrt{3}.$

Whence, $\qquad\qquad\qquad\qquad\quad x = 6 \pm \sqrt{3}.$

Since neither $6 + \sqrt{3}$ nor $6 - \sqrt{3}$ satisfies the equation $(x-6)(x-5) = 0$, both roots may be retained.

2. Solve the equation $\dfrac{1}{2+x} - \dfrac{1}{2-x} = \dfrac{x^2 + 3x - 6}{x^2 - 4}.$

We may write it $\qquad \dfrac{1}{x+2} + \dfrac{1}{x-2} = \dfrac{x^2 + 3x - 6}{x^2 - 4}.$

Multiplying each term by $x^2 - 4$,

$$x - 2 + x + 2 = x^2 + 3x - 6.$$

Or, $\qquad\qquad\qquad\qquad x^2 + x = 6.$

Multiplying by 4, and adding 1^2 to both members,

$$4x^2 + 4x + 1 = 25.$$

Extracting square roots, $\quad 2x + 1 = \pm 5.$

Then, $\qquad\qquad\qquad\quad 2x = -1 \pm 5 = 4 \text{ or } -6.$

Whence, $\qquad\qquad\qquad\quad x = 2 \text{ or } -3.$

Since 2 satisfies the equation $x^2 - 4 = 0$, it must be rejected, and the only solution is $x = -3$.

452. Literal Equations involving Quadratics.

In solving literal equations which involve complete quadratics, the methods of § 449 are usually the most convenient.

Ex. Solve the equation $acx^2 - adx + bcx - bd = 0$.

We write the equation $acx^2 - (ad - bc)x = bd$.

Multiplying by $4\,ac$, and adding $(ad - bc)^2$ to both members,

$$4\,a^2c^2x^2 - 4\,ac(ad - bc)x + (ad - bc)^2$$
$$= 4\,abcd + a^2d^2 - 2\,abcd + b^2c^2 = a^2d^2 + 2\,abcd + b^2c^2.$$

Extracting square roots,

$$2\,acx - (ad - bc) = \pm\,(ad + bc).$$

$$2\,acx = ad - bc \pm (ad + bc) = 2\,ad \text{ or } -2\,bc.$$

Whence, $\qquad\qquad x = \dfrac{d}{c} \text{ or } -\dfrac{b}{a}.$

If several terms contain the same power of x, the coefficient of that power should be enclosed in parentheses, as shown above.

The above equation may be solved more easily by the method of § 183; thus, by § 156, the equation may be written

$$(ax + b)(cx - d) = 0.$$

Then, $\qquad\qquad ax + b = 0, \text{ or } x = -\dfrac{b}{a};$

and $\qquad\qquad cx - d = 0, \text{ or } x = \dfrac{d}{c}.$

Several equations in Exercise 51 may be solved most easily by the method of § 183.

As a general rule, literal quadratics are best solved by formula.

453. Equations leading to Quadratics, having the Unknown Number under Radical Signs.

In solving equations of this kind, only solutions which satisfy the given equation should be retained.

In verifying solutions, only *principal values of the roots are considered* (§ 397).

1. Solve the equation $\sqrt{5 + x} + \sqrt{5 - x} = \dfrac{12}{\sqrt{5 - x}}.$

Clearing of fractions, $\quad \sqrt{25 - x^2} + 5 - x = 12.$

Transposing, $\qquad\qquad\qquad \sqrt{25 - x^2} = x + 7.$

Squaring, $\qquad\qquad\qquad 25 - x^2 = x^2 + 14\,x + 49.$

Or, $\qquad\qquad\qquad 2\,x^2+14\,x=-24.$

Multiplying by 2, and adding 7^2 to both members,

$$4\,x^2+28\,x+49=1.$$

Extracting square roots, $\qquad 2\,x+7=\pm 1.$

$$2\,x=-7\pm 1=-6\text{ or }-8.$$

Whence, $\qquad\qquad\qquad\qquad\qquad x=-3\text{ or }-4.$

Putting $x=-3$, the given first member becomes

$$\sqrt{2}+\sqrt{8}=\sqrt{2}+2\,\sqrt{2}=3\,\sqrt{2}.$$

The second member becomes $\dfrac{12}{\sqrt{8}}=\dfrac{3\times 2\times 2}{2\,\sqrt{2}}=3\,\sqrt{2}.$

Then, the solution $x=-3$ is correct.

Putting $x=-4$, the given first member becomes $1+\sqrt{9}=4.$

The second member becomes $\dfrac{12}{\sqrt{9}}=4.$

Then, the solution $x=-4$ is correct.

2. Solve the equation $\sqrt{x-1}+\sqrt{3\,x+3}=4.$

Transposing $\sqrt{x-1}$, $\qquad \sqrt{3\,x+3}=4-\sqrt{x-1}.$

Squaring, $\qquad\qquad\qquad 3\,x+3=16-8\,\sqrt{x-1}+x-1.$

Transposing, $\qquad\qquad\quad 8\,\sqrt{x-1}=12-2\,x.$

Or, $\qquad\qquad\qquad\qquad 4\,\sqrt{x-1}=6-x.$

Squaring, $\qquad\qquad\qquad 16\,x-16=36-12\,x+x^2.$

Or, $\qquad\qquad\qquad\qquad x^2-28\,x=-52.$

Completing the square,

$$x^2-28\,x+14^2=144.$$

Extracting square roots, $\qquad x-14=\pm 12.$

Whence, $\qquad\qquad\qquad\qquad x=14\pm 12=26\text{ or }2.$

Putting $x=26$, the given first member becomes $5+9$, or 14.
Then, the solution $x=26$ is not correct.

Putting $x=2$, the given first member becomes $1+3$, or 4.
Then, $x=2$ is the only correct solution.

EXERCISE 51

Solve the following :

1. $\dfrac{2x}{3} - \dfrac{5}{4x} = \dfrac{7x}{9} - \dfrac{21}{4x}$.

2. $\dfrac{5}{6x} - \dfrac{13}{9x^2} = \dfrac{1}{18}$.

3. $\dfrac{3}{4x} + \dfrac{4x}{3} = -\dfrac{85}{18}$.

4. $x^2 + 2mx = 1 - m^2$.

5. $x^2 - 2ax = -6a + 9$.

6. $x^2 + ax + bx = -ab$.

7. $x^2 - (n-1)x = n$.

8. $\dfrac{6x+5}{4x-3} - \dfrac{4x+4}{x-3} = 0$.

9. $x^2 - m^2nx + mn^2x = m^3n^3$.

10. $x^2 - 4ax - 10x = -40a$.

11. $\dfrac{10x^2-3}{18} = \dfrac{5x^2+6}{9} - \dfrac{6x^2-1}{9x^2-2}$.

12. $6x^2 + 4ax - 15bx = 10ab$.

13. $amx^2 + anx + bmx + bn = 0$.

14. $\sqrt{5x^2 - 3x - 41} = 3x - 7$.

15. $6 - \sqrt{5x^2 - 9} = 12$.

16. $\sqrt{7x+8} - \sqrt{5x-4} = 2$.

17. $\dfrac{3a}{x-5b} - \dfrac{x+5b}{3a-10b} = 0$.

18. $\dfrac{1}{x+3} - \dfrac{1}{x-5} = \dfrac{x^2-17}{x^2-2x-15}$.

19. $\dfrac{1}{x-2} + \dfrac{7x}{24(x+2)} = \dfrac{15}{x^2-4}$.

20. $\dfrac{x-2}{x+5} - \dfrac{x+4}{x-3} = -\dfrac{7}{3}$.

21. $\dfrac{x-a}{x+a} - \dfrac{x+a}{x-a} = \dfrac{x^2-5a^2}{x^2-a^2}$.

22. $\sqrt{(a+2b)x - 2ab} = x - 4b$.

23. $2x + \sqrt{4x^2 - 7} = \dfrac{21}{\sqrt{4x^2 - 7}}$.

24. $\dfrac{a}{2x+a} - \dfrac{a}{3x-4a} = \dfrac{4}{3}$.

25. $2\sqrt{3x+4} + 3\sqrt{3x+7} = \dfrac{8}{\sqrt{3x+4}}$.

26. $(a+x)^3 + (b-x)^3 = (a+b)^3$.

27. $\sqrt{x-a} + \sqrt{2x+3a} = \sqrt{5a}$.

28. $3\sqrt{x-1} - \dfrac{4}{\sqrt{x-1}} = 4$.

29. $\dfrac{x}{a+b} + \dfrac{a+b}{x} = \dfrac{2(a^2+b^2)}{a^2-b^2}$.

30. $\dfrac{x^2-1}{x} = \dfrac{4ab}{a^2-b^2}$.

31. $\dfrac{3x}{4-5x} - \dfrac{4-5x}{3x} = -\dfrac{5}{6}$.

32. $\dfrac{1}{x^2-3x} - \dfrac{1}{x^2+4x} = \dfrac{14}{15x^2}$.

33. $\dfrac{2x+1}{3x-2} + \dfrac{3x-2}{2x+1} = \dfrac{17}{4}$.

34. $\dfrac{1}{a-b+x} = \dfrac{1}{a} - \dfrac{1}{b} + \dfrac{1}{x}$.

35. $\dfrac{1}{3}\left(\dfrac{1}{4x-1} - \dfrac{1}{2}\right) = 3\left(\dfrac{1}{3x+1} - \dfrac{1}{3}\right)$.

36. $\dfrac{1}{x^2-4} - \dfrac{1}{3(x+2)} = 1 + \dfrac{3}{2-x}$.

37. $3\sqrt{x+a} + 2\sqrt{x+6a} = \dfrac{24a}{\sqrt{x+a}}$.

38. $\dfrac{3x^2-4}{x^2+5} - \dfrac{4x^2+3}{2x^2-1} - \dfrac{9x^2-123}{2x^4+9x^2-5} = 1$.

39. $\dfrac{5}{2x+3} + \dfrac{7}{3x-4} = \dfrac{8x^2-13x-64}{6x^2+x-12}.$

40. $\dfrac{x+4a}{2x-3a} - \dfrac{3x-2a}{3x+a} = \dfrac{30ax-a^2}{6x^2-7ax-3a^2}.$

41. $\dfrac{a}{x+a-c} + \dfrac{b}{x+b-c} = 2.$

45. $\dfrac{3}{x-1} - \dfrac{x+4}{x^2+x+1} = \dfrac{5+4x}{x^3-1} - 2.$

42. $\sqrt{mx} + \sqrt{(m-n)x+mn} = 2m.$

46. $\dfrac{3x^2+x-2}{2x^2-4x-6} = \dfrac{3x^2+4x-1}{2x^2-2x-1}.$

43. $\dfrac{28(3x+10)}{8x^3-27} - \dfrac{25}{2x^2-3x} = 0.$

47. $a^2c^2(1+x)^2 - b^2d^2(1-x)^2 = 0.$

44. $\dfrac{2x-3n}{3x+n} + \dfrac{3x+n}{2x-3n} = \dfrac{10}{3}.$

48. $\dfrac{2x+1}{\sqrt{x+1}} = \dfrac{2n+1}{\sqrt{n+1}}.$

49. $\dfrac{1}{\sqrt{1+x^2}+\sqrt{1-x^2}} + \dfrac{1}{\sqrt{1+x^2}-\sqrt{1-x^2}} = \dfrac{\sqrt{2}}{x^2}.$

50. $\dfrac{x}{x+4} - \dfrac{x+4}{x} + \dfrac{x}{x-5} - \dfrac{x-5}{x} = 0.$

51. $\sqrt{6-5x} + \sqrt{2-7x} = \sqrt{12+6x}.$

52. $\dfrac{x+a}{x-a} + \dfrac{x-a}{x+a} = \dfrac{a+b}{a-b} + \dfrac{a+b}{a-b}.$

53. $\sqrt{a^2+bx} - \sqrt{b^2+ax} = a-b.$

54. $(x-2a+3b)^2 + (x+3a-2b)^2 = 25a^2 - 30ab + 13b^2.$

55. $\dfrac{\sqrt{x^2+1}+\sqrt{x^2-1}}{\sqrt{x^2+1}-\sqrt{x^2-1}} - \dfrac{\sqrt{x^2+1}-\sqrt{x^2-1}}{\sqrt{x^2+1}+\sqrt{x^2-1}} = 2\sqrt{16x^2-1}.$

56. $(a-b+2c)x^2 - (2a+b+c)x = -a-2b+c.$

57. $\sqrt{a^2+ax+x^2} + \sqrt{a^2-ax+x^2} = a(\sqrt{7}+\sqrt{13}).$

58. $\dfrac{x+1}{x-1} + \dfrac{x+2}{x-2} + \dfrac{x+3}{x-3} = 3.$

59. $\dfrac{x+5}{x-4} - \dfrac{x-7}{x+6} - \dfrac{x+9}{x-8} = -1.$

60. $\sqrt{1+x+x^2} + \sqrt{1-x+x^2} = x(1+\sqrt{3}).$

61. $(x+a-2b)^3 - (x-2a+b)^3 = 9(a-b)^3.$

62. $\dfrac{6}{x+3} - \dfrac{1}{x-5} - \dfrac{2}{x+7} = \dfrac{3}{x-9}.$

63. $\sqrt{3x^2+4x+10} - \sqrt{3x^2+2x-8} = 2.$

64. $\dfrac{1}{x+a} + \dfrac{1}{a} + \dfrac{1}{x+b} + \dfrac{1}{b} = 0.$

65. $\dfrac{1}{x} - \dfrac{1}{b-x} + \dfrac{1}{a} + \dfrac{1}{a+b} = 0.$

66. $(3mn+n^2)x^2 - (6m^2-7mn-2n^2)x + 2mn - 3n^2 = 0.$

67. $\dfrac{x+1}{x+7} - \dfrac{x+3}{x+5} = \dfrac{x+2}{x+8} - \dfrac{x+4}{x+6}.$

68. $(8\,a^2 + 10\,ab - 3\,b^2)x^2 - (16\,a^2 + 6\,b^2)x + 8\,a^2 - 10\,ab - 3\,b^2 = 0.$

69. $\dfrac{a}{x-a} + \dfrac{b}{x-b} = \dfrac{a}{b} + \dfrac{b}{a}.$ **70.** $\dfrac{x-1}{x-2} + \dfrac{x-2}{x-3} = \dfrac{x-4}{x-5} + \dfrac{x-5}{x-6}.$

71. $\sqrt{x^2 + 2\,x - 3} - \sqrt{x^2 - 2\,x - 3} = \sqrt{2\,x^2 - 6}.$

72. $\sqrt{x^2 + 7\,ax + 12\,a^2} + \sqrt{x^2 - 7\,ax + 12\,a^2} = \sqrt{2\,x^2 + 24\,a^2}.$

73. $\dfrac{1}{x+2\,a+3\,b} + \dfrac{1}{x-2\,a-3\,b} + \dfrac{1}{x+2\,a-3\,b} + \dfrac{1}{x-2\,a+3\,b} = 0.$

74. $\dfrac{x^2 + 6\,x + 1}{x+6} + \dfrac{4\,x^2 + 12\,x + 1}{x+3} = \dfrac{2\,x^2 - 12\,x - 1}{x-6} + \dfrac{3\,x^2 - 9\,x - 1}{x-3}.$

75. $\dfrac{x+1}{x-1} + \dfrac{x+2}{x-2} + \dfrac{x+3}{x-3} = -3.$

76. $\left(x - \dfrac{4}{x}\right)\left(x - \dfrac{9}{x}\right)\left(x - \dfrac{16}{x}\right) = (x+2)(x+3)(x+4).$

77. $(x^2 + 1)(a^2 - b^2 - c^2 + 2\,bc) = 2\,x\,(a^2 + b^2 - 2\,bc + c^2).$

THEORY OF QUADRATIC EQUATIONS

454. *A quadratic equation cannot have more than two different roots.*

Every quadratic equation can be reduced to the form

$$ax^2 + bx + c = 0.$$

If possible, let this equation have three different roots, r_1, r_2, and r_3; then, by § 110,

$$ar_1^2 + br_1 + c = 0, \tag{1}$$
$$ar_2^2 + br_2 + c = 0, \tag{2}$$

and $$ar_3^2 + br_3 + c = 0. \tag{3}$$

Subtracting (2) from (1),

$$a(r_1^2 - r_2^2) + b(r_1 - r_2) = 0.$$

Then, $a(r_1 + r_2)(r_1 - r_2) + b(r_1 - r_2) = 0,$

or, $(r_1 - r_2)(ar_1 + ar_2 + b) = 0.$

Whence, either $r_1 - r_2 = 0$, or else $ar_1 + ar_2 + b = 0$ (§ 49).

But $r_1 - r_2$ cannot be zero, for, by hypothesis, r_1 and r_2 are different.

Hence, $ar_1 + ar_2 + b = 0. \tag{4}$

In like manner, by subtracting (3) from (1), we have

$$ar_1 + ar_3 + b = 0. \tag{5}$$

Subtracting (5) from (4), $ar_2 - ar_3 = 0$, or $r_2 - r_3 = 0$.

But this is impossible, for, by hypothesis, r_2 and r_3 are different.

Hence, a quadratic equation cannot have more than two different roots.

455. Sum and Product of Roots.

Let r_1 and r_2 denote the roots of $ax^2 + bx + c = 0$.

Then, by § 450,

$$r_1 = \frac{-b + \sqrt{b^2 - 4\,ac}}{2\,a}, \text{ and } r_2 = \frac{-b - \sqrt{b^2 - 4\,ac}}{2\,a}.$$

Adding these values, $\quad r_1 + r_2 = \dfrac{-2\,b}{2\,a} = -\dfrac{b}{a}$.

Multiplying them together,

$$r_1 r_2 = \frac{b^2 - (b^2 - 4\,ac)}{4\,a^2}(\S\ 132) = \frac{4\,ac}{4\,a^2} = \frac{c}{a}.$$

Hence, *if a quadratic equation is in the form* $ax^2 + bx + c = 0$, *the sum of the roots equals minus the coefficient of x divided by the coefficient of x^2, and the product of the roots equals the independent term divided by the coefficient of x^2.*

1. Find by inspection the sum and product of the roots of

$$3\,x^2 - 7\,x - 15 = 0.$$

The sum of the roots is $\dfrac{7}{3}$, and their product $\dfrac{-15}{3}$, or -5.

2. One root of the equation $6\,x^2 + 31\,x = -35$ is $-\dfrac{7}{2}$; find the other.

The equation can be written $6\,x^2 + 31\,x + 35 = 0$.

Then, the sum of the roots is $-\dfrac{31}{6}$, and their product $\dfrac{35}{6}$.

Then, the other root is $-\dfrac{31}{6} + \dfrac{7}{2}$, or $\dfrac{35}{6} \div -\dfrac{7}{2}$; that is, $-\dfrac{5}{3}$.

EXERCISE 52

Find by inspection the sum and product of the roots of:

1. $x^2 + 7x + 6 = 0$.
2. $x^2 - x + 12 = 0$.
3. $x^2 + 3x - 1 = 0$.
4. $3x^2 - x - 6 = 0$

5. $4x - 12x^2 = 3$.
6. $9x - 21x^2 + 7 = 0$.
7. $6x^2 + x + 4 = 0$.
8. $6ax^2 + 7abx = 20b^2$.

9. One root of $x^2 + 7x = 98$ is 7; find the other.

10. One root of $28x^2 - x - 15 = 0$ is $-\frac{5}{7}$; find the other.

11. One root of $x^2 - 9x + x\sqrt{3} + 2 - 7\sqrt{3} = 0$ is $5 + 2\sqrt{3}$; find the other.

12. If r_1 and r_2 are the roots of $ax^2 + bx + c = 0$, express the following in terms of r_1 and r_2:

(a) $r_1^2 + r_1r_2 + r_2^2$.   (b) $\dfrac{r_1^2 + r_2^2}{r_1r_2}$.   (c) $\dfrac{1}{r_1^2} + \dfrac{1}{r_2^2}$.   (d) $r_1^3 + r_2^3$.

456. Discussion of General Solution.

By § 448, the roots of $ax^2 + bx + c = 0$ are

$$r_1 = \frac{-b + \sqrt{b^2 - 4ac}}{2a} \text{ and } r_2 = \frac{-b - \sqrt{b^2 - 4ac}}{2a}.$$

We will now discuss these results for all possible real values of a, b, and c.

I. $b^2 - 4ac$ *positive.*

In this case, r_1 and r_2 are *real* and *unequal.*

II. $b^2 - 4ac = 0$.

In this case, r_1 and r_2 are *real* and *equal.*

III. $b_2 - 4ac$ *negative.*

In this case, r_1 and r_2 are *imaginary* (§ 407), or *complex* (§ 415).

IV. $b = 0$.

In this case, the equation takes the form

$$ax^2 + c = 0; \text{ whence, } x = \pm\sqrt{-\frac{c}{a}}.$$

If a and c are of unlike sign, the roots are *real, equal in absolute value,* and *unlike in sign.*

If a and c are of like sign, both roots are *imaginary*.

V. $c = 0$.

In this case, the equation takes the form
$$ax^2 + bx = 0; \text{ whence, } x = 0, \text{ or } -\frac{b}{a}.$$

Hence, the roots are both *real*, one being *zero*.

VI. $b = 0$, *and* $c = 0$.

In this case, the equation takes the form $ax^2 = 0$.
Hence, both roots equal zero.

The roots are both *rational*, or both *irrational*, according as $b^2 - 4\,ac$ is, or is not, a perfect square.

Ex. Determine by inspection the nature of the roots of
$$2\,x^2 - 5\,x - 18 = 0.$$

Here $a = 2, b = -5, c = -18$; and $b^2 - 4\,ac = 25 + 144 = 169$.

Since $b^2 - 4\,ac$ is positive, the roots are real and unequal.

Since $b^2 - 4\,ac$ is a perfect square, both roots are rational.

EXERCISE 53

Determine by inspection the nature of the roots of:

1. $6\,x^2 + 7\,x - 5 = 0$.
2. $4\,x^2 - x = 0$.
3. $10\,x^2 + 17\,x + 3 = 0$.
4. $4\,x^2 - 20\,x + 25 = 0$.
5. $x^2 - 21\,x + 200 = 0$.

6. $16\,x^2 - 9 = 0$.
7. $9\,x^2 = 12\,x + 1$.
8. $25\,x^2 + 30\,x + 9 = 0$.
9. $7\,x^2 + 3\,x = 0$.
10. $41\,x - 20\,x^2 = 20$.

FACTORING

457. Factoring of Quadratic Expressions.

A *quadratic expression* is an expression of the form
$$ax^2 + bx + c.$$

In § 174, we showed how to factor certain expressions of this form *by inspection*; we will now derive a rule for factoring any quadratic expression.

We have,

$$ax^2 + bx + c = a\left(x^2 + \frac{bx}{a} + \frac{c}{a}\right)$$

$$= a\left[x^2 + \frac{bx}{a} + \left(\frac{b}{2\,a}\right)^2 - \frac{b^2}{4\,a^2} + \frac{c}{a}\right]$$

$$= a\left[\left(x + \frac{b}{2\,a}\right)^2 - \frac{b^2 - 4\,ac}{4\,a^2}\right]$$

$$= a\left(x + \frac{b}{2\,a} + \frac{\sqrt{b^2 - 4\,ac}}{2\,a}\right)\left(x + \frac{b}{2\,a} - \frac{\sqrt{b^2 - 4\,ac}}{2\,a}\right),$$

by § 171.   (1)

But by § 450, the roots of $ax^2 + bx + c = 0$ are

$$-\frac{b}{2\,a} + \frac{\sqrt{b^2 - 4\,ac}}{2\,a} \text{ and } -\frac{b}{2\,a} - \frac{\sqrt{b^2 - 4\,ac}}{2\,a}.$$

Hence, *to factor a quadratic expression, place it equal to zero, and solve the equation thus formed.*

Then the required factors are the coefficient of x^2 in the given expression, x minus the first root, and x minus the second.

1. Factor $6\,x^2 + 7\,x - 3$.

Solving the equation $6\,x^2 + 7\,x - 3 = 0$, by § 450,

$$x = \frac{-7 \pm \sqrt{49 + 72}}{12} = \frac{-7 \pm 11}{12} = \frac{1}{3} \text{ or } -\frac{3}{2}.$$

Then, $6\,x^2 + 7\,x - 3 = 6\left(x - \frac{1}{3}\right)\left(x + \frac{3}{2}\right)$

$$= 3\left(x - \frac{1}{3}\right) \times 2\left(x + \frac{3}{2}\right)$$

$$= (3\,x - 1)(2\,x + 3).$$

The example may also be solved by using (1) as a *formula.*

2. Factor $4 + 13\,x - 12\,x^2$.

Solving the equation $4 + 13\,x - 12\,x^2 = 0$, we have

$$x = \frac{-13 \pm \sqrt{169 + 192}}{-24} = \frac{-13 \pm 19}{-24} = -\frac{1}{4} \text{ or } \frac{4}{3}.$$

Whence, $4 + 13x - 12x^2 = -12\left(x + \frac{1}{4}\right)\left(x - \frac{4}{3}\right)$

$$= 4\left(x + \frac{1}{4}\right) \times \left(-3\right)\left(x - \frac{4}{3}\right)$$

$$= (1 + 4x)(4 - 3x).$$

3. Factor $2x^2 - 3xy - 2y^2 - 7x + 4y + 6$.

We solve the equation

$$2x^2 - x(3y + 7) - 2y^2 + 4y + 6 = 0.$$

By § 450, $\quad x = \dfrac{3y + 7 \pm \sqrt{(3y + 7)^2 + 16y^2 - 32y - 48}}{4}$

$$= \frac{3y + 7 \pm \sqrt{25y^2 + 10y + 1}}{4}$$

$$= \frac{3y + 7 \pm (5y + 1)}{4}$$

$$= \frac{8y + 8}{4} \text{ or } \frac{-2y + 6}{4} = 2y + 2 \text{ or } \frac{-y + 3}{2}.$$

Then, $\quad 2x^2 - 3xy - 2y^2 - 7x + 4y + 6$

$$= 2[x - (2y + 2)]\left[x - \frac{-y + 3}{2}\right]$$

$$= (x - 2y - 2)(2x + y - 3).$$

458. If the coefficient of x^2 is a perfect square, it is preferable to factor the expression by completing the square as in § 447, and then using § 171.

1. Factor $9x^2 - 9x - 4$.

By § 447, $9x^2 - 9x$ will become a perfect square by adding to it the square of $\dfrac{9}{2 \times 3}$, or $\dfrac{3}{2}$; then,

$$9x^2 - 9x - 4 = 9x^2 - 9x + \left(\frac{3}{2}\right)^2 - \frac{9}{4} - 4$$

$$= \left(3x - \frac{3}{2}\right)^2 - \frac{25}{4}.$$

Then, $9\,x^2 - 9\,x - 4 = \left(3\,x - \dfrac{3}{2} + \dfrac{5}{2}\right)\left(3\,x - \dfrac{3}{2} - \dfrac{5}{2}\right)$ (§ 171)

$$= (3\,x + 1)(3\,x - 4).$$

If the x^2 term is negative, the entire expression should be enclosed in parentheses preceded by a $-$ sign.

2. Factor $3 - 12\,x - 4\,x^2$.

$$\begin{aligned}
3 - 12\,x - 4\,x^2 &= -(4\,x^2 + 12\,x - 3) \\
&= -(4\,x^2 + 12\,x + 9 - 9 - 3) \\
&= -[(2\,x + 3)^2 - 12] \\
&= (2\,x + 3 + \sqrt{12}) \times (-1)(2\,x + 3 - \sqrt{12}) \\
&= (2\sqrt{3} + 3 + 2\,x)(2\sqrt{3} - 3 - 2\,x).
\end{aligned}$$

In certain cases, the factors of a quadratic expression involve complex numbers.

3. Factor $x^2 - 4\,x + 9$.

$$\begin{aligned}
x^2 - 4\,x + 9 &= (x^2 - 4\,x + 4) + 5 \\
&= (x - 2)^2 - (-5) \\
&= (x - 2 + \sqrt{-5})(x - 2 - \sqrt{-5}).
\end{aligned}$$

EXERCISE 54

Factor the following by the method of § 457 :

1. $x^2 + 14\,x + 33$.
2. $x^2 - 13\,x + 40$.
3. $x^2 - x - 42$.
4. $4\,x^2 + 3\,x - 7$.
5. $3\,x^2 - 11\,x - 20$.
6. $2\,x^2 + 9\,x + 9$.
7. $5\,x^2 - 36\,x + 36$.
8. $9 - 8\,x - x^2$.
9. $20 + 19\,x - 6\,x^2$.
10. $8\,x^2 + 18\,x - 5$.
11. $6\,x^2 + 7\,x + 2$.
12. $12\,x^2 + 7\,x - 45$.
13. $14\,x^2 - 23\,xa + 3\,a^2$.
14. $24\,x^2 - 17\,xy + 3\,y^2$.
15. $28\,x^2 - mx - 2\,m^2$.
16. $5 - 26\,x - 24\,x^2$.
17. $8 + 14\,x - 15\,x^2$.
18. $21\,x^2 + 23\,xy^2 + 6\,y^4$.
19. $x^2 - xy - 6\,y^2 - 6\,x + 13\,y + 5$.

20. $x^2 - 3xy - 4y^2 + 6x - 4y + 8.$

21. $x^2 - 6xy + 5y^2 - 2x - 2y - 3.$

22. $2a^2 + 5ab + 2b^2 + 7a + 5b + 3.$

23. $3x^2 + 7xy - 6y^2 - 10xz - 8yz + 8z^2.$

24. $2 - 7y - 7x + 3y^2 + xy - 4x^2.$

Factor the following by the method of § 458 :

25. $4x^2 - 12x - 7.$

26. $32 - 12x - 9x^2.$

27. $16x^2 + 56x + 33.$

28. $9x^2 + 24x - 2.$

29. $4x^2 + 20x + 19.$

30. $1 + 2x - x^2.$

31. $16x^2 - 16x + 1.$

32. $25x^2 - 25x + 6.$

33. $36x^2 + 72x + 29.$

34. $11 + 10x - 25x^2.$

459. We will now take up the factoring of expressions of the forms $x^4 + ax^2y^2 + y^4$, or $x^4 + y^4$, when the factors involve surds. (Compare § 172.)

1. Factor $a^4 + 2a^2b^2 + 25b^4.$

$$a^4 + 2a^2b^2 + 25b^4 = (a^4 + 10a^2b^2 + 25b^4) - 8a^2b^2$$
$$= (a^2 + 5b^2)^2 - (ab\sqrt{8})^2$$
$$= (a^2 + 5b^2 + ab\sqrt{8})(a^2 + 5b^2 - ab\sqrt{8})$$
$$= (a^2 + 2ab\sqrt{2} + 5b^2)(a^2 - 2ab\sqrt{2} + 5b^2).$$

The above expression may also be expressed as the product of two factors involving complex numbers.

2. Factor $x^4 + 1.$

$$x^4 + 1 = (x^4 + 2x^2 + 1) - 2x^2$$
$$= (x^2 + 1)^2 - (x\sqrt{2})^2$$
$$= (x^2 + x\sqrt{2} + 1)(x^2 - x\sqrt{2} + 1).$$

EXERCISE 55

In each of the following, obtain two sets of factors, where this can be done without bringing in imaginary numbers :

1. $x^4 - 7x^2 + 4.$

2. $a^4 + b^4.$

3. $9m^4 - 11m^2 + 1.$

4. $4a^4 + 6a^2 + 9.$

5. $36x^4 - 92x^2 + 49.$

6. $25m^4 + 28m^2n^2 + 16n^4.$

460. Solution of Equations by Factoring.

In § 183, we showed how to solve equations whose first members could be resolved by inspection into first degree factors, and whose second members were zero.

We will now take up equations whose first members can be resolved into factors partly of the first and partly of the second, or entirely of the second degree.

1. Solve the equation $x^3 - 1 = 0$.

Factoring the first member, $(x - 1)(x^2 + x + 1) = 0$.

Then, $\qquad x - 1 = 0$, or $x = 1$;

and $\qquad x^2 + x + 1 = 0$; whence, by § 450,

$$x = \frac{-1 \pm \sqrt{1-4}}{2} = \frac{-1 \pm \sqrt{-3}}{2}.$$

2. Solve the equation $x^4 + 1 = 0$.

By Ex. 2, § 459,

$$x^4 + 1 = (x^2 + x\sqrt{2} + 1)(x^2 - x\sqrt{2} + 1).$$

Solving $x^2 + x\sqrt{2} + 1 = 0$, we have

$$x = \frac{-\sqrt{2} \pm \sqrt{2-4}}{2} = \frac{-\sqrt{2} \pm \sqrt{-2}}{2}.$$

Solving $x^2 - x\sqrt{2} + 1 = 0$, we have

$$x = \frac{\sqrt{2} \pm \sqrt{2-4}}{2} = \frac{\sqrt{2} \pm \sqrt{-2}}{2}.$$

EXERCISE 56

Solve the following equations :

1. $3x^3 - 2x^2 + 15x - 10 = 0$. $\qquad$ **2.** $x^4 + 4x^2 - 32 = 0$.

3. $x^3 - 64 = 0$. $\qquad$ **5.** $27x^3 + 8 = 0$. $\qquad$ **7.** $64x^3 - 125 = 0$.

4. $3x^4 + 24x = 0$. $\qquad$ **6.** $16x^4 - 81 = 0$. $\qquad$ **8.** $x^6 - 729a^6 = 0$.

9. $\dfrac{x^2 + 2x + 4}{x^2 - 2x - 4} = \dfrac{4}{x^2}$. $\qquad$ **10.** $\dfrac{x^2(x+4a) - 9a^3}{x^2(x-4a) - 9a^3} + \dfrac{x^2 - 2a^2}{x^2 + 2a^2} = 0$.

11. $x^4 + 81 = 0$. $\qquad$ **13.** $x^4 + 2x^2 + 25 = 0$. $\qquad$ **15.** $x^8 - 256a^8 = 0$.

12. $x^4 - 5x^2 + 1 = 0$. $\qquad$ **14.** $x^4 - 18x^2 + 9 = 0$. $\qquad$ **16.** $9x^4 - x^2 + 4 = 0$.

461. Maxima and Minima Values of Quadratic Expressions.

The greatest or least value of a quadratic expression may sometimes be found by the artifice of completing the square.

1. Find the minimum value of $x^2 - 5x + 7$.

We have $\quad x^2 - 5x + 7 = \left(x - \dfrac{5}{2}\right)^2 + \dfrac{3}{4}$.

Since $\left(x - \dfrac{5}{2}\right)^2$ is positive for every real value of x, the least

value of $\left(x - \dfrac{5}{2}\right)^2 + \dfrac{3}{4}$ is when $x = \dfrac{5}{2}$.

Thus, the minimum value of the expression is $\dfrac{3}{4}$.

2. Find the maximum value of $4 - 3x - 2x^2$.

We may write the expression

$$4 - 2\left(x^2 + \frac{3}{2}x\right) = 4 - 2\left[\left(x + \frac{3}{4}\right)^2 - \frac{9}{16}\right] = \frac{41}{8} - 2\left(x + \frac{3}{4}\right)^2.$$

The greatest value is when $x = -\dfrac{3}{4}$.

Thus, the greatest value of the expression is $\dfrac{41}{8}$.

EXERCISE 57

Find the maxima and minima values of the following, and determine which:

1. $x^2 + 3x - 1$.	3. $4x^2 - 8x - 5$.	5. $3x^2 + 5x + 4$.
2. $6 - 8x - x^2$.	4. $3 + x - x^2$.	6. $-2 - 9x - 9x^2$.
7. $6x^2 - 7x + 3$.		8. $-7 + 2x - 5x^2$.

PROBLEMS INVOLVING QUADRATIC EQUATIONS WITH ONE UNKNOWN NUMBER

462. In solving problems which involve quadratic equations, there will usually be two values of the unknown number; only those values should be retained which satisfy the conditions of the problem.

The considerations of §§ 261 and 262 hold for equations of any degree.

1. A man sold a watch for $\$21$, and lost as many per cent as the watch cost dollars. Find the cost of the watch.

Let $\qquad\qquad x =$ number of dollars the watch cost.

Then, $\qquad\qquad x =$ the per cent of loss,

and $\qquad x \times \dfrac{x}{100}$, or $\dfrac{x^2}{100} =$ number of dollars lost.

By the conditions, $\qquad \dfrac{x^2}{100} = x - 21$.

Solving, $\qquad\qquad x = 30$ or 70.

Then, the cost of the watch was either $\$30$ or $\$70$; for either of these answers satisfies the conditions of the problem.

2. A farmer bought some sheep for $\$72$. If he had bought 6 more for the same money, they would have cost him $\$1$ apiece less. How many did he buy?

Let $\qquad\qquad x =$ number bought.

Then, $\qquad\qquad \dfrac{72}{x} =$ number of dollars paid for one,

and $\qquad\qquad \dfrac{72}{x+6} =$ number of dollars paid for one if there had been 6 more.

By the conditions, $\qquad \dfrac{72}{x} = \dfrac{72}{x+6} + 1$.

Solving, $\qquad\qquad x = 18$ or -24.

Only the *positive* value of x is admissible, for the negative value does not satisfy the conditions of the problem.

Therefore, the number of sheep was 18.

If, in the enunciation of the problem, the words "6 more" had been changed to "6 fewer," and "$\$1$ apiece less" to "$\$1$ apiece more," we should have found the answer 24. (Compare § 261.)

EXERCISE 58

1. What number added to its reciprocal gives $2\frac{1}{6}$?

2. Divide the number 24 into two parts such that twice the square of the greater shall exceed 5 times the square of the less by 45.

3. Find three consecutive numbers such that the sum of their squares shall be 434.

4. Find two numbers whose difference is 7, and the difference of whose cubes is 1267.

5. Find five consecutive numbers such that the quotient of the first by the second, added to the quotient of the fifth by the fourth, shall equal $\frac{23}{12}$.

6. Find four consecutive numbers such that if the sum of the squares of the second and fourth be divided by the sum of the squares of the first and third, the quotient shall be $\frac{13}{10}$.

7. The area of a certain square field exceeds that of another square field by 1008 square yards. And the perimeter of the greater exceeds one-half that of the smaller by 120 yards. Find the dimensions of each field.

8. A fast train runs 8 miles an hour faster than a slow train, and takes 3 hours less to travel 288 miles. Find the rates of the trains.

9. The perimeter of a rectangular field is 184 feet, and its area 1920 square feet. Find its dimensions.

10. A merchant sold goods for $ 22.75, and lost as many per cent as the goods cost dollars. What was the cost ?

11. A merchant sold two pieces of cloth of different quality for $ 40.25, the poorer containing 28 yards. He received for the finer as many dollars a yard as there were yards in the piece ; and 7 yards of the poorer sold for as much as 2 yards of the finer. Find the value of each piece.

12. A merchant sold goods for $ 50.69, and gained as many per cent as the goods cost dollars. What was the cost ?

13. A has five-fourths as much money as B. After giving A $ 6, B's money is equal to A's multiplied by a fraction whose numerator is 15, and whose denominator is the number of dollars A had at first. How much had each at first ?

14. A and B set out at the same time from places 247 miles apart, and travel towards each other. A travels at the rate of 9 miles an hour ; and B's rate in miles an hour is less by 3 than the number of hours at the end of which they meet. Find B's rate.

15. A man buys a certain number of shares of stock, paying for each as many dollars as he buys shares. After the price has advanced as many dimes per share as he has shares, he sells, and gains $ 722.50. How many shares did he buy ?

16. The two digits of a number differ by 1 ; and if the square of the number be added to the square of the given number with its digits reversed, the sum is 585. Find the number.

17. A gives $ 336, in equal amounts, to a certain number of persons. B gives the same sum, in equal amounts, to 18 fewer persons, and gives to each $ 6 more than A. How much does A give to each person ?

18. The telegraph poles along a certain road are at equal intervals. If the interval between the poles were increased by 22 feet, there would be 8 fewer in a mile. How many are there in a mile?

19. A merchant bought a cask of wine for $45. Having lost 3 gallons by leakage, he sells the remainder at $1.50 a gallon above cost, and makes a profit of 33⅓ per cent on his entire outlay. How many gallons did the cask contain?

20. The men in a regiment can be arranged in a column twice as long as it is wide. If their number were 224 less, they could be arranged in a hollow square 4 deep, having in each outer side of the square as many men as there were in the length of the column. Find the number of men.

21. The denominator of a fraction exceeds twice the numerator by 2, and the difference between the fraction and its reciprocal is $\dfrac{55}{24}$. Find the fraction.

22. A man started to walk 3 miles, intending to arrive at a certain time. After walking a mile, he was detained 10 minutes, and was in consequence obliged to walk the rest of the way a mile an hour faster. What was his original speed?

23. A regiment, in solid square, has 24 fewer men in front than when in a hollow square 6 deep. How many men are there in the regiment?

24. A rectangular field is surrounded by a fence 160 feet long. The cost of this fence, at 96 cents a foot, was one-tenth as many dollars as there are square feet in the area of the field. What are the dimensions of the field?

25. A crew can row down stream 18 miles, and back again, in 7½ hours. Their rate up stream is 1½ miles an hour less than the rate of the stream. Find the rate of the stream, and of the crew in still water.

26. A man put $5000 in a savings-bank paying a certain rate of interest. At the end of a year he withdrew $75, leaving the remainder at interest. At the end of another year, the amount due him was $5278.50. Find the rate of interest.

27. A square garden has a square plot of grass at its centre, surrounded by a path 4 feet in width. The area of the garden outside the path exceeds by 768 square feet the area of the path; and the side of the garden is less by 16 feet than three times the side of the plot. Find the dimensions of the garden.

28. A merchant has a cask full of wine. He draws out 6 gallons, and fills the cask with water. Again he draws out 6 gallons, and fills the cask with water. There are now 25 gallons of pure wine in the cask. How many gallons does the cask hold?

29. A and B sell a quantity of corn for $22, A selling 10 bushels more than B. If A had sold as many bushels as B did, he would have received $8 ; while if B had sold as many bushels as A did, he would have received $15. How many bushels did each sell, and at what price ?

30. Two men are employed to do a certain piece of work. The first receives $48 ; and the second, who works 6 days less, receives $27. If the second had worked all the time, and the first 6 days less, they would have received equal amounts. How many days did each work, and at what wages ?

31. A and B run around a course, starting from the same point, in opposite directions. A reaches the starting-point 4 minutes, and B 9 minutes, after they have met on the road. If they continue to run at the same rates, in how many minutes will they meet at the starting-point ?

32. A carriage-wheel, 15 feet in circumference, revolves in a certain number of seconds. If it revolved in a time longer by one second, the carriage would travel 14400 feet less in an hour. In how many seconds does it revolve ?

DISCUSSION OF PROBLEMS INVOLVING QUADRATIC EQUATIONS WITH ONE UNKNOWN NUMBER

463. Interpretation of Complex Results.

Prob. Let it be required to find two real numbers whose sum shall be 10, and product 26.

Let $x =$ one number.

Then, $10 - x =$ the other.

By the conditions, $x(10 - x) = 26$.

Solving, $x = 5 \pm \sqrt{-1}$.

We conclude that the given conditions cannot be satisfied, and the problem is impossible.

Hence, *imaginary or complex results show that the problem is impossible.*

464. The Problem of the Lights.

To find upon the line which joins two lights, A and B, the point equally illuminated by them ; it being given that the intensity of a light, at a certain distance, equals its intensity at the distance 1, divided by the square of the given distance.

Let B be c units to the right of A.

Let a and b denote the intensities of A and B, respectively, at the distance 1.

Let the point of equal illumination be x units to the *right* of A.

Then it will be $c - x$ units from B.

By the conditions of the problem, the intensity of A at the distance x units, is $\dfrac{a}{x^2}$; and the intensity of B at the distance $c - x$ units, is $\dfrac{b}{(c - x)^2}$.

Then,
$$\frac{a}{x^2} = \frac{b}{(c - x)^2}.$$

Solving this equation, $x = \dfrac{c\sqrt{a}}{\sqrt{a} + \sqrt{b}}$ or $\dfrac{c\sqrt{a}}{\sqrt{a} - \sqrt{b}}$.

Since there are two lights, c must always be positive; then, neither a, b, nor c can equal zero.

The problem then admits of only three different hypotheses:

1. $a > b$.

In this case, $\dfrac{\sqrt{a}}{\sqrt{a} + \sqrt{b}}$ is < 1, and $> \dfrac{1}{2}$.

Then, the first value of x is $< c$, and $> \dfrac{c}{2}$.

Thus, the first point of equal illumination is at C, between the lights, and nearer B, the lesser light.

Again, $\dfrac{\sqrt{a}}{\sqrt{a} - \sqrt{b}}$ is > 1.

Then, the second value of x is $> c$.

Thus, the second point of equal illumination is at C', in AB produced, to the right of the lesser light.

2. $a < b$.

In this case, $\dfrac{\sqrt{a}}{\sqrt{a} + \sqrt{b}}$ is $< \dfrac{1}{2}$, and the first value of $x < \dfrac{c}{2}$.

Then, the first point of equal illumination is between the lights, and nearer A, the lesser light.

Again, the second value of x is *negative*.

Then, the second point of equal illumination is at C'', in BA produced, to the left of the lesser light.

3. $a = b$.

In this case, $\dfrac{\sqrt{a}}{\sqrt{a} + \sqrt{b}} = \dfrac{1}{2}$, and the first value of $x = \dfrac{c}{2}$.

Then, the first point of equal illumination is midway between the lights.

Again, $\dfrac{c\sqrt{a}}{\sqrt{a} - \sqrt{b}} = \infty$ (§ 247).

Then, there is no second point of equal illumination in AB, or AB produced.

In this case, as $\sqrt{a} - \sqrt{b}$ approaches the limit zero, the second value of x increases without limit.

That is, as the difference between the intensities of the lights approaches the limit zero, the distance from A to the second point of equal illumination increases without limit.

GRAPHICAL REPRESENTATION OF QUADRATIC EXPRESSIONS WITH ONE UNKNOWN NUMBER

465. The graph of a quadratic expression, with one unknown number, may be found as in § 279.

Ex. Find the graph of $x^2 - 2x - 3$.

Put $y = x^2 - 2x - 3$.

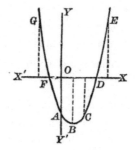

If $x = 0$, $y = -3$. (A)

If $x = 1$, $y = -4$. (B)

If $x = 2$, $y = -3$. (C)

If $x = 3$, $y = 0$. (D)

If $x = 4$, $y = 5$. (E)

If $x = -1$, $y = 0$. (F)

If $x = -2$, $y = 5$. (G) .

The graph is the *curve GBE*.

By taking other values for x, the curve may be traced beyond E and G.

It extends in either direction to an indefinitely great distance from XX'.

To determine the *lowest* point of the curve, we must know what negative value of y has the greatest absolute value; this may be found as in § 461.

We have, $\qquad x^2 - 2x - 3 = (x-1)^2 - 4.$

The latter expression has its negative value of greatest absolute value when $x = 1$, being then equal to -4.

Then, the lowest point of the curve has the co-ordinates $(1, -4)$; and is therefore the point B.

466. The principle of § 280 holds for the graph of the first member of any quadratic equation, with one unknown number.

Thus, the above graph intersects XX' twice; once at $x = 3$, and once at $x = -1$; and the roots of the equation $x^2 - 2x - 3 = 0$ are 3 and -1.

467. Graphs of the First Members of Quadratic Equations having Equal or Complex Roots.

1. Consider the equation $x^2 - 4x + 4 = 0$.

By § 183, the two roots are 2 and 2.

To find the graph of the first member, put $y = (x - 2)^2$.

If $x = 0$, $y = 4$. If $x = 2$, $y = 0$.

If $x = 1$, $y = 1$. If $x = 3$, $y = 1$; etc.

The graph is the curve ABC, which extends beyond A and C to an indefinitely great distance from XX'.

Since y cannot be negative, the graph is *tangent* to XX' at the point whose co-ordinates are $(2, 0)$.

It is evident from this that, if a quadratic equation, with one unknown number, has equal roots, the graph of its first member is tangent to XX'.

2. Consider the equation $x^2 + x + 2 = 0$.

Solving, $x = \dfrac{-1 \pm \sqrt{-7}}{2}$.

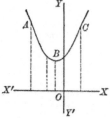

To find the graph of the first member, put $y = x^2 + x + 2$.

If $x = 0$, $y = 2$. If $x = -1$, $y = 2$.

If $x = 1$, $y = 4$. If $x = -2$, $y = 4$; etc.

The graph is the curve ABC, which extends beyond A and C to an indefinitely great distance from XX'.

To find the point B, where the curve is nearest to XX', we have

$$x^2 + x + 2 = \left(x + \frac{1}{2}\right)^2 + \frac{7}{4}.$$

The latter expression has its least value, $\dfrac{7}{4}$, when $x = -\dfrac{1}{2}$.

Then, B has the co-ordinates $\left(-\dfrac{1}{2}, \dfrac{7}{4}\right)$.

It is evident from this that, if a quadratic equation, with one unknown number, has complex roots, the graph of its first member does not intersect XX'.

The equation $a^2 x^2 - b^2 = 0$ may be written $(ax + b)(ax - b) = 0$.

The graph of the first member in this case is a pair of straight lines parallel to YY', respectively, $\dfrac{b}{a}$ to the right and $\dfrac{b}{a}$ to the left, of that line.

EXERCISE 59

Find the graph of the first member of each of the following, determine its lowest point, and verify the principles of §§ 280 and 467 in the results :

1. $x^2 - 5x + 4 = 0$.   3. $4x^2 + 7x = 0$.   5. $4x^2 + 12x + 9 = 0$.

2. $x^2 + x - 6 = 0$.   4. $8x^2 - 14x - 15 = 0$.   6. $2x^2 + 4x + 5 = 0$.

Find the graphs of the first members of the following, and verify the principle of § 280 in the results :

7. $x^2 - 16 = 0$.   8. $9x^2 - 25 = 0$.

XX. EQUATIONS SOLVED LIKE QUAD-
RATICS

468. Equations in the Quadratic Form.

An equation is said to be in the *quadratic form* when it is in the form
$$ax^{2n} + bx^n + c = 0,$$

where n is an integer or fraction; as,
$$x^6 - 6 x^3 - 16 = 0,$$

and
$$x^{-3} + x^{-\frac{3}{2}} = 72.$$

Such equations are readily solved by the methods of the preceding chapter.

1. Solve the equation $x^6 - 6 x^3 = 16$.

Completing the square by the rule of § 445,
$$x^6 - 6 x^3 + 9 = 16 + 9 = 25.$$

Extracting square roots, $x^3 - 3 = \pm 5$.

Then, $x^3 = 3 \pm 5 = 8$ or -2.

Extracting cube roots, . $x = 2$ or $-\sqrt[3]{2}$.

There are also four imaginary roots, which may be found by the method of § 460.

2. Solve the equation $2 x + 3 \sqrt{x} = 27$.

Since $\sqrt{x}$ is the same as $x^{\frac{1}{2}}$, this is in the quadratic form. Multiplying by 8, and adding 3^2 to both members,
$$16 x + 24 \sqrt{x} + 9 = 216 + 9 = 225.$$

Extracting square roots, $4 \sqrt{x} + 3 = \pm 15$.

Then, $4 \sqrt{x} = -3 \pm 15 = 12$ or -18.

Or, $\sqrt{x} = 3$ or $-\dfrac{9}{2}$.

But only *principal roots* are considered.

Therefore, $\sqrt{x}$ cannot be negative, and the only solution is

$$\sqrt{x} = 3, \text{ or } x = 9.$$

In solving an equation of the form

$$ax^{\frac{2p}{q}} + bx^{\frac{p}{q}} + c = 0,$$

any value of $x^{\frac{p}{q}}$ which is not a principal root, should be rejected.

For example, if $x^{-\frac{3}{4}} = -2$, the corresponding solution should be rejected.

3. Solve the equation $2\,x^{-\frac{2}{3}} - 11\,x^{-\frac{1}{3}} + 12 = 0$.

By formula (1), § 450,

$$x^{-\frac{1}{3}} = \frac{11 \pm \sqrt{121 - 96}}{4} = \frac{11 \pm 5}{4} = 4 \text{ or } \frac{3}{2}.$$

In this case, neither value is rejected.

Extracting square roots, $x^{-\frac{1}{6}} = \pm 2 \text{ or } \pm \left(\frac{3}{2}\right)^{\frac{1}{2}}$.

Raising to third power, $x^{-1} = \pm 8 \text{ or } \pm \left(\frac{3}{2}\right)^{\frac{3}{2}}$.

Inverting, $\qquad \cdot \qquad x = \pm \frac{1}{8} \text{ or } \pm \left(\frac{2}{3}\right)^{\frac{3}{2}}$.

To solve an equation of the form $x^{\frac{p}{q}} = a$, first extract the root corresponding to the numerator of the fractional exponent, and afterwards raise to the power corresponding to the denominator; careful attention must be given to algebraic signs.

469. An equation may sometimes be solved with reference to an *expression*, by regarding it as a single letter.

1. Solve the equation $(x+5)^{\frac{1}{2}} - 3(x+5)^{\frac{1}{4}} = 40$.

Completing the square,

$$(x+5)^{\frac{1}{2}} - 3(x+5)^{\frac{1}{4}} + \left(\frac{3}{2}\right)^2 = 40 + \frac{9}{4} = \frac{169}{4}.$$

Extracting square roots, $(x+5)^{\frac{1}{4}} - \frac{3}{2} = \pm \frac{13}{2}$.

Then, $\qquad\qquad (x+5)^{\frac{1}{4}} = \frac{3}{2} \pm \frac{13}{2} = 8 \text{ or } -5.$

We reject the value $(x+5)^{\frac{3}{4}} = -5$; the only solution is
$$(x+5)^{\frac{3}{4}} = 8.$$

Extracting cube root, $(x+5)^{\frac{1}{4}} = 2$.

Raising to fourth power, $x + 5 = 16$, and $x = 11$.

Certain equations of the fourth degree may be solved by the rules for quadratics.

2. Solve the equation $x^4 + 12\,x^3 + 34\,x^2 - 12\,x - 35 = 0$.

The equation may be written
$$(x^4 + 12\,x^3 + 36\,x^2) - 2\,x^2 - 12\,x = 35.$$

Or, $(x^2 + 6\,x)^2 - 2\,(x^2 + 6\,x) = 35.$

Completing the square,
$$(x^2 + 6\,x)^2 - 2\,(x^2 + 6\,x) + 1 = 36.$$

Extracting square roots, $(x^2 + 6\,x) - 1 = \pm 6$.

Then, $x^2 + 6\,x = 7$ or -5.

Completing the square, $x^2 + 6\,x + 9 = 16$ or 4.

Extracting square roots, $x + 3 = \pm 4$ or ± 2.

Then, $x = -3 \pm 4$ or $-3 \pm 2 = 1, -7, -1$, or -5.

In solving equations like the above, the first step is to complete the square with reference to the x^4 and x^3 terms; by § 447, the third term of the square is the square of the quotient obtained by dividing the x^3 term by twice the square root of the x^4 term.

3. Solve the equation $x^2 - 6\,x + 5\sqrt{x^2 - 6\,x + 20} = 46$.

Adding 20 to both members,
$$(x^2 - 6\,x + 20) + 5\sqrt{x^2 - 6\,x + 20} = 66.$$

Completing the square,
$$(x^2 - 6\,x + 20) + 5\sqrt{x^2 - 6\,x + 20} + \frac{25}{4} = 66 + \frac{25}{4} = \frac{289}{4}.$$

Extracting square roots, $\sqrt{x^2 - 6\,x + 20} + \frac{5}{2} = \pm\frac{17}{2}$.

Then, $\sqrt{x^2 - 6\,x + 20} = 6$ or -11.

The only solution is $\sqrt{x^2 - 6x + 20} = 6.$

Squaring, $x^2 - 6x + 20 = 36.$

Completing the square, $x^2 - 6x + 9 = 25.$

Extracting square roots, $x - 3 = \pm 5$, and $x = 8$ or -2.

In solving equations of the above form, add such an expression to both members that the expression without the radical sign in the first member may be the same as that within, or some multiple of it.

4. Solve the equation $2x^2 + 5x - 2x\sqrt{x^2 + 5x - 3} = 12.$

The equation may be written

$$x^2 + 5x - 2x\sqrt{x^2 + 5x - 3} + x^2 = 12.$$

Subtracting 3 from both members,

$$(x^2 + 5x - 3) - 2x\sqrt{x^2 + 5x - 3} + x^2 = 9.$$

Extracting square roots, $\sqrt{x^2 + 5x - 3} - x = \pm 3.$

Or, $\sqrt{x^2 + 5x - 3} = x \pm 3.$

Squaring, $x^2 + 5x - 3 = x^2 \pm 6x + 9.$

Then, $-x$ or $11x = 12$, and $x = -12$ or $\dfrac{12}{11}.$

Neither value satisfies the given equation.

5. Solve the equation $\dfrac{x^2 - 3}{x^2 - x} + \dfrac{x^2 - x}{x^2 - 3} = \dfrac{5}{2}.$

Representing $\dfrac{x^2 - 3}{x^2 - x}$ by y, the equation becomes

$$y + \frac{1}{y} = \frac{5}{2}, \text{ or } 2y^2 + 2 = 5y.$$

Solving this, $y = \dfrac{1}{2}$ or 2; that is, $\dfrac{x^2 - 3}{x^2 - x} = \dfrac{1}{2}$ or 2.

Taking first value, $2x^2 - 6 = x^2 - x.$

Or, $x^2 + x = 6.$

Solving, $x = 2$ or -3.

Taking second value, $x^2 - 3 = 2x^2 - 2x.$

Or, $-x^2 + 2x = 3.$

Solving, $x = 1 \pm \sqrt{-2}.$

EXERCISE 60

Solve the following:

1. $x^4 - 29 x^2 = -100$.

2. $x^{-6} + 19 x^{-3} = 216$.

3. $x^{\frac{4}{3}} + 10 x^{\frac{2}{3}} + 9 = 0$.

4. $x^{\frac{5}{2}} - 33 x^{\frac{5}{4}} = -32$.

5. $64 + 63 x^{-\frac{3}{2}} - x^{-3} = 0$.

6. $3 x^{-2} + 14 x^{-1} = 5$.

7. $5 x^{-\frac{6}{5}} + 7 x^{-\frac{3}{5}} = -2$.

8. $4 x^{\frac{2}{5}} - \dfrac{18}{x^{\frac{2}{5}}} = -21$.

9. $6 x - 2 = 11 \sqrt{x}$.

10. $x^{-\frac{10}{3}} + 244 x^{-\frac{5}{3}} = -243$.

11. $2 x^{-8} - 35 x^{-4} + 48 = 0$.

12. $27 x^6 + 46 x^3 = 16$.

13. $32 x^{\frac{5}{2}} - 33 = -x^{-\frac{5}{2}}$.

14. $16 x^8 - 33 x^4 - 243 = 0$.

15. $161 x^5 + 5 = -32 x^{10}$.

16. $81 x^{-\frac{3}{4}} - 308 - 64 x^{\frac{3}{4}} = 0$.

17. $(2 x^2 + 3 x)^2 - 4(2 x^2 + 3 x) = 45$.

18. $x^4 + 12 x^3 + 14 x^2 - 132 x - 135 = 0$.

19. $5 x + 12 - 5 \sqrt{5 x + 12} = -4$.

20. $\dfrac{x^2 - 3}{2 x} + \dfrac{2 x}{x^2 - 3} = -\dfrac{17}{4}$.

21. $3 x^2 + x + 5 \sqrt{3 x^2 + x + 6} = 30$.

22. $8 x^2 - 1 + 6 x \sqrt{8 x^2 - 1} = -8 x^2$.

23. $x^4 - 2 ax^3 - 17 a^2x^2 + 18 a^3x + 72 a^4 = 0$.

24. $18\left(x - \dfrac{1}{x}\right)^2 + 21\left(x - \dfrac{1}{x}\right) = -5$.

25. $\dfrac{x^2 + 2}{2 x - 5} - \dfrac{2 x - 5}{x^2 + 2} = \dfrac{35}{6}$.

26. $x^2 - 6 \sqrt{x^2 - 4 x + 11} = 4 x - 19$.

27. $x^2 + 3 x + 4 - \sqrt{x^2 + 3 x + 4} = 2$.

28. $(4 x^2 + 2 x - 7)^2 + 4 x^2 + 2 x - 189 = 0$.

29. $\sqrt{x^2 - 3 x - 3} = x^2 - 3 x - 23$.

30. $(2 x^2 - 3 x - 1)^3 - 6(2 x^2 - 3 x - 1)^{\frac{3}{2}} = 16$.

31. $3 \sqrt[3]{x^2 - 12 x} - 7 \sqrt[6]{x^2 - 12 x} = -2$.

32. $x^4 - 18 x^3 + 109 x^2 - 252 x + 180 = 0$.

33. $\sqrt{3 x^2 - 2 x + 16} + 2 \sqrt[4]{3 x^2 - 2 x + 16} - 15 = 0$.

34. $7(x^3 - 28)^{-\frac{6}{5}} + 8(x^3 - 28)^{-\frac{3}{5}} = -1$.

35. $(3 x + 15)^{\frac{1}{2}} + 9(3 x + 15)^{\frac{1}{4}} = 22$.

36. $5 x^2 + 5 x - 165 = 4 x\sqrt{x^2 + 5 x - 8}$.

37. $10(1 - x^2) - 12\,x - \sqrt{5\,x^2 + 6\,x - 2} = 0.$

38. $x^4 + 28\,x^3 + 190\,x^2 - 84\,x - 135 = 0.$

39. $9(x + a)^{\frac{4}{3}} - 22\,b^2(x + a)^{\frac{2}{3}} + 8\,b^4 = 0.$

40. $x^2 + 1 + \sqrt{x^2 - 8\,x + 37} = 8(x + 12).$

41. $25(x + 1)^{-1} - 15(x + 1)^{-\frac{1}{2}} = -2.$

42. $(3\,x - 2\,a)^2 - 4\,x(3\,x - 2\,a) = 4(x + 4\,a)^2 + 8\,x(x + 4\,a).$

43. $\dfrac{x^2 - 5\,x + 1}{x^2 - 2\,x + 2} - \dfrac{x^2 - 2\,x + 2}{x^2 - 5\,x + 1} = -\dfrac{8}{3}.$

44. $9\,x(7 - x) + 9\sqrt{x^2 - 7\,x - 5} = -43.$

45. $\dfrac{3\,x^2 + 2\,x - 5}{4\,x^2 - 7\,x - 1} + \dfrac{4\,x^2 - 7\,x - 1}{3\,x^2 + 2\,x - 5} = \dfrac{5}{2}.$

46. $9\,x^4 - 30\,x^3 - 185\,x^2 + 350\,x + 1176 = 0.$

47. $\sqrt{\dfrac{x^2 + 3\,x + 10}{x^2 - 5\,x + 2}} + \sqrt{\dfrac{x^2 - 5\,x + 2}{x^2 + 3\,x + 10}} = \dfrac{26}{5}.$

48. $\sqrt{\dfrac{x^2 + 3}{x}} - \sqrt{\dfrac{x}{x^2 + 3}} = \dfrac{3}{2}.$

XXI. SIMULTANEOUS QUADRATIC EQUATIONS

On the double signs $\pm$ and $\mp$.

If two or more double signs are used in an equation, it will be understood that the equation can be read in two ways; first, reading all the *upper* signs; second, reading all the *lower* signs.

Thus, the equation $a \pm b = \pm c$ can be read either

$$a + b = c, \text{ or } a - b = -c.$$

And the equation $a \pm b = \mp c$ can be read either

$$a + b = -c, \text{ or } a - b = c.$$

The same notation will be used in the case of a system of equations, each involving double signs.

Thus, the equations $x = \pm 2$, $y = \pm 3$, can be read either

$$x = +2, \ y = +3, \text{ or } x = -2, \ y = -3.$$

And the equations $x = \pm 2$, $y = \mp 3$, can be read either

$$x = +2, \ y = -3, \text{ or } x = -2, \ y = +3.$$

The principles demonstrated in §§ 233 to 236, inclusive, hold for simultaneous equations of any degree.

470. The following principle is of frequent use in solving simultaneous equations of higher degree than the first:

The system of equations

$$\begin{cases} A \times B = 0, & (1) \\ C \times D = 0, & (2) \end{cases}$$

where A, B, C, and D are rational and integral expressions which involve the unknown numbers, is equivalent to the systems

$$\begin{cases} A = 0, \\ C = 0, \end{cases} \quad \begin{cases} A = 0, \\ D = 0, \end{cases} \quad \begin{cases} B = 0, \\ C = 0, \end{cases} \text{ and } \begin{cases} B = 0, \\ D = 0. \end{cases} \quad (3)$$

For any solution of (1) and (2) makes $A \times B$ and $C \times D$ identically equal to 0.

It then makes at least one factor of $A \times B$ and $C \times D$ identically equal to 0, and hence satisfies some one of the systems (3).

Again, any solution of any one of the systems (3) makes either A or B, and also either C or D, identically equal to 0; and hence satisfies (1) and (2).

Then, the system (1) and (2) is equivalent to (3).

The principle holds for any number of equations, with any number of factors.

471. Two equations of the second degree (§ 113) with two unknown numbers will generally produce, by elimination, an equation of the *fourth* degree with one unknown number.

Consider, for example, the equations

$$\begin{cases} x^2 + y = a. & (1) \\ x + y^2 = b. & (2) \end{cases}$$

From (1), $y = a - x^2$; substituting in (2),

$$x + a^2 - 2\, ax^2 + x^4 = b\,;$$

an equation of the fourth degree in x.

The methods already given are, therefore, not sufficient for the solution of every system of simultaneous quadratic equations, with two unknown numbers.

In certain cases, however, the solution may be effected.

472. Case I. *When each equation is in the form*

$$ax^2 + by^2 = c.$$

In this case, either x^2 or y^2 can be eliminated by addition or subtraction.

1. Solve the equations $\begin{cases} 3\,x^2 + \frac{1}{4}\,y^2 = 76. & (1) \\ 3\,y^2 - 1\frac{1}{1}\,x^2 = 4. & (2) \end{cases}$

Multiply (1) by 3,	$9\,x^2 + 12\,y^2 = 228.$
Multiply (2) by 4,	$12\,y^2 - 44\,x^2 = 16.$
Subtracting,	$53\,x^2 = 212.$
Or,	$x^2 = 4.$ (3)
Whence,	$x = \pm 2.$

Substituting $x = \pm\, 2$ in (1), $12 + 4\, y^2 = 76$.

Then, $\qquad\qquad\qquad\qquad\qquad y^2 = 16.$ (4)

Whence, $\qquad\qquad\qquad\qquad\qquad y = \pm\, 4.$

The solution is $x = 2,\ y = \pm\, 4$; or, $x = -\, 2,\ y = \pm\, 4.$ (5)

It follows, precisely as in Ex. 1, § 238, that the given system is equivalent to the system (3) and (4).

Now (3) and (4) may be·written

$$(x + 2)(x - 2) = 0,\ \text{and}\ (y + 4)(y - 4) = 0.$$

And by § 470, these are equivalent to

$$\begin{cases} x + 2 = 0, \\ y + 4 = 0, \end{cases} \begin{cases} x + 2 = 0, \\ y - 4 = 0, \end{cases} \begin{cases} x - 2 = 0, \\ y + 4 = 0, \end{cases} \text{and} \begin{cases} x - 2 = 0, \\ y - 4 = 0; \end{cases}$$

which are the same as (5).

The method of elimination by addition or subtraction may be used in other examples.

2. Solve the equations $\begin{cases} 3\, x^2 - 4\, y = \quad 47. & (1) \\ 7\, x^2 + 6\, y = \quad 33. & (2) \end{cases}$

Multiply (1) by 3, $\qquad 9\, x^2 - 12\, y = 141.$

Multiply (2) by 2, $\qquad \underline{14\, x^2 + 12\, y = \quad 66.}$

Adding, $\qquad\qquad\qquad\quad 23\, x^2 = 207.$

Then, $\qquad\qquad\qquad\qquad x^2 = 9,\ \text{and}\ x = \pm\, 3.$

Substituting $x = \pm\, 3$ in (1), $27 - 4\, y = 47.$

Then, $\qquad\qquad\qquad\qquad -\, 4\, y = 20,\ \text{and}\ y = -\, 5.$

It is possible to eliminate one unknown number, in examples (1) and (2), by *substitution* (§ 239), or by *comparison* (§ 240).

EXERCISE 61

Solve the following:

1. $\begin{cases} 3\, x^2 + 2\, y^2 = 66. \\ 9\, x^2 + 5\, y^2 = 189. \end{cases}$

2. $\begin{cases} 3\, x - 5\, y^2 = -\, 116. \\ 7\, x + 4\, y^2 = 121. \end{cases}$

3. $\begin{cases} 3\, x^2 - 2\, xy = 24. \\ 4\, x^2 - 5\, xy = 46. \end{cases}$

4. $\begin{cases} 4\, x^2 + 9\, y^2 = 13. \\ 8\, x^2 - 27\, y^2 = 6. \end{cases}$

5. $\begin{cases} 5\, xy + \quad y^2 = -\, 75. \\ \quad xy - 3\, y^2 = -\, 95. \end{cases}$

6. $\begin{cases} 11\, x^2 - \quad 6\, y^2 = 84. \\ \ 7\, x^2 + 15\, y^2 = 204. \end{cases}$

7. $\begin{cases} 2\,x^2 - xy - 3\,y^2 = 0. \\ x^2 + xy + 3\,y^2 = 27. \end{cases}$
   9. $\begin{cases} 2\,x^2 + 3\,y^2 = 67 - x. \\ x^2 - 2\,y^2 = 17. \end{cases}$

8. $\begin{cases} 4\,x^2 - y^2 = (3\,a+b)(a+3\,b). \\ 4\,y^2 - x^2 = (3\,a-b)(a-3\,b). \end{cases}$
   10. $\begin{cases} y^2 + 4\,xy - 3\,y = 42. \\ 2\,y^2 - xy + 5\,y = -10. \end{cases}$

11. $\begin{cases} \dfrac{3\,x+2\,y}{3\,x-2\,y} + \dfrac{3\,x-2\,y}{3\,x+2\,y} = \dfrac{41}{20}. \\ 8\,y^2 + 3\,x^2 = 29. \end{cases}$

12. $\begin{cases} (3\,x+4\,y)^2 - (6\,x - y)(6\,x + 5\,y) = 57. \\ (5\,x - 2\,y)^2 - 4(x - 4\,y)(2\,x + 3\,y) = 225. \end{cases}$

473. CASE II. *When one equation is of the second degree, and the other of the first.*

Equations of this kind may be solved by finding the value of one of the unknown numbers in terms of the other from the first degree equation, and substituting this value in the other equation.

Ex. Solve the equations $\quad\begin{cases} 2\,x^2 - xy = 6\,y. & \text{(1)} \\ x + 2\,y = 7. & \text{(2)} \end{cases}$

From (2), $\qquad\qquad\qquad\qquad\qquad y = \dfrac{7-x}{2}.$ (3)

Substituting in (1), $\quad 2\,x^2 - x\left(\dfrac{7-x}{2}\right) = 6\left(\dfrac{7-x}{2}\right).$ (4)

Clearing of fractions, $\quad 4\,x^2 - 7\,x + x^2 = 42 - 6\,x.$

Or, $\qquad\qquad\qquad\qquad 5\,x^2 - x = 42.$ (5)

Solving, $\qquad\qquad\qquad\qquad x = 3 \text{ or } -\dfrac{14}{5}.$

Substituting in (3), $y = \dfrac{7-3}{2}$ or $\dfrac{7+\dfrac{14}{5}}{2} = 2$ or $\dfrac{49}{10}.$

The solution is $x = 3$, $y = 2$; or, $x = -\dfrac{14}{5}$, $y = \dfrac{49}{10}.$ (6)

By § 236, the given system is equivalent to (3) and (4); or, since (4) is equivalent to (5), to the system (3) and (5).

Now, (5) can be written $(x - 3)(5\,x + 14) = 0.$

Then, by § 470, the system (3) and (5) is equivalent to the systems (3) and $x - 3 = 0$, and (3) and $5\,x + 14 = 0$; that is, to (6).

EXERCISE 62

Solve the following :

1. $\begin{cases} x^2 + 3\,y^2 = 37. \\ x\ -2\,y\ =9. \end{cases}$

2. $\begin{cases} xy = 2\,a^2 + 3\,a - 2. \\ 3\,x + 4\,y = 11\,a + 2. \end{cases}$

3. $\begin{cases} 2\,xy + x = -36. \\ xy - 3\,y = -5. \end{cases}$

4. $\begin{cases} x^2 - 2\,y^2 + 3\,x = -8. \\ x^2 - 2\,y^2 - 4\,y = -2. \end{cases}$

5. $\begin{cases} x^2 - xy + 2\,y^2 = 8. \\ \quad\quad\ 3\,x + y = 10. \end{cases}$

6. $\begin{cases} 3\,x^2 - xy - y^2 = -3. \\ \quad\quad\ 2\,x - 3\,y = 5. \end{cases}$

7. $\begin{cases} \dfrac{2\,x}{3} + \dfrac{3\,y}{2} = 2. \\[2mm] \dfrac{3}{2\,x} + \dfrac{2}{3\,y} = 2. \end{cases}$

8. $\begin{cases} \dfrac{2\,x}{y} - 5\,x = \dfrac{11}{2}. \\[2mm] \dfrac{3\,y}{x} + 4\,y = \dfrac{2}{3}. \end{cases}$

9. $\begin{cases} x - \dfrac{2}{y} = -\dfrac{a}{b}. \\[2mm] y + \dfrac{2}{x} = \dfrac{3\,b}{a}. \end{cases}$

10. $\begin{cases} 4\,x + y - 3\,xy = -6. \\ x - 5\,y + 2\,xy = 10. \end{cases}$

11. $\begin{cases} \dfrac{x}{x-y} - \dfrac{x-y}{x} = -\dfrac{40}{21}. \\[2mm] \quad\quad 2\,y + 3\,x = -1. \end{cases}$

12. $\begin{cases} \dfrac{x}{2\,y} - \dfrac{y}{3\,x} = \dfrac{29}{24}. \\[2mm] \quad\ 4\,y - x = -2. \end{cases}$

13. $\begin{cases} x^2 + 4\,xy = 13. \\ 2\,xy + 9\,y^2 = 87. \end{cases}$

14. $\begin{cases} \dfrac{x-1}{3} - \dfrac{y-1}{2} = 0. \\[2mm] \dfrac{x^2 - y}{32} - \dfrac{y^2 - x}{15} = 0. \end{cases}$

15. $\begin{cases} x^2y^2 - 24\,xy + 95 = 0. \\ \quad\quad\ 3\,x - 2\,y = -13. \end{cases}$

16. $\begin{cases} 3\,x^2 - 5\,xy = (2\,a - b)(a + 7\,b). \\ \quad\quad x + y = 3\,(a - b). \end{cases}$

474. Case III. *When the given equations are symmetrical with respect to x and y; that is, when x and y can be interchanged without changing the equation.*

Equations of this kind may be solved by combining them in such a way as to obtain the values of $x + y$ and $x - y$.

1. Solve the equations $\begin{cases} x + y = 2. \\ \quad\ xy = -15. \end{cases}$

$\qquad\qquad\qquad\qquad\qquad\qquad\qquad\qquad\qquad (1)$
$\qquad\qquad\qquad\qquad\qquad\qquad\qquad\qquad\qquad (2)$

Squaring (1),	$x^2 + 2\,xy + y^2 = \quad 4.$	(3)
Multiplying (2) by 4,	$4\,xy \quad\quad = -60.$	(4)
Subtracting,	$x^2 - 2\,xy + y^2 = \quad 64.$	(5)
Extracting square roots,	$x - y = \pm\,8.$	(6)

Adding (1) and (6), $2x = 2 \pm 8 = 10$ or -6.

Whence, $x = 5$ or -3.

Subtracting (6) from (1), $2y = 2 \mp 8 = -6$ or 10.

Whence, $y = -3$ or 5.

The solution is $x = 5$, $y = -3$; or, $x = -3$, $y = 5$.   (7)

In subtracting ± 8 from 2, we have 2 ∓ 8, in accordance with the notation explained on page 298.

In operating with double signs, $\pm$ is changed to $\mp$, and $\mp$ to $\pm$, whenever $+$ should be changed to $-$.

Equation (4) is equivalent to (2); but (3) is equivalent to $x + y = 2$ and $x + y = -2$.

If, then, we use only the value $+2$ for $x + y$, the given system is equivalent to (3) and (4).

By § 234, the system (3) and (4) is equivalent to (3) and (5).

Then, the given system is equivalent to the positive value of $x + y$ in (3), and (5); that is, to (1) and (5).

Now (5) may be written $(x - y - 8)(x - y + 8) = 0$.

Then, by § 470, the system (1) and (5) is equivalent to (1) and $x - y - 8 = 0$, and (1) and $x - y + 8 = 0$; that is, to (7).

The above equations may also be solved by the method of Case II; but the symmetrical method is shorter and neater.

2. Solve the equations
$$\begin{cases} x^2 + y^2 = 50. & (1) \\ xy = -7. & (2) \end{cases}$$

Multiply (2) by 2, $2xy = -14.$ (3)

Add (1) and (3) $x^2 + 2xy + y^2 = 36.$ (4)

Whence, $x + y = \pm 6.$ (5)

Subtract (3) from (1), $x^2 - 2xy + y^2 = 64.$ (6)

Whence, $x - y = \pm 8.$ (7)

Add (5) and (7), $2x = 6 \pm 8$, or $-6 \pm 8.$

Whence, $x = 7, -1, 1,$ or $-7.$

Subtract (7) from (5), $2y = 6 \mp 8$, or $-6 \mp 8.$

Whence, $y = -1, 7, -7,$ or $1.$

The solution is $x = \pm 7$, $y = \mp 1$; or, $x = \pm 1$, $y = \mp 7.$

The given system is equivalent to the system (4) and (6).

Now (4) and (6) can be written

$$(x + y + 6)(x + y - 6) = 0, \text{ and } (x - y + 8)(x - y - 8) = 0.$$

Then, the system (4) and (6) is equivalent to (5) and (7), with every possible combination of signs.

We may solve by the method of Case III other systems in which the equations are symmetrical, except in the *signs* of terms ; as, for example, the system

$$\begin{cases} x - y = a. \\ \quad xy = b. \end{cases}$$

We may also solve certain non-symmetrical systems ; as, for example, the system

$$\begin{cases} a^2x^2 + b^2y^2 = c. \\ \quad ax + by = d. \end{cases}$$

EXERCISE 63

Solve the following :

1. $\begin{cases} x^2 + y^2 = 29. \\ x + y = -3. \end{cases}$

2. $\begin{cases} x - y = 11. \\ xy = -28. \end{cases}$

3. $\begin{cases} x^2 + y^2 = 130. \\ x - y = -8. \end{cases}$

4. $\begin{cases} x + y = 2a - 1. \\ xy = a^2 - a - 2. \end{cases}$

5. $\begin{cases} x^2 + y^2 = \dfrac{a^6 + b^6}{a^2b^2}. \\ xy = ab. \end{cases}$

6. $\begin{cases} x^2 + xy + y^2 = 63. \\ x - y = 3. \end{cases}$

7. $\begin{cases} \dfrac{x}{y} + \dfrac{y}{x} = -\dfrac{10}{3}. \\ x - y = 1. \end{cases}$

8. $\begin{cases} x^2 - xy + y^2 = a^2 + 3b^2. \\ x + y = 2a. \end{cases}$

9. $\begin{cases} x^2 + xy + y^2 = \dfrac{31}{4}. \\ x^2 - xy + y^2 = \dfrac{91}{4}. \end{cases}$

10. $\begin{cases} \dfrac{1}{x^2} + \dfrac{1}{y^2} = 74. \\ \dfrac{1}{x} - \dfrac{1}{y} = 12. \end{cases}$

11. $\begin{cases} \dfrac{1}{x^2} + \dfrac{1}{y^2} = \dfrac{289}{36}. \\ \dfrac{1}{xy} = \dfrac{10}{3}. \end{cases}$

12. $\begin{cases} x^2 + 9y^2 = 50. \\ x - 3y = 0. \end{cases}$

13. $\begin{cases} xy = -16. \\ 2x + y = 14. \end{cases}$

14. $\begin{cases} \dfrac{1}{xy} = 24. \\ x + y = 11xy. \end{cases}$

15. $\begin{cases} \dfrac{1}{x^2} + \dfrac{1}{xy} + \dfrac{1}{y^2} = 49. \\[2mm] \dfrac{1}{x} + \dfrac{1}{y} = 8. \end{cases}$

16. $\begin{cases} \dfrac{x^2 - xy + y^2}{x^2 y^2} = \dfrac{7}{324}. \\[2mm] \dfrac{x - y}{xy} = \dfrac{1}{18}. \end{cases}$

17. $\begin{cases} 36\,x^2 + 64\,y^2 = 85. \\ 6\,x + 8\,y = 11. \end{cases}$

18. $\begin{cases} 25\,x^2 + 16\,y^2 = 544. \\ 5\,x - 4\,y = 32. \end{cases}$

19. $\begin{cases} 2\,x^2 - 3\,xy + 2\,y^2 = 92. \\ 5\,x^2 + 4\,xy + 5\,y^2 = 161. \end{cases}$

20. $\begin{cases} 16\,x^2 y^2 - 104\,xy = -105. \\ x - y = -2. \end{cases}$

21. $\begin{cases} \dfrac{1}{x^2} + \dfrac{1}{xy} + \dfrac{1}{y^2} = \dfrac{3\,a^4 - 3\,a^2 b^2 + b^4}{a^2(a-b)^2}. \\[2mm] \dfrac{1}{x^2} - \dfrac{1}{xy} + \dfrac{1}{y^2} = \dfrac{a^4 - a^2 b^2 + b^4}{a^2(a-b)^2}. \end{cases}$

475. CASE IV. *When each equation is of the second degree, and homogeneous; that is, when each term involving the unknown numbers is of the second degree with respect to them.*

Certain equations of this form may be solved by the method of Case I or Case III. (See Exs. 1, § 472, and 2, § 474.) The method of Case IV should be used only when the example cannot be solved by Cases I or III.

Ex. Solve the equations $\quad \begin{cases} x^2 - 2\,xy = 5. \\ x + y = 29. \end{cases}$

Putting in the given equations $\qquad y = vx,$ $\hfill (1)$

we have $\qquad x^2 - 2\,vx^2 = 5; \text{ or, } x^2 = \dfrac{5}{1 - 2\,v};$ $\hfill (2)$

and $\qquad x^2 + v^2 x^2 = 29; \text{ or, } x^2 = \dfrac{29}{1 + v^2}.$ $\hfill (3)$

Equating values of x^2, $\qquad \dfrac{5}{1 - 2\,v} = \dfrac{29}{1 + v^2}.$ $\hfill (4)$

Or, $\qquad 5\,v^2 + 58\,v = 24.$ $\hfill (5)$

Solving this equation, $\qquad v = \dfrac{2}{5} \text{ or } -12.$

Substituting these values in (2), we have

$$x^2 = \frac{5}{1 - \dfrac{4}{5}} \text{ or } \frac{5}{1 + 24} = 25 \text{ or } \frac{1}{5}; \text{ then, } x = \pm 5 \text{ or } \pm \frac{1}{\sqrt{5}}.$$

Substituting the values of v and x in the equation $y = vx$,

$$y = \frac{2}{5}(\pm 5) \text{ or } -12\left(\pm \frac{1}{\sqrt{5}}\right) = \pm 2 \text{ or } \mp \frac{12}{\sqrt{5}}.$$

The solution is $x = \pm 5$, $y = \pm 2$; or, $x = \pm \dfrac{1}{\sqrt{5}}$, $y = \mp \dfrac{12}{\sqrt{5}}$.

The given system, and (1), are three equations with three unknown numbers; by § 236, they are equivalent to the system (1), (2), and (3).

Then, precisely as in Ex., § 240, the system (1), (2), and (3) is equivalent to (1), (2), and (4), or to (1), (2), and (5).

We may write (5) in the form $(5v - 2)(v + 12) = 0$.

Then, the system (1), (2), and (5) is equivalent to the systems (1), (2), and $5v - 2 = 0$, and (1), (2), and $v + 12 = 0$.

Then, the given system is equivalent to the systems

$$y = \frac{2}{5}x, \quad x^2 = \frac{5}{1 - \dfrac{4}{5}}, \text{ and } y = -12x, \quad x^2 = \frac{5}{1 + 24}.$$

In finding y from the equation $y = vx$, care must be taken to multiply each value of x by the value of v which was used to obtain it.

EXERCISE 64

Solve the following:

1. $\begin{cases} x^2 + y^2 = 25. \\ x^2 - xy = 4. \end{cases}$

7. $\begin{cases} x^2 - 2xy - 4y^2 = -41. \\ x^2 - 5xy + 8y^2 = 58. \end{cases}$

2. $\begin{cases} x^2 + 3xy = -5. \\ 2xy - y^2 = -24. \end{cases}$

8. $\begin{cases} 2x^2 + 7xy + 4y^2 = 2. \\ 3x^2 + 8xy - 4y^2 = -72. \end{cases}$

3. $\begin{cases} x^2 + xy + y^2 = 19. \\ 2x^2 + xy = -2. \end{cases}$

9. $\begin{cases} 11x^2 - xy - y^2 = 45. \\ 7x^2 + 3xy - 2y^2 = 20. \end{cases}$

4. $\begin{cases} 4x^2 - xy - y^2 = -16. \\ 3xy + y^2 = 28. \end{cases}$

10. $\begin{cases} 5x^2 + xy - 3y^2 = 27. \\ 4x^2 - 4xy + 3y^2 = 72. \end{cases}$

5. $\begin{cases} \dfrac{5}{x^2} - \dfrac{1}{y^2} = 9. \\ \dfrac{1}{xy} - \dfrac{3}{y^2} = -90. \end{cases}$

11. $\begin{cases} \dfrac{2}{x^2} + \dfrac{1}{xy} + \dfrac{5}{y^2} = 44. \\ \dfrac{1}{xy} - \dfrac{1}{y^2} = -12. \end{cases}$

6. $\begin{cases} x^2 + xy - 5y^2 = 25. \\ x^2 + 4y^2 = 40. \end{cases}$

12. $\begin{cases} 4x^2 - 2xy - y^2 = -16. \\ 4x^2 + 7xy + 2y^2 = 104. \end{cases}$

13. $\begin{cases} 3y^2 - xy - 40x^2 = 30x^2y^2. \\ 5y^2 - 3xy - 72x^2 = 38x^2y^2. \end{cases}$

476. Solution of Simultaneous Equations of Higher Degree by Factoring.

1. Solve the equations $\begin{cases} (x-y)(x+2\,y-1)=0. \\ (x+y)(x-3\,y+2)=0. \end{cases}$

By § 470, the given system is equivalent to the systems

$$\begin{cases} x-y=0, \\ x+y=0, \end{cases} \qquad \begin{cases} x-y=0, \\ x-3\,y+2=0, \end{cases}$$

$$\begin{cases} x+2\,y-1=0, \\ x+y=0, \end{cases} \text{ and } \begin{cases} x+2\,y-1=0, \\ x-3\,y+2=0. \end{cases}$$

The solutions of these are

$$x=0,\ y=0;\ x=1,\ y=1;\ x=-1,\ y=1;\ x=-\frac{1}{5},\ y=\frac{3}{5}.$$

2. Solve the equations $\begin{cases} x^2+xy-2\,y^2=0. \\ 2\,x+3\,y+6=0. \end{cases}$ \hfill (1)

We may write (1) in the form $(x+2\,y)(x-y)=0$.
Then the given system is equivalent to the systems

$$\begin{cases} x+2\,y=0, \\ 2\,x+3\,y+6=0, \end{cases} \text{ and } \begin{cases} x-y=0, \\ 2\,x+3\,y+6=0. \end{cases}$$

Solving these, $x=-12,\ y=6;$ or, $x=-\dfrac{6}{5},\ y=-\dfrac{6}{5}.$

The example can be solved by the method of § 473; but the above method is shorter.

3. Solve the equations $\begin{cases} 3\,x^2+y^2=7\,x. \\ xy+y^2=2\,x. \end{cases}$ \hfill (1)
\hfill (2)

Multiplying (1) by 2, $\quad 6\,x^2+2\,y^2=14\,x.$
Multiplying (2) by 7, $\quad 7\,xy+7\,y^2=14\,x.$
Subtracting, $\quad \overline{6\,x^2-7\,xy-5\,y^2=0}$, or $(2\,x+y)(3\,x-5\,y)=0.$

Then, the given system is equivalent to the systems

$$\begin{cases} 3\,x^2+y^2=7\,x, \\ 2\,x+y=0, \end{cases} \text{ and } \begin{cases} 3\,x^2+\ y^2=7\,x, \\ 3\,x-5\,y=0. \end{cases}$$

Solving these, $x=0,\ y=0;\ x=1,\ y=-2;$ or, $x=\dfrac{25}{12},\ y=\dfrac{5}{4}.$

4. Solve the equations $\begin{cases} x^2 = x + y. \\ y^2 = 3y - x. \end{cases}$

Subtracting, $x^2 - y^2 = 2x - 2y$, or $(x-y)(x+y-2) = 0$.

Then, $\begin{cases} x^2 = x + y, \\ x - y = 0, \end{cases}$ and $\begin{cases} x^2 = x + y, \\ x + y - 2 = 0. \end{cases}$

Solving these, $x = 0,\ y = 0;\ \ x = 2,\ y = 2;\ $ or, $\ x = \pm\sqrt{2},$ $y = 2 \mp \sqrt{2}.$

EXERCISE 65

Solve the following :

1. $\begin{cases} (2x - 3y)(x - 4y + 1) = 0. \\ \qquad\qquad 5x + 4y = 23. \end{cases}$

2. $\begin{cases} (2x + y)(3x - 4y + 5) = 0. \\ (x - 3y)(2x + 5y - 8) = 0. \end{cases}$

3. $\begin{cases} x^2 - 3xy - 4y^2 = 0. \\ \quad 3x - 5y = 46. \end{cases}$

4. $\begin{cases} 2x^2 - xy - 15y^2 = 0. \\ \quad 5x + 2y = 21. \end{cases}$

5. $\begin{cases} 12x^2 - 11xy + 2y^2 = 0. \\ \qquad 7x - 3y = -5. \end{cases}$

6. $\begin{cases} 2x^2 - xy = 0. \\ x^2 + 2y^2 = 9. \end{cases}$

7. $\begin{cases} \quad x^2 - 2xy = 0. \\ 2x^2 + xy + y^2 = 44. \end{cases}$

8. $\begin{cases} (x + 2y)(4x - 3y) = 0. \\ 3x^2 - 5xy - 4y^2 = 18. \end{cases}$

9. $\begin{cases} x^2 - 4y^2 = 3x. \\ xy + 8y^2 = x. \end{cases}$

10. $\begin{cases} 3x^2 + xy - 2y^2 = -4y. \\ 6x^2 - 2xy + y^2 = 3y. \end{cases}$

11. $\begin{cases} 3x^2 + 3y^2 = 10xy. \\ \dfrac{1}{x} + \dfrac{1}{y} = \dfrac{4}{3}. \end{cases}$

12. $\begin{cases} (x - y)(x^2 - xy - 6y^2) = 0. \\ \quad 2x - 5y + 1 = 0. \end{cases}$

13. $\begin{cases} 2x^3 + 5x^2y - 8xy^2 - 20y^3 = 0. \\ \qquad\qquad 3x + 4y = 7. \end{cases}$

14. $\begin{cases} x^2 = mx - ny. \\ y^2 = nx - my. \end{cases}$

477. Solution by Division.

Consider the equations $\begin{cases} A \times B = a \times b, & (1) \\ \quad B = b; & (2) \end{cases}$

where A and B are rational and integral expressions which involve the unknown numbers, and a and b any numbers.

By § 236, the given system is equivalent to

$$\begin{cases} A \times b = a \times b, \\ \quad B = b; \end{cases} \text{ or, to } \begin{cases} A = a, \\ B = b. \end{cases} \qquad (3)$$

Here the first member of (3) is obtained by dividing the first member of (1) by the first member of (2), and the second member by dividing the second member of (1) by the second member of (2).

Ex. Solve the equations $\begin{cases} x^3 - y^3 = 9. & (1) \\ x - y = 3. & (2) \end{cases}$

Divide (1) by (2), $x^2 + xy + y^2 = 3.$ (3)

Squaring (2), $x^2 - 2xy + y^2 = 9.$ (4)

Subtract (4) from (3), $3xy = -6$, or $xy = -2.$ (5)

Add (3) and (5), $x^2 + 2xy + y^2 = 1.$

Extracting square roots, $x + y = \pm 1.$ (6)

Add (2) and (6), $2x = 3 \pm 1 = 4$ or 2.

Then, $x = 2$ or 1.

Subtract (2) from (6), $2y = -3 \pm 1 = -2$ or $-4.$

Then, $y = -1$ or $-2.$

The solution is $x = 2$, $y = -1$; or, $x = 1$, $y = -2.$

The equations (2) and (3), though not symmetrical, are solved as in § 474.

478. Consider the equations $\begin{cases} A \times B = C \times D, \\ B = D; \end{cases}$

where A, B, C, and D are rational and integral expressions which involve the unknown numbers.

By § 236, the given system is equivalent to

$$\begin{cases} A \times B = C \times B, \\ B = D; \end{cases} \text{ or, to } \begin{cases} B(A - C) = 0, \\ B = D. \end{cases}$$

By § 470, the latter is equivalent to the systems

$$\begin{cases} B = 0, \\ D = D, \end{cases} \text{ and } \begin{cases} A - C = 0, \\ B = D. \end{cases}$$

Then, the given system is equivalent to the systems

$$\begin{cases} B = 0, \\ D = 0, \end{cases} \text{ and } \begin{cases} A = C, \\ B = D. \end{cases}$$

Ex. Solve the equations $\begin{cases} x^2 - y^2 = 27\,x^3 + 8. & (1) \\ x - y = 3\,x + 2. & (2) \end{cases}$

Dividing (1) by (2), the given system is equivalent to the systems

$$\begin{cases} x - y = 0, \\ 3\,x + 2 = 0, \end{cases} \text{ and } \begin{cases} x + y = 9\,x^2 - 6\,x + 4, \\ x - y = 3\,x + 2. \end{cases} \quad (3)$$

The solution of the first system is $x = -\dfrac{2}{3},\ y = -\dfrac{2}{3}.$

To solve the second, add (2) and (3); then,

$$2\,x = 9\,x^2 - 3\,x + 6, \text{ or } 9\,x^2 - 5\,x + 6 = 0.$$

By § 450, $\qquad x = \dfrac{5 \pm \sqrt{25 - 216}}{18} = \dfrac{5 \pm \sqrt{-191}}{18}.$

By (2), $\qquad y = -2\,x - 2 = -\dfrac{5 \pm \sqrt{-191}}{9} - 2$

$$= \dfrac{-23 \mp \sqrt{-191}}{9}.$$

If we try to solve by substituting the value of y from (2) in (1), we shall have an equation of the third degree in x.

EXERCISE 66

Solve the following :

1. $\begin{cases} x^3 - y^3 = 26. \\ x - y = 2. \end{cases}$

2. $\begin{cases} x^3 + y^3 = 280. \\ x^2 - xy + y^2 = 28. \end{cases}$

3. $\begin{cases} x + y = 35. \\ \sqrt[3]{x} + \sqrt[3]{y} = 5. \end{cases}$

4. $\begin{cases} x^3 - 8\,y^3 = 189. \\ x - 2\,y = 9. \end{cases}$

5. $\begin{cases} \dfrac{1}{x^3} + \dfrac{1}{y^3} = -19. \\ \dfrac{1}{x} + \dfrac{1}{y} = -1. \end{cases}$

6. $\begin{cases} \dfrac{1}{x^3} - \dfrac{1}{y^3} = 72. \\ \dfrac{1}{x^2} + \dfrac{1}{xy} + \dfrac{1}{y^2} = 12. \end{cases}$

7. $\begin{cases} x^2 y + xy^2 = 56. \\ x + y = -1. \end{cases}$

8. $\begin{cases} x^4 + x^2 y^2 + y^4 = 481. \\ x^2 - xy + y^2 = 37. \end{cases}$

9. $\begin{cases} (x^2 - 16)(9\,y^2 - 4) = -2100. \\ (x + 4)(3\,y - 2) = 50. \end{cases}$

10. $\begin{cases} 25\,x^2 - 25\,y^2 = 24\,x^2 y^2. \\ 5\,x + 5\,y = -4\,xy. \end{cases}$

11. $\begin{cases} 8x^3 + 27y^3 = 91. \\ 4x^2 - 6xy + 9y^2 = 13. \end{cases}$

12. $\begin{cases} x^4 - y^4 = x^2y^2 - 1. \\ x^2 - y^2 = xy - 1. \end{cases}$

13. $\begin{cases} \dfrac{x^2}{y} + \dfrac{y^2}{x} = \dfrac{19}{6}. \\ \dfrac{1}{x} + \dfrac{1}{y} = \dfrac{1}{6}. \end{cases}$

14. $\begin{cases} \dfrac{x^2}{y} - \dfrac{y^2}{x} = \dfrac{98}{15}. \\ x - y = 2. \end{cases}$

15. $\begin{cases} x^2 - y^2 + 3x - 3y = 12. \\ (x-y)(3x - 5y - 4) = -9. \end{cases}$

16. $\begin{cases} x^2y + y^2x = 42. \\ \dfrac{1}{x} + \dfrac{1}{y} = \dfrac{7}{6}. \end{cases}$

479. Special Methods for the Solution of Simultaneous Equations of Higher Degree.

1. Solve the equations $\qquad \begin{cases} x^3 - y^3 = 19. & (1) \\ x^2y - xy^2 = 6. & (2) \end{cases}$

Multiply (2) by 3, $\qquad 3x^2y - 3xy^2 = 18.$ (3)

Subtract (3) from (1), $x^3 - 3x^2y + 3xy^2 - y^3 = 1.$

Extracting cube roots, $\qquad x - y = 1.$ (4)

Dividing (2) by (4), $\qquad xy = 6.$ (5)

Solving equations (4) and (5) by the method of § 474, we find $x = 3,\ y = 2$; or, $x = -2,\ y = -3$.

2. Solve the equations $\begin{cases} x^3 + y^3 = 9xy. \\ x + y = 6. \end{cases}$

Putting $x = u + v$ and $y = u - v$,

$\qquad (u+v)^3 + (u-v)^3 = 9(u+v)(u-v);$ (1)

and $\qquad (u+v) + (u-v) = 6.$ (2)

Reducing (1), $\qquad 2u^3 + 6uv^2 = 9(u^2 - v^2).$ (3)

Reducing (2), $\qquad 2u = 6,$ or $u = 3.$

Putting $u = 3$ in (3), $54 + 18v^2 = 9(9 - v^2).$

Whence, $\qquad v^2 = 1,$ or $v = \pm 1.$

Therefore, $\qquad x = u + v = 3 \pm 1 = 4$ or 2;

and $\qquad y = u - v = 3 \mp 1 = 2$ or $4.$

The artifice of substituting $u + v$ and $u - v$ for x and y is advantageous in any case where the given equations are *symmetrical* (§ 474) with respect to x and y. See also Ex. 4.

3. Solve the equations $\begin{cases} x^2 + y^2 + 2x + 2y = 23. & (1) \\ xy = 6. & (2) \end{cases}$

Multiplying (2) by 2, $\qquad\qquad\qquad 2xy = 12.$ (3)

Add (1) and (3), $\qquad x^2 + 2xy + y^2 + 2x + 2y = 35.$

Or, $\qquad\qquad\qquad\qquad (x+y)^2 + 2(x+y) = 35.$

Completing the square, $\quad (x+y)^2 + 2(x+y) + 1 = 36.$

Then, $\quad (x+y) + 1 = \pm 6$; and $x + y = 5$ or -7.   (4)

Squaring (4), $\qquad\quad x^2 + 2xy + y^2 = 25$ or $49.$

Multiplying (2) by 4, $\quad \underline{ 4xy \qquad = 24.}$

Subtracting, $\qquad\quad x^2 - 2xy + y^2 = 1$ or $25.$

Whence, $\qquad\qquad\qquad\quad x - y = \pm 1$ or $\pm 5.$ (5)

Adding (4) and (5), $\qquad\qquad 2x = 5 \pm 1,$ or $-7 \pm 5.$

Whence, $\qquad\qquad\qquad x = 3, 2, -1,$ or $-6.$

Subtracting (5) from (4), $\qquad 2y = 5 \mp 1,$ or $-7 \mp 5.$

Whence, $\qquad\qquad\qquad y = 2, 3, -6,$ or $-1.$

4. Solve the equations $\begin{cases} x^4 + y^4 = 97. \\ x + y = -1. \end{cases}$

Putting $x = u + v$ and $y = u - v,$

$$(u+v)^4 + (u-v)^4 = 97, \qquad (1)$$

and $\qquad\qquad (u+v) + (u-v) = -1. \qquad (2)$

Reducing (1), $\quad 2u^4 + 12u^2v^2 + 2v^4 = 97.$ (3)

Reducing (2), $\qquad\qquad\qquad 2u = -1,$ or $u = -\dfrac{1}{2}.$

Substituting in (3), $\quad \dfrac{1}{8} + 3v^2 + 2v^4 = 97.$

Solving this, $v^2 = \dfrac{25}{4}$ or $-\dfrac{31}{4}$; and $v = \pm\dfrac{5}{2}$ or $\pm\dfrac{\sqrt{-31}}{2}.$

Therefore, $x = u + v = -\dfrac{1}{2} \pm \dfrac{5}{2},$ or $-\dfrac{1}{2} \pm \dfrac{\sqrt{-31}}{2}$

$$= 2, -3, \text{ or } \frac{-1 \pm \sqrt{-31}}{2}.$$

And, $y = u - v = -\dfrac{1}{2} \mp \dfrac{5}{2}$, or $-\dfrac{1}{2} \mp \dfrac{\sqrt{-31}}{2}$

$$= -3, 2, \text{ or } \frac{-1 \mp \sqrt{-31}}{2}.$$

In solving fractional simultaneous equations of higher degree, we must reject any solution which satisfies the equation obtained by equating to zero the L. C. M. of the given denominators (§ 222).

Also, in solving simultaneous equations of higher degree having unknown numbers under radical signs, we retain only those solutions which satisfy the given equations, when the *principal values* of the roots are taken (§ 397).

EXERCISE 67

Solve the following:

1. $\begin{cases} x^4 + y^4 = 257. \\ x - y = 5. \end{cases}$

2. $\begin{cases} x^2 + y^2 + x - y = 32. \\ xy = 6. \end{cases}$

3. $\begin{cases} x^3 + y^3 = 2 a^3 + 24 a. \\ x^2y + xy^2 = 2 a(a^2 - 4). \end{cases}$

4. $\begin{cases} x^2 + 9 y^2 + 4 x = 9. \\ xy + 2 y = -2. \end{cases}$

5. $\begin{cases} x + y + xy = 11. \\ (x + y)^2 + x^2y^2 = 61. \end{cases}$

6. $\begin{cases} xy - x + y = -9. \\ x^2y - xy^2 = -20. \end{cases}$

7. $\begin{cases} 9 x^2 - 13 xy - 3 x = -123. \\ xy + 4 y^2 + 2 y = 125. \end{cases}$

8. $\begin{cases} \sqrt{2 x^2 - 9} = 3 y + 6. \\ \sqrt{x^4 - 17 y^2} = x^2 - 5. \end{cases}$

9. $\begin{cases} x^2 + y = -3. \\ y^2 - 10 x^3 + 17 x^2 + 10 x = 33. \end{cases}$

10. $\begin{cases} x^2y - x = -6. \\ x^6y^3 - x^3 = -72. \end{cases}$

11. $\begin{cases} x - y + \sqrt{xy} = 11. \\ \sqrt{x^3y} - \sqrt{xy^3} = 30. \end{cases}$

12. $\begin{cases} x^2 + y^2 = xy + 1. \\ x^4 + y^4 = x^2y^2 + 1. \end{cases}$

13. $\begin{cases} x + y = -2. \\ x^5 + x^3y^2 + x^2y^3 + y^5 = -1120. \end{cases}$

14. $\begin{cases} xy + x + y = 169. \\ \sqrt{xy} - \sqrt{x + y} = 7. \end{cases}$

15. $\begin{cases} x^2y^2 + x^2 + y^2 = 169. \\ xy\sqrt{x^2 + y^2} = -60. \end{cases}$

16. $\begin{cases} x^2(1 + y) + y^2(1 + x) = 109. \\ xy = 12. \end{cases}$

17. $\begin{cases} x^5 - y^5 = 211. \\ x - y = 1. \end{cases}$

18. $\begin{cases} (x^3 + y^3)(x + y) = 112. \\ x^2 + xy + y^2 = 13. \end{cases}$

19. $\begin{cases} x^4 + 2 x^3y - 6 x^2y^2 + 2 xy^3 + y^4 = 0. \\ x + y = xy. \end{cases}$

20. $\begin{cases} \sqrt{2 x^2 + 6 y + 10} = 19 - x^2 - 3 y, \\ x^2 + y^2 - 4 y = 1, \end{cases}$

SIMULTANEOUS QUADRATIC EQUATIONS WITH MORE
THAN ONE UNKNOWN NUMBER

480. **1.** Solve the equations $\begin{cases} x^2 + y^2 + z^2 = 14. & (1) \\ 2x - 3y + z = 11. & (2) \\ x + 2y - z = -6. & (3) \end{cases}$

Add (2) and (3), $\qquad 3x - y = 5$; or, $y = 3x - 5.$ (4)

By (3), $\qquad z = x + 2y + 6 = x + 6x - 10 + 6 = 7x - 4.$ (5)

Substitute values of y and z in (1),

$$x^2 + 9x^2 - 30x + 25 + 49x^2 - 56x + 16 = 14.$$

Or, $\qquad\qquad\qquad\qquad 59x^2 - 86x = -27.$

By § 450, $\quad x = \dfrac{43 \pm \sqrt{1849 - 1593}}{59} = \dfrac{43 \pm 16}{59} = 1 \text{ or } \dfrac{27}{59}.$

Then by (4), $y = 3 - 5$ or $\dfrac{81}{59} - 5 = -2$ or $-\dfrac{214}{59}.$

And by (5), $z = 7 - 4$ or $\dfrac{189}{59} - 4 = 3$ or $-\dfrac{47}{59}.$

2. Solve the equations $\begin{cases} (y - b)(z - c) = a^2. & (1) \\ (z - c)(x - a) = b^2. & (2) \\ (x - a)(y - b) = c^2. & (3) \end{cases}$

Multiply (1), (2), and (3),

$$(x - a)^2(y - b)^2(z - c)^2 = a^2 b^2 c^2.$$

Whence, $\qquad\qquad (x - a)(y - b)(z - c) = \pm\, abc.$ (4)

Divide (4) by (1), $\quad x - a = \pm \dfrac{bc}{a}$, or $x = \dfrac{a^2 \pm bc}{a}.$

Divide (4) by (2), $\quad y - b = \pm \dfrac{ca}{b}$, or $y = \dfrac{b^2 \pm ca}{b}.$

Divide (4) by (3), $\quad z - c = \pm \dfrac{ab}{c}$, or $z = \dfrac{c^2 \pm ab}{c}.$

3. Solve the equations $\begin{cases} x(x + y + z) = a^2. & (1) \\ y(x + y + z) = b^2. & (2) \\ z(x + y + z) = c^2. & (3) \end{cases}$

Add (1), (2), and (3), $(x + y + z)^2 = a^2 + b^2 + c^2.$

Then, $x + y + z = \pm \sqrt{a^2 + b^2 + c^2}.$ (4)

Divide (1) by (4), $x = \pm \dfrac{a^2}{\sqrt{a^2 + b^2 + c^2}}.$

Divide (2) by (4), $y = \pm \dfrac{b^2}{\sqrt{a^2 + b^2 + c^2}}.$

Divide (3) by (4), $z = \pm \dfrac{c^2}{\sqrt{a^2 + b^2 + c^2}}.$

EXERCISE 68

(The note on page 313 applies with equal force to the following examples.)

Solve the following :

1.
$$\begin{cases} xy = a^2 b^2. \\ yz = -ab^3. \\ zx = -a^3 b. \end{cases}$$

2.
$$\begin{cases} x^2 yz = 12. \\ xy^2 z = 6. \\ xyz^2 = 18. \end{cases}$$

3.
$$\begin{cases} xy + yz = -8. \\ yz + zx = -3. \\ zx + xy = -35. \end{cases}$$

4.
$$\begin{cases} (x + y)(x + z) = 14. \\ (y + z)(y + x) = 2. \\ (z + x)(z + y) = 7. \end{cases}$$

5.
$$\begin{cases} 3x^2 - xy - xz = 4. \\ 5x - 2y = 1. \\ 4x + 3z = -5. \end{cases}$$

6.
$$\begin{cases} \dfrac{1}{x} + \dfrac{1}{y} - \dfrac{1}{z} = 13. \\ \dfrac{1}{y} - \dfrac{1}{x} = 1. \\ \dfrac{2}{xy} + \dfrac{1}{z} = 0. \end{cases}$$

7.
$$\begin{cases} xy + xz = 18 - x^2. \\ yz + yx = 27 - y^2. \\ zx + zy = 36 - z^2. \end{cases}$$

8.
$$\begin{cases} xy + yz - zx = b. \\ xy - yz + zx = c. \\ -xy + yz + zx = a. \end{cases}$$

9.
$$\begin{cases} 2x^2 + y^2 - z^2 = 43. \\ x - 3y + z = 17. \\ x + y - 3z = 13. \end{cases}$$

10.
$$\begin{cases} x + y + z = 12. \\ xy + yz + zx = 47. \\ x^2 + y^2 - z^2 = 0. \end{cases}$$

11.
$$\begin{cases} 6x + 6y = 5xyz. \\ 3y + 3z = 2xyz. \\ 2z + 2x = xyz. \end{cases}$$

12.
$$\begin{cases} x^2 + y^2 + z^2 = 110. \\ x + y - z = 4. \\ xz + yz = 77. \end{cases}$$

PROBLEMS INVOLVING SIMULTANEOUS EQUATIONS OF A HIGHER DEGREE THAN THE FIRST

481. In solving problems which involve simultaneous equations of a higher degree than the first, there will usually be more than one set of values of the unknown numbers; only those values should be retained which satisfy the conditions of the problem.

The considerations of §§ 261, 262, and 463, hold for simultaneous equations of any degree.

EXERCISE 69

1. The product of the sum of two numbers by the smaller is 21, and the product of their difference by the greater is 4. Find the numbers.

2. The difference of the squares of two numbers is 260 ; and the sum of the numbers is $\frac{13}{5}$ their difference. Find the numbers.

3. The sum of the squares of two numbers is 61, and the product of their squares is 900. Find the numbers.

4. The difference of the cubes of two numbers is 316 ; and if the product of the numbers be added to the sum of their squares, the sum is 79. Find the numbers.

5. Two numbers are expressed by the same two digits in reverse order. The sum of the numbers equals the square of the sum of the digits, and the difference of the numbers equals 5 times the square of the smaller digit. Find the numbers.

6. A party at a hotel spent a certain sum. Had there been five more, and each had spent fifty cents less, the bill would have been $24.75. Had there been three less, and each had spent fifty cents more, the bill would have been $9.75. How many were there, and what did each spend ?

7. The square of the sum of two numbers exceeds their product by 84 and the sum of the numbers, plus the square root of their product, equals 14. Find the numbers.

8. The difference of the cubes of two numbers is 728 ; and if the product of the numbers be multiplied by their difference, the result is 72. Find the numbers.

9. If $700 be put at simple interest for a certain number of years, at a certain rate, it amounts to $883.75. If the time were 4 years less, and the rate $1\frac{1}{2}$ per cent more, the amount would be $810.25. Find the time and the rate.

10. If the digits of a number of two figures be inverted, the quotient of this number by the given number is $\frac{4}{7}$, and their product 2268. Find the number.

11. The square of the smaller of two numbers, added to twice their product, gives 7 times the smaller number. And the square of the greater exceeds the product of the numbers by 6 times the smaller number. Find the numbers.

12. A and B travel from P to Q, 14 miles, at uniform rates, B taking 20 minutes longer than A to perform the journey. On the return, each travels one mile an hour faster, and B now takes 15 minutes longer than A. Find the rates of travelling.

13. A and B run a race around a course two miles long, B winning by two minutes. A now increases his speed by two miles an hour, and B diminishes his by the same amount, and A wins by two minutes. Find their original rates.

14. A man ascends the last half of a mountain at a rate one-half mile an hour less than his rate during the first half, and reaches the top in $3\frac{2}{5}$ hours. On the descent, his rate is one mile an hour greater than during the first half of the ascent, and he accomplishes it in $2\frac{2}{3}$ hours. Find the distance to the top, and his rate during the first half of the ascent.

15. The square of the second digit of a number of three digits exceeds twice the sum of the first and third by 3. The sum of the first and second digits exceeds 4 times the third by 1. And if 495 be subtracted from the number, the digits will be inverted. Find the number.

16. A rectangular piece of cloth, when wet, shrinks $\frac{1}{6}$ in its length, and $\frac{1}{12}$ in its width. If the area is diminished by $10\frac{5}{8}$ square feet, and the length of the four sides by $5\frac{1}{2}$ feet, what were the original dimensions?

17. A ship has provisions for 36 days. If the crew were 16 greater, and the daily ration one-half pound less, the provisions would last 30 days. If the crew were 2 less, and the daily ration one pound greater, they would last 24 days. Find the number of men, and the daily ration.

18. The sum of two numbers is 5, and the sum of their fifth powers is 1025. Find the numbers.

19. A man lends $2100 in two amounts, at different rates of interest, and the two sums produce equal returns. If the first portion had been loaned at the second rate, it would have produced $48; and if the second portion had been loaned at the first rate, it would have produced $27. Find the rates.

20. A can do a piece of work in two hours less time than B; and together they can do the work in $1\frac{1}{5}$ hours less time than A alone. How long does each alone take to do the work?

21. A starts to travel from P to Q, and at the same time B starts to travel from Q to P, both travelling at constant rates. A reaches Q in 8 hours, and B reaches P in 18 hours, after they have met on the road. How many hours does each take to perform the journey?

22. A and B travel from P to Q and back. A starts one hour after B, overtakes him at a point two miles from Q, meets him 32 minutes afterwards, and reaches P $1\frac{1}{2}$ hours before B. Find the distance from P to Q, and the rates of travel of A and B.

GRAPHICAL REPRESENTATION OF SIMULTANEOUS QUADRATIC EQUATIONS WITH TWO UNKNOWN NUMBERS

482. 1. Consider the equation $y^2 = 4x + 4$.

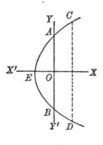

We have $y = \pm 2\sqrt{x+1}$.

If $x = 0$, $y = \pm 2$. (A, B)

If $x = 1$, $y = \pm 2\sqrt{2}$. (C, D)

If $x = -1$, $y = 0$. (E)

etc.

For any positive value of x, or for any negative value between 0 and -1, y has two values; the graph extends to an indefinitely great distance to the right of O.

For any negative value of $x < -1$, y is *imaginary;* then, no part of the graph lies to the left of a perpendicular to XX' at E.

2. Consider the equation $x^2 - 2y^2 = 1$.

Here, $y^2 = \dfrac{x^2 - 1}{2}$,

or $\qquad y = \pm \sqrt{\dfrac{x^2 - 1}{2}}$.

If $x = \pm 1$, $y = 0$. (A, A')

If x is between 1 and -1, y is imaginary; then, no part of the graph lies between perpendiculars to XX' at A and A'.

If $x = \pm 2$, $y = \pm \sqrt{\dfrac{3}{2}}$. (B, C, B', C')

For any positive value of $x > 1$, or any negative value < -1, y has two values; then, the graph has two branches, each of which extends to an indefinitely great distance from O.

3. Consider the equation $x^2 + y^2 - 4x + 2y = 4$.

In this case, it is convenient to first locate the points where the graph intersects the axes.

If $y = 0$, $x^2 - 4x = 4$,

and $x = 2 \pm \sqrt{8}$. (A, B)

If $x = 0$, $y^2 + 2y = 4$,

and $y = -1 \pm \sqrt{5}$. (C, D)

We may write the given equation

$$y^2 + 2y + 1 = 5 + 4x - x^2;$$

or, $(y + 1)^2 = (1 + x)(5 - x)$.

If $x = -1$ or 5, $y + 1 = 0$, and $y = -1$. (E, F)

If x has any positive value > 5, or any negative value < -1, $(1 + x)(5 - x)$ is negative, and $y + 1$ imaginary; then, no part of the graph extends to the right of F, or to the left of E.

Again, we may write the given equation

$$x^2 - 4x + 4 = 8 - 2y - y^2; \quad \text{or,} \quad (x - 2)^2 = (4 + y)(2 - y).$$

If $y = -4$ or 2, $x - 2 = 0$, and $x = 2$. (G, H)

If y has any positive value > 2, or any negative value < -4, $(4 + y)(2 - y)$ is negative; then, no part of the graph extends above H, or below G.

It is shown, in works on Analytic Geometry, that the graph of any equation of the second degree, with two unknown numbers, is one of the *conic sections*, so-called from being the sections of a cone made by a plane; either a *circle*, a *parabola*, an *ellipse*, a *hyperbola*, or a *pair of straight lines*.

The graph of Ex. 1 is a parabola, as also is the graph of any equation of the form $y^2 = ax$, or $y^2 = ax + b$.

(The graphs of §§ 465 and 467 are parabolas.)

The graph of Ex. 2 is a hyperbola, as also is the graph of any equation of the form $ax^2 - by^2 = c$, if a and b are numbers of like sign.

(The hyperbola has two branches. The graph of any equation of the form $xy = a$ is a hyperbola.)

The graph of Ex. 3 is a circle; as also is the graph of any equation of the form $x^2 + y^2 = a$, or $x^2 + y^2 + ax + by + c = 0$.

The graph of any equation of the form $ax^2 + by^2 = c$, where a, b, and c are numbers of like sign, and a and b unequal, is an ellipse.

(The graph of any equation of the form $a^2x^2 - b^2y^2 = 0$ is the pair of straight lines whose equations are $y = \pm \dfrac{ax}{b}$.)

483. Graphical Representation of Solutions of Systems of Simultaneous Quadratic Equations.

1. Consider the equations $\begin{cases} y^2 = 4\,x. \\ 3\,x - y = 5. \end{cases}$

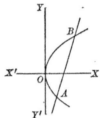

The graph of $y^2 = 4\,x$ is the parabola AOB.

The graph of $3\,x - y = 5$ is the straight line AB, intersecting the parabola at the points A and B, respectively.

To find the co-ordinates of A and B, we solve the given equations (§ 277); the solution is $x = 1$, $y = -2$, and $x = \dfrac{25}{9}$, $y = \dfrac{10}{3}$.

It may be verified in the figure that these are the co-ordinates of A and B, respectively.

Hence (compare § 277), *if any two graphs intersect, the co-ordinates of any point of intersection form a solution of the system of equations represented by the graphs.*

2. Consider the equations

$$\begin{cases} x^2 + y^2 = 17. \\ xy = 4. \end{cases}$$

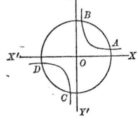

The graph of $x^2 + y^2 = 17$ is the circle AD, whose centre is at O, and whose radius is $\sqrt{17}$.

The graph of $xy = 4$ is a hyperbola, having its branches in the angles XOY and $X'OY'$, respectively, and intersecting the circle at the points A and B in angle XOY, and at the points C and D in angle $X'OY'$.

The solution of the given equations is

$x = 4, y = 1; \; x = 1, y = 4; \; x = -1, y = -4; \;$ and $x = -4, y = -1.$

It may be verified in the figure that these are the co-ordinates of A, B, C, and D, respectively.

3. Consider the equations

$$\begin{cases} x^2 + 4\,y^2 = 4. \\ 2\,x + 3\,y = -5. \end{cases}$$

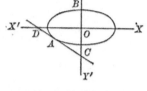

The graph of $x^2 + 4\,y^2 = 4$ is the ellipse AB, intersecting XX' at points 2 to the right and 2 to the left of O, and YY' at points 1 above and 1 below O.

The graph of $2\,x + 3\,y = -5$ is the straight line CD.

Substituting $x = -\dfrac{3\,y + 5}{2}$ in $x^2 + 4\,y^2 = 4$, we obtain the equation $25\,y^2 + 30\,y + 9 = 0$, which has equal roots.

Thus, $y = -\dfrac{3}{5};$ and $x = -\dfrac{-\dfrac{9}{5} + 5}{2} = -\dfrac{8}{5}.$

The equal roots signify that the two points of intersection coincide, and the line is therefore tangent to the ellipse.

In general, if the equation obtained by eliminating one of the unknown numbers has equal roots, the graphs are tangent to each other.

4. Consider the equations

$$\begin{cases} 9\,x^2 - y^2 = -9. \\ x - 2\,y = -2. \end{cases}$$

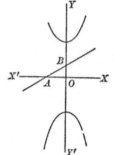

The graph of $9\,x^2 - y^2 = -9$ is a hyperbola, having its branches above and below O, respectively.

The graph of $x - 2\,y = -2$ is the straight line AB.

Substituting $x = 2\,y - 2$ in $9\,x^2 - y^2 = -9$, we obtain the equation $35\,y^2 - 72\,y + 45 = 0$, which has complex roots.

Then, the graphs have no point of intersection.

In general, if the equation obtained by eliminating one of the unknown numbers has no real root, the graphs do not intersect each other.

EXERCISE 70

Find the graphs of the following :

1. $xy = -6.$

3. $x^2 + y^2 = 4.$

5. $9x^2 - 4y^2 = 0.$

2. $x^2 = 3y.$

4. $y^2 = 5x - 1.$

6. $4x^2 + 9y^2 = 36.$

7. $4x^2 - y^2 = -4.$

8. $x^2 + y^2 + 6x - 2y = 15.$

Find the graphs of the following systems, and in each case verify the principles of § 483 :

9. $\begin{cases} x^2 + 4y^2 = 4. \\ x - y = 1. \end{cases}$

12. $\begin{cases} x^2 - y^2 = 9. \\ 5x - 4y = -9. \end{cases}$

15. $\begin{cases} x^2 + y^2 = 29. \\ xy = 10. \end{cases}$

10. $\begin{cases} x^2 + y^2 = 16. \\ y^2 = 6x. \end{cases}$

13. $\begin{cases} 2x^2 - 3y = 5. \\ 5x + 6y = -12. \end{cases}$

16. $\begin{cases} 2x^2 + 5y^2 = 53. \\ 3x^2 - 4y^2 = -24. \end{cases}$

11. $\begin{cases} y^2 - 3x = -3. \\ x + 2y = -2. \end{cases}$

14. $\begin{cases} 9x^2 + y^2 = 148. \\ xy = -8. \end{cases}$

17. $\begin{cases} x^2 + y^2 + 3x = 22. \\ 4x^2 - 9y^2 = 0. \end{cases}$

XXII. INDETERMINATE LINEAR EQUATIONS

484. It was shown in § 269 that a system of m independent linear equations containing more than m unknown numbers, has an indefinitely great number of solutions.

Such a system is called *indeterminate* (§ 266).

If, however, the unknown numbers are required to satisfy other conditions, the number of solutions may be finite.

485. Solution of Indeterminate Linear Equations in Positive Integers.

We shall consider in the present chapter the solution of indeterminate linear equations, in which the unknown numbers are restricted to positive integral values.

1. Solve $7x + 5y = 118$ in positive integers.

Dividing by 5, the smaller of the two coefficients,

$$x + \frac{2x}{5} + y = 23 + \frac{3}{5}; \text{ or, } \frac{2x-3}{5} = 23 - x - y.$$

Since, by the conditions of the problem, x and y must be positive integers, $\frac{2x-3}{5}$ must be an integer.

Let this integer be represented by p.

Then, $\qquad \frac{2x-3}{5} = p$, or $2x - 3 = 5p$. $\qquad\qquad$ (1)

Dividing (1) by 2,

$$x - 1 - \frac{1}{2} = 2p + \frac{p}{2}; \text{ or, } x - 1 - 2p = \frac{p+1}{2}.$$

Since x and p are integers, $x - 1 - 2p$ is an integer; and therefore $\frac{p+1}{2}$ must be an integer.

Let this integer be represented by q.

Then, $\qquad\qquad\qquad \frac{p+1}{2} = q$, or $p = 2q - 1$.

Substituting in (1), $2x - 3 = 10q - 5$.

Whence, $\qquad\qquad x = 5q - 1.$ $\qquad\qquad$ (2)

Substituting this value in the given equation,

$$35q - 7 + 5y = 118; \text{ or, } y = 25 - 7q. \qquad (3)$$

Equations (2) and (3) form the *general solution in integers* of the given equation.

By giving to q the value zero, or any positive or negative integer, we shall obtain sets of integral values of x and y which satisfy the given equation.

If q is zero, or any negative integer, x will be negative.

If q is any positive integer > 3, y will be negative.

Hence, the only *positive integral* values of x and y which satisfy the given equation are those obtained from the values 1, 2, 3 of q.

That is, $x = 4$, $y = 18$; $x = 9$, $y = 11$; and $x = 14$, $y = 4$.

2. Solve $8x - 13y = 100$ in positive integers.

Dividing by 8, the coefficient of smaller absolute value,

$$x - y - \frac{5y}{8} = 12 + \frac{4}{8}; \text{ or, } x - y - 12 = \frac{5y + 4}{8}.$$

Then, $\dfrac{5y + 4}{8}$ must be an integer.

Multiplying by 5, $\dfrac{25y + 20}{8}$ must also be an integer.

Then, $3y + \dfrac{y}{8} + 2 + \dfrac{4}{8}$ must be an integer, and hence $\dfrac{y + 4}{8}$ must be an integer; let this be represented by p.

Then, $\qquad\qquad \dfrac{y + 4}{8} = p, \text{ or } y = 8p - 4.$

Substituting in the given equation,

$$8x - 104p + 52 = 100, \text{ or } x = 13p + 6.$$

In this case p may be any positive integer.

If $p = 1$, $x = 19$ and $y = 4$; if $p = 2$, $x = 32$ and $y = 12$; etc. Thus, the number of solutions is indefinitely great.

The artifice of multiplying $\dfrac{5y+4}{8}$ by 5 saves much work in Ex. 2.

The rule in any case is to multiply the numerator of the fraction by such a number that the coefficient of the unknown quantity shall exceed some multiple of the denominator by unity.

If this had not been done, the last part of the solution would have stood as follows :

Let $\qquad\qquad \dfrac{5y+4}{8}=p,$ or $5y+4=8p.$ $\qquad$ (1)

Divide by 5, $y+\dfrac{4}{5}=p+\dfrac{3p}{5}$; then $\dfrac{3p-4}{5}$ must be an integer.

Let $\qquad\qquad \dfrac{3p-4}{5}=q,$ or $3p-4=5q.$ $\qquad$ (2)

Divide by 3, $p-1-\dfrac{1}{3}=q+\dfrac{2q}{3}$; then $\dfrac{2q+1}{3}$ must be an integer.

Let $\qquad\qquad \dfrac{2q+1}{3}=r,$ or $2q+1=3r.$ $\qquad$ (3)

Divide by 2, $q+\dfrac{1}{2}=r+\dfrac{r}{2}$; then $\dfrac{r-1}{2}$ must be an integer.

Let $\qquad\qquad \dfrac{r-1}{2}=s,$ $\qquad$ or $r=2s+1.$

Substituting in (3), $2q+1=6s+3,$ $\quad$ or $q=3s+1.$

Substituting in (2), $3p-4=15s+5,$ $\quad$ or $p=5s+3.$

Substituting in (1), $5y+4=40s+24,$ $\quad$ or $y=8s+4.$

Substituting in the given equation,

$\qquad 8x-104s-52=100,$ $\qquad$ or $x=13s+19.$

These values of x and y differ in form from those obtained above ; but it is to be observed that $13s+19$ and $8s+4$, for the values 0, 1, 2, etc., of s, give rise to the *same series of positive integers* as $13p+6$ and $8p-4$ for the values 1, 2, 3, etc., of p.

We will now show how to solve in positive integers two equations involving three unknown numbers.

3. In how many ways can the sum of $ 14.40 be paid with dollars, half-dollars, and dimes, the number of dimes being equal to the number of dollars and half-dollars together ?

Let $\qquad\qquad\qquad x =$ number of dollars,

$\qquad\qquad\qquad\qquad y =$ number of half-dollars,

and $\qquad\qquad\qquad z =$ number of dimes.

Then by the conditions,

$$\begin{cases} 10\,x + 5\,y + z = 144, \\ x + y = z. \end{cases} \tag{1}$$

Adding, $\qquad 11\,x + 6\,y + z = 144 + z,$

or, $\qquad\qquad\qquad 11\,x + 6\,y = 144. \tag{2}$

Dividing by 6, $\quad x + \dfrac{5\,x}{6} + y = 24.$

Then $\dfrac{5\,x}{6}$ must be an integer; or, x must be a multiple of 6.

Let $\qquad\qquad\qquad\qquad x = 6\,p,$ where p is an integer.

Substitute in (2), $66\,p + 6\,y = 144,$ or $y = 24 - 11\,p.$

Substitute in (1), $\qquad\qquad z = 6\,p + 24 - 11\,p = 24 - 5\,p.$

The only positive integral solutions are when $p = 1$ or 2.

Therefore, the number of ways is two; either 6 dollars, 13 half-dollars, and 19 dimes; or 12 dollars, 2 half-dollars, and 14 dimes.

EXERCISE 71

Solve the following in positive integers :

1. $3\,x + 5\,y = 29.$
2. $7\,x + 2\,y = 39.$
3. $6\,x + 29\,y = 274.$
4. $4\,x + 31\,y = 473.$

5. $10\,x + 7\,y = 297.$
6. $23\,x + 17\,y = 183.$
7. $8\,x + 71\,y = 1933.$
8. $13\,x + 50\,y = 1089.$

Solve the following in least positive integers :

9. $6\,x - 7\,y = 13.$
10. $5\,x - 8\,y = 31.$
11. $14\,x - 5\,y = 64.$

12. $8\,x - 31\,y = 10.$
13. $15\,x - 38\,y = -47.$
14. $64\,x - 19\,y = 507.$

Solve the following in positive integers :

15. $\begin{cases} 12\,x + 7\,y + 2\,z = 53. \\ 2\,x - 11\,y + z = -25. \end{cases}$

16. $\begin{cases} 3\,x - 3\,y + 7\,z = 101. \\ 4\,x + 2\,y - 3\,z = 5. \end{cases}$

17. In how many different ways can \$1.65 be paid with quarter-dollars and dimes ?

18. In how many many different ways can £2 1s. be paid with half-crowns, worth 2s. 6d. each, and florins, worth 2s. each ?

19. Find two fractions whose denominators are 5 and 7, respectively, whose numerators are the smallest possible positive integers, and whose difference is $\frac{17}{35}$.

20. In how many different ways can $7.15 be paid with fifty-cent pieces, twenty-five-cent pieces, and twenty-cent pieces, so that twice the number of fifty-cent pieces, plus twice the number of twenty-cent pieces, shall exceed the number of twenty-five-cent pieces by 31 ?

21. A farmer purchased a certain number of pigs, sheep, and calves, for $138. The pigs cost $4 each, the sheep $7 each, and the calves $9 each ; and the whole number of animals purchased was 23. How many of each did he buy ?

22. In how many different ways can $5.45 be paid with quarter-dollars, twenty-cent pieces, and dimes, so that twice the number of quarters, plus 5 times the number of twenty-cent pieces, shall exceed the number of dimes by 36 ?

486. Every linear equation, with two unknown numbers, x and y, can be reduced to one of the forms

$$ax \pm by = \pm c,$$

where $a, b,$ and c are positive integers which have no common divisor.

The equation $ax + by = -c$ cannot be solved in positive integers; for, if $x, y, a,$ and b are positive integers, $ax + by$ must also be a positive integer.

Again, the equations $ax \pm by = c$ and $ax - by = -c$ cannot be solved in positive integers if a and b have a common divisor.

For, if x and y are positive integers, this common divisor must also be a divisor of $ax \pm by$, and consequently of c; which is contrary to the hypothesis that $a, b,$ and c have no common divisor.

XXIII. RATIO AND PROPORTION

487. The **Ratio** of one number a to another number b is the quotient of a divided by b.

Thus, the ratio of a to b is $\dfrac{a}{b}$; it is also expressed $a : b$.

In the ratio $a : b$, a is called the *first term*, or *antecedent*, and b the *second term*, or *consequent*.

If a is $> b$, the ratio $a : b$ is called a ratio of *greater inequality;* if a is $< b$, it is called a ratio of *less inequality.*

The ratio of the product of the antecedents of a series of ratios to the product of the consequents, is said to be *compounded* of the given ratios.

Thus, $ac : bd$ is compounded of the ratios $a : b$ and $c : d$.

The ratio $a^2 : b^2$ is called the *duplicate ratio*, the ratio $a^3 : b^3$ the *triplicate ratio*, and the ratio $\sqrt{a} : \sqrt{b}$ the *sub-duplicate ratio*, of $a : b$.

RATIO OF CONCRETE MAGNITUDES

488. In § 487, we considered the ratio of *abstract numbers* only; it is, however, necessary to consider the ratio of two concrete magnitudes of the same kind.

If a concrete magnitude is a times a certain unit, and another b times the same unit, we define the ratio of the first magnitude to the second as being the ratio of a to b.

Thus, the ratio of two lines whose lengths are $2\tfrac{1}{3}$ and $3\tfrac{1}{2}$ inches, respectively, is $2\tfrac{1}{3} \div 3\tfrac{1}{2}$, or $\dfrac{2}{3}$.

If the ratio can be expressed as a *rational* number, as in the above illustration, the magnitudes are said to be **Commensurable.**

If it cannot be expressed as a rational number, they are said to be **Incommensurable.**

PROPORTION

489. A **Proportion** is an equation whose members are equal ratios.

Thus, if $a:b$ and $c:d$ are equal ratios,

$$a:b=c:d, \text{ or } \frac{a}{b}=\frac{c}{d},$$

is a proportion.

The symbol :: is sometimes used in place of the sign of equality in a proportion.

490. In the proportion $a:b=c:d$, a is called the *first term*, b the *second*, c the *third*, and d the *fourth*.

The first and third terms of a proportion are called the *antecedents*, and the second and fourth terms the *consequents*.

The first and fourth terms are called the *extremes*, and the second and third terms the *means*.

If the means of a proportion are equal, either mean is called a **Mean Proportional** between the first and last terms, and the last term is called a **Third Proportional** to the first and second terms.

Thus, in the proportion $a:b=b:c$, b is a mean proportional between a and c, and c is a third proportional to a and b.

A **Fourth Proportional** to three numbers is the fourth term of a proportion whose first three terms are the three numbers taken in their order.

Thus, in the proportion $a:b=c:d$, d is a fourth proportional to a, b, and c.

A **Continued Proportion** is a series of equal ratios, in which each consequent is the same as the following antecedent; as,

$$a:b=b:c=c:d=d:e.$$

PROPERTIES OF PROPORTIONS

491. *In any proportion, the product of the extremes is equal to the product of the means.*

Let the proportion be $a:b=c:d$.

Then by § 489, $\qquad \frac{a}{b}=\frac{c}{d}.$

Clearing of fractions, $\qquad ad=bc.$

492. From the equation $ad = bc$ (§ 491), we obtain

$$a = \frac{bc}{d}, \ b = \frac{ad}{c}, \ c = \frac{ad}{b}, \text{ and } d = \frac{bc}{a}.$$

That is, *in any proportion, either extreme equals the product of the means divided by the other extreme; and either mean equals the product of the extremes divided by the other mean.*

493. (Converse of § 491.) *If the product of two numbers be equal to the product of two others, one pair may be made the extremes, and the other pair the means, of a proportion.*

Let $ad = bc.$ (1)

Dividing by bd, $\dfrac{a}{b} = \dfrac{c}{d}.$

Then, $a : b = c : d,$ or $c : d = a : b.$

In like manner, by dividing the members of (1) by ab, then by cd, and then by ac, we have

$$d : b = c : a, \text{ or } c : a = d : b,$$
$$a : c = b : d, \text{ or } b : d = a : c,$$

and $d : c = b : a,$ or $b : a = d : c.$

494. *In any proportion, the terms are in proportion by* **alternation**; *that is, the means can be interchanged.*

Let the proportion be $a : b = c : d.$

Then by § 491, $ad = bc.$ (1)

Whence, by § 493, $a : c = b : d.$

We also have from (1), by § 493,

$$d : b = c : a.$$

That is, *in any proportion, the extremes can be interchanged.*

495. *In any proportion, the terms are in proportion by* **Inversion**; *that is, the second term is to the first as the fourth term is to the third.*

Let the proportion be $a : b = c : d.$

Then by § 491, $ad = bc.$

Whence, by § 493, $b : a = d : c.$

It follows from the above that, *in any proportion, the means can be written as the extremes, and the extremes as the means.*

496. *A mean proportional between two numbers is equal to the square root of their product.*

Let the proportion be $a : b = b : c.$

Then by § 491, $b^2 = ac,$ and $b = \sqrt{ac}.$

497. *In any proportion, the terms are in proportion by* **Composition**; *that is, the sum of the first two terms is to the first term as the sum of the last two terms is to the third term.*

Let the proportion be $a : b = c : d.$

Then, $ad = bc.$

Adding each member of the equation to $ac,$

$$ac + ad = ac + bc, \text{ or } a(c + d) = c(a + b).$$

Then by § 493, $a + b : a = c + d : c.$

We may also prove $a + b : b = c + d : d.$

498. *In any proportion, the terms are in proportion by* **Division**; *that is, the difference of the first two terms is to the first term as the difference of the last two terms is to the third term.*

Let the proportion be $a : b = c : d.$

Then, $ad = bc.$

Subtracting each member of the equation from $ac,$

$$ac - ad = ac - bc, \text{ or } a(c - d) = c(a - b).$$

Then, $a - b : a = c - d : c.$

We may also prove $a - b : b = c - d : d.$

499. *In any proportion, the terms are in proportion by* **Composition and Division**; *that is, the sum of the first two terms is to their difference as the sum of the last two terms is to their difference.*

Let the proportion be $a : b = c : d$

Then by § 497, $$\frac{a+b}{a}=\frac{c+d}{c}. \qquad (1)$$

And by § 498, $$\frac{a-b}{a}=\frac{c-d}{c}. \qquad (2)$$

Dividing (1) by (2), $\dfrac{a+b}{a-b}=\dfrac{c+d}{c-d}.$

Whence, $\qquad a+b : a-b = c+d : c-d.$

500. *In any proportion, if the first two terms be multiplied by any number, as also the last two, the resulting numbers will be in proportion.*

Let the proportion be $\quad a : b = c : d.$

Then, $\dfrac{a}{b}=\dfrac{c}{d}$; and hence $\dfrac{ma}{mb}=\dfrac{nc}{nd}.$

Therefore, $\qquad ma : mb = nc : nd.$

We may also prove $\qquad \dfrac{a}{m}:\dfrac{b}{m}=\dfrac{c}{n}:\dfrac{d}{n}.$

(Either m or n may be unity; that is, the terms of either ratio may be multiplied or divided without multiplying or dividing the terms of the other.)

501. *In any proportion, if the first and third terms be multiplied by any number, as also the second and fourth terms, the resulting numbers will be in proportion.*

Let the proportion be $\quad a : b = c : d.$

Then, $\dfrac{a}{b}=\dfrac{c}{d}$; and hence $\dfrac{ma}{nb}=\dfrac{mc}{nd}.$

Therefore, $\qquad ma : nb = mc : nd.$

We may also prove $\qquad \dfrac{a}{m}:\dfrac{b}{n}=\dfrac{c}{m}:\dfrac{d}{n}.$

(Either m or n may be unity.)

502. *In any number of proportions, the products of the corresponding terms are in proportion.*

Let the proportions be $a : b = c : d,$

and $\qquad\qquad\qquad e : f = g : h.$

Then, $$\frac{a}{b} = \frac{c}{d}, \text{ and } \frac{e}{f} = \frac{g}{h}.$$

Multiplying, $$\frac{a}{b} \times \frac{e}{f} = \frac{c}{d} \times \frac{g}{h}, \text{ or } \frac{ae}{bf} = \frac{cg}{dh}.$$

Whence, $$ae : bf = cg : dh.$$

In like manner, the theorem may be proved for any number of proportions.

503. *The quotients of the corresponding terms of two proportions are in proportion.*

Let the proportions be $a : b = c : d,$

and $$e : f = g : h.$$

Then, $$\frac{a}{b} = \frac{c}{d}, \text{ and } \frac{f}{e} = \frac{h}{g}.$$

Whence, $$\frac{a}{b} \times \frac{f}{e} = \frac{c}{d} \times \frac{h}{g}; \text{ or, } \frac{a}{e} \div \frac{b}{f} = \frac{c}{g} \div \frac{d}{h}.$$

Then, $$\frac{a}{e} : \frac{b}{f} = \frac{c}{g} : \frac{d}{h}.$$

504. *In any proportion, like powers or like principal roots of the terms are in proportion.*

Let the proportion be $a : b = c : d.$

Then, $\dfrac{a}{b} = \dfrac{c}{d}$; and hence $\dfrac{a^n}{b^n} = \dfrac{c^n}{d^n}.$

Therefore, $$a^n : b^n = c^n : d^n.$$

We may also prove $$\sqrt[n]{a} : \sqrt[n]{b} = \sqrt[n]{c} : \sqrt[n]{d}.$$

505. *In a series of equal ratios, any antecedent is to its consequent as the sum of all the antecedents is to the sum of all the consequents.*

Let $$a : b = c : d = e : f.$$

Then by § 491, $$ad = bc,$$

and $$af = be.$$

Also, $$ab = ba.$$

Adding, $\qquad a(b+d+f)=b(a+c+e)$.

Whence, $\qquad\qquad\qquad a:b=a+c+e:b+d+f.$ (§ 493)

In like manner, the theorem may be proved for any number of equal ratios.

506. *To prove that if* $\qquad \dfrac{a}{b}=\dfrac{c}{d}=\dfrac{e}{f}=\cdots,$

then each of these equal ratios equals $\left(\dfrac{pa^n+qc^n+re^n+\cdots}{pb^n+qd^n+rf^n+\cdots}\right)^{\frac{1}{n}}.$

If $\dfrac{a}{b}=\dfrac{c}{d}=\dfrac{f}{e}=\cdots=k$, then $a=bk$, $c=dk$, $e=fk$, etc.

Then, $\quad pa^n+qc^n+re^n+\cdots=p(bk)^n+q(dk)^n+r(fk)^n+\cdots$
$$=k^n(pb^n+qd^n+rf^n+\cdots).$$

Therefore, $\qquad\qquad k^n=\dfrac{pa^n+qc^n+re^n+\cdots}{pb^n+qd^n+rf^n+\cdots}.$

Or, $\qquad\qquad\qquad k=\left(\dfrac{pa^n+qc^n+re^n+\cdots}{pb^n+qd^n+rf^n+\cdots}\right)^{\frac{1}{n}}.$

507. *If three numbers are in continued proportion, the first is to the third as the square of the first is to the square of the second.*

Let the proportion be $a:b=b:c$.

Then, $\qquad\qquad\qquad \dfrac{a}{b}=\dfrac{b}{c}.$

Therefore, $\qquad \dfrac{a}{b}\times\dfrac{b}{c}=\dfrac{a}{b}\times\dfrac{a}{b}$, or $\dfrac{a}{c}=\dfrac{a^2}{b^2}.$

Whence, $\qquad\qquad a:c=a^2:b^2.$

508. *If four numbers are in continued proportion, the first is to the fourth as the cube of the first is to the cube of the second.*

Let the proportion be $a:b=b:c=c:d$.

Then, $\qquad\qquad\qquad \dfrac{a}{b}=\dfrac{b}{c}=\dfrac{c}{d}.$

Therefore, $\quad \dfrac{a}{b}\times\dfrac{b}{c}\times\dfrac{c}{d}=\dfrac{a}{b}\times\dfrac{a}{b}\times\dfrac{a}{b}$, or $\dfrac{a}{d}=\dfrac{a^3}{b^3}.$

Whence, $\qquad\qquad a:d=a^3:b^3.$

509. Examples.

1. If $x : y = (x + z)^2 : (y + z)^2$, prove z a mean proportional between x and y.

From the given proportion, by § 491,

$y(x + z)^2 = x(y + z)^2$, or $x^2 y + 2\,xyz + yz^2 = xy^2 + 2\,xyz + xz^2$.

Transposing, $x^2 y - xy^2 = xz^2 - yz^2$.

Dividing by $x - y$, $xy = z^2$.

Therefore, z is a mean proportional between x and y.

The theorem of § 499 saves work in the solution of a certain class of fractional equations.

2. Solve the equation $\dfrac{x^2 + x - 1}{x^2 - x - 1} = \dfrac{x - 2}{x + 2}$.

By composition and division,

$$\frac{2\,x^2 - 2}{2\,x} = \frac{2\,x}{-4}; \text{ or,} \frac{x^2 - 1}{x} = -\frac{x}{2}.$$

Clearing of fractions, $2\,x^2 - 2 = -x^2$.

Then, $3\,x^2 = 2$, and $x = \pm \sqrt{\dfrac{2}{3}}$.

3. Prove that if $\dfrac{a}{b} = \dfrac{c}{d}$, then

$$a^2 - b^2 : a^2 - 3\,ab = c^2 - d^2 : c^2 - 3\,cd.$$

Let $\dfrac{a}{b} = \dfrac{c}{d} = x$; then, $a = bx$.

Therefore,

$$\frac{a^2 - b^2}{a^2 - 3\,ab} = \frac{b^2 x^2 - b^2}{b^2 x^2 - 3\,b^2 x} = \frac{x^2 - 1}{x^2 - 3\,x} = \frac{\dfrac{c^2}{d^2} - 1}{\dfrac{c^2}{d^2} - \dfrac{3\,c}{d}} = \frac{c^2 - d^2}{c^2 - 3\,cd}.$$

Then $a^2 - b^2 : a^2 - 3\,ab = c^2 - d^2 : c^2 - 3\,cd$.

EXERCISE 72

1. Find the third term of a proportion whose first, second, and fourth terms are $\dfrac{3}{4}$, $\dfrac{5}{6}$, and $\dfrac{8}{9}$, respectively.

2. Find a third proportional to $\dfrac{14}{9}$ and $\dfrac{7}{12}$.

3. Find a mean proportional between $1\frac{11}{14}$ and $24\frac{3}{5}$.

4. Find a fourth proportional to $4\frac{1}{3}$, $5\frac{5}{8}$, and $1\frac{5}{7}$.

5. Find a third proportional to $a^3 + 27$ and $a + 3$.

6. Find a mean proportional between $\dfrac{x^2 - x - 12}{x - 5}$ and $\dfrac{x^2 - 9x + 20}{x + 3}$.

Solve the following equations :

7. $\dfrac{3x - 8}{3x + 4} = \dfrac{2x - 5}{2x + 7}$.

8. $\dfrac{x^2 + 2x - 3}{x^2 - 2x - 3} = \dfrac{3x + 2}{3x - 2}$.

9. $\dfrac{x^2 + 3x - 1}{x^2 - 3x + 1} = \dfrac{x^2 + 2x + 1}{x^2 - 2x - 1}$.

10. $\dfrac{\sqrt{x^2 + 1} + \sqrt{x^2 - 1}}{\sqrt{x^2 + 1} - \sqrt{x^2 - 1}} = \dfrac{\sqrt{a^2 - 2a + 2} + \sqrt{a^2 - 2a}}{\sqrt{a^2 - 2a + 2} - \sqrt{a^2 - 2a}}$.

11. $\begin{cases} \dfrac{x + y}{x - y} = \dfrac{a + b}{a - b}. \\[2mm] \dfrac{x^2 + x + y^2}{x^2 - x + y^2} = \dfrac{a^2 + a + b^2}{a^2 - a + b^2}. \end{cases}$

12. If $a : b = c : d$ and $e : f = g : h$, prove
$$ae + bf : ae - bf = cg + dh : cg - dh.$$

13. Find two numbers such that, if 9 be added to the first, and 7 subtracted from the second, they will be in the ratio $9 : 2$; while if 9 be subtracted from the first, and 7 added to the second, they will be in the ratio $9 : 11$.

14. Find two numbers in the ratio $a : b$, such that, if each be increased by c, they shall be in the ratio $m : n$.

15. Find three numbers in continued proportion whose sum is $28\frac{1}{2}$, such that the quotient of the first by the second shall be $\dfrac{2}{3}$.

16. Find a number such that, if it be added to each term of the ratio $8 : 5$, the result is $\dfrac{11}{20}$ of what it would have been if the same number had been subtracted from each term.

17. The second of three numbers is a mean proportional between the other two. The third number exceeds the sum of the other two by 20 ; and the sum of the first and third exceeds three times the second by 4. Find the numbers.

18. If $8a - 5b : 7a - 4b = 8b - 5c : 7b - 4c$, prove c a third proportional to a and b.

19. If $a + b + c + d : a + b = a - b + c - d : a - b$, prove
$$a : b = c : d.$$

20. If $x + y : y + z = \sqrt{x^2 - y^2} : \sqrt{y^2 - z^2}$, prove y a mean proportional between x and z.

21. A is following B along a certain road, when B turns and walks in the opposite direction; if A and B approach each other five times as fast as before, compare their rates.

22. If 4 silver coins and 11 copper coins are worth as much as 2 gold coins, and 5 silver coins and 19 copper coins as much as 3 gold coins, find the ratio of the value of a gold coin, and the value of a silver coin, to the value of a copper coin.

23. Given $2(a^2 + ab)x + (a^2 + 2b^2)y = (a^2 - b^2)x + (2a^2 + b^2)y$, find the ratio of x to y.

24. Given $\dfrac{x}{b} + \dfrac{y}{a} = \dfrac{x}{c} + \dfrac{z}{a} = \dfrac{y}{c} + \dfrac{z}{b}$, find the ratio of x to y, and of x to z.

25. If $\dfrac{a}{b} = \dfrac{c}{d}$, prove,

    (a) $3a^2 - 4ab : 2ab + 7b^2 = 3c^2 - 4cd : 2cd + 7d^2$.

    (b) $a^3 + 6ab^2 : a^2b - 5b^3 = c^3 + 6cd^2 : c^2d - 5d^3$.

26. The sum of four numbers in proportion is 32. The sum of the means exceeds the sum of the extremes by 4; and the sum of the consequents exceeds the sum of the antecedents by 16. Find the numbers.

27. A passenger observes that a train passes him, moving in the opposite direction, in 3 seconds; while, if it had been moving in the same direction, it would have passed him in 13 seconds. Compare the rates of the trains.

28. Each of two vessels contains a mixture of wine and water. A mixture consisting of equal measures from the two vessels is composed of wine and water in the ratio $3:4$; another mixture consisting of 14 measures from the first and 21 measures from the second, is composed of wine to water in the ratio $2:3$. Find the ratio of wine to water in each vessel.

29. If $\dfrac{a}{b} = \dfrac{c}{d} = \dfrac{e}{f}$, prove

(a) $a^2 + c^2 + e^2 : b^2 + d^2 + f^2 = ac + ce + ea : bd + df + fb$.

(b) $a^4 + c^4 + e^4 : b^4 + d^4 + f^4 = (a^2 + c^2 + e^2)^2 : (b^2 + d^2 + f^2)^2$.

30. If $a + b$, $b + c$, and $c + a$ are in continued proportion, prove

$$a + b : b + c = c - a : a - b.$$

31. Find four numbers in proportion such that the sum of the means is 21, and of the extremes 39; and twice the last term exceeds three times the sum of the first two terms by 36.

32. If a, b, c, and d are in continued proportion, prove

$$3a + 4d : 2a - 5d = 3a^3 + 4b^3 : 2a^3 - 5b^3.$$

XXIV. VARIATION

510. One variable number (§ 245) is said to *vary directly* as another when the ratio of any two values of the first equals the ratio of the corresponding values of the second.

It is usual to omit the word "directly," and simply say that one number *varies* as another.

Thus, if a workman receives a fixed number of dollars per diem, the number of dollars received in m days will be to the number received in n days as m is to n.

Then, the ratio of any two numbers of dollars received equals the ratio of the corresponding numbers of days worked.

Hence, the number of dollars which the workman receives *varies* as the number of days during which he works.

The symbol $\propto$ is used to express variation; thus, $a \propto b$ is read "a varies as b."

511. One variable is said to *vary inversely* as another when the first varies directly as the *reciprocal* of the second.

Thus, the number of hours in which a railway train will traverse a fixed route varies inversely as the speed; if the speed be *doubled*, the train will traverse its route in *one-half* the number of hours.

One variable is said to vary as two others *jointly* when it varies directly as their product.

Thus, the number of dollars received by a workman in a certain number of days varies jointly as the number which he receives in one day, and the number of days during which he works.

One variable is said to vary directly as a second and inversely as a third, when it varies jointly as the second and the reciprocal of the third.

Thus, the attraction of a body varies directly as the amount of matter, and inversely as the square of the distance.

512. *If $x \propto y$, then x equals y multiplied by a constant number.*

Let x' and y' denote a *fixed* pair of corresponding values of x and y, and x and y any other pair.

By the definition of § 510, $\dfrac{x}{y} = \dfrac{x'}{y'}$; or, $x = \dfrac{x'}{y'}y$.

Denoting the constant ratio $\dfrac{x'}{y'}$ by m, we have

$$x = my.$$

513. It follows from §§ 511 and 512 that:

1. *If x varies inversely as y,* $x = \dfrac{m}{y}$.

2. *If x varies jointly as y and z,* $x = myz$.

3. *If x varies directly as y and inversely as z,* $x = \dfrac{my}{z}$.

The converse of each statement of §§ 512 and 513 is also true ; that is, if x equals y multiplied by a constant, $x \propto y$, etc.

514. *If $x \propto y$, and $y \propto z$, then $x \propto z$.*

By § 512, if $x \propto y$, $x = my$.   (1)

And if $y \propto z$, $y = nz$.

Substituting in (1), $x = mnz$.

Whence, by § 513, $x \propto z$.

515. *If $x \propto y$ when z is constant, and $x \propto z$ when y is constant, then $x \propto yz$ when both y and z vary.*

Let y' and z' be the values of y and z, respectively, when x has the value x'.

Let y be changed from y' to y'', z remaining constantly equal to z', and let x be changed in consequence from x' to X.

Then by § 510, $\dfrac{x'}{X} = \dfrac{y'}{y''}$.   (1)

Now let z be changed from z' to z'', y remaining constantly equal to y'', and let x be changed in consequence from X to x''

Then, $\dfrac{X}{x''} = \dfrac{z'}{z''}$.   (2)

Multiplying (1) by (2), $\dfrac{x'}{x''} = \dfrac{y'z'}{y''z''}$.   (3)

Now if *both* changes are made, that is, y from y' to y'' and z from z' to z'', x is changed from x' to x'', and yz is changed from $y'z'$ to $y''z''$.

Then by (3), the ratio of any two values of x equals the ratio of the *corresponding values* of yz; and, by §510, $x \propto yz$.

In like manner it may be proved that if there are any number of variables x, y, z, u, etc., such that $x \propto y$ when z, u, etc., are constant, $x \propto z$ when y, u, etc., are constant, etc., then if all the variables y, z, u, etc., vary, x varies as their product.

The following is an illustration of the above theorem :

It is known, by Geometry, that the area of a triangle varies as the base when the altitude is constant, and as the altitude when the base is constant.

Hence, when both base and altitude vary, the area varies as their product.

PROBLEMS

516. Problems in variation are readily solved by converting the variation into an equation by aid of §§ 512 or 513.

1. If x varies inversely as y, and equals 9 when $y = 8$, find the value of x when $y = 18$.

If x varies inversely as y, $x = \dfrac{m}{y}$ (§ 513).

Putting $x = 9$ and $y = 8$, $9 = \dfrac{m}{8}$, or $m = 72$.

Then, $x = \dfrac{72}{y}$; and, if $y = 18$, $x = \dfrac{72}{18} = 4$.

2. Given that the area of a triangle varies jointly as its base and altitude, what will be the base of a triangle whose altitude is 12, equivalent to the sum of two triangles whose bases are 10 and 6, and altitudes 3 and 9, respectively ?

Let B, H, and A denote the base, altitude, and area, respectively, of any triangle, and B' the base of the required triangle.

Since A varies jointly as B and H, $A = mBH$ (§ 513).

Then the area of the first triangle is $m \times 10 \times 3$, or $30\,m$, and the area of the second is $m \times 6 \times 9$, or $54\,m$; whence, the area of the required triangle is $30\,m + 54\,m$, or $84\,m$.

But the area of the required triangle is also $m \times B' \times 12$.

Therefore, $12\,mB' = 84\,m$, and $B' = 7$.

EXERCISE 73

1. If x varies inversely as y, and equals $\frac{2}{3}$ when $y = \frac{3}{4}$, what is the value of y when $x = \frac{3}{2}$?

2. If $y \propto z^2$, and equals 40 when $z = 10$, what is the value of y in terms of z^2?

3. If z varies jointly as x and y, and equals $\frac{2}{3}$ when $x = \frac{3}{4}$ and $y = \frac{4}{5}$, what is the value of z when $x = \frac{4}{3}$ and $y = \frac{5}{4}$?

4. If x varies directly as y and inversely as z, and is equal to $\frac{9}{16}$ when $y = 27$ and $z = 64$, what is the value of x when $y = 9$ and $z = 32$?

5. If $5x + 8 \propto 6y - 1$, and $x = 6$ when $y = -3$, what is the value of x when $y = 7$?

6. If $x^4 \propto y^3$, and $x = 4$ when $y = 4$, what is the value of y when $x = \frac{1}{2}$?

7. The surface of a cube varies as the square of its edge. If the surface of a cube whose edge is $2\frac{1}{4}$ inches is $32\frac{1}{4}$ square inches, what will be the edge of a cube whose surface is $30\frac{3}{8}$ square inches?

8. The distance fallen by a body from a position of rest varies as the square of the time during which it falls. If a body falls $1029\frac{1}{4}$ feet in 8 seconds, how long will it take to fall $402\frac{1}{12}$ feet?

9. If 7 men in 4 weeks earn \$238, how many men will earn \$127.50 in 3 weeks; it being given that the amount earned varies jointly as the number of men and the number of weeks during which they work.

10. A circular plate of lead, 17 inches in diameter, is melted and formed into three circular plates of the same thickness. If the diameters of two of the plates are 8 and 9 inches, respectively, find the diameter of the other; it being given that the area of a circle varies as the square of its diameter.

11. If y equals the sum of two numbers which vary directly as x^3 and inversely as x, respectively, and $y = -53$ when $x = -3$, and $y = \frac{29}{2}$ when $x = 2$, what is the value of y when $x = \frac{1}{2}$?

12. If x equals the sum of two numbers, one of which varies directly as y^2 and the other inversely as z^2, and $x = 45$ when $y = 1$ and $z = 1$, and $x = 40$ when $y = 2$ and $z = 3$, find the value of y when $x = 37$ and $z = 1$.

13. If y equals the sum of three numbers, the first of which is constant, and the second and third vary as x^2 and x^3, respectively, and $y = -50$ when $x = 2$, 30 when $x = -2$, and 110 when $x = -3$, find the expression for y in terms of x.

14. The volume of a circular coin varies jointly as its thickness and the square of the radius of its face. Two coins whose thicknesses are 5 and 7, and radii of faces 60 and 30, respectively, are melted, and formed into 100 coins, each 3 units thick. Find the radius of the face of the new coin.

15. The distance travelled by a man, in any hour after the first, equals a constant number of miles, plus a number of miles which varies inversely as the number of hours travelled *before* that hour. If he travels 12 miles in the 6th hour, and 8 in the 11th, how far does he travel in the 21st hour?

16. If the weight of a spherical shell, two inches thick, is $\dfrac{19}{27}$ of its weight if solid, find its diameter; it being given that the volume of a sphere varies as the cube of its diameter.

17. The illumination from a source of light varies inversely as the square of the distance. If a book, now 10 inches off, be moved $10(\sqrt{5}-1)$ inches farther away, how much will the light received be reduced?

18. Prove that if $x \propto z$, and $y \propto z$, then $x \pm y \propto z$, and $\sqrt{xy} \propto z$.

19. Prove that if $x \propto y$, and $z \propto u$, then $xz \propto yu$.

20. Prove that if $x \propto y$, then $x^n \propto y^n$.

ARITHMETIC PROGRESSION

517. An **Arithmetic Progression** is a series (§ 283) in which each term, after the first, is obtained by adding to the preceding term a constant number called the *Common Difference*.

Thus, 1, 3, 5, 7, 9, 11, ⋯ is an arithmetic progression in which the common difference is 2.

Again, 12, 9, 6, 3, 0, − 3, ⋯ is an arithmetic progression in which the common difference is − 3.

An Arithmetic Progression is also called an *Arithmetic Series.*

518. *Given the first term, a, the common difference, d, and the number of terms, n, to find the last term, l.*

The progression is $a, a+d, a+2d, a+3d, \cdots$.

We observe that the coefficient of d in any term is less by 1 than the number of the term.

Then, in the nth term the coefficient of d will be $n-1$.

That is, $$l = a + (n-1)d. \tag{I}$$

519. *Given the first term, a, the last term, l, and the number of terms, n, to find the sum of the terms, S.*

$$S = a + (a+d) + (a+2d) + \cdots + (l-d) + l.$$

Writing the terms in reverse order,

$$S = l + (l-d) + (l-2d) + \cdots + (a+d) + a.$$

Adding these equations term by term,

$$2S = (a+l) + (a+l) + (a+l) + \cdots + (a+l) + (a+l).$$

Therefore, $2S = n(a+l)$, and $S = \dfrac{n}{2}(a+l).$ $\qquad$ (II)

The *first term, common difference, number of terms, last term,* and *sum of the terms,* are called the *elements* of the progression.

Substituting in (II) the value of l from (I), we have

$$S = \frac{n}{2}[2a + (n-1)d].$$

520. *Ex.* In the progression 8, 5, 2, -1, -4, $\cdot$, to 27 terms, find the last term and the sum.

Here, $a = 8$, $d = 5 - 8 = -3$, $n = 27$.

Substitute in   (I), $l = 8 + (27 - 1)(-3) = -70$.

Substitute in (II), $S = \dfrac{27}{2}(8 - 70) = -837$.

The common difference may be found by subtracting the first term from the second, or any term from the next following term.

EXERCISE 74

In each of the following, find the last term and the sum:

1. 5, 14, 23, $\cdots$ to 18 terms.
2. 9, 2, -5, $\cdots$ to 23 terms.
3. -51, -43, -35, $\cdots$ to 15 terms.
4. $-\dfrac{7}{4}$, $-\dfrac{19}{8}$, -3, $\cdots$ to 16 terms.
5. $\dfrac{5}{6}$, $\dfrac{1}{6}$, $-\dfrac{1}{2}$, $\cdots$ to 28 terms.
6. $\dfrac{8}{9}$, $\dfrac{47}{36}$, $\dfrac{31}{18}$, $\cdots$ to 25 terms.
7. $-\dfrac{11}{8}$, $-\dfrac{19}{16}$, -1, $\cdots$ to 39 terms.
8. $-\dfrac{3}{10}$, $-\dfrac{5}{6}$, $-\dfrac{41}{30}$, $\cdots$ to 52 terms.
9. $3a + 4b$, $8a + 2b$, $13a$, $\cdots$ to 10 terms.
10. $\dfrac{x - 2y}{3}$, $\dfrac{x}{6}$, $\dfrac{2y}{3}$, $\cdots$ to 9 terms.

521. If any three of the five elements of an arithmetic progression are given, the other two may be found by substituting the known values in the fundamental formulæ (I) and (II), and solving the resulting equations.

1. Given $a = -\dfrac{5}{3}$, $n = 20$, $S = -\dfrac{5}{3}$; find d and l.

Substituting the given values in (II),

$$-\frac{5}{3} = 10\left(-\frac{5}{3} + l\right), \text{ or } -\frac{1}{6} = -\frac{5}{3} + l; \text{ then, } l = \frac{5}{3} - \frac{1}{6} = \frac{3}{2}.$$

Substituting the values of a, n, and l in (I),

$$\frac{3}{2} = -\frac{5}{3} + 19\,d; \text{ whence, } 19\,d = \frac{19}{6}, \text{ and } d = \frac{1}{6}.$$

2. Given $d = -3$, $l = -39$, $S = -264$; find a and n.

Substituting in (I),

$$-39 = a + (n-1)(-3), \text{ or } a = 3\,n - 42. \tag{1}$$

Substituting the values of l, S, and a in (II),

$$-264 = \frac{n}{2}(3\,n - 42 - 39), \text{ or } -528 = 3\,n^2 - 81\,n,$$

or $n^2 - 27\,n = -176.$

Whence, $n = \dfrac{27 \pm \sqrt{729 - 704}}{2} = \dfrac{27 \pm 5}{2} = 16 \text{ or } 11.$

Substituting in (1), $a = 48 - 42$ or $33 - 42 = 6$ or -9.
The solution is, $a = 6$, $n = 16$; or, $a = -9$, $n = 11$.

The significance of the two answers is as follows :

If $a = 6$ and $n = 16$, the progression is
6, 3, 0, -3, -6, -9, -12, -15, -18, -21, -24, -27, -30, -33, -36, -39.

If $a = -9$ and $n = 11$, the progression is
-9, -12, -15, -18, -21, -24, -27, -30, -33, -36, -39.
In each of these the sum is -264.

3. Given $a = \dfrac{1}{3}$, $d = -\dfrac{1}{12}$, $S = -\dfrac{3}{2}$; find l and n.

Substituting in (I), $l = \dfrac{1}{3} + (n-1)\left(-\dfrac{1}{12}\right) = \dfrac{5-n}{12}.$ (1)

Substituting the values of a, S, and l in (II),

$$-\frac{3}{2} = \frac{n}{2}\left(\frac{1}{3} + \frac{5-n}{12}\right), \text{ or } -3 = n\left(\frac{9-n}{12}\right), \text{ or } n^2 - 9\,n = 36.$$

Solving this, $n = 12$ or -3.

The value $n = -3$ must be rejected, for the number of terms in a progression must be a *positive integer*.

Substituting $n = 12$ in (1), $l = \dfrac{5-12}{12} = -\dfrac{7}{12}.$

Any value of n which is not a positive integer must be rejected, together with all other values dependent on it.

From (I) and (II), *general formulœ* for the solution of examples like the above may be readily derived.

4. Given a, d, and S; derive the formula for n.

By § 519, $2\,S = n[2\,a + (n-1)\,d]$, or $dn^2 + (2\,a - d)\,n = 2\,S$.

This is a quadratic in n; solving by formula (1), § 450,

$$n = \frac{d - 2\,a \pm \sqrt{(2\,a - d)^2 + 8\,d\,S}}{2\,d}.$$

EXERCISE 75

1. Given $d = 8$, $l = 147$, $n = 19$; find a and S.

2. Given $d = -6$, $n = 14$, $S = -616$; find a and l.

3. Given $a = -69$, $n = 16$, $l = 36$; find d and S.

4. Given $a = 8$, $n = 25$, $S = -2500$; find d and l.

5. Given $a = \dfrac{3}{4}$, $l = -\dfrac{51}{4}$, $S = -78$; find d and n.

6. Given $l = \dfrac{229}{4}$, $n = 25$, $S = \dfrac{2925}{4}$; find a and d.

7. Given $a = -\dfrac{6}{5}$, $d = -\dfrac{3}{10}$, $S = -\dfrac{306}{5}$; find n and l.

8. Given $a = -\dfrac{1}{3}$, $l = \dfrac{61}{2}$, $d = \dfrac{5}{6}$; find n and S.

9. Given $d = -\dfrac{1}{12}$, $n = 55$, $S = -165$; find a and l.

10. Given $l = \dfrac{227}{12}$, $n = 24$, $S = 241$; find a and d.

11. Given $l = \dfrac{95}{6}$, $d = \dfrac{5}{6}$, $S = \dfrac{935}{6}$; find a and n.

12. Given $a = -\dfrac{4}{5}$, $l = -\dfrac{97}{10}$, $S = -\dfrac{315}{2}$; find d and n.

13. Given $a = -\dfrac{9}{22}$, $n = 21$, $S = \dfrac{21}{22}$; find d and l.

14. Given $l = \dfrac{23}{12}$, $d = \dfrac{5}{12}$, $S = -\dfrac{58}{3}$; find a and n.

15. Given $a = -\dfrac{31}{6}$, $d = \dfrac{1}{3}$, $S = -\dfrac{77}{2}$; find n and l.

16. Given a, l, and n; derive the formula for d.
17. Given a, n, and S; derive the formulæ for d and l.
18. Given d, n, and S; derive the formulæ for a and l.
19. Given a, d, and l; derive the formulæ for n and S.
20. Given d, l, and n; derive the formulæ for a and S.
21. Given l, n, and S; derive the formulæ for a and d.
22. Given a, d, and S; derive the formula for l.
23. Given a, l, and S; derive the formulæ for d and n.
24. Given d, l, and S; derive the formulæ for a and n.

522. Arithmetic Means.

To find an arithmetic progression of $m + 2$ terms, whose first and last terms are two given numbers, a and b, is called *inserting m arithmetic means between a and b.*

Ex. Insert 5 arithmetic means between 3 and -5.

We find an arithmetic progression of 7 terms, in which $a = 3$, and $l = -5$; substituting $n = 7$, $a = 3$, and $l = -5$ in (I),

$$-5 = 3 + 6\,d, \text{ or } d = -\frac{4}{3}.$$

The progression is 3, $\dfrac{5}{3}$, $\dfrac{1}{3}$, -1, $-\dfrac{7}{3}$, $-\dfrac{11}{3}$, -5.

523. Let x denote the arithmetic mean between a and b.

Then, $\qquad x - a = b - x$, or $2x = a + b$.

Whence, $\qquad\qquad x = \dfrac{a + b}{2}.$

That is, *the arithmetic mean between two numbers equals one-half their sum.*

EXERCISE 76

1. Insert 7 arithmetic means between 4 and 10.

2. Insert 6 arithmetic means between $-\dfrac{5}{6}$ and $-\dfrac{11}{2}$.

3. Insert 9 arithmetic means between $-\dfrac{7}{3}$ and 6.

4. Insert 8 arithmetic means between -3 and $-\dfrac{33}{4}$.

5. Insert 5 arithmetic means between $\dfrac{5}{9}$ and $-\dfrac{1}{3}$.

6. How many arithmetic means are inserted between $-\dfrac{3}{2}$ and $\dfrac{29}{10}$, when the sum of the second and last is $\dfrac{9}{5}$?

7. If m arithmetic means are inserted between a and b, find the first three.

Find the arithmetic mean between:

8. $1\frac{7}{9}$ and $-2\frac{1}{8}$.   **9.** $(3\,m+n)^2$ and $(m-3\,n)^2$.

   10. $\dfrac{x}{x-1}$ and $-\dfrac{x}{x^3-1}$.

524. Problems.

1. The sixth term of an arithmetic progression is $\dfrac{5}{6}$, and the fifteenth term is $\dfrac{16}{3}$. Find the first term.

The common difference must be one-ninth the result obtained by subtracting the sixth term from the fifteenth.

Then, $d=\dfrac{1}{9}\left(\dfrac{16}{3}-\dfrac{5}{6}\right)=\dfrac{1}{2}.$

Again, the first term must equal the sixth term minus five times the common difference.

Then, $a=\dfrac{5}{6}-\dfrac{5}{2}=-\dfrac{5}{3}.$

2. Find four numbers in arithmetic progression such that the product of the first and fourth shall be 45, and the product of the second and third 77.

Let the numbers be represented by $x-3\,y$, $x-y$, $x+y$, and $x+3\,y$, respectively.

Then by the conditions, $\begin{cases} x^2-9\,y^2=45. \\ x^2-\ \ y^2=77. \end{cases}$

Solving these equations,

   $x=9,\ y=\pm\,2\,;\ \text{or},\ x=-9,\ y=\pm\,2\ (\S\ 472).$

Then the numbers are 3, 7, 11, 15; or, $-3,\ -7,\ -11,\ -15$.

In problems like the above, it is convenient to represent the unknown numbers by *symmetrical* expressions.

Thus, if five numbers had been required to be found, we should have represented them by $x-2\,y$, $x-y$, x, $x+y$, and $x+2\,y$.

EXERCISE 77

1. The seventh term of an arithmetic progression is $-\dfrac{13}{6}$, and the thirteenth term $-\dfrac{7}{2}$. Find the twenty-second term.

2. The first term of an arithmetic progression is 1, and the sum of the sixth and tenth terms is 37. Find the second, third, and fourth terms.

3. The first term of an arithmetic progression of eleven terms is $\dfrac{3}{4}$, and the seventh term -3. Find the sum of the terms.

4. In an arithmetic progression, the sum of the first and last terms is two-ninths the sum of all the terms. Find the number of terms.

5. How many positive integers of three digits are multiples of 13? What is their sum?

. 6. Find five numbers in arithmetic progression such that their sum shall be 25, and the sum of their squares 135.

7. Find four numbers in arithmetic progression such that the product of the first and third shall be -21, and the product of the second and fourth 24.

8. If the constant difference of an arithmetic progression equals twice the first term, the quotient of the sum of the terms by the first term is a perfect square.

9. In any arithmetic progression, the sum of the first m terms, less twice the sum of the first $m+1$ terms, plus the sum of the first $m+2$ terms, equals the common difference.

10. The sum of the first ten terms of an arithmetic progression is to the sum of the first five terms as 13 to 4. Find the ratio of the first term to the common difference.

11. The sum of six numbers in arithmetic progression is 36, and the sum of their squares is 286. Find the numbers.

12. A man travels $\dfrac{1995}{2}$ miles. He travels 20 miles the first day, and increases his speed one-half mile in each succeeding day. How many days does the journey require?

13. Find three numbers in arithmetic progression, such that the square of the first added to the product of the other two gives 16, and the square of the second added to the product of the other two gives 14.

14. A traveller sets out from a certain place, and goes $3\frac{1}{2}$ miles the first hour, $3\frac{3}{4}$ the second hour, 4 the third hour, and so on. After he has been gone 5 hours, another sets out, and travels $8\frac{1}{4}$ miles an hour. After how many hours are the travellers together?
(Interpret the two answers.)

15. Find the sum of the terms of an arithmetic progression of 11 terms, in which 121 is the middle term.

16. A man climbing a mountain, ascends the first hour 1000 feet, the second hour 800 feet, the third hour 600 feet, and so on. After how many hours will he be at the height of 2800 feet?

(Interpret the two answers.)

17. If a person saves $120 each year, and puts this sum at simple interest at $3\frac{1}{2}$ per cent at the end of each year, to how much will his property amount at the end of 18 years?

18. There are 12 equidistant balls in a straight line. A person starts from a position in line with the balls, and beyond them, his distance from the first ball being the same as the distance between the balls, and picks them up in succession, returning with each to his original position. He finds that he has walked 5460 feet. Find the distance between the balls.

19. A and B travel around the world, the circuit being 23661 miles. A goes east one mile the first day, two miles the second day, three miles the third day, and so on. B goes west at a uniform rate of 20 miles a day. After how many days will they meet?

(Interpret the negative answer.)

GEOMETRIC PROGRESSION

525. A **Geometric Progression** is a series in which each term, after the first, is obtained by multiplying the preceding term by a constant number called the *Ratio*.

Thus, 2, 6, 18, 54, 162, ⋯ is a geometric progression in which the ratio is 3.

9, 3, 1, $\frac{1}{3}$, $\frac{1}{9}$, ⋯ is a geometric progression in which the ratio is $\frac{1}{3}$.

− 3, 6, − 12, 24, − 48, ⋯ is a geometric progression in which the ratio is − 2.

A Geometric Progression is also called a *Geometric Series*.

526. *Given the first term, a, the ratio, r, and the number of terms, n, to find the last term, l.*

The progression is a, ar, ar^2, ar^3, ⋯.

We observe that the exponent of r in any term is less by 1 than the number of the term.

Then, in the nth term the exponent of r will be $n-1$.

That is, $\qquad\qquad l = ar^{n-1}.$ (I)

527. *Given the first term, a, the last term, l, and the ratio, r, to find the sum of the terms, S.*

$$S = a + ar + ar^2 + \cdots + ar^{n-3} + ar^{n-2} + ar^{n-1}.$$ (1)

Multiplying each term by r,

$$rS = ar + ar^2 + ar^3 + \cdots + ar^{n-2} + ar^{n-1} + ar^n.$$ (2)

Subtracting (1) from (2), $rS - S = ar^n - a$, or $S = \dfrac{ar^n - a}{r-1}$.

But by (I), § 526, $\qquad rl = ar^n.$

Therefore, $\qquad\qquad S = \dfrac{rl - a}{r-1}.$ (II)

The *first term*, *ratio*, *number of terms*, *last term*, and *sum of the terms*, are called the *elements* of the progression.

528. Examples.

1. In the progression $3, 1, \frac{1}{3}, \cdots$, to 7 terms, find the last term and the sum.

Here, $a = 3$, $r = \frac{1}{3}$, $n = 7$; substituting in (I) and (II),

$$l = 3\left(\frac{1}{3}\right)^6 = \frac{1}{3^5} = \frac{1}{243}.$$

$$S = \frac{\frac{1}{3} \times \frac{1}{243} - 3}{\frac{1}{3} - 1} = \frac{\frac{1}{729} - 3}{-\frac{2}{3}} = \frac{-\frac{2186}{729}}{-\frac{2}{3}} = \frac{1093}{243}.$$

The ratio may be found by dividing the second term by the first, or any term by the next preceding term.

2. In the progression $-2, 6, -18, \cdots$, to 8 terms, find the last term and the sum.

Here, $a = -2$, $r = \frac{6}{-2} = -3$, $n = 8$; therefore,

$$l = -2(-3)^7 = -2 \times (-2187) = 4374.$$
$$S = \frac{-3 \times 4374 - (-2)}{-3 - 1} = \frac{-13122 + 2}{-4} = 3280.$$

EXERCISE 78

In each of the following, find the last term and the sum of the terms:

1. $1, -2, 4, \cdots$ to 10 terms.

2. $-3, -12, -48, \cdots$ to 6 terms.

3. $-\dfrac{5}{6}, \dfrac{5}{2}, -\dfrac{15}{2}, \cdots$ to 9 terms.

4. $\dfrac{2}{10}, \dfrac{3}{2}, \dfrac{15}{2}, \cdots$ to 5 terms.

5. $\dfrac{8}{9}, \dfrac{4}{3}, 2, \cdots$ to 7 terms.

6. $-\dfrac{3}{4}, 1, -\dfrac{4}{3}, \cdots$ to 7 terms.

7. $\dfrac{16}{3}, -\dfrac{4}{3}, \dfrac{1}{3}, \cdots$ to 6 terms.

8. $\dfrac{5}{3}, \dfrac{2}{3}, \dfrac{4}{15}, \cdots$ to 5 terms.

9. $-\dfrac{1}{12}, \dfrac{1}{8}, -\dfrac{3}{16}$, to 8 terms.

529. If any three of the five elements of a geometric progression are given, the other two may be found by substituting the given values in the fundamental formulæ (I) and (II), and solving the resulting equations.

But in certain cases the operation involves the solution of an equation of a degree higher than the second; and in others the unknown number appears as an exponent, the solution of which form of equation can usually only be affected by the aid of logarithms (§ 604).

In all such cases in the present chapter, the equations may be solved by inspection.

1. Given $a = -2$, $n = 5$, $l = -32$; find r and S.

Substituting the given values in (I), we have

$$-32 = -2\,r^4; \text{ whence, } r^4 = 16, \text{ or } r = \pm 2.$$

Substituting in (II),

If $\quad r = 2, \ S = \dfrac{2(-32)-(-2)}{2-1} = -64 + 2 = -62.$

If $\quad r = -2, \ S = \dfrac{(-2)(-32)-(-2)}{-2-1} = \dfrac{64+2}{-3} = -22.$

The solution is, $r = 2$, $S = -62$; or, $r = -2$, $S = -22$.

The significance of the two answers is as follows:

If $r = 2$, the progression is $-2, -4, -8, -16, -32$, whose sum is -62.

If $r = -2$, the progression is $-2, \ 4, -8, \ 16, -32$, whose sum is -22.

2. Given $a = 3$ $r = -\frac{1}{3}$, $S = \frac{1640}{729}$; find n and l.

Substituting in (II), $\dfrac{1640}{729} = \dfrac{-\frac{1}{3}l - 3}{-\frac{1}{3} - 1} = \dfrac{l+9}{4}$.

Whence, $\qquad l + 9 = \dfrac{6560}{729}$; or, $l = -\dfrac{1}{729}$.

Substituting the values of a, r, and l in (I),

$$-\frac{1}{729} = 3\left(-\frac{1}{3}\right)^{n-1}; \text{ or, } \left(-\frac{1}{3}\right)^{n-1} = -\frac{1}{2187}.$$

Whence, by inspection, $n - 1 = 7$, or $n = 8$.

From (I) and (II) general formulæ may be derived for the solution of cases like the above.

If the given elements are n, l, and S, equations for a and r may be found, but there are no definite formulæ for their values.

The same is the case when the given elements are a, n, and S.

The general formulæ for n involve logarithms; these cases are discussed in § 604.

EXERCISE 79

1. Given $r = 3$, $n = 8$, $l = 2187$; find a and S.
2. Given $a = 6$, $n = 7$, $l = \frac{128}{243}$; find r and S.
3. Given $r = -5$, $n = 5$, $S = -1042$; find a and l.
4. Given $a = -3$, $r = -\frac{1}{2}$, $l = \frac{3}{128}$; find n and S.
5. Given $r = -2$, $n = 10$, $S = -\frac{5115}{2}$; find a and l.
6. Given $a = \frac{25}{2}$, $n = 6$, $l = -\frac{16}{125}$; find r and S.
7. Given $a = -\frac{1}{3}$, $l = -\frac{243}{64}$, $S = -\frac{463}{192}$; find r and n.
8. Given $a = \frac{3}{4}$, $r = \frac{3}{4}$, $S = \frac{2343}{1024}$; find l and n.
9. Given $l = 384$, $r = -4$, $S = \frac{2457}{8}$; find a and n.
10. Given $a = \frac{2}{9}$, $l = 1458$, $S = \frac{9842}{9}$; find r and n.

11. Given a, r, and S; derive the formula for l.

12. Given a, l, and S; derive the formula for r.

13. Given r, l, and S; derive the formula for a.

14. Given r, n, and l; derive the formulæ for a and S.

15. Given r, n, and S; derive the formulæ for a and l.

16. Given a, n, and l; derive the formulæ for r and S.

530. Sum of a Geometric Progression to Infinity.

The limit (§ 245) to which the sum of the terms of a *decreasing* geometric progression approaches, when the number of terms is indefinitely increased, is called the *sum of the series to infinity.*

Formula (II), § 527, may be written

$$S = \frac{a - rl}{1 - r}.$$

It is evident that, by sufficiently continuing a decreasing geometric progression, the absolute value of the last term may be made less than any assigned number, however small.

Hence, when the number of terms is indefinitely increased, l, and therefore rl, approaches the limit 0.

Then, the fraction $\dfrac{a - rl}{1 - r}$ approaches the limit $\dfrac{a}{1 - r}$.

Therefore, the sum of a decreasing geometric progression to infinity is given by the formula

$$S = \frac{a}{1 - r}. \tag{III}$$

1. Find the sum of the series 4, $-\dfrac{8}{3}$, $\dfrac{16}{9}$, $\cdots$ to infinity.

Here, $a = 4$, $r = -\dfrac{2}{3}$.

Substituting in (III), $S = \dfrac{4}{1 + \dfrac{2}{3}} = \dfrac{12}{5}$.

This signifies that, the greater the number of terms taken, the more nearly does their sum approach to $\frac{12}{5}$; but the sum will never exactly equal this value.

A *repeating decimal* is a decreasing geometric progression, and its value may be found by formula (III).

2. Find the value of .85151 ···

We have, .85151 ··· = .8 + .051 + .00051 + ···

The terms after the first constitute a decreasing geometric progression, in which $a = .051$, and $r = .01$.

Substituting in (III), $S = \dfrac{.051}{1 - .01} = \dfrac{.051}{.99} = \dfrac{51}{990} = \dfrac{17}{330}$.

Then, the value of the given decimal is $\dfrac{8}{10} + \dfrac{17}{330}$, or $\dfrac{281}{330}$.

EXERCISE 80

Find the sum of the following to infinity:

1. $6, -2, 1, \cdots$.

2. $12, 3, \dfrac{3}{4}, \cdots$.

3. $-4, -\dfrac{2}{3}, -\dfrac{1}{9}, \cdots$.

4. $-\dfrac{25}{6}, \dfrac{25}{9}, -\dfrac{50}{27}, \cdots$.

5. $\dfrac{8}{5}, \dfrac{14}{15}, \dfrac{49}{90}, \cdots$.

6. $-\dfrac{1}{10}, \dfrac{2}{25}, -\dfrac{8}{125}, \cdots$.

7. $-\dfrac{3}{4}, \dfrac{15}{32}, -\dfrac{75}{256}, \cdots$.

8. $\dfrac{5}{6}, \dfrac{5}{27}, \dfrac{10}{243}, \cdots$.

Find the values of the following:

9. .8181 ···.

10. .629629 ···.

11. .91777 ···.

12. .75959 ···.

13. .23135135 ···.

14. .587474 ···.

531. Geometric Means.

To find a geometric progression of $m + 2$ terms, whose first and last terms are two given numbers, a and b, is called *inserting m geometric means between a and b*.

Ex. Insert 5 geometric means between 2 and $\dfrac{128}{729}$.

We find a geometric progression of 7 terms, in which $a = 2$, and $l = \dfrac{128}{729}$; substituting $n = 7$, $a = 2$, and $l = \dfrac{128}{729}$ in (I),

$$\frac{128}{729} = 2\,r^6; \text{ whence, } r^6 = \frac{64}{729}, \text{ and } r = \pm\frac{2}{3}.$$

The result is $2,\ \pm\dfrac{4}{3},\ \dfrac{8}{9},\ \pm\dfrac{16}{27},\ \dfrac{32}{81},\ \pm\dfrac{64}{243},\ \dfrac{128}{729}$.

532. Let x denote the geometric mean between a and b.

Then, $\dfrac{x}{a}=\dfrac{b}{x}$, or $x^2=ab$.

Whence, $x=\sqrt{ab}$.

That is, *the geometric mean between two numbers is equal to the square root of their product.*

EXERCISE 81

1. Insert 8 geometric means between $\dfrac{3}{8}$ and -192.

2. Insert 7 geometric means between -3 and -19683.

3. Insert 6 geometric means between $\dfrac{5}{16}$ and 5120.

4. Insert 4 geometric means between $-\dfrac{1}{6}$ and $\dfrac{512}{729}$.

5. Insert 5 geometric means between -48 and $-\dfrac{3}{256}$.

6. Insert 3 geometric means between $\dfrac{125}{32}$ and $\dfrac{1}{10}$.

7. If m geometric means are inserted between a and b, what are the last two means ?

Find the geometric mean between :

8. $4\frac{2}{3}$ and $2\frac{5}{8}$.

9. $\dfrac{x^2+xy}{xy-y^2}$ and $\dfrac{x^2-y^2}{xy}$.

10. $a^2-4\,ab+4\,b^2$ and $4\,a^2+4\,ab+b^2$.

533. Problem.

Find 3 numbers in geometric progression such that their sum shall be 14, and the sum of their squares 84.

Let the numbers be represented by a, ar, and ar^2.

Then, by the conditions, $\begin{cases} a+ar+ar^2=14. & (1) \\ a^2+a^2r^2+a^2r^4=84. & (2) \end{cases}$

Divide (2) by (1), $a-ar+ar^2=6.$ (3)

Subtract (3) from (1), $2\,ar=8$, or $r=\dfrac{4}{a}$.   (4)

PROGRESSIONS

PROGRESSIONS   357

Substituting in (1), $a + 4 + \dfrac{16}{a} = 14$, or $a^2 - 10\,a + 16 = 0$.

Solving this equation, $\qquad a = 8$ or 2.

Substituting in (4), $\qquad r = \dfrac{4}{8}$ or $\dfrac{4}{2} = \dfrac{1}{2}$ or 2.

Then, the numbers are 2, 4, and 8.

EXERCISE 82

1. What number must be added to each of the numbers a, b, and c, so that the resulting numbers shall form a geometric progression?

2. The sixth term of a geometric progression is $\dfrac{4}{27}$, and the eleventh term $-\dfrac{128}{6561}$. Find the third term.

3. Find an arithmetic progression whose first term is 2, and whose first, fourth, and tenth terms form a geometric progression.

4. The product of the first five terms of a geometric progression is 243. Find the third term.

5. Find four numbers in geometric progression such that the sum of the first and fourth is 27, and of the second and third 18.

6. Find six numbers in geometric progression such that the sum of the first, third, and fifth is 147, and of the second, fourth, and sixth 294.

7. The sum of the terms of a geometric progression whose first term is 1, ratio 3, and number of terms 4, equals the sum of the terms of an arithmetic progression whose first term is 4, and common difference 4. Find the number of terms in the arithmetic progression.

8. A man who saved every year five-fourths as much as in the preceding year, had saved in four years $9225. How much did he save the first year?

9. The population of a state increases from 100000 to 161051 in five years. What is the rate of increase per year?

10. The difference between two numbers is 72, and their arithmetic mean exceeds their geometric mean by 8. Find the numbers.

11. The sum of the first eight terms of a decreasing geometric progression is to the sum to infinity as 16 to 25. Find the ratio.

12. There are three numbers in geometric progression whose sum is $6\frac{1}{4}$. If the first be multiplied by $\dfrac{9}{8}$, the second by $\dfrac{5}{4}$, and the third by $\dfrac{7}{6}$, the resulting numbers will be in arithmetic progression. What are the numbers?

13. The digits of a number of three figures are in geometric progression, and their sum is 14. If 594 be subtracted from the number, the digits will be reversed. Find the number.

14. The mth term of a geometric progression is p, and the nth term is q; prove that the first term is $^{m-n}\sqrt{p^{1-n}q^{m-1}}$.

15. The sum of three rational numbers in geometric progression is $\frac{13}{15}$, and the sum of their reciprocals $\frac{65}{3}$. Find the numbers.

16. If the numbers a, b, and c are in geometric progression, prove

$$\frac{1}{a^3} + \frac{1}{b^3} + \frac{1}{c^3} = \frac{a^3 + b^3 + c^3}{a^2 b^2 c^2}.$$

17. The sum of the first four terms of a geometric progression is 45, and of the first six terms 189. Find the first term and the ratio.

18. If x, y, and z are, respectively, the pth, qth, and rth terms of a geometric progression, prove

$$x^{q-r} \times z^{p-q} = y^{p-r}.$$

HARMONIC PROGRESSION

534. A **Harmonic Progression** is a series of terms whose reciprocals form an arithmetic progression.

Thus, $1, \frac{1}{3}, \frac{1}{5}, \frac{1}{7}, \frac{1}{9}, \cdots$ is a harmonic progression, because the reciprocals of the terms, $1, 3, 5, 7, 9, \cdots$, form an arithmetic progression.

A Harmonic Progression is also called a *Harmonic Series.*

Any problem in harmonic progression, which is susceptible of solution, may be solved by taking the reciprocals of the terms, and applying the formulæ of the arithmetic progression.

There is, however, no general method for finding the *sum of the terms* of a harmonic series.

Ex. In the progression $2, \frac{2}{3}, \frac{2}{5}, \cdots$ to 36 terms, find the last term.

Taking the reciprocals of the terms, we have the arithmetic progression $\frac{1}{2}, \frac{3}{2}, \frac{5}{2}, \cdots$.

Here, $a = \frac{1}{2}$, $d = 1$, $n = 36$.

Substituting in (I), § 518, $l = \frac{1}{2} + (36 - 1) \times 1 = \frac{71}{2}$.

Then, $\frac{2}{71}$ is the last term of the given harmonic series.

535. Harmonic Means.

To find a harmonic progression of $m + 2$ terms, whose first and last terms are two given numbers, a and b, is called *inserting m harmonic means between a and b.*

Ex. Insert 5 harmonic means between 2 and -3.

We have to insert 5 arithmetic means between $\frac{1}{2}$ and $-\frac{1}{3}$.

Substituting $a = \frac{1}{2}$, $l = -\frac{1}{3}$, $n = 7$, in (I), § 518,

$$-\frac{1}{3} = \frac{1}{2} + 6\,d, \text{ or } d = -\frac{5}{36}.$$

Then the arithmetic series is

$$\frac{1}{2}, \frac{13}{36}, \frac{2}{9}, \frac{1}{12}, -\frac{1}{18}, -\frac{7}{36}, -\frac{1}{3}.$$

Therefore, the required harmonic series is

$$2, \frac{36}{13}, \frac{9}{2}, 12, -18, -\frac{36}{7}, -3.$$

536.
Let x denote the harmonic mean between a and b.

Then, $\frac{1}{x}$ is the arithmetic mean between $\frac{1}{a}$ and $\frac{1}{b}$.

Then, by § 523, $\frac{1}{x} = \frac{\frac{1}{a} + \frac{1}{b}}{2} = \frac{a+b}{2\,ab}$, and $x = \frac{2\,ab}{a+b}$.

EXERCISE 83

In each of the following, find the last term :

1. $\frac{4}{5}, \frac{12}{43}, \frac{12}{71}, \cdots$ to 22 terms.

2. $-\frac{4}{3}, -\frac{6}{5}, -\frac{12}{11}, \cdots$ to 19 terms.

3. -3, 2, $\dfrac{3}{4}$, $\cdots$ to 26 terms.

4. $\dfrac{1}{11}$, $\dfrac{4}{39}$, $\dfrac{2}{17}$, $\cdots$ to 11 terms.

5. $-\dfrac{5}{6}$, $-\dfrac{2}{3}$, $-\dfrac{5}{9}$, $\cdots$ to 37 terms.

6. Insert 6 harmonic means between 2 and $-\dfrac{10}{9}$.

7. Insert 8 harmonic means between $-\dfrac{4}{5}$ and $-\dfrac{1}{5}$.

8. Insert 7 harmonic means between $\dfrac{2}{7}$ and $-\dfrac{2}{5}$.

Find the harmonic mean between :

9. $\dfrac{2}{3}$ and $-\dfrac{3}{4}$.   **10.** $\dfrac{a+b}{a-b}$ and $\dfrac{a^2-b^2}{a^2+b^2}$.

11. Find the $(n-1)$th term of the harmonic progression a, b, $\cdots$ to n terms.

12. If m harmonic means are inserted between a and b, what is the third mean ?

13. The first term of a harmonic progression is p, and the second term q. Continue the series to three more terms.

14. The arithmetic mean between two numbers is 1, and the harmonic mean -15. Find the numbers.

15. The fifth term of a harmonic progression is $-\dfrac{4}{3}$, and the eleventh term $-\dfrac{1}{3}$. Find the fifteenth term.

16. The geometric mean between two numbers is 4, and the harmonic mean $\dfrac{16}{5}$. Find the numbers.

17. The arithmetic mean between two numbers exceeds the geometric mean by $\dfrac{1}{2}$, and the geometric mean exceeds the harmonic mean by $\dfrac{6}{13}$. Find the numbers.

(Represent the sum of the numbers by x, and their product by y.)

18. Prove that, if any three consecutive terms of a harmonic progression be taken, the first is to the third as the first minus the second is to the second minus the third.

19. If a^2, b^2, and c^2 are in arithmetic progression, prove that $b+c$, $c+a$, and $a+b$ are in harmonic progression.

20. If a, b, and c are in arithmetic progression, b, c, and d in geometric progression, and c, d, and e in harmonic progression, prove a, c, and e in geometric progression.

537. Let A, G, and H denote the arithmetic, geometric, and harmonic means, respectively, between a and b.

Then, by §§ 523, 532, and 536,

$$A=\frac{a+b}{2},\ G=\sqrt{ab},\text{ and }H=\frac{2\,ab}{a+b}.$$

But, $$\frac{a+b}{2}\times\frac{2\,ab}{a+b}=ab=(\sqrt{ab})^2.$$

Whence, $$A\times H=G^2,\text{ or }G=\sqrt{A\times H}.$$

That is, *the geometric mean between two numbers is also the geometric mean between their arithmetic and harmonic means.*

538. Let a and b be two positive real numbers.

By § 537, their geometric mean is intermediate in value between their arithmetic and harmonic means.

But, $$\frac{a+b}{2}-\frac{2\,ab}{a+b}=\frac{(a+b)^2-4\,ab}{2(a+b)}=\frac{(a-b)^2}{2(a+b)};$$

a *positive* number.

Hence, of the three means, the arithmetic is the greatest, the geometric next, and the harmonic the least.

XXVI. CONVERGENCY AND DIVERGENCY OF SERIES

539. An Infinite Series (§ 283) may be developed by Division, or by Evolution.

Let it be required, for example, to divide 1 by $1 - x$.

$$
1 - x)1(1 + x + x^2 + \cdots
$$
$$
\underline{1 - x}
$$
$$
x
$$
$$
\underline{x - x^2}
$$
$$
x^2
$$

The quotient is obtained in the form of the infinite series $1 + x + x^2 + \cdots$.

Again, let it be required to find the square root of $1 + x$.

$$
1 + x \left|\; 1 + \frac{x}{2} - \frac{x^2}{8} + \cdots \right.
$$
$$
\underline{1}
$$
$$
2 + \frac{x}{2} \;\bigg|\; x
$$
$$
x + \frac{x^2}{4}
$$
$$
\overline{2 + x - \frac{x^2}{8}} \bigg| - \frac{x^2}{4}
$$

The result is obtained in the form of the infinite series $1 + \frac{x}{2} - \frac{x^2}{8} + \cdots$.

Infinite series may also be developed by other methods, one of the most important of which will be considered in Chap. XXVII.

540. Convergent and Divergent Series.

An infinite series is said to be *Convergent* when the sum of the first n terms approaches a fixed finite number as a limit (§ 245), when n is indefinitely increased.

This limit is called the *Value of the Series*.

A *finite* series may be regarded as a convergent series.

An infinite series is said to be *Divergent* when the sum of the first n terms can be made numerically greater than any assigned number, however great, by taking n sufficiently great.

Consider, for example, the infinite series

$$1 + x + x^2 + x^3 + \cdots,$$

developed by the fraction $\dfrac{1}{1-x}$ (§ 539).

I. Suppose $x = x_1$, where x_1 is numerically < 1.

In this case, the given series is a decreasing Geometric Progression; and by § 530, the sum of the first n terms approaches the limit $\dfrac{1}{1-x_1}$ when n is indefinitely increased.

That is, the sum of the first n terms approaches a fixed finite number as a limit, when n is indefinitely increased.

Hence, the series is *convergent* when x is numerically < 1.

Let us take, for example, $x = .1$.

The series now takes the form $1 + .1 + .01 + \cdots$; while the value of the fraction from which the series was developed is $\dfrac{1}{1 - .1}$, or $\dfrac{10}{9}$.

In this case, however great the number of terms taken, their sum never exactly equals $\dfrac{10}{9}$, but approaches this value as a limit (§ 530).

Thus, if an infinite series is *convergent*, the *value of the series* (§ 540) equals the value of the expression from which the series was developed.

II. Suppose $x = x_1$, where x_1 is numerically > 1.

The sum of the first n terms is now

$$1 + x_1 + x_1^2 + \cdots + x_1^{n-1} = \frac{x_1^n - 1}{x_1 - 1} \text{ (§ 143).}$$

By taking n sufficiently great, $\dfrac{x_1^n - 1}{x_1 - 1}$ can be made to numerically exceed any assigned number, however great.

Hence, the series is *divergent* when x is numerically > 1.

Let us take, for example, $x = 10$.

The series now takes the form $1 + 10 + 100 + \cdots$; while the value of the fraction from which the series was developed is $\dfrac{1}{1 - 10}$, or $-\dfrac{1}{9}$.

In this case, the greater the number of terms taken, the more does their sum diverge from the value $-\frac{1}{9}$.

Thus, if an infinite series is *divergent*, the greater the number of terms taken, the more does their sum diverge from the value of the expression from which the series was developed.

III. Suppose $x = 1$.

In this case, each term of the series equals 1, and the sum of the first n terms equals n; and this sum can be made to exceed any assigned number, however great, by taking n sufficiently great.

Hence, the series is *divergent* when $x = 1$.

IV. Suppose $x = -1$.

In this case the series takes the form
$$1 - 1 + 1 - 1 + \cdots;$$
and the sum of the first n terms is either 1 or 0 according as n is odd or even.

If the sum of the first n terms of an infinite series neither approaches a fixed finite limit, nor exceeds any assigned number, however great, when n is indefinitely increased, the series is called an *Oscillating Series*.

Hence, the series is an *oscillating series* when $x = -1$.

541. It follows from § 540 that *an infinite series cannot be used for the purposes of demonstration unless it is convergent.*

It will be understood, throughout the remainder of the work, that, in every expression involving a convergent infinite series, the *value* of the series is meant. For example, the product of two convergent infinite series will be understood as signifying the product of their values.

THEOREMS ON CONVERGENCY AND DIVERGENCY OF SERIES

542. *If an infinite series is convergent, the last term approaches the limit zero, when the number of terms is indefinitely increased.*

Let the series be $u_1 + u_2 + \cdots + u_n + u_{n+1} + \cdots$.

By § 540, $u_1 + u_2 + \cdots + u_n$ and $u_1 + u_2 + \cdots + u_n + u_{n+1}$ approach *the same finite limit* when n is indefinitely increased.

But the limit of the difference between $u_1 + u_2 + \cdots + u_n$ and $u_1 + u_2 + \cdots + u_n + u_{n+1}$ is the difference of their limits (§ 255).

Whence, u_{n+1} approaches the limit 0 when n is indefinitely increased.

543. *An infinite series is convergent if the sum of the first n terms is finite, and the sum of any finite number of terms commencing with the $(n + 1)$th approaches the limit zero, when n is indefinitely increased.*

Let U represent the sum of the first n terms, and V the sum of the m terms $u_{n+1} + u_{n+2} + \cdots + u_{n+m}$, of the series $u_1 + u_2 + \cdots$.

By § 254, the limit of $U + V$, when n is indefinitely increased, is the sum of the limits of U and V.

But since V approaches the limit 0, when n is indefinitely increased, $U + V$ approaches the *same limit* as U.

Since this is the case whatever the number of terms in V, U must approach a *fixed* finite limit when n is indefinitely increased; and the series is convergent.

Take, for example, the series $1 + \dfrac{1}{2} + \dfrac{1}{2^2} + \cdots$.

The sum of the first n terms is $\dfrac{1 - \dfrac{1}{2^n}}{1 - \dfrac{1}{2}}$ (§ 143), which is finite however great n may be.

The sum of the terms from the $(n + 1)$th to the $(n + m)$th is

$$\frac{1}{2^n} + \frac{1}{2^{n+1}} + \cdots + \frac{1}{2^{n+m-1}}, \text{ or } \frac{1}{2^n}\left(1 + \frac{1}{2} + \cdots + \frac{1}{2^{m-1}}\right), \text{ or } \frac{1}{2^n}\left(\frac{1 - \dfrac{1}{2^m}}{1 - \dfrac{1}{2}}\right);$$

which approaches the limit 0 when n is indefinitely increased.

Then, the series is convergent.

(This series was proved convergent in § 540, I.)

544. *If an infinite series is convergent or divergent, it will remain convergent or divergent after any finite number of terms have been added to, or subtracted from it.*

For in the case of a convergent series, the sum of the first n terms still approaches a fixed finite limit when n is indefinitely increased.

And in the case of a divergent, the sum of the first n terms still exceeds any assigned number, however great, when n is indefinitely increased.

Then, in testing a series for convergency or divergency, we may commence *at any assigned term*, taking no account of the preceding terms.

545. *If all the terms of an infinite series are positive, and the sum of any n consecutive terms is finite however great n may be, the series is convergent.*

For, the greater the number of terms taken, the greater will be their sum; but this sum is always finite.

Then, when n is indefinitely increased, the sum of the first n terms must approach a *fixed finite limit;* and the series is convergent.

Thus, in the illustrative example of § 543, the sum of the first n terms is finite, however great n may be ; and hence, the series is convergent.

546. The following theorem, and that of § 547, are of great importance in testing the convergency or divergency of series

If, commencing with a certain assigned term, each term of a series of positive terms is less than the corresponding term of a series of positive terms, which is known to be convergent, the first series is convergent.

For the sum of the first n terms is finite, however great n may be, and the series is convergent by § 545.

Ex. Prove the infinite series

$$1 + \frac{1}{2} + \frac{1}{3^2} + \frac{1}{4^3} + \cdots$$

convergent.

Each term, commencing with the third, is less than the corresponding term of the series

$$1 + \frac{1}{2} + \frac{1}{2^2} + \frac{1}{2^3} + \cdots,$$

which was proved convergent in § 540, I.

Then, the given series is convergent.

547. *If, commencing with a certain assigned term, each term of a series of positive terms is greater than the corresponding term of a series of positive terms, which is known to be divergent, the given series is divergent.*

For, the sum of the first n terms may be made to exceed any assigned number, however great, by taking n sufficiently great.

Thus, commencing with the second term, each term of the series

$$1 + 2 + 2^2 + 2^3 + \cdots$$

is greater than the corresponding term of the series

$$1 + 1 + 1 + 1 + \cdots,$$

which was proved divergent in § 540, III.

Then, the given series is divergent.

(This was also proved in § 540, II.)

548. *To prove the infinite series*

$$1 + \frac{1}{2^k} + \frac{1}{3^k} + \frac{1}{4^k} + \cdots$$

convergent when k is > 1, and divergent when $k = 1$ or $k < 1$.

I. If k is > 1, the second and third terms are together $<$ $\frac{1}{2^k} + \frac{1}{2^k}$, or $\frac{2}{2^k}$; the next four terms are together $< \frac{4}{4^k}$; the next eight are together $< \frac{8}{8^k}$; and so on.

Then, the series is less than the series

$$1 + \frac{2}{2^k} + \frac{4}{4^k} + \frac{8}{8^k} + \cdots, \text{ or } 1 + \frac{1}{2^{k-1}} + \frac{1}{4^{k-1}} + \frac{1}{8^{k-1}} + \cdots,$$

$$\text{or } 1 + \frac{1}{2^{k-1}} + \left(\frac{1}{2^{k-1}}\right)^2 + \left(\frac{1}{2^{k-1}}\right)^3 + \cdots;$$

which was proved, in § 530, to approach a finite limit when the number of terms was indefinitely increased.

Therefore, the given series is convergent.

II. If $k = 1$, the series becomes

$$1 + \frac{1}{2} + \frac{1}{3} + \frac{1}{4} + \cdots. \tag{1}$$

The third and fourth terms are together $> \frac{2}{4}$ or $\frac{1}{2}$; the next four terms are together $> \frac{4}{8}$ or $\frac{1}{2}$; and so on.

Then, by taking a sufficiently great number of terms, their sum may be made greater than any assigned number, however great, and the series is divergent.

The series (1) is a *harmonic series* (§ 534).

III. If k is < 1, each term of the given series, commencing with the second, is greater than the corresponding term of (1), and the series is divergent (§ 547).

As examples of the above general theorem, the series

$$1 + \frac{1}{2^2} + \frac{1}{3^2} + \frac{1}{4^2} + \cdots$$

is convergent ; and the series

$$1 + \frac{1}{\sqrt{2}} + \frac{1}{\sqrt{3}} + \frac{1}{\sqrt{4}} + \cdots$$

is divergent.

549. *If, commencing with a certain assigned term, each term of a series of positive terms is greater than some assigned finite number, however small, the series is divergent.*

For the sum of the first n terms can be made to exceed any assigned number, however great, by taking n sufficiently great.

Thus, in the series $\quad \frac{1}{2} + \frac{2}{3} + \frac{3}{4} + \frac{4}{5} + \cdots$,

each term, commencing with the second, is greater than $\frac{1}{2}$.

Then, the series is divergent.

550. *If, in two series of positive terms, the ratio of two corresponding terms is always finite, the first series is convergent if the second is convergent, and divergent if it is divergent.*

Let the series be $u_1 + u_2 + u_3 + \cdot$, and $v_1 + v_2 + v_3 + \cdots$.

I. Let the second series be convergent.

Let k be a finite number greater than the greatest of the ratios $\frac{u_1}{v_1}, \frac{u_2}{v_2}, \cdots$; then, $\frac{u_1}{v_1} < k, \frac{u_2}{v_2} < k, \cdots, \frac{u_n}{v_n} < k$.

Then, $u_1 < kv_1, \ u_2 < kv_2, \ \cdots, \ u_n < kv_n.$

Adding these inequalities, we have

$$(u_1 + u_2 + \cdots + u_n) < k(v_1 + v_2 + \cdots + v_n).$$

But since the second series is convergent, $v_1 + v_2 + \cdots + v_n$ is finite, however great n may be; also, k is finite.

Then, $u_1 + u_2 + \cdots + u_n$ is finite, however great n may be, and the first series is convergent (§ 545).

II. Let the second series be divergent.

Let k be a finite number smaller than the least of the ratios

$$\frac{u_1}{v_1}, \ \frac{u_2}{v_2}, \ \cdots; \ \text{then,} \ \frac{u_1}{v_1} > k, \ \frac{u_2}{v_2} > k, \ \cdots, \ \frac{u_n}{v_n} > k.$$

Then, $u_1 > kv_1, \ u_2 > kv_2, \ \cdots, \ u_n > kv_n.$

Whence, $(u_1 + u_2 + \cdots + u_n) > k(v_1 + v_2 + \cdots + v_n).$

Now, since the second series is divergent, $v_1 + v_2 + \cdots + v_n$ can be made greater than any assigned number, however great, by sufficiently increasing n.

Then, $u_1 + u_2 + \cdots + u_n$ can be made greater than any assigned number, however great, by sufficiently increasing n, and the first series is divergent.

1. Prove the series $\dfrac{1}{1 \times 2} + \dfrac{1}{2 \times 3} + \dfrac{1}{3 \times 4} + \cdots$ convergent.

We compare the series with the series

$$1 + \frac{1}{2^2} + \frac{1}{3^2} + \cdots,$$

which was shown to be convergent in § 548.

The ratio of the nth term of this to the nth term of the given series is $\dfrac{\dfrac{1}{n^2}}{\dfrac{1}{n(n+1)}}$, or $\dfrac{n(n+1)}{n^2}$, or $1 + \dfrac{1}{n}$.

This is always between 1 and 2, and is therefore finite for every value of n.

Then the given series is convergent.

2. Prove the series $\dfrac{1}{1 \times 2} + \dfrac{2^2}{3 \times 4} + \dfrac{3^2}{5 \times 6} + \cdots$ divergent.

We compare it with the series
$$1 + 1 + 1 + \cdots, \qquad (1)$$
which was shown to be divergent in § 540, III.

The ratio of the nth term of the given series to the nth term of (1) is
$$\frac{n^2}{2n(2n-1)}, \text{ or } \frac{1}{2\left(2 - \dfrac{1}{n}\right)}.$$

This is always between $\dfrac{1}{2}$ and $\dfrac{1}{4}$, and is therefore finite for every value of n; then the given series is divergent.

> **551.** *If, commencing with a certain assigned term, the ratio of each term of an infinite series of positive terms to the preceding term is numerically less than a fixed positive number, which is itself less than unity, the series is convergent.*

Let the series be $u_1 + u_2 + u_3 + \cdots$. $\qquad$ (1)

Suppose $\dfrac{u_2}{u_1} < k,\ \dfrac{u_3}{u_2} < k,\ \cdot\ ,\ \dfrac{u_n}{u_{n-1}} < k,\ \cdot\ ,$ where k is < 1.

By § 540, I, since k is < 1, the infinite series
$$1 + k + k^2 + k^3 + \cdots$$
is convergent.

Then, by § 550, since u_1 is finite, the series
$$u_1(1 + k + k^2 + k^3 + \cdots) \qquad (2)$$
is convergent.

Multiplying together the first $n - 1$ of the above inequalities (§ 338), we have
$$\frac{u_2 u_3 \cdots u_n}{u_1 u_2 \cdots u_{n-1}} < k^{n-1}; \text{ whence, } \frac{u_n}{u_1} < k^{n-1}, \text{ or } u_n < u_1 k^{n-1}.$$

That is, the nth term of (1) is less than the nth term of (2); and by § 546, series (1) is convergent.

The ratio of u_{n+1} to u_n is called the *Ratio of Convergency* of the infinite series $u_1 + u_2 + u_3 + \cdots$.

Ex. Prove the series $1 + \dfrac{2^2}{\lfloor 2} + \dfrac{2^3}{\lfloor 3} + \dfrac{2^4}{\lfloor 4} + \cdots$ convergent.

The ratio of the $(n+1)$th term to the nth is

$$\frac{\dfrac{2^{n+1}}{\underline{|n+1}}}{\dfrac{2^n}{\underline{|n}}}, \text{ or } \frac{2}{n+1}.$$

If $n=2$, the ratio equals $\frac{2}{3}$; and for any value of $n > 2$, the ratio is $< \frac{2}{3}$.

Then, commencing with the fourth term, the ratio of each term to the preceding is $< \frac{2}{3}$, and the series is convergent.

552. *If, commencing with a certain assigned term, the ratio of each term of an infinite series of positive terms to the preceding term is either equal to, or greater than, unity, the series is divergent.*

For, commencing with the assigned term, each term of the series is either equal to, or greater than, the assigned term; and the series is divergent by § 549.

Ex. Prove the series $\dfrac{2}{1 \times 2} + \dfrac{2^2}{2 \times 3} + \dfrac{2^3}{3 \times 4} + \cdots$ divergent.

The ratio of the $(n+1)$th term to the nth is

$$\frac{\dfrac{2^{n+1}}{(n+1)(n+2)}}{\dfrac{2^n}{n(n+1)}}, \text{ or } \frac{2n}{n+2}.$$

If $n=2$, the ratio equals 1; and for any value of $n > 2$, the ratio is > 1.

Then, commencing with the third term, the ratio of each term to the preceding is equal to, or greater than, 1, and the series is divergent.

553. The method of § 551 does not apply when the ratio of the $(n+1)$th term to the nth is less than 1, but approaches the limit 1 when n is indefinitely increased.

For in this case the ratio will not always be less than a fixed positive number, which is itself less than 1.

In such cases, the convergency or divergency of the series must be determined by other tests.

Consider, for example, the series

$$1+\frac{1}{3}+\frac{1}{5}+\frac{1}{7}+\cdots.$$

The ratio of the $(n+1)$th term to the nth is

$$\frac{\dfrac{1}{2\,n+1}}{\dfrac{1}{2\,n-1}}=\frac{2\,n-1}{2\,n+1}=\frac{2-\dfrac{1}{n}}{2+\dfrac{1}{n}}.$$

This is always <1, but approaches the limit 1 when n is indefinitely increased.

The series is divergent, which may be shown as in § 548, II.

554. *If an infinite series of positive terms is convergent, it will remain so after the signs of any of its terms have been changed.*

For the sum of the first n terms will still be finite, however great n may be, and the series is convergent by § 545.

It follows from the above that the theorems of §§ 546 and 551 hold when any or all of the terms are negative; and also the first statement of § 550 when all the terms are negative.

555. It follows from §§ 551, 552, and 554 that

I. *If the ratio of the $(n+1)$th term of an infinite series to the nth term approaches a limit numerically <1, when n is indefinitely increased, the series is convergent.*

Thus, in the example of § 551, $\dfrac{2}{n+1}$ approaches the limit 0, when n is indefinitely increased.

Then, the series is convergent.

II. *If the ratio of the $(n+1)$th term of an infinite series to the nth term approaches a limit numerically >1, when n is indefinitely increased, the series is divergent.*

Thus, in the example of § 552, the ratio of the $(n+1)$th term to the nth term can be written $\dfrac{2}{1+\dfrac{2}{n}}$; and this approaches the limit 2 when n is indefinitely increased.

Then, the series is divergent.

If the ratio of the $(n+1)$th term to the nth term approaches the limit 1, when n is indefinitely increased, other tests must be applied to determine whether the series is convergent or divergent (§ 553).

556. *If the terms of an infinite series are alternately positive and negative, and each term numerically less than the preceding term, the series is convergent if the nth term approaches the limit 0 when n is indefinitely increased.*

Let the series be $u_1 - u_2 + u_3 - u_4 + \cdots$.

It may be written in the forms

$$(u_1 - u_2) + (u_3 - u_4) + (u_5 - u_6) + \cdots, \tag{1}$$

and $\qquad u_1 - (u_2 - u_3) - (u_4 - u_5) - \cdots. \tag{2}$

Since each of the expressions $u_1 - u_2$, $u_3 - u_4$, etc., is positive, it is evident from (1) and (2) that the sum of the first n terms is positive, and $< u_1$.

That is, the sum of the first n terms of the given series is finite, however great n may be.

The sum of the m terms commencing with the $(n+1)$th is

$$\pm (u_{n+1} - u_{n+2} + \cdots \pm u_{n+m}); \tag{3}$$

the upper or lower sign being taken before u_{n+m} according as m is odd or even.

The expression in parentheses can be written in the forms

$$(u_{n+1} - u_{n+2}) + (u_{n+3} - u_{n+4}) + \cdots,$$

and $\qquad u_{n+1} - (u_{n+2} - u_{n+3}) - (u_{n+4} - u_{n+5}) + \cdots;$

which shows that it is positive and $< u_{n+1}$.

Now, if n is indefinitely increased, u_{n+1}, and therefore expression (3), approaches the limit 0.

Thus, the sum of any finite number of terms commencing with the $(n+1)$th approaches the limit 0 when n is indefinitely increased, and the series is convergent by § 543.

As an example of the above theorem, the series

$$1 - \frac{1}{2} + \frac{1}{3} - \frac{1}{4} + \cdots$$

is convergent.

557. *To prove the infinite series*

$$1 + x + \frac{x^2}{2} + \frac{x^3}{3} + \cdots$$

convergent when x is numerically < 1.

The ratio of the $(n + 1)$th term to the nth term is

$$\frac{x^n}{n} \div \frac{x^{n-1}}{n-1} = \frac{x(n-1)}{n} = x\left(1 - \frac{1}{n}\right),$$

which approaches the limit x when n is indefinitely increased.

Then, if x is numerically < 1, the series is convergent (§ 555, I).

558. *To prove the infinite series*

$$1 + x + \frac{x^2}{\lfloor 2} + \frac{x^3}{\lfloor 3} + \cdots$$

convergent for every value of x.

The ratio of the $(n + 1)$th term to the nth is $\dfrac{\dfrac{x^n}{\lfloor n}}{\dfrac{x^{n-1}}{\lfloor n-1}}$, or $\dfrac{x}{n}$,

which approaches the limit 0 when n is indefinitely increased.

Then, the series is convergent (§ 555, I).

559. *To prove the infinite series*

$$1 + nx + \frac{n(n-1)}{\lfloor 2} x^2 + \frac{n(n-1)(n-2)}{\lfloor 3} x^3 + \cdots,$$

where n is any positive fraction, or negative integer or fraction, convergent when x is numerically < 1.

By § 287, the ratio of the $(r + 1)$th term to the rth term is

$$\frac{n(n-1)\cdots(n-r+1)}{\lfloor r} x^r \div \frac{n(n-1)\cdots(n-r+2)}{\lfloor r-1} x^{r-1}.$$

That is, $\qquad \dfrac{n-r+1}{r}x,$ or $\left(\dfrac{n+1}{r}-1\right)x.$

If n does not equal -1, this approaches the limit $-x$ when r is indefinitely increased; and the series is convergent if x is numerically <1 (§ 555, I).

If $n=-1$, the series takes the form $1-x+x^2-x^3+\cdots$, which is convergent when x is numerically <1 by § 556.

560. *The infinite series*

$$a+bx+cx^2+dx^3+\cdots+kx^{n-1}+lx^n+\cdots$$

is convergent when the numerical value of x is taken sufficiently small, and for any numerically smaller value of x, including zero.

For the ratio of the $(n+1)$th term to the nth is $\dfrac{lx^n}{kx^{n-1}}$, or $\dfrac{lx}{k}$.

Whatever the values of k and l, x may be taken so small that $\dfrac{lx}{k}$ shall always be numerically $<q$, where q is numerically <1.

Then, for this value of x the series is convergent.

And by § 546, it is convergent for any numerically smaller value of x, including 0.

561. If x has any value (not including zero) which makes the series

$$a+bx+cx^2+\cdots \qquad (1)$$

convergent, $a+bx+cx^2+\cdot$, and therefore $bx+cx^2+\cdot$, or $x(b+cx+\cdot)$, is *finite*, for this value of x.

Then, since x is not zero, $b+cx+\cdots$ is finite for this value of x; and $x(b+cx+\cdot)$, or $bx+cx^2+\cdots$ approaches the limit 0 when x is indefinitely decreased.

Since $b+cx+\cdots$ is finite for any value of x, except 0, which makes series (1) convergent, it is itself convergent for this value of x (§ 545).

562. Absolutely and Conditionally Convergent Series.

A convergent infinite series, having negative terms, is said to be *absolutely convergent* when it remains convergent after the signs of the negative terms are changed.

It is said to be *conditionally convergent* when this is not the case.

Thus, the convergent infinite series (§ 556)

$$1 - \frac{1}{2} + \frac{1}{3} - \frac{1}{4} + \cdots, \tag{1}$$

if the signs of the negative terms are changed, becomes

$$1 + \frac{1}{2} + \frac{1}{3} + \frac{1}{4} + \cdots,$$

which was proved divergent in § 548.

Then, the series (1) is conditionally convergent.

In a conditionally convergent series, the sum of the terms approaches a different limit by a different arrangement of the terms.

Thus, in series (1), we may write the terms

$$\left(1 - \frac{1}{2} + \frac{1}{3}\right) - \left(\frac{1}{4} - \frac{1}{5}\right) - \left(\frac{1}{6} - \frac{1}{7}\right) - \cdots,$$

which shows that the sum of the terms is $< \left(1 - \frac{1}{2} + \frac{1}{3}\right)$, or $\frac{5}{6}$.

We may also write the terms

$$\left(1 + \frac{1}{3} - \frac{1}{2}\right) + \left(\frac{1}{5} + \frac{1}{7} - \frac{1}{4}\right) + \left(\frac{1}{9} + \frac{1}{11} - \frac{1}{6}\right) + \cdots,$$

which shows that the sum of the terms is $> \frac{5}{6}$.

Then the terms of a series cannot be arranged in any desired order unless the series is absolutely convergent.

EXERCISE 84

Expand each of the following to four terms:

1. $\dfrac{3 + 4x}{1 + 2x}$.

2. $\dfrac{1 - 5x^2}{1 - 5x - 2x^2}$.

3. $\dfrac{4x}{2 + 6x - x^2}$.

4. $\dfrac{2 + 4x - 5x^3}{3 - 6x^2 + 7x^3}$.

5. $\sqrt{1 + 3x}$.

6. $\sqrt{x^2 + xy + y^2}$.

7. $\sqrt{9a^4 - 3b^2}$.

8. $\sqrt[3]{8x^8 - 1}$.

9. $\sqrt[3]{a^6 + 2b}$.

Determine whether the following infinite series are convergent or divergent:

10. $\dfrac{1}{2} + \dfrac{2}{2^2} + \dfrac{3}{2^3} + \dfrac{4}{2^4} + \cdots$.

11. $1 + \dfrac{1}{\lfloor 3} + \dfrac{1}{\lfloor 5} + \dfrac{1}{\lfloor 7} + \cdots$.

12. $\dfrac{1}{1 \cdot 2} + \dfrac{1}{3 \cdot 4} + \dfrac{1}{5 \cdot 6} + \cdots$.

13. $1 + \dfrac{2^2}{\lfloor 2} + \dfrac{3^3}{\lfloor 3} + \cdots$.

14. $1 - \dfrac{1}{2^2} + \dfrac{1}{3^2} - \dfrac{1}{4^2} + \cdots$.

15. $\dfrac{1}{3} + \dfrac{1 \cdot 3}{3 \cdot 6} + \dfrac{1 \cdot 3 \cdot 5}{3 \cdot 6 \cdot 9} + \cdots$.

16. $\dfrac{1}{3} + \dfrac{1}{6} + \dfrac{1}{9} + \cdots$.

17. $\dfrac{1}{1} + \dfrac{\lfloor 2}{1 \cdot 3} + \dfrac{\lfloor 3}{1 \cdot 3 \cdot 5} + \cdots$.

18. $1 + \dfrac{1}{2^2} + \dfrac{1}{3^3} + \dfrac{1}{4^4} + \cdots$.

19. $\dfrac{1}{3} + \dfrac{1 \cdot 2}{3 \cdot 5} + \dfrac{1 \cdot 2 \cdot 3}{3 \cdot 5 \cdot 7} + \cdots$.

20. $1 + \dfrac{2^3}{\lfloor 2} + \dfrac{3^3}{\lfloor 3} + \dfrac{4^3}{\lfloor 4} + \cdots$.

21. $\dfrac{2}{2 \cdot 3} + \dfrac{4}{3 \cdot 4} + \dfrac{6}{4 \cdot 5} + \cdots$.

22. $\dfrac{1}{3} - \dfrac{1}{2 \cdot 3^2} + \dfrac{1}{3 \cdot 3^3} - \dfrac{1}{4 \cdot 3^4} + \cdots$.

23. $\dfrac{2}{1} + \dfrac{3}{1 \cdot 2} + \dfrac{4}{2 \cdot 3} + \dfrac{5}{3 \cdot 4} + \cdots$.

Determine for what values of x each of the following infinite series is convergent or divergent:

24. $1 + 2^2 x + 3^2 x^2 + \cdots$.

25. $1 + \dfrac{x}{1 \cdot 2} + \dfrac{x^2}{2 \cdot 3} + \dfrac{x^3}{3 \cdot 4} + \cdots$.

26. Prove the infinite series

$$\dfrac{1}{1 + x} + \dfrac{1}{1 + x^2} + \dfrac{1}{1 + x^3} + \cdots$$

convergent when x is > 1, and divergent when $x = 1$ or $x < 1$.

27. Prove the infinite series

$$\dfrac{1}{1 + x} + \dfrac{x}{1 + x^2} + \dfrac{x^2}{1 + x^4} + \cdots$$

convergent for every value of x.

In determining the convergency or divergency of a series, it is usually best to commence with the tests of § 555 ; if the limit approached is 1, then other methods may be tried.

XXVII. UNDETERMINED COEFFICIENTS

THE THEOREM OF UNDETERMINED COEFFICIENTS

563. An important method for expanding expressions into series is based on the following theorem:

Let the members of the equation

$$A + Bx + Cx^2 + Dx^3 + \cdots = A' + B'x + C'x^2 + D'x^3 + \cdots \quad (1)$$

be infinite series which are equal for any value of x which makes them both convergent; then, the coefficients of like powers of x in the series will be equal; that is,

$$A = A', \; B = B', \; C = C', \text{ etc.}$$

By § 560, each series is convergent for a certain finite value of x, and for all smaller values; and since this is the case, each of the expressions

$$Bx + Cx^2 + \cdots \text{ and } B'x + C'x^2 + \cdots$$

approaches the limit 0 when x is indefinitely decreased (§ 561).

Then, the given series approach the limits A and A', respectively, when x is indefinitely decreased.

Now, since the given series are functions of x, which are equal for every value of x which makes them both convergent, their limits when x is indefinitely decreased are equal (§ 252).

Therefore, $A = A'$,

and hence $Bx + Cx^2 + \cdots = B'x + C'x^2 + \cdots$.

Since x is not 0, we may divide through by x.

Then, $B + Cx + \cdots = B' + C'x + \cdots$.   (2)

By § 561, each member of (2) is convergent for the same values of x as the corresponding member of (1).

That is, (2) is satisfied by any value of x which makes both members convergent; and letting x be indefinitely decreased, we have $B = B'$.

Proceeding in this way, we may prove $C = C'$, etc.

The above proof holds when either or both of the given series are finite.

EXPANSION OF FRACTIONS

564. 1. Expand $\dfrac{2 - 3x^2 - x^3}{1 - 2x + 3x^2}$ in ascending powers of x.

We saw, in § 539, that a fraction could be expanded into a series by dividing the numerator by the denominator.

We therefore know that the proposed expansion is possible. Assume then

$$\frac{2 - 3x^2 - x^3}{1 - 2x + 3x^2} = A + Bx + Cx^2 + Dx^3 + Ex^4 + \cdots; \quad (1)$$

where A, B, C, D, E, $\cdots$, are numbers independent of x.

Clearing of fractions, and collecting the terms in the second member involving like powers of x, we have

$$2 - 3x^2 - x^3 = A + \begin{matrix} B \\ -2A \\ +3A \end{matrix} \Big| x + \begin{matrix} C \\ -2B \\ +3A \end{matrix} \Big| x^2 + \begin{matrix} D \\ -2C \\ +3B \end{matrix} \Big| x^3 + \begin{matrix} E \\ -2D \\ +3C \end{matrix} \Big| x^4 + \cdots. \quad (2)$$

A vertical line, called a *bar*, is often used in place of parentheses.

Thus, $\quad \begin{matrix} +B \\ -2A \end{matrix} \Big| x$ is equivalent to $(B - 2A)x$.

Equations (1) and (2) are satisfied when x has any value which makes the second member a convergent series.

Then, by § 563, the coefficients of like powers of x in (2) must be equal; that is,

$$A = 2.$$
$$B - 2A = 0; \text{ or, } B = 2A = 4.$$
$$C - 2B + 3A = -3; \text{ or, } C = 2B - 3A - 3 = -1.$$
$$D - 2C + 3B = -1; \text{ or, } D = 2C - 3B - 1 = -15.$$
$$E - 2D + 3C = 0; \text{ or, } E = 2D - 3C = -27; \text{ etc.}$$

Substituting these values in (1), we have

$$\frac{2 - 3x^2 - x^3}{1 - 2x + 3x^2} = 2 + 4x - x^2 - 15x^3 - 27x^4 - \cdots.$$

The result may be verified by division.

The series expresses the value of the fraction only for such values of x as make it convergent (§ 540).

If the numerator and denominator contain only *even* powers of x, the operation may be abridged by assuming a series containing only the even powers of x.

Thus, if the fraction were $\dfrac{2 + 4\,x^2 - x^4}{1 - 3\,x^2 + 5\,x^4}$, we should assume it equal to $A + Bx^2 + Cx^4 + Dx^6 + Ex^8 + \cdots$.

In like manner, if the numerator contains only *odd* powers of x, and the denominator only even powers, we should assume a series containing only the odd powers of x.

If every term of the numerator contains x, we may assume a series commencing with the lowest power of x in the numerator.

If every term of the denominator contains x, we determine by actual division what power of x will occur in the first term of the expansion, and then assume the fraction equal to a series commencing with this power of x, the exponents of x in the succeeding terms increasing by unity as before.

2. Expand $\dfrac{1}{3\,x^2 - x^3}$ in ascending powers of x.

Dividing 1 by $3\,x^2$, the quotient is $\dfrac{x^{-2}}{3}$.

We then assume,

$$\frac{1}{3\,x^2 - x^3} = Ax^{-2} + Bx^{-1} + C + Dx + Ex^2 + \cdots. \qquad (3)$$

Clearing of fractions,

$$1 = 3\,A + 3\,B\Big|x + 3\,C\Big|x^2 + 3\,D\Big|x^3 + 3\,E\Big|x^4 + \cdots.$$
$$ - A\Big| \quad - B\Big| \quad - C\Big| \quad - D\Big|$$

Equating coefficients of like powers of x,

$$3\,A = 1;$$
$$3\,B - A = 0;$$
$$3\,C - B = 0;$$
$$3\,D - C = 0;$$
$$3\,E - D = 0;\ \text{etc.}$$

Whence, $A = \dfrac{1}{3}$, $B = \dfrac{1}{9}$, $C = \dfrac{1}{27}$, $D = \dfrac{1}{81}$, $E = \dfrac{1}{243}$, etc.

Substituting in (3), we have

$$\frac{1}{3\,x^2 - x^3} = \frac{x^{-2}}{3} + \frac{x^{-1}}{9} + \frac{1}{27} + \frac{x}{81} + \frac{x^2}{243} + \cdots.$$

In Ex. 1, $E = 2\,D - 3\,C$; that is, the coefficient of x^4 equals twice the coefficient of the preceding term, minus three times the coefficient of the next but one preceding.

It is evident that this law holds for the succeeding terms; thus, the coefficient of x^5 is $2 \times (-27) - 3 \times (-15)$, or -9.

After the law of coefficients has been found in any expansion, the terms may be found more easily than by long division; and for this reason the method of § 564 is to be preferred when a large number of terms is required.

The law for Ex. 2 is that each coefficient is one-third the preceding.

EXERCISE 85

Expand each of the following to five terms :

1. $\dfrac{3 + 2\,x}{1 - x}$.

2. $\dfrac{1 - 6\,x}{1 + 4\,x}$.

3. $\dfrac{4 + x^2}{1 - 3\,x^2}$.

4. $\dfrac{2\,x}{3 - 5\,x^2}$.

5. $\dfrac{1 + 4\,x - x^2}{1 - x + 3\,x^2}$.

6. $\dfrac{2 - x + 3\,x^2}{1 + 2\,x^2}$.

7. $\dfrac{1 + 4\,x^2}{1 + 4\,x - x^2}$.

8. $\dfrac{x - 7\,x^3 - 4\,x^4}{1 - 5\,x - 2\,x^2}$.

9. $\dfrac{x^2 - 3\,x^3}{3 - x - 2\,x^3}$.

10. $\dfrac{2 - 3\,x^2}{3 - 2\,x + x^3}$.

11. $\dfrac{2 + x - 3\,x^2}{1 - 4\,x + 5\,x^2}$.

12. $\dfrac{3 - 4\,x^3}{2 + x^2 - 3\,x^3}$.

13. $\dfrac{3}{2\,x^3 + x^4}$.

14. $\dfrac{3 + 5\,x - 2\,x^3}{x^2 - 3\,x^3 + x^4}$.

15. $\dfrac{1 - 4\,x^2 + 6\,x^3}{x + 2\,x^2 - x^3}$.

16. $\dfrac{1 - 4\,x + 2\,x^3}{2\,x^3 - 3\,x^5 - x^6}$.

EXPANSION OF SURDS

565. *Ex.* Expand $\sqrt{1 - x}$ in ascending powers of x.

We saw, in § 539, that the square root of an imperfect square could be expanded into a series by Evolution.

We therefore know that the proposed expansion is possible. Assume then,

$$\sqrt{1 - x} = A + Bx + Cx^2 + Dx^3 + Ex^4 + \cdots. \qquad (1)$$

Squaring both members, we have by § 134,

$$1 - x = A^2 \begin{vmatrix} x + \\ + 2\,AB \end{vmatrix} \begin{vmatrix} B^2 \\ + 2\,AC \end{vmatrix} x^2 \begin{vmatrix} x^3 + \\ + 2\,AD \\ + 2\,BC \end{vmatrix} \begin{vmatrix} C^2 \\ + 2\,AE \\ + 2\,BD \end{vmatrix} x^4 + \cdots.$$

Equating coefficients of like powers of x,

$$A^2 = \quad 1; \text{ or, } A = 1.$$

$$2\,AB = -1; \text{ or, } B = -\frac{1}{2\,A} = -\frac{1}{2}.$$

$$B^2 + 2\,AC = \quad 0; \text{ or, } C = -\frac{B^2}{2\,A} = -\frac{1}{8}.$$

$$2\,AD + 2\,BC = \quad 0; \text{ or, } D = -\frac{BC}{A} = -\frac{1}{16}.$$

$$C^2 + 2\,AE + 2\,BD = \quad 0; \text{ or, } E = -\frac{C^2 + 2\,BD}{A} = -\frac{5}{128}; \text{ etc.}$$

Substituting these values in (1), we have

$$\sqrt{1 - x} = 1 - \frac{x}{2} - \frac{x^2}{8} - \frac{x^3}{16} - \frac{5\,x^4}{128} - \cdots.$$

The result may be verified by Evolution.

The series expresses the value of $\sqrt{1 - x}$ only for such values of x as make it convergent.

EXERCISE 86

Expand each of the following to five terms:

1. $\sqrt{1 - 4\,x}$.   3. $\sqrt{1 + 2\,x - x^2}$.   5. $\sqrt[3]{1 + 3\,x}$.

2. $\sqrt{1 + 5\,x}$.   4. $\sqrt{1 - x + 3\,x^2}$.   6. $\sqrt[3]{1 - x - 2\,x^2}$.

PARTIAL FRACTIONS

566. If the denominator of a fraction can be resolved into factors, each of the first degree in x, and the numerator is of a lower degree than the denominator, the Theorem of Undetermined Coefficients enables us to express the given fraction as the sum of two or more *partial fractions*, whose denominators are factors of the given denominator, and whose numerators are independent of x.

567. CASE I.   *No factors of the denominator equal.*

1. Separate $\dfrac{19\,x+1}{(3\,x-1)(5\,x+2)}$ into partial fractions.

Assume $\dfrac{19\,x+1}{(3\,x-1)(5\,x+2)}=\dfrac{A}{3\,x-1}+\dfrac{B}{5\,x+2}$,   (1)

where A and B are numbers independent of x.

Clearing of fractions, we have

$$19\,x+1=A(5\,x+2)+B(3\,x-1)$$
$$=(5\,A+3\,B)x+2\,A-B.   \text{(2)}$$

The second member of (1) must express the value of the given fraction for every value of x.

Hence, equation (2) is satisfied by every value of x; and by § 563, the coefficients of like powers of x in the two members are equal.

That is, $5\,A+3\,B=19,$

and $2\,A-\ B=1.$

Solving these equations, we obtain $A=2$ and $B=3$.

Substituting in (1), we have

$$\frac{19\,x+1}{(3\,x-1)(5\,x+2)}=\frac{2}{3\,x-1}+\frac{3}{5\,x+2}.$$

The result may be verified by finding the sum of the partial fractions.

2. Separate $\dfrac{x+4}{2\,x-x^2-x^3}$ into partial fractions.

The factors of $2\,x-x^2-x^3$ are x, $1-x$, and $2+x$.

Assume then $\dfrac{x+4}{2\,x-x^2-x^3}=\dfrac{A}{x}+\dfrac{B}{1-x}+\dfrac{C}{2+x}.$

Clearing of fractions, we have

$$x+4=A(1-x)(2+x)+Bx(2+x)+Cx(1-x).$$

This equation, being satisfied by every value of x, is satisfied when $x=0$.

Putting $x = 0$, we have $4 = 2\,A$, or $A = 2$.

Again, the equation is satisfied when $x = 1$.

Putting $x = 1$, we have $5 = 3\,B$, or $B = \dfrac{5}{3}$.

The equation is also satisfied when $x = -2$.

Putting $x = -2$, we have $2 = -6\,C$, or $C = -\dfrac{1}{3}$.

Then, $\dfrac{x+4}{2\,x - x^2 - x^3} = \dfrac{2}{x} + \dfrac{\frac{5}{3}}{1-x} + \dfrac{-\frac{1}{3}}{2+x}$

$= \dfrac{2}{x} + \dfrac{5}{3\,(1-x)} - \dfrac{1}{3\,(2+x)}.$

The student should compare the above method of finding A and B with that used in Ex. 1.

568. CASE II.   *All the factors of the denominator equal.*

Let it be required to separate $\dfrac{x^2 - 11\,x + 26}{(x-3)^3}$ into partial fractions.

Substituting $y + 3$ for x, the fraction becomes

$$\dfrac{(y+3)^2 - 11\,(y+3) + 26}{y^3} = \dfrac{y^2 - 5\,y + 2}{y^3} = \dfrac{1}{y} - \dfrac{5}{y^2} + \dfrac{2}{y^3}.$$

Replacing y by $x - 3$, the result takes the form

$$\dfrac{1}{x-3} - \dfrac{5}{(x-3)^2} + \dfrac{2}{(x-3)^3}.$$

This shows that the given fraction can be expressed as the sum of three partial fractions, whose numerators are independent of x, and whose denominators are the powers of $x - 3$ beginning with the first and ending with the third.

Similar considerations hold with respect to any example under Case II; the number of partial fractions in any case being the same as the number of equal factors in the denominator of the given fraction.

Ex. Separate $\dfrac{6\,x + 5}{(3\,x + 5)^2}$ into partial fractions.

In accordance with the above principle, we assume the given fraction equal to the sum of *two* partial fractions, whose denominators are the powers of $3x + 5$ beginning with the first and ending with the *second*.

That is,

$$\frac{6x + 5}{(3x + 5)^2} = \frac{A}{3x + 5} + \frac{B}{(3x + 5)^2}.$$

Clearing of fractions, $6x + 5 = A(3x + 5) + B$

$$= 3Ax + 5A + B.$$

Equating coefficients of like powers of x,

$$3A = 6,$$

and

$$5A + B = 5.$$

Solving these equations, $A = 2$ and $B = -5$.

Whence,

$$\frac{6x + 5}{(3x + 5)^2} = \frac{2}{3x + 5} - \frac{5}{(3x + 5)^2}.$$

569. CASE III. *Some of the factors of the denominator equal.*

Ex. Separate $\dfrac{3x + 2}{x(x + 1)^3}$ into partial fractions.

The method in Case III is a combination of the methods of Cases I and II; we assume

$$\frac{3x + 2}{x(x + 1)^3} = \frac{A}{x} + \frac{B}{x + 1} + \frac{C}{(x + 1)^2} + \frac{D}{(x + 1)^3}. \tag{1}$$

Clearing of fractions,

$$3x + 2 = A(x + 1)^3 + Bx(x + 1)^2 + Cx(x + 1) + Dx$$
$$= (A + B)x^3 + (3A + 2B + C)x^2$$
$$+ (3A + B + C + D)x + A.$$

Equating coefficients of like powers of x,

$$A + B = 0,$$
$$3A + 2B + C = 0,$$
$$3A + B + C + D = 3,$$

and

$$A = 2.$$

Solving, we have $A = 2$, $B = -2$, $C = -2$, and $D = 1$.

Substituting in (1),

$$\frac{3x+2}{x(x+1)^3} = \frac{2}{x} - \frac{2}{x+1} - \frac{2}{(x+1)^2} + \frac{1}{(x+1)^3}.$$

The following general rule for Case III will be found convenient :

A fraction of the form $\dfrac{X}{(x+a)(x+b)\cdots(x+m)^r \cdots}$ should be assumed equal to

$$\frac{A}{x+a} + \frac{B}{x+b} + \cdots + \frac{E}{x+m} + \frac{F}{(x+m)^2} + \cdots + \frac{K}{(x+m)^r} + \cdots.$$

Single factors like $x + a$ and $x + b$ having single partial fractions corresponding, arranged as in Case I ; and repeated factors like $(x+m)^r$ having r partial fractions corresponding, arranged as in Case II.

EXERCISE 87

Separate the following into partial fractions :

1. $\dfrac{8x-6}{4x^2-9}.$

2. $\dfrac{19x-30}{5x^2-6x}.$

3. $\dfrac{2x-10}{(2x-3)^2}.$

4. $\dfrac{2x^2+15x+34}{(x+5)^3}.$

5. $\dfrac{5x^2-75}{x^3-25x}.$

6. $\dfrac{9x^2-15x}{(3x-1)^3}.$

7. $\dfrac{43x+6}{6x^2+5x-6}.$

8. $\dfrac{8x^2}{(2x-3)^3}.$

9. $\dfrac{5x^2+4x-1}{(5x+2)^3}.$

10. $\dfrac{5ax^2-2a^2x-8a^3}{x^3+3ax^2-4a^2x}.$

11. $\dfrac{4x^2-22x+63}{x(x-3)^2}.$

12. $\dfrac{42-27x}{8-14x+5x^2}.$

13. $\dfrac{62x-38}{(2x-1)(12x^2-x-6)}.$

14. $\dfrac{2x^3+19x^2-17x+12}{x^4+4x^3}.$

15. $\dfrac{x^3-x-4}{(x-1)^4}.$

16. $\dfrac{18x-4\sqrt{2}}{9x^2+6x-1}.$

17. $\dfrac{9x^2-9x-18}{(x^2-2x)(x^2-9)}.$

18. $\dfrac{14x^2+11x+29}{(3x-1)(2x+3)^2}.$

19. $\dfrac{x^3+14x^2+9x}{(x+2)^4}.$

20. $\dfrac{x^3-3x^2-7x+4}{x^2(x-1)^2}.$

21. $\dfrac{9x^3-24x^2+20x-4}{(3x-2)^4}.$

22. $\dfrac{2x^3+12x^2+12x+4}{x(x+1)(x+2)^2}.$

23. $\dfrac{19x-32}{(2x-3)(8x^2-10x-3)}.$

570. If the degree of the numerator is equal to, or greater than, that of the denominator, the preceding methods are inapplicable.

In such a case, we divide the numerator by the denominator until a remainder is obtained which is of a lower degree than the denominator.

Ex. Separate $\dfrac{x^3 - 3x^2 - 1}{x^2 - x}$ into an integral expression and partial fractions.

We have, by division, $\dfrac{x^3 - 3x^2 - 1}{x^2 - x} = x - 2 + \dfrac{-2x - 1}{x^2 - x}.$ (1)

We can now separate $\dfrac{-2x - 1}{x^2 - x}$ into partial fractions by the method of Case I; the result is $\dfrac{1}{x} - \dfrac{3}{x - 1}.$

Substituting in (1), $\dfrac{x^3 - 3x^2 - 1}{x^2 - x} = x - 2 + \dfrac{1}{x} - \dfrac{3}{x - 1}.$

Another way to solve the above example is to combine the methods of §§ 564 and 567, and assume the given fraction equal to

$$Ax + B + \frac{C}{x} + \frac{D}{x - 1}.$$

EXERCISE 88

Separate the following into integral expressions and partial fractions :

1. $\dfrac{9x^3 + 21x^2 + 22x - 17}{(x + 2)(3x - 1)}.$

2. $\dfrac{4x^3 - 26x^2 + 20x - 1}{(x - 2)^3}.$

3. $\dfrac{2x^6 - 2x^5 - 3x^2 + 1}{x^4 - x^3}.$

4. $\dfrac{6x^5 + 6x^4 - 2x^3 + 5x + 1}{x^2(x + 1)^3}.$

5. $\dfrac{5x^6 + 15x^5 + 3x^4 - 14x^2 - 18}{x^4 + 3x^3}.$

571. If the denominator of a fraction can be resolved into factors partly of the first and partly of the second, or all of the second degree, in x, and the numerator is of a lower degree than the denominator, the Theorem of Undetermined Coefficients enables us to express the given fraction as the sum of two or more partial fractions, whose denominators are factors of the given denominator, and whose numerators are independent of x in the case of fractions corresponding to factors of the first degree, and of the form $Ax + B$ in the case of fractions corresponding to factors of the second degree.

The only exceptions occur when the factors of the denominator are of the second degree and all equal.

Ex. Separate $\dfrac{1}{x^3+1}$ into partial fractions.

The factors of the denominator are $x+1$ and x^2-x+1.

Assume then $\qquad \dfrac{1}{x^3+1}=\dfrac{A}{x+1}+\dfrac{Bx+C}{x^2-x+1}.$ $\qquad\qquad$ (1)

Clearing of fractions, we have

$$1 = A(x^2-x+1)+(Bx+C)(x+1)$$
$$= (A+B)x^2+(-A+B+C)x+A+C.$$

Equating coefficients of like powers of x,

$$A+B=0,$$
$$-A+B+C=0,$$

and $\qquad\qquad\qquad\qquad A+C=1.$

Solving these equations, $A=\dfrac{1}{3},\ \ B=-\dfrac{1}{3},\ \ $ and $\ C=\dfrac{2}{3}.$

Substituting in (1), $\dfrac{1}{x^3+1}=\dfrac{1}{3(x+1)}-\dfrac{x-2}{3(x^2-x+1)}.$

EXERCISE 89

Separate the following into partial fractions:

1. $\dfrac{6x^2+5x+2}{x^3+1}.$

2. $\dfrac{5x^2+x-14}{(3x+1)(x^2-x+3)}.$

3. $\dfrac{3x^2-x+25}{2x^3-5x^2+4x-10}.$

4. $\dfrac{4x^3-5x^2+6x+3}{x^4-1}.$

5. $\dfrac{22x-6}{8x^3-27}.$

6. $\dfrac{4x^3+18x+8}{x^4+3x^2+4}.$

572. We will now show how to find an expression for the nth term of the expansion of a fraction in ascending powers of x, when the denominator can be resolved into binomial factors of the first or second degree in x.

Ex. Find the nth term in the expansion of the fraction $\dfrac{1+7x}{1+2x-3x^2}$ in ascending powers of x.

Separating the fraction into partial fractions by the method of § 567, we have

$$\frac{1+7\,x}{1+2\,x-3\,x^2} = \frac{2}{1-x} - \frac{1}{1+3\,x}. \tag{1}$$

By division, $\dfrac{2}{1-x} = 2\,(1+x+x^2+x^3+\cdots)$, $\qquad$ (2)

and $\qquad\qquad \dfrac{1}{1+3\,x} = 1 - 3\,x + 3^2x^2 - 3^3x^3 + \cdots. \tag{3}$

The nth term of (2) is $2\,x^{n-1}$, and the nth term of (3) is $(-3)^{n-1}x^{n-1}$.

Subtracting, the nth term of (1) is

$$2\,x^{n-1} - (-3)^{n-1}x^{n-1}, \text{ or } [\,2 - (-3)^{n-1}\,]\,x^{n-1}.$$

The above may be used as a *formula* to obtain the successive terms of the expansion.

If $n = 1$, the expression becomes $(2-1)x^0$, or 1.

If $n = 2$, the expression becomes $(2+3)x$, or $5\,x$.

If $n = 3$, the expression becomes $(2-9)x^2$, or $-7\,x^2$; etc.

Then, $\dfrac{1+7\,x}{1+2\,x-3\,x^2} = 1 + 5\,x - 7\,x^2 + \cdots.$

EXERCISE 90

In each of the following, find the nth term of the expansion of the fraction in ascending powers of x :

1. $\dfrac{3}{1-x-2\,x^2}.$

2. $\dfrac{2\,x-1}{1-9\,x+20\,x^2}.$

3. $\dfrac{6+11\,x}{2+5\,x-3\,x^2}.$

4. $\dfrac{5\,x-12}{6\,x^2+5\,x-6}.$

5. $\dfrac{7+4\,x-x^2}{6+3\,x-4\,x^2-2\,x^3}.$

6. $\dfrac{1+5\,x+6\,x^2}{(1-x)(1+x^2)}.$

In Exs. 5 and 6, it should be observed that there are *two forms* for the nth term according as n is even or odd.

REVERSION OF SERIES

573. To *revert* a given series $y = a + bx^m + cx^n + \cdots$ is to express x in the form of a series proceeding in ascending powers of y.

Ex.   Revert the series $y = 2\,x - 3\,x^2 + 4\,x^3 - 5\,x^4 + \cdots$.

Assume, $x = Ay + By^2 + Cy^3 + Dy^4 + \cdots.$ (1)

Substituting in this the given value of y,

$$x = A(2\,x - 3\,x^2 + 4\,x^3 - 5\,x^4 + \cdots)$$
$$+ B(4\,x^2 + 9\,x^4 - 12\,x^3 + 16\,x^4 + \cdots)$$
$$+ C(8\,x^3 - 36\,x^4 + \cdots) + D(16\,x^4 + \cdots) + \cdots.$$

That is, $x = 2\,Ax - 3\,A \begin{vmatrix} x^2 + \\ \end{vmatrix} \begin{matrix} 4\,A \\ -12\,B \\ +8\,C \end{matrix} \begin{vmatrix} x^3 - \\ \end{vmatrix} \begin{matrix} 5\,A \\ +25\,B \\ -36\,C \\ +16\,D \end{matrix} \begin{vmatrix} x^4 + \cdots. \\ \end{vmatrix}$

$\qquad\qquad\quad +4\,B$

Equating coefficients of like powers of x,

$$2\,A = 1;$$
$$-3\,A + 4\,B = 0;$$
$$4\,A - 12\,B + 8\,C = 0;$$
$$-5\,A + 25\,B - 36\,C + 16\,D = 0;\ \text{etc.}$$

Solving, $A = \dfrac{1}{2}$, $B = \dfrac{3}{8}$, $C = \dfrac{5}{16}$, $D = \dfrac{35}{128}$, etc.

Substituting in (1), $x = \dfrac{1}{2}y + \dfrac{3}{8}y^2 + \dfrac{5}{16}y^3 + \dfrac{35}{128}y^4 + \cdots.$

If the even powers of x are wanting in the given series, the operation may be abridged by assuming x equal to a series containing only the *odd* powers of y.

Thus, to revert the series $y = x - x^3 + x^5 - x^7 + \cdots$, we assume $x = Ay + By^3 + Cy^5 + Dy^7 + \cdots.$

If the *odd* powers of x are wanting in the given series, we substitute t for x^2, and revert the series, expressing t in ascending powers of y; by taking the square root of this result, x itself may be expressed in ascending powers of y.

If the first term of the given series is independent of x, it is impossible to express x in ascending powers of y, though it is possible to express it in the form of a series whose terms are functions of y.

Thus, let it be required to revert the series

$$y = 1 + x + \frac{x^2}{\lfloor 2} + \frac{x^3}{\lfloor 3} + \cdots.$$

The series may be written $y - 1 = x + \frac{x^2}{\lfloor 2} + \frac{x^3}{\lfloor 3} + \cdots.$

We then assume

$$x = A(y-1) + B(y-1)^2 + C(y-1)^3 + D(y-1)^4 + \cdots.$$

Proceeding as before, we find

$$x = (y-1) - \frac{1}{2}(y-1)^2 + \frac{1}{3}(y-1)^3 - \frac{1}{4}(y-1)^4 + \cdots.$$

EXERCISE 91

Revert each of the following to four terms :

1. $y = x + 3x^2 + 5x^3 + 7x^4 + \cdots.$

2. $y = x - 2x^2 + 3x^3 - 4x^4 + \cdots.$

3. $y = x - \frac{x^2}{2} + \frac{x^3}{3} - \frac{x^4}{4} + \cdots.$

4. $y = 1 + 2x + 5x^2 + 8x^3 + 11x^4 + \cdots.$

5. $y = \frac{x}{2} - \frac{x^2}{4} + \frac{x^3}{6} - \frac{x^4}{8} + \cdots.$

6. $y = \frac{x}{3} + \frac{x^2}{6} + \frac{x^3}{9} + \cdots.$

7. $y = 2x - 4x^3 + 6x^5 - 8x^7 + \cdots.$

8. $y = x + \frac{x^3}{\lfloor 3} + \frac{x^5}{\lfloor 5} + \frac{x^7}{\lfloor 7} + \cdots.$

XXVIII. THE BINOMIAL THEOREM

ANY RATIONAL EXPONENT

574. It was proved in § 285 that, if n is a positive integer,

$$(1+x)^n = 1 + nx + \frac{n(n-1)}{\lfloor 2}x^2 + \frac{n(n-1)(n-2)}{\lfloor 3}x^3 + \cdots. \quad (1)$$

In this case, the second member is a finite series of $n+1$ terms.

If n is a negative integer, or a positive or negative fraction, the series in the second member becomes infinite; for no one of the expressions $n-1$, $n-2$, etc., can equal zero.

We will now prove that in this case the series gives the value of $(1+x)^n$, provided it is *convergent;* this we know to be the case when x is numerically < 1 (§ 559).

575. Proof of the Binomial Theorem for Any Rational Exponent.

If m and n are *positive integers,*

$$(1+x)^m = 1 + mx + \frac{m(m-1)}{\lfloor 2}x^2 + \cdots, \quad (2)$$

and

$$(1+x)^n = 1 + nx + \frac{n(n-1)}{\lfloor 2}x^2 + \cdots. \quad (3)$$

But, $(1+x)^m \times (1+x)^n = (1+x)^{m+n}$.

Then the product of the series in the second members of (2) and (3) must equal the expanded form of $(1+x)^{m+n}$; that is,

$$\left[1 + mx + \frac{m(m-1)}{\lfloor 2}x^2 + \cdots\right] \times \left[1 + nx + \frac{n(n-1)}{\lfloor 2}x^2 + \cdots\right]$$

$$= 1 + (m+n)x + \frac{(m+n)(m+n-1)}{\lfloor 2}x^2 + \cdots. \quad (4)$$

We proved the above result on the hypothesis that both m and n were positive integers.

But the *form* of the product will evidently be the same whatever the values of m and n.

Therefore, (4) holds for *all rational values* of m and n, provided x is numerically <1; for in this case each series is convergent.

(We assume that the product of two convergent series is convergent.)

Now let the symbol $f(m)$ stand for the series

$$1 + mx + \frac{m(m-1)}{\underline{|2}}x^2 + \cdots,$$

for any rational value of m.

Then, if m is a positive integer, $f(m) = (1+x)^m$.   (5)

Then, by § 251, (4) may be written

$$f(m) \times f(n) = f(m+n), \tag{6}$$

which holds for all rational values of m and n.

Then by (6), if p is also a rational number,

$$f(m) \times f(n) \times f(p) = [f(m+n)] \times f(p) = f(m+n+p); \text{ etc.}$$

Thus, $f(m) \times f(n) \times f(p) \times \cdots$ to r factors

$$= f(m+n+p+\cdots \text{ to } r \text{ terms}). \tag{7}$$

Now let $m, n, p, \cdots$ be each equal to $\frac{q}{r}$, where q and r are positive integers; then (7) becomes

$$\left[f\left(\frac{q}{r}\right) \right]^r = f\left(\frac{q}{r} \times r\right) = f(q).$$

But since q is a positive integer, $f(q) = (1+x)^q$.

Then, $\left[f\left(\frac{q}{r}\right) \right]^r = (1+x)^q.$

Taking the rth root of both members,

$$(1+x)^{\frac{q}{r}} = f\left(\frac{q}{r}\right) = 1 + \frac{q}{r}x + \frac{\frac{q}{r}\left(\frac{q}{r}-1\right)}{\underline{|2}}x^2 + \cdots; \tag{8}$$

which proves the theorem for a positive fractional exponent.

The result is proved only for the case where x is numerically <1.

Again, in (6), let $m = -n$, where n is a positive integer or a positive fraction.

Then, $f(-n) \times f(n) = f(-n+n) = f(0)$.

But $f(0)$ stands for $(1+x)^0$, which equals 1 (§ 359).

Therefore, $f(-n) = \dfrac{1}{f(n)}$.

Now since n is a positive integer or a positive fraction, it follows from (5) and (8) that $f(n) = (1+x)^n$.

Whence, $f(-n) = \dfrac{1}{(1+x)^n}$.

Then,
$$(1+x)^{-n} = f(-n) = 1 + (-n)x + \frac{(-n)(-n-1)}{\lfloor 2} x^2 + \cdots ;$$

which proves the theorem for a negative integral or negative fractional exponent.

The result is proved only in the case where x is numerically < 1.

576. Putting $\dfrac{x}{a}$ for x, in (1), § 574,

$$\left(1 + \frac{x}{a}\right)^n = 1 + n\frac{x}{a} + \frac{n(n-1)}{\lfloor 2} \frac{x^2}{a^2} + \cdots. \qquad (9)$$

Multiplying each term by a^n, we have

$$(a+x)^n = a^n + na^{n-1}x + \frac{n(n-1)}{\lfloor 2} a^{n-2}x^2 + \cdots. \qquad (10)$$

We know that the second member of (9) is convergent when $\dfrac{x}{a}$ is numerically < 1.

Hence, the second member of (10) is convergent when x is numerically $< a$.

If x is numerically $> a$, we can expand $(a+x)^n$ in ascending powers of a; thus,

$$(x+a)^n = x^n + nx^{n-1}a + \frac{n(n-1)}{\lfloor 2} x^{n-2}a^2 + \cdots ;$$

and this series will be convergent, since a is numerically $< x$.

577. Examples.

In expanding expressions by the Binomial Theorem when the exponent is fractional or negative, the exponents and coefficients of the terms may be found by the laws of § 285, which hold for all rational values of the exponent.

1. Expand $(a + x)^{\frac{2}{3}}$ to five terms.

The exponent of a in the first term is $\frac{2}{3}$, and decreases by 1 in each succeeding term.

The exponent of x in the second term is 1, and increases by 1 in each succeeding term.

The coefficient of the first term is 1; of the second term, $\frac{2}{3}$.

Multiplying $\frac{2}{3}$, the coefficient of the second term, by $-\frac{1}{3}$, the exponent of a in that term, and dividing the product by the exponent of x increased by 1, or 2, we have $-\frac{1}{9}$ as the coefficient of the third term; and so on.

Then,

$$(a + x)^{\frac{2}{3}} = a^{\frac{2}{3}} + \frac{2}{3} a^{-\frac{1}{3}} x - \frac{1}{9} a^{-\frac{4}{3}} x^2 + \frac{4}{81} a^{-\frac{7}{3}} x^3 - \frac{7}{243} a^{-\frac{10}{3}} x^4 + \cdots.$$

It follows from § 576 that the series expresses the value of $(a + x)^{\frac{2}{3}}$ only when x is numerically $< a$.

If x is numerically $> a$, $(a + x)^{\frac{2}{3}}$ is equal to

$$x^{\frac{2}{3}} + \frac{2}{3} x^{-\frac{1}{3}} a - \frac{1}{9} x^{-\frac{4}{3}} a^2 + \frac{4}{81} x^{-\frac{7}{3}} a^3 - \cdots.$$

2. Expand $(1 + 2 x^{-\frac{1}{2}})^{-2}$ to five terms.

Enclosing $2 x^{-\frac{1}{2}}$ in parentheses, we have

$$(1 + 2 x^{-\frac{1}{2}})^{-2} = [1 + (2 x^{-\frac{1}{2}})]^{-2}$$
$$= 1^{-2} - 2 \cdot 1^{-3} \cdot (2 x^{-\frac{1}{2}}) + 3 \cdot 1^{-4} \cdot (2 x^{-\frac{1}{2}})^2$$
$$- 4 \cdot 1^{-5} \cdot (2 x^{-\frac{1}{2}})^3 + 5 \cdot 1^{-6} \cdot (2 x^{-\frac{1}{2}})^4 - \cdots.$$
$$= 1 - 4 x^{-\frac{1}{2}} + 12 x^{-1} - 32 x^{-\frac{3}{2}} + 80 x^{-2} + \cdots.$$

By writing the exponents of 1, in expanding $[1 + (2 x^{-\frac{1}{2}})]^{-2}$, we can make use of the fifth law of § 285.

The series expresses the value of $(1 + 2\,x^{-\frac{1}{2}})^{-2}$ only when $2\,x^{-\frac{1}{2}}$ is numerically < 1, or $x^{-\frac{1}{2}}$ numerically $< \dfrac{1}{2}$.

That is, when $x^{\frac{1}{2}}$ is numerically > 2, or when x is positive and > 4.

3. Expand $\dfrac{1}{\sqrt[3]{a^{-1} - 3\,x^{\frac{1}{3}}}}$ to four terms.

Enclosing a^{-1} and $-\,3\,x^{\frac{1}{3}}$ in parentheses, we have

$$\frac{1}{\sqrt[3]{a^{-1} - 3\,x^{\frac{1}{3}}}} = \frac{1}{(a^{-1} - 3\,x^{\frac{1}{3}})^{\frac{1}{3}}} = [(a^{-1}) + (-\,3\,x^{\frac{1}{3}})]^{-\frac{1}{3}}$$

$$= (a^{-1})^{-\frac{1}{3}} - \frac{1}{3}(a^{-1})^{-\frac{4}{3}}(-\,3\,x^{\frac{1}{3}}) + \frac{2}{9}(a^{-1})^{-\frac{7}{3}}(-\,3\,x^{\frac{1}{3}})^2$$

$$- \frac{14}{81}(a^{-1})^{-\frac{10}{3}}(-\,3\,x^{\frac{1}{3}})^3 + \cdots$$

$$= a^{\frac{1}{3}} + a^{\frac{4}{3}}x^{\frac{1}{3}} + 2\,a^{\frac{7}{3}}x^{\frac{2}{3}} + \frac{14}{3}\,a^{\frac{10}{3}}x + \cdots.$$

The result expresses the value of the given fraction only when $3\,x^{\frac{1}{3}}$ is numerically $< a^{-1}$; if $3\,x^{-\frac{1}{3}}$ is numerically $> a^{-1}$, the fraction can be expanded in ascending powers of a^{-1}.

EXERCISE 92

Expand each of the following to five terms:

1. $(a + x)^{\frac{1}{2}}$.

2. $(1 + x)^{-8}$.

3. $(1 - x)^{\frac{5}{3}}$.

4. $\sqrt[5]{a - x}$.

5. $\dfrac{1}{(a + b)^6}$.

6. $\dfrac{1}{\sqrt[6]{1 - x}}$.

7. $(x^{\frac{2}{3}} - 2\,y)^{\frac{5}{2}}$.

8. $\left(m^{-2} + \dfrac{n^{-\frac{1}{6}}}{3}\right)^{-4}$.

9. $(a^4 - 2\,x^{\frac{1}{2}})^{-\frac{7}{2}}$.

10. $\dfrac{1}{x^{\frac{1}{4}} + 3\,y^{-\frac{4}{3}}}$

11. $\sqrt[3]{[(x^{-3} + 6\,yz)^7]}$.

12. $\dfrac{1}{(m^{\frac{1}{2}} - 2\,n^{-\frac{2}{3}})^6}$.

13. $\left(\dfrac{a}{b} + \dfrac{b}{a}\right)^{-\frac{3}{4}}$.

14. $(x^{-\frac{3}{5}} - 3\,y^{\frac{2}{4}})^{-\frac{4}{3}}$.

15. $\left(\dfrac{1}{16\sqrt[4]{a^3}} - \sqrt[5]{x^2}\right)^{\frac{3}{4}}$.

578. The formula for the rth term of $(a + x)^n$ (§ 287) holds for fractional or negative values of n, since it was derived from an expansion which has been proved to hold for all rational values of the exponent.

Ex. Find the 7th term of $(a - 3\,x^{-\frac{3}{2}})^{-\frac{1}{3}}$.

Enclosing $-3\,x^{-\frac{3}{2}}$ in parentheses, we have

$$(a - 3\,x^{-\frac{3}{2}})^{-\frac{1}{3}} = [a + (-3\,x^{-\frac{3}{2}})]^{-\frac{1}{3}}.$$

The exponent of $(-3\,x^{-\frac{3}{2}})$ is $7 - 1$, or 6.

The exponent of a is $-\dfrac{1}{3} - 6$, or $-\dfrac{19}{3}$.

The first factor of the numerator is $-\dfrac{1}{3}$, and the last factor $-\dfrac{19}{3} + 1$, or $-\dfrac{16}{3}$.

The last factor of the denominator is 6.

Hence, the 7th term

$$= \frac{-\dfrac{1}{3} \cdot -\dfrac{4}{3} \cdot -\dfrac{7}{3} \cdot -\dfrac{10}{3} \cdot -\dfrac{13}{3} \cdot -\dfrac{16}{3}}{1 \cdot 2 \cdot 3 \cdot 4 \cdot 5 \cdot 6}\, a^{-\frac{19}{3}}(-3\,x^{-\frac{3}{2}})^6$$

$$= \frac{728}{3^8}\, a^{-\frac{19}{3}}(3^6 x^{-9}) = \frac{728}{9}\, a^{-\frac{19}{3}} x^{-9}.$$

EXERCISE 93

Find the

1. 6th term of $(a + x)^{\frac{4}{3}}$.
2. 5th term of $(a + b)^{-\frac{1}{5}}$.
3. 12th term of $(1 - x)^{-5}$.
4. 7th term of $(x^{-1} + 2\,y^{\frac{1}{2}})^{-2}$.
5. 9th term of $(a + 2\,x)^{\frac{7}{2}}$.
6. 5th term of $\dfrac{1}{\sqrt{(1-x)^5}}$.

7. 7th term of $(a^4 - x^{\frac{1}{2}})^{\frac{3}{5}}$.
8. 10th term of $\dfrac{1}{(x + m)^6}$.
9. 8th term of $(m^{\frac{1}{4}} - 2\,n^{-4})^{-\frac{3}{2}}$.
10. 9th term of $\sqrt{(a - x)^3}$.
11. 6th term of $(a^{\frac{5}{2}} - 4\,b^{-2})^{-\frac{3}{4}}$.
12. 8th term of $(x^{-3} + 3\,y^{-\frac{1}{3}})^{-\frac{2}{3}}$.

13. Term involving x^{-14} in $\left(x\,\sqrt{y^3} + \dfrac{1}{\sqrt[3]{z^2}}\right)^{-4}$.

14. Term involving $a^{-\frac{9}{4}}$ in $(a^{\frac{1}{3}} - 4\,b^{-\frac{2}{5}})^{\frac{3}{4}}$.

579. Extraction of Roots.

The Binomial Theorem may sometimes be used to find the approximate root of a number, which is not a perfect power of the same degree as the index of the root.

Ex.   Find $\sqrt[3]{25}$ approximately to five places of decimals.

The nearest perfect cube to 25 is 27.

We have $\sqrt[3]{25} = \sqrt[3]{27 - 2} = [(3^3) + (-2)]^{\frac{1}{3}}$

$$= (3^3)^{\frac{1}{3}} + \frac{1}{3}(3^3)^{-\frac{2}{3}}(-2) - \frac{1}{9}(3^3)^{-\frac{5}{3}}(-2)^2$$

$$+ \frac{5}{81}(3^3)^{-\frac{8}{3}}(-2)^3 - \cdots$$

$$= 3 - \frac{2}{3 \cdot 3^2} - \frac{4}{9 \cdot 3^5} - \frac{40}{81 \cdot 3^8} - \cdots.$$

Expressing each fraction approximately to the nearest fifth decimal place, we have

$$\sqrt[3]{25} = 3 - .07407 - .00183 - .00008 - \cdots = 2.92402.$$

In any case, we separate the number into two parts, the first of which is the next less or next greater perfect power of the same degree as the required root; choice being made of the one which makes the smaller second term, provided the series is convergent (§ 576).

Thus, in finding $\sqrt[3]{17}$, we should take $(3^3 - 10)^{\frac{1}{3}}$, and not $(2^3 + 9)^{\frac{1}{3}}$; for although the latter has the smaller second term, the series is not convergent (§ 576).

_____

If the ratio of the second term of the binomial to the first is a small proper fraction, the terms of the expansion diminish rapidly; but if this ratio is but little less than 1, it requires a great many terms to insure any degree of accuracy.

EXERCISE 94

Find the approximate value of each of the following to five places of decimals:

1. $\sqrt{51}$.   3. $\sqrt[3]{130}$.   5. $\sqrt[4]{79}$. ,

2. $\sqrt{118}$.   4. $\sqrt[4]{18}$.   6. $\sqrt[5]{223}$.

XXIX. LOGARITHMS

580. Any positive real number, m, can be expressed in the form a^x, where a is any positive real number except unity.

If $a^x = m$, x is called the *Logarithm of m to the Base a*; a relation which is expressed

$$x = \log_a m.$$

A negative number is not considered as having a logarithm.

581. The Common System.

Logarithms of numbers to the base 10 are called *Common Logarithms*, and collectively form the *Common System*.

They are the only ones used for numerical computation.

It is customary, in writing common logarithms, to omit the subscript 10 which indicates the base; thus,

$$\log_{10} 13 \text{ is written simply } \log 13.$$

Any positive real number, except unity, may be taken as the base of a system of logarithms.

582. By §§ 359 and 360,

$10^0 = 1,$	$10^{-1} = .1,$
$10^1 = 10,$	$10^{-2} = .01,$
$10^2 = 100,$	$10^{-3} = .001, \text{ etc.}$

Whence, by the definition of § 581,

$\log 1 = 0,$	$\log .1 = -1 = 9 - 10,$
$\log 10 = 1,$	$\log .01 = -2 = 8 - 10,$
$\log 100 = 2,$	$\log .001 = -3 = 7 - 10, \text{ etc.}$

The second form for log .1, log .01, etc., is preferable in practice. Where no base is expressed, the base 10 is understood.

It is evident from the above that the common logarithm of a number greater than 1 is positive, and of a number between 0 and 1 negative.

If a number is not an exact power of 10, its common logarithm can only be expressed approximately; the integral part of the logarithm is called the *characteristic*, and the decimal part the *mantissa*.

For example, $\log 13 = 1.1139$.

Here, the characteristic is 1, and the mantissa .1139.

A negative logarithm is always expressed with a positive mantissa, which is done by adding and subtracting 10.

Thus, the negative logarithm -2.5863 is written

$$(10 - 2.5863) - 10, \text{ or } 7.4137 - 10.$$

In this case, $7 - 10$ is the characteristic.

The negative logarithm $7.4137 - 10$ is sometimes written $\bar{3}.4137$; the negative sign over the characteristic showing that it alone is negative, the mantissa being always positive.

583. If a number has five places in its integral part, it lies between 10^4 and 10^5; and hence its common logarithm lies between 4 and 5.

Therefore, the characteristic of its logarithm is 4.

In general, if a number has n places in its integral part, it lies between 10^{n-1} and 10^n; and the characteristic of its logarithm is $n - 1$.

Hence, *the characteristic of the logarithm of a number greater than* 1 *is* 1 *less than the number of places to the left of the decimal point.*

584. If a decimal has three ciphers between its decimal point and first significant figure, it lies between 10^{-4} and 10^{-3}; and hence its common logarithm lies between $6 - 10$ and $7 - 10$.

Therefore, the characteristic of its logarithm is $6 - 10$.

In general, if a decimal has n ciphers between its decimal point and first significant figure, it lies between $10^{-(n+1)}$ and 10^{-n}; and its common logarithm lies between $-(n+1)$ and $-n$, or $(9 - n) - 10$ and $(10 - n) - 10$.

That is, the characteristic of its logarithm is $(9 - n) - 10$.

Hence, *to find the characteristic of the logarithm of a number between zero and 1, subtract the number of ciphers between the decimal point and first significant figure from 9, writing −10 after the mantissa.*

PROPERTIES OF LOGARITHMS

585. *In any system, the logarithm of unity is zero.*

For by § 359, $a^0 = 1$; whence, by § 580, $\log_a 1 = 0$.

586. *In any system, the logarithm of the base is unity.*

For $a^1 = a$; whence, $\log_a a = 1$.

587. *In any system whose base is greater than unity, the logarithm of zero is minus infinity.*

For if a is >1, $a^{-\infty} = \dfrac{1}{a^\infty} = \dfrac{1}{\infty} = 0$ (§ 248).

Whence, by § 580, $\log_a 0 = -\infty$.

The above result must be interpreted as follows :

If, in any system whose base is greater than unity, a number approaches the limit 0, its logarithm is negative, and increases without limit in absolute value. (Compare § 248.)

588. *In any system whose base is less than unity, the logarithm of zero is infinity.*

For if a is <1, $a^\infty = 0$; whence, $\log_a 0 = \infty$.

This means that if, in any system whose base is less than unity, a number approaches the limit 0, its logarithm increases without limit.

589. *In any system, the logarithm of a product is equal to the sum of the logarithms of its factors.*

Assume the equations $a^x = m$, $a^y = n$.

Then, by § 580, $x = \log_a m$, $y = \log_a n$.

Multiplying the assumed equations,

$$a^x \times a^y = mn, \text{ or } a^{x+y} = mn.$$

Whence, $\log_a mn = x + y = \log_a m + \log_a n$.

In like manner, the theorem may be proved for the product of any number of factors.

By aid of the above theorem, the logarithm of any positive integer may be found when the logarithms of its factors are known.

Ex. Given $\log 2 = .3010$, and $\log 3 = .4771$; find $\log 72$.

$$\log 72 = \log (2 \times 2 \times 2 \times 3 \times 3)$$
$$= \log 2 + \log 2 + \log 2 + \log 3 + \log 3$$
$$= 3 \times \log 2 + 2 \times \log 3$$
$$= .9030 + .9542 = 1.8572.$$

590. *In any system, the logarithm of a fraction is equal to the logarithm of the numerator minus the logarithm of the denominator.*

Assume the equations $a^x = m$, $a^y = n$.

Then, $x = \log_a m$, $y = \log_a n$.

Dividing the assumed equations, $\dfrac{a^x}{a^y} = \dfrac{m}{n}$, or $a^{x-y} = \dfrac{m}{n}$.

Whence, $\log_a \dfrac{m}{n} = x - y = \log_a m - \log_a n$.

Ex. Given $\log 2 = .3010$; find $\log 5$.

$$\log 5 = \log \tfrac{10}{2} = \log 10 - \log 2 = 1 - .3010 = .6990.$$

591. *In any system, the logarithm of any power of a quantity is equal to the logarithm of the quantity multiplied by the exponent of the power.*

Assume the equation $a^x = m$; whence, $x = \log_a m$.

Raising both members of the assumed equation to the pth power,
$$a^{px} = m^p; \text{ whence, } \log_a (m^p) = px = p \log_a m.$$

592. *In any system, the logarithm of any root of a quantity is equal to the logarithm of the quantity divided by the index of the root.*

For, $\log_a \sqrt[r]{m} = \log_a (m^{\frac{1}{r}}) = \dfrac{1}{r} \log_a m$ (§ 591).

593. **Examples.**

1. Given $\log 2 = .3010$; find $\log 2^{\frac{5}{3}}$.

$$\log 2^{\frac{5}{3}} = \frac{5}{3} \times \log 2 = \frac{5}{3} \times .3010 = .5017.$$

To multiply a logarithm by a fraction, multiply first by the numerator, and divide the result by the denominator.

2. Given $\log 3 = .4771$; find $\log \sqrt[8]{3}$.

$$\log \sqrt[8]{3} = \frac{\log 3}{8} = \frac{.4771}{8.} = .0596.$$

3. Given $\log 2 = .3010$, $\log 3 = .4771$, find $\log (2^{\frac{1}{3}} \times 3^{\frac{5}{4}})$.

By § 589,

$$\log (2^{\frac{1}{3}} \times 3^{\frac{5}{4}}) = \log 2^{\frac{1}{3}} + \log 3^{\frac{5}{4}} = \frac{1}{3} \log 2 + \frac{5}{4} \log 3 = .6967.$$

EXERCISE 95

Given $\log 2 = .3010$, $\log 3 = .4771$, $\log 7 = .8451$, find the logarithm of:

1. 84.	**6.** $2^{\frac{5}{6}}$.	**11.** $\sqrt[5]{105}$.	**16.** 18522.
2. 392.	**7.** $\sqrt[3]{3}$.	**12.** $4\frac{1}{56}$.	**17.** $\dfrac{3^{\frac{3}{5}}}{\sqrt{35}}$.
3. $\frac{48}{7}$.	**8.** 5292.	**13.** 280^7.	**18.** $\left(\dfrac{18}{5}\right)^{\frac{1}{4}}$.
4. $12\frac{12}{27}$.	**9.** $\frac{405}{14}$.	**14.** $75^{\frac{7}{4}}$.	**19.** $\dfrac{\sqrt[3]{36}}{7^{\frac{2}{3}}}$.
5. 7^6.	**10.** 45^3.	**15.** $\sqrt[7]{98}$.	**20.** $(2^{\frac{2}{3}} \times 15^{\frac{1}{2}})$.

594. *To prove the relation*

$$\log_b m = \frac{\log_a m}{\log_a b}.$$

Assume the equations $a^x = m$, $b^y = m$.

Then, $x = \log_a m$, $y = \log_b m$.

From the assumed equations, $a^x = b^y$, or $a^{\frac{x}{y}} = b$.

Therefore, $\log_a b = \frac{x}{y}$, or $y = \frac{x}{\log_a b}$.

That is, $\log_b m = \dfrac{\log_a m}{\log_a b}.$

By aid of this relation, if the logarithm of a number m to a certain base a is known, its logarithm to any other base b may be found by dividing by the logarithm of b to the base a.

595. *To prove the relation*

$$\log_b a \times \log_a b = 1.$$

Putting $m = a$ in the result of § 594,

$$\log_b a = \frac{\log_a a}{\log_a b} = \frac{1}{\log_a b} \quad (\S\ 586).$$

Whence, $\log_b a \times \log_a b = 1.$

596. *In the common system, the mantissæ of the logarithms of numbers having the same sequence of figures are equal.*

Suppose, for example, that $\log 3.053 = .4847$.

Then, $\log\ 305.3 = \log(100 \times 3.053) = \log 100 + \log 3.053$

$$= 2 + .4847 = 2.4847\,;$$

$$\log .03053 = \log (.01 \times 3.053) = \log .01 + \log 3.053$$

$$= 8 - 10 + .4847 = 8.4847 - 10\,;\ \text{etc.}$$

In general, if n is any positive or negative integer,

$$\log (10^n \times m) = n \log 10 + \log m = n + \log m.$$

But $10^n \times m$ is a number which differs from m only in the position of its decimal point, and $n + \log m$ is a number having the same decimal part as $\log m$.

Hence, if two numbers have the same sequence of figures, the mantissæ of their logarithms are equal.

For this reason, only mantissæ are given, in a table of Common Logarithms; for to find the logarithm of any number, we have only to find the mantissa corresponding to its sequence of figures, and then prefix the characteristic in accordance with the rules of §§ 583 and 584.

This property of logarithms only holds for the common system, and constitutes its superiority over other systems for numerical computation.

Ex. Given $\log 2 = .3010$, $\log 3 = .4771$; find $\log .00432$.

$\log 432 = \log(2^4 \times 3^3) = 4 \log 2 + 3 \log 3 = 2.6353$.

Then, the *mantissa* of the result is .6353.

Whence by § 584, $\log .00432 = 7.6353 - 10$.

EXERCISE 96

Given $\log 2 = .3010$, $\log 3 = .4771$, $\log 7 = .8451$, find the logarithm of:

1. 87.5.	**3.** 6750.	**5.** .0324.	**7.** .784.
2. 2.592.	**4.** 274.4.	**6.** .000175.	**8.** .001875.

USE OF THE TABLE

597. The table (pages 406 and 407) gives the mantissæ of the logarithms of all integers from 100 to 1000, calculated to four places of decimals.

598. *To find the logarithm of a number of three figures.*

Look in the column headed "No." for the first two significant figures of the given number.

Then the required mantissa will be found in the corresponding horizontal line, in the vertical column headed by the third figure of the number.

Finally, prefix the characteristic in accordance with the rules of §§ 583 and 584.

For example, $\log 168 = 2.2253$;

$$\log .344 = 9.5366 - 10; \text{ etc.}$$

For a number consisting of one or two significant figures, the column headed 0 may be used.

Thus, let it be required to find $\log 83$ and $\log 9$.

By § 596, $\log 83$ has the same mantissa as $\log 830$, and $\log 9$ the same mantissa as $\log 900$.

Hence, $\log 83 = 1.9191$, and $\log 9 = 0.9542$.

599. *To find the logarithm of a number of more than three figures.*

No.	0	1	2	3	4	5	6	7	8	9
10	0000	0043	0086	0128	0170	0212	0253	0294	0334	0374
11	0414	0453	0492	0531	0569	0607	0645	0682	0719	0755
12	0792	0828	0864	0899	0934	0969	1004	1038	1072	1106
13	1139	1173	1206	1239	1271	1303	1335	1367	1399	1430
14	1461	1492	1523	1553	1584	1614	1644	1673	1703	1732
15	1761	1790	1818	1847	1875	1903	1931	1959	1987	2014
16	2041	2068	2095	2122	2148	2175	2201	2227	2253	2279
17	2304	2330	2355	2380	2405	2430	2455	2480	2504	2529
18	2553	2577	2601	2625	2648	2672	2695	2718	2742	2765
19	2788	2810	2833	2856	2878	2900	2923	2945	2967	2989
20	3010	3032	3054	3075	3096	3118	3139	3160	3181	3201
21	3222	3243	3263	3284	3304	3324	3345	3365	3385	3404
22	3424	3444	3464	3483	3502	3522	3541	3560	3579	3598
23	3617	3636	3655	3674	3692	3711	3729	3747	3766	3784
24	3802	3820	3838	3856	3874	3892	3909	3927	3945	3962
25	3979	3997	4014	4031	4048	4065	4082	4099	4116	4133
26	4150	4166	4183	4200	4216	4232	4249	4265	4281	4298
27	4314	4330	4346	4362	4378	4393	4409	4425	4440	4456
28	4472	4487	4502	4518	4533	4548	4564	4579	4594	4609
29	4624	4639	4654	4669	4683	4698	4713	4728	4742	4757
30	4771	4786	4800	4814	4829	4843	4857	4871	4886	4900
31	4914	4928	4942	4955	4969	4983	4997	5011	5024	5038
32	5051	5065	5079	5092	5105	5119	5132	5145	5159	5172
33	5185	5198	5211	5224	5237	5250	5263	5276	5289	5302
34	5315	5328	5340	5353	5366	5378	5391	5403	5416	5428
35	5441	5453	5465	5478	5490	5502	5514	5527	5539	5551
36	5563	5575	5587	5599	5611	5623	5635	5647	5658	5670
37	5682	5694	5705	5717	5729	5740	5752	5763	5775	5786
38	5798	5809	5821	5832	5843	5855	5866	5877	5888	5899
39	5911	5922	5933	5944	5955	5966	5977	5988	5999	6010
40	6021	6031	6042	6053	6064	6075	6085	6096	6107	6117
41	6128	6138	6149	6160	6170	6180	6191	6201	6212	6222
42	6232	6243	6253	6263	6274	6284	6294	6304	6314	6325
43	6335	6345	6355	6365	6375	6385	6395	6405	6415	6425
44	6435	6444	6454	6464	6474	6484	6493	6503	6513	6522
45	6532	6542	6551	6561	6571	6580	6590	6599	6609	6618
46	6628	6637	6646	6656	6665	6675	6684	6693	6702	6712
47	6721	6730	6739	6749	6758	6767	6776	6785	6794	6803
48	6812	6821	6830	6839	6848	6857	6866	6875	6884	6893
49	6902	6911	6920	6928	6937	6946	6955	6964	6972	6981
50	6990	6998	7007	7016	7024	7033	7042	7050	7059	7067
51	7076	7084	7093	7101	7110	7118	7126	7135	7143	7152
52	7160	7168	7177	7185	7193	7202	7210	7218	7226	7235
53	7243	7251	7259	7267	7275	7284	7292	7300	7308	7316
54	7324	7332	7340	7348	7356	7364	7372	7380	7388	7396
No.	0	1	2	3	4	5	6	7	8	9

No.	0	1	2	3	4	5	6	7	8	9
55	7404	7412	7419	7427	7435	7443	7451	7459	7466	7474
56	7482	7490	7497	7505	7513	7520	7528	7536	7543	7551
57	7559	7566	7574	7582	7589	7597	7604	7612	7619	7627
58	7634	7642	7649	7657	7664	7672	7679	7686	7694	7701
59	7709	7716	7723	7731	7738	7745	7752	7760	7767	7774
60	7782	7789	7796	7803	7810	7818	7825	7832	7839	7846
61	7853	7860	7868	7875	7882	7889	7896	7903	7910	7917
62	7924	7931	7938	7945	7952	7959	7966	7973	7980	7987
63	7993	8000	8007	8014	8021	8028	8035	8041	8048	8055
64	8062	8069	8075	8082	8089	8096	8102	8109	8116	8122
65	8129	8136	8142	8149	8156	8162	8169	8176	8182	8189
66	8195	8202	8209	8215	8222	8228	8235	8241	8248	8254
67	8261	8267	8274	8280	8287	8293	8299	8306	8312	8319
68	8325	8331	8338	8344	8351	8357	8363	8370	8376	8382
69	8388	8395	8401	8407	8414	8420	8426	8432	8439	8445
70	8451	8457	8463	8470	8476	8482	8488	8494	8500	8506
71	8513	8519	8525	8531	8537	8543	8549	8555	8561	8567
72	8573	8579	8585	8591	8597	8603	8609	8615	8621	8627
73	8633	8639	8645	8651	8657	8663	8669	8675	8681	8686
74	8692	8698	8704	8710	8716	8722	8727	8733	8739	8745
75	8751	8756	8762	8768	8774	8779	8785	8791	8797	8802
76	8808	8814	8820	8825	8831	8837	8842	8848	8854	8859
77	8865	8871	8876	8882	8887	8893	8899	8904	8910	8915
78	8921	8927	8932	8938	8943	8949	8954	8960	8965	8971
79	8976	8982	8987	8993	8998	9004	9009	9015	9020	9025
80	9031	9036	9042	9047	9053	9058	9063	9069	9074	9079
81	9085	9090	9096	9101	9106	9112	9117	9122	9128	9133
82	9138	9143	9149	9154	9159	9165	9170	9175	9180	9186
83	9191	9196	9201	9206	9212	9217	9222	9227	9232	9238
84	9243	9248	9253	9258	9263	9269	9274	9279	9284	9289
85	9294	9299	9304	9309	9315	9320	9325	9330	9335	9340
86	9345	9350	9355	9360	9365	9370	9375	9380	9385	9390
87	9395	9400	9405	9410	9415	9420	9425	9430	9435	9440
88	9445	9450	9455	9460	9465	9469	9474	9479	9484	9489
89	9494	9499	9504	9509	9513	9518	9523	9528	9533	9538
90	9542	9547	9552	9557	9562	9566	9571	9576	9581	9586
91	9590	9595	9600	9605	9609	9614	9619	9624	9628	9633
92	9638	9643	9647	9652	9657	9661	9666	9671	9675	9680
93	9685	9689	9694	9699	9703	9708	9713	9717	9722	9727
94	9731	9736	9741	9745	9750	9754	9759	9763	9768	9773
95	9777	9782	9786	9791	9795	9800	9805	9809	9814	9818
96	9823	9827	9832	9836	9841	9845	9850	9854	9859	9863
97	9868	9872	9877	9881	9886	9890	9894	9899	9903	9908
98	9912	9917	9921	9926	9930	9934	9939	9943	9948	9952
99	9956	9961	9965	9969	9974	9978	9983	9987	9991	9996
No.	0	1	2	3	4	5	6	7	8	9

1. Required the logarithm of 32.76.

We find from the table, $\log 32.7 = 1.5145$,

$$\log 32.8 = 1.5159.$$

That is, an increase of one-tenth of a unit in the number produces an increase of 0014 in the logarithm.

Therefore, an increase of six-hundredths of a unit in the number will produce an increase of $.6 \times .0014$ in the logarithm, or .0008 to the nearest fourth decimal place.

Hence, $\log 32.76 = 1.5145 + .0008 = 1.5153.$

The above method is based on the assumption that the differences of logarithms are proportional to the differences of their corresponding numbers ; which, though not strictly accurate, is sufficiently exact for practical purposes.

The difference between any mantissa in the table and the mantissa of the next higher number of these figures, is called the *Tabular Difference.*

The following rule is derived from the above :

Find from the table the mantissa of the first three significant figures, and the tabular difference

Multiply the latter by the remaining figures of the number, with a decimal point before them.

Add the result to the mantissa of the first three figures, and prefix the proper characteristic.

In finding the correction to the nearest units' figure, the decimal portion should be omitted, provided that if it is .5, or greater than .5, the units' figure is increased by 1 ; thus 13.26 would be taken as 13, 30.5 as 31, and 22.803 as 23.

2. Find the logarithm of .021508.

Mantissa $215 = .3324$	Tab. diff. $= 21$
2	$.08$
$.3326$	Correction $= 1.68 = 2$, nearly.

The result is $8.3326 - 10$.

600. *To find the number corresponding to a logarithm.*

1. Required the number whose logarithm is 0.6571.

Find in the table the mantissa 6571.

In the corresponding line, in the column headed "No.," we find 45, the first two figures of the required number, and at the head of the column we find 4, the third figure.

Since the characteristic is 0, there must be one place to the left of the decimal point (§ 583).

Hence, the number corresponding to 0.6571 is 4.54.

2. Required the number whose logarithm is 1.3934.

We find in the table the mantissæ 3927 and 3945.

The numbers corresponding to the logarithms 1.3927 and 1.3945 are 24.7 and 24.8, respectively.

That is, an increase of .0018 in the mantissa produces an increase of one-tenth of a unit in the number corresponding.

Then, an increase of .0007 in the mantissa will produce an increase of $\frac{7}{18}$ of one-tenth of a unit in the number, or .04, nearly.

Hence, the number corresponding is 24.7 + .04, or 24.74.

The following rule is derived from the above:

Find from the table the next less mantissa, the three figures corresponding, and the tabular difference.

Subtract the next less from the given mantissa, and divide the remainder by the tabular difference.

Annex the quotient to the first three figures of the number, and point off the result.

The rules for pointing off are the reverse of those of §§ 583 and 584:

I. *If* − 10 *is not written after the mantissa, add* 1 *to the characteristic, giving the number of places to the left of the decimal point.*

II. *If* − 10 *is written after the mantissa, subtract the positive part of the characteristic from* 9, *giving the number of ciphers to be placed between the decimal point and first significant figure.*

3. Find the number whose logarithm is 8.5265 − 10.

$$5265$$

Next less mant. = 5263; figures corresponding, 336.

Tab. diff. 13)2.00(.15 = .2, nearly.

$$\frac{13}{70}$$

By the above rule, there will be one cipher to be placed between the decimal point and first significant figure.

The result is .03362.

The correction can usually be depended upon to only one decimal place; the division should be carried to two places to determine the last figure accurately.

EXERCISE 97

Find the logarithm of :

1. 70.	**4.** .0337.	**7.** .9617.	**10.** .0064685.
2. .59.	**5.** 82.95.	**8.** .0003788.	**11.** 4072.6.
3. 98.4.	**6.** 253.07.	**9.** 7.803.	**12.** .013592.

Find the number corresponding to :

13. 1.7782.	**17.** 0.8744.	**21.** 1.8077.
14. 8.4314 − 10.	**18.** 3.3565.	**22.** 7.6899 − 10.
15. 0.6522.	**19.** 6.2998 − 10.	**23.** 9.9108 − 10.
16. 9.0128 − 10.	**20.** 8.9646 − 10.	**24.** 2.5524.

APPLICATIONS

601. The approximate value of a number in which the operations indicated involve only multiplication, division, involution, or evolution may be conveniently found by logarithms.

The utility of the process consists in the fact that addition takes the place of multiplication, subtraction of division, multiplication of involution, and division of evolution.

In computations with four-place logarithms, the result cannot usually be depended upon to more than *four* significant figures.

1. Find the value of .0631 × 7.208 × .51272.

By § 589, log (.0631 × 7.208 × .51272)

$$= \log .0631 + \log 7.208 + \log .51272.$$

$$
\begin{aligned}
\log\ .0631 &= 8.8000 - 10 \\
\log\ 7.208 &= 0.8578 \\
\log .51272 &= 9.7099 - 10 \\
\text{Adding, log of result} &= 19.3677 - 20 \\
&= 9.3677 - 10 \text{ (See Note below.)}
\end{aligned}
$$

Number corresponding to $9.3677 - 10 = .2332$.

If the sum is a negative logarithm, it should be written in such a form that the negative portion of the characteristic may be -10.

Thus, $19.3677 - 20$ is written $9.3677 - 10$.

2. Find the value of $\dfrac{336.8}{7984}$.

By § 590, $\qquad \log \dfrac{336.8}{7984} = \log 336.8 - \log 7984.$

$$\log 336.8 = 12.5273 - 10 \text{ (See Note below.)}$$
$$\log 7984 = \underline{3.9022}$$

Subtracting, log of result $= 8.6251 - 10$

Number corresponding $= .04218$.

To subtract a greater logarithm from a less, or a negative logarithm from a positive, increase the characteristic of the minuend by 10, writing -10 after the mantissa to compensate.

Thus, to subtract 3.9022 from 2.5273, write the minuend in the form $12.5273 - 10$; subtracting 3.9022 from this, the result is $8.6251 - 10$.

3. Find the value of $(.07396)^5$.

By § 591, $\log (.07396)^5 = 5 \times \log .07396.$

$$\log .07396 = 8.8690 - 10$$
$$\underline{5}$$
$$44.3450 - 50$$
$$= 4.3450 - 10 = \log .000002213.$$

4. Find the value of $\sqrt[3]{.035063}$.

By § 592, $\log \sqrt[3]{.035063} = \dfrac{1}{3} \log .035063.$

$$\log .035063 = 8.5449 - 10$$
$$3\overline{)28.5449 - 30} \text{ (See Note below.)}$$
$$9.5150 - 10 = \log .3274.$$

To divide a negative logarithm, write it in such a form that the negative portion of the characteristic may be exactly divisible by the divisor, with -10 as the quotient.

Thus, to divide $8.5449 - 10$ by 3, we write the logarithm in the form $28.5449 - 30$. Dividing this by 3, the quotient is $9.5150 - 10$.

602. **Arithmetical Complement.**

The *Arithmetical Complement* of the logarithm of a number, or, briefly, the *Cologarithm* of the number, is the logarithm of the reciprocal of that number.

Thus, $\operatorname{colog} 409 = \log \dfrac{1}{409} = \log 1 - \log 409.$

$$\log 1 = 10. \quad \cdot \ -10 \quad \text{(See Ex. 2, § 601.)}$$
$$\log 409 = \underline{\ 2.6117\ }$$
$$\therefore \ \operatorname{colog} 409 = \ 7.3883 - 10.$$

Again, $\operatorname{colog} .067 = \log \dfrac{1}{.067} = \log 1 - \log .067.$

$$\log 1 = 10. \quad\quad -10$$
$$\log .067 = \underline{\ 8.8261 - 10\ }$$
$$\therefore \ \operatorname{colog} .067 = \ 1.1739.$$

It follows from the above that *the cologarithm of a number may be found by subtracting its logarithm from* $10 - 10$.

The cologarithm may be found by subtracting the last *significant* figure of the logarithm from 10 and each of the others from 9, $-$ 10 being written after the result in the case of a positive logarithm.

Ex.   Find the value of $\dfrac{.51384}{8.708 \times .0946}$.

$$\log \frac{.51384}{8.708 \times .0946} = \log\left(.51384 \times \frac{1}{8.708} \times \frac{1}{.0946}\right)$$
$$= \log .51384 + \log \frac{1}{8.708} + \log \frac{1}{.0946}$$
$$= \log .51384 + \operatorname{colog} 8.708 + \operatorname{colog} .0946.$$

$$\log .51384 = 9.7109 - 10$$
$$\operatorname{colog} 8.708 = 9.0601 - 10$$
$$\operatorname{colog} .0946 = \underline{1.0241\ }$$
$$9.7951 - 10 = \log .6239.$$

It is evident from the above example that, to find the logarithm of a fraction whose terms are the product of factors, we *add together the logarithms of the factors of the numerator, and the cologarithms of the factors of the denominator.*

The value of the fraction may be found without using cologarithms by the following formula :

$$\log \frac{.51384}{8.708 \times .0946} = \log .51384 - (\log 8.708 + \log .0946) \quad (\S\S\ 589,\ 590).$$

The advantage in using cologarithms is that the written work of computation is exhibited in a more compact form.

603. Examples.

1. Find the value of $\dfrac{2\sqrt[3]{5}}{3^{\frac{5}{6}}}$.

$$\log \frac{2\sqrt[3]{5}}{3^{\frac{5}{6}}} = \log 2 + \log \sqrt[3]{5} + \operatorname{colog} 3^{\frac{5}{6}} \quad (\S\ 602)$$

$$= \log 2 + \frac{1}{3}\log 5 + \frac{5}{6}\operatorname{colog} 3.$$

$$\log 2 = .3010$$
$$\log 5 = .6990; \qquad \div\ 3 = .2330$$
$$\operatorname{colog} 3 = 9.5229 - 10; \quad \times \frac{5}{6} = 9.6024 - 10$$
$$\overline{\qquad\qquad .1364 = \log 1.369.}$$

A *negative* number has no common logarithm (§ 580).

If such numbers occur in computation, they may be treated as if they were positive, and the *sign* of the result determined irrespective of the logarithmic work.

Thus, to find the value of $721.3 \times (-3.0528)$, we find the value of 721.3×3.0528, and put a negative sign before the result.

2. Find the value of $\sqrt[3]{\dfrac{-.03296}{7.962}}$.

$$\log \sqrt[3]{\frac{.03296}{7.962}} = \frac{1}{3}\log \frac{.03296}{7.962}$$

$$= \frac{1}{3}(\log .03296 - \log 7.962).$$

$$\log .03296 = 8.5180 - 10$$
$$\log\ \ 7.962 = 0.9010$$
$$\overline{\quad 3)27.6170 - 30\quad}$$
$$9.2057 - 10 = \log .1606.$$

The result is $-.1606$.

EXERCISE 98

Find by logarithms the values of the following :

1. $2414.7 \times .09348$. **3.** $(-54.375) \times (-.00061488)$.

2. 832.4×4.1639. **4.** $.38142 \times (-.0053909)$.

5. $\dfrac{51.29}{6.348}$. **7.** $\dfrac{.004497}{.09769}$. **9.** $\dfrac{718 \times (-.02415)}{(-.5157) \times 1420.6}$.

6. $\dfrac{834.32}{2192.4}$. **8.** $\dfrac{3.3629}{-.75438}$. **10.** $\dfrac{.87028 \times 3.74}{.0006589 \times (-42.318)}$.

11. $\dfrac{(-.009213) \times (-73.36)}{(-.0832) \times 2.8087}$. **12.** $\dfrac{3.8961 \times .6945 \times .01382}{4694 \times .00457}$.

13. $(2.514)^5$. **19.** $\sqrt[4]{.1994}$. **25.** $\sqrt[6]{\dfrac{3}{5}} \div \sqrt[3]{\dfrac{7}{8}}$.

14. $(-83.28)^8$. **20.** $\sqrt[5]{-.037368}$. **26.** $\dfrac{\sqrt[4]{.0009657}}{\sqrt[3]{.0049784}}$.

15. $(.035127)^4$. **21.** $\dfrac{(.01)^{\frac{3}{2}}}{\sqrt[3]{7}}$. **27.** $\dfrac{-(.25693)^{\frac{6}{5}}}{(-.8346)^{\frac{7}{3}}}$.

16. $100^{\frac{3}{4}}$. **22.** $\dfrac{\sqrt{.1}}{(-9)^{\frac{2}{5}}}$. **28.** $\left(\dfrac{76.1 \times .0593}{1.307}\right)^{\frac{3}{4}}$.

17. $(-.007795)^{\frac{10}{7}}$. **23.** $\sqrt[7]{-\dfrac{75.43}{31}}$. **29.** $\sqrt[3]{-\dfrac{7.544}{31.4 \times .415}}$.

18. $\sqrt[6]{1553}$. **24.** $\left(\dfrac{4400}{6937}\right)^{\frac{2}{5}}$. **30.** $\sqrt[8]{5106.5 \times .00003109}$.

31. $(837.5 \times .0094325)^{\frac{2}{7}}$. **36.** $.83184 \times (.2682)^3 \times (56.1)^{\frac{5}{2}}$.

32. $\dfrac{\sqrt{3929} \times \sqrt[4]{65.48}}{\sqrt[6]{721.33}}$. **37.** $\dfrac{.0005616 \times \sqrt[7]{424.65}}{(6.73)^4 \times (.03194)^{\frac{3}{5}}}$.

33. $\dfrac{\sqrt[5]{.05287}}{\sqrt[3]{.374} \times \sqrt[9]{.0078359}}$. **38.** $\dfrac{485.7 \times (.7301)^7 \times \sqrt[6]{1000}}{(9.1273)^6 \times (.7095)^{\frac{2}{5}}}$.

34. $\dfrac{(-.0001916)^{\frac{2}{3}} \times \sqrt{68.1}}{.27556}$. **39.** $\sqrt[3]{\left[\dfrac{(-.95048)^5 \times (8473)^{\frac{4}{3}}}{(-2080.9) \times \sqrt[8]{.0572}}\right]}$.

35. $\dfrac{3801.4}{\sqrt[5]{.04142} \times (-.947^{\frac{3}{4}})}$. **40.** $\dfrac{\sqrt[5]{-.003012} \times 1955}{(-.843)^3 \times \sqrt[4]{17959} \times (-560.6)^{\frac{2}{7}}}$.

41. $\sqrt[5]{\left[\dfrac{\sqrt[9]{-.04813} \times (5.6074)^{\frac{3}{4}} \times (.65034)^4}{(10.115)^5 \times (-.002988)^{\frac{2}{5}} \times \sqrt[3]{731.27}}\right]}$.

EXPONENTIAL AND LOGARITHMIC EQUATIONS

604. An **Exponential Equation** is an equation in which the unknown number occurs as an exponent.

To solve an equation of this form, take the logarithms of both members; the result will be an equation which can be solved by ordinary algebraic methods.

1. Given $31^x = 23$; find the value of x.

Taking the logarithms of both members,

$$\log (31^x) = \log 23; \text{ or } x \log 31 = \log 23 \text{ (§ 591)}.$$

Then, $\qquad x = \dfrac{\log 23}{\log 31} = \dfrac{1.3617}{1.4914} = .9130+.$

2. Solve the equation $.2^x = 3$.

Taking the logarithms of both members, $x \log .2 = \log 3$.

Then, $x = \dfrac{\log 3}{\log .2} = \dfrac{.4771}{9.3010 - 10} = \dfrac{.4771}{-.699} = -.6825+.$

An equation of the form $a^x = b$ may be solved by inspection if b can be expressed as an exact power of a.

3. Solve the equation $16^x = 128$.

We may write the equation $(2^4)^x = 2^7$, or $2^{4x} = 2^7$.

Then, by inspection, $4x = 7$; and $x = \dfrac{7}{4}$.

If the equation were $16^x = \dfrac{1}{128}$, we could write it $(2^4)^x = \dfrac{1}{2^7} = 2^{-7}$; then $4x$ would equal -7, and $x = -\dfrac{7}{4}$.

Certain logarithmic equations are readily solved by aid of the principles of §§ 589 to 591.

4. Given $2 \log_a x = m$; find the value of x.

By § 591, $2 \log_a x = \log_a (x^2)$; whence, $\log_a (x^2) = m$.

Then by § 580, $a^m = x^2$; whence, $x = \pm \sqrt{a^m} = \pm a^{\frac{m}{2}}$.

5. Given $\log (x + 4) - \log x = 3$; find the value of x.

By § 590, $\log (x + 4) - \log x = \log \dfrac{x + 4}{x}$.

Then, $\log \dfrac{x+4}{x} = 3$; and by § 581, $10^3 = \dfrac{x+4}{x}$.

Therefore, $1000\,x = x + 4$, and $x = \dfrac{4}{999}$.

EXERCISE 99

Solve the following :

1. $13^x = 8.$

2. $.06^x = .9.$

3. $9.347^x = .0625.$

4. $.005038^x = 816.3.$

5. $3^{4x-1} = 4^{2x+3}.$

6. $7^{3x+2} = .8^x.$

7. $.2^{x+5} = .5^{x-4}.$

8. $.3^{x-4} = 100.$

9. $16^x = 32.$

10. $32^x = \dfrac{1}{128}.$

11. $\left(\dfrac{1}{16}\right)^x = 8.$

12. $\left(\dfrac{1}{27}\right)^x = \dfrac{1}{81}.$

13. $5^{2x-1} = \dfrac{1}{25}.$

14. $\left(\dfrac{1}{a}\right)^{x+1} = a^2.$

15. $\left(\dfrac{2}{7}\right)^{x-3} = \dfrac{7}{2}.$

16. Given a, r, and l; derive the formula for n (§ 529).

17. Given a, r, and S; derive the formula for n.

18. Given a, l, and S; derive the formula for n.

19. Given r, l, and S; derive the formula for n.

Solve the following :

20. $3 \log_a x = 4 \log_a m.$

21. $\log (x-5) - \log (2x+1) = 2.$

22. $\log 5 + \log (3x-2) = 3.$

23. $\log 3 - \log (x+1) = -1.$

24. $\log x + \log (4x+3) = 1.$

25. $\log 2 + 2 \log x = \log (5x-2).$

605. **Logarithm of a Number to Any Base.**

1. Find the logarithm of .3 to the base 7.

By § 594,

$$\log_7 .3 = \frac{\log_{10} .3}{\log_{10} 7} = \frac{9.4771 - 10}{.8451} = -\frac{.5229}{.8451} = -.6187 +.$$

Examples of this kind may be solved by inspection, if the number can be expressed as an exact power of the base.

2. Find the logarithm of 128 to the base 16.

Let $\log_{16} 128 = x$; then, by § 580, $16^x = 128$.

Then, as in Ex. 3, § 604, $x = \dfrac{7}{4}$; that is, $\log_{16} 128 = \dfrac{7}{4}$.

Find the values of the following:

1. $\log_7 59$.   **3.** $\log_4 82$.   **5.** $\log_{68} 2.915$.

2. $\log_6 .7$.   **4.** $\log_9 .00453$.   **6.** $\log_{21} .06038$.

Find by inspection the values of the following:

7. $\log_{25} 125$.   **8.** $\log_{49}\left(\dfrac{1}{7}\right)$.   **9.** $\log_{\frac{1}{27}}(3)$.   **10.** $\log_{\frac{1}{32}}\left(\dfrac{1}{256}\right)$.

EXPONENTIAL AND LOGARITHMIC SERIES.

606. Let n be a real number greater than unity.

By § 364, $\left[\left(1+\dfrac{1}{n}\right)^n\right]^x=\left(1+\dfrac{1}{n}\right)^{nx}.$

Expanding both members by the Binomial Theorem,

$$\left[1+n\cdot\frac{1}{n}+\frac{n(n-1)}{\lfloor 2}\cdot\frac{1}{n^2}+\frac{n(n-1)(n-2)}{\lfloor 3}\cdot\frac{1}{n^3}+\cdots\right]^x$$

$$=1+nx\cdot\frac{1}{n}+\frac{nx(nx-1)}{\lfloor 2}\cdot\frac{1}{n^2}$$

$$+\frac{nx(nx-1)(nx-2)}{\lfloor 3}\cdot\frac{1}{n^3}+\cdots.\quad(1)$$

Since, by hypothesis, n is >1, $\dfrac{1}{n}$ is numerically <1; and both members of (1) are convergent series (§ 559).

We may write equation (1) in the form

$$\left[1+1+\frac{1-\dfrac{1}{n}}{\lfloor 2}+\frac{\left(1-\dfrac{1}{n}\right)\left(1-\dfrac{2}{n}\right)}{\lfloor 3}+\cdots\right]^x$$

$$=1+x+\frac{x\left(x-\dfrac{1}{n}\right)}{\lfloor 2}+\frac{x\left(x-\dfrac{1}{n}\right)\left(x-\dfrac{2}{n}\right)}{\lfloor 3}+\cdots;\quad(2)$$

which holds however great n may be.

Now let n be indefinitely increased.

Then, the limit of each of the terms $\dfrac{1}{n}$, $\dfrac{2}{n}$, etc., is 0 (§ 248).

Hence, the limiting value of the first member of (2) is

$$\left[1+1+\frac{1}{\underline{|2}}+\frac{1}{\underline{|3}}+\cdots\right]^x,$$

and the limiting value of the second member is

$$1+x+\frac{x^2}{\underline{|2}}+\frac{x^3}{\underline{|3}}+\cdots.$$

By § 252, these limits are equal; that is,

$$\left[1+1+\frac{1}{\underline{|2}}+\frac{1}{\underline{|3}}+\cdots\right]^x=1+x+\frac{x^2}{\underline{|2}}+\frac{x^3}{\underline{|3}}+\cdots.$$

The series in the second member is convergent for every value of x (§ 558); and the series in brackets is also convergent, for it is obtained from the series in the second member by putting 1 in place of x.

Denoting the series in brackets by e, we have

$$e^x=1+x+\frac{x^2}{\underline{|2}}+\frac{x^3}{\underline{|3}}+\cdots; \qquad (3)$$

which holds for every value of x.

Putting mx for x, in (3),

$$e^{mx}=1+mx+\frac{m^2x^2}{\underline{|2}}+\frac{m^3x^3}{\underline{|3}}+\cdots. \qquad (4)$$

Let $m=\log_e a$, where a is any positive real number.

Then $e^m=a$ (§ 580), and $e^{mx}=a^x$.

Substituting these values in (4), we obtain

$$a^x=1+(\log_e a)\,x+(\log_e a)^2\frac{x^2}{\underline{|2}}+(\log_e a)^3\frac{x^3}{\underline{|3}}+\cdots; \qquad (5)$$

which holds for all values of x, and all positive real values of a.

The result (5) is called the *Exponential Series*.

607. The system of logarithms which has e for its base is called the *Napierian System*, from Napier, the inventor of logarithms.

Napierian logarithms are also called *Natural Logarithms*.

The approximate value of e may be readily calculated from the series of § 606,

$$e = 1 + 1 + \frac{1}{\underline{|2}} + \frac{1}{\underline{|3}} + \cdots,$$

and will be found to equal 2.7182818....

608. *To expand* $\log_e(1 + x)$ *in ascending powers of* x.

Substituting in (5), § 606, $1 + x$ for a, and y for x,

$$(1 + x)^y = 1 + [\log_e(1 + x)]y + \text{terms in } y^2, y^3, \text{etc.};$$

which holds for all values of y, provided x is real, and algebraically greater than -1.

Expanding the first member by the Binomial Theorem,

$$1 + yx + \frac{y(y-1)}{\underline{|2}}x^2 + \frac{y(y-1)(y-2)}{\underline{|3}}x^3 + \cdots$$

$$= 1 + [\log_e(1 + x)]y + \text{terms in } y^2, y^3, \text{etc.} \qquad (6)$$

The first member of (6) is convergent when x is numerically less than 1 (§ 559).

Hence, (6) holds for all values of y, provided x is real, and numerically less than 1.

Then, by the Theorem of Undetermined Coefficients, the coefficients of y in the two series are equal; that is,

$$x - \frac{\underline{|1}}{\underline{|2}}x^2 + \frac{\underline{|2}}{\underline{|3}}x^3 - \frac{\underline{|3}}{\underline{|4}}x^4 + \cdots = \log_e(1 + x).$$

Or, $$\log_e(1 + x) = x - \frac{x^2}{2} + \frac{x^3}{3} - \frac{x^4}{4} + \frac{x^5}{5} - \cdots; \qquad (7)$$

which holds for all values of x numerically less than 1.

This result is called the *Logarithmic Series*.

It was proved in § 557 that this series was convergent when x was numerically less than 1.

It was also shown in § 556 that it was convergent when $x = 1$, and in § 548 that it was divergent when $x = -1$.

Then, series (7) can be used to calculate Napierian logarithms, provided x is taken equal to, or numerically less than, 1.

Unless x is small, it requires the sum of a great many terms to ensure any degree of accuracy.

609. We will now derive a more convenient series for the calculation of Napierian logarithms.

Putting $-x$ for x, in (7), § 608, we have

$$\log_e(1 - x) = -x - \frac{x^2}{2} - \frac{x^3}{3} - \frac{x^4}{4} - \frac{x^5}{5} - \cdots. \tag{8}$$

Subtracting (8) from (7), we obtain

$$\log_e(1 + x) - \log_e(1 - x) = 2x + \frac{2x^3}{3} + \frac{2x^5}{5} + \cdots.$$

Or (§ 590), $$\log_e\frac{1 + x}{1 - x} = 2\left(x + \frac{x^3}{3} + \frac{x^5}{5} + \cdots\right). \tag{9}$$

Let $x = \dfrac{m - n}{m + n}$; m and n being positive, and $m > n$.

This is a valid substitution, since in this case $\dfrac{m - n}{m + n} < 1.$

Then, $$\frac{1 + x}{1 - x} = \frac{1 + \dfrac{m - n}{m + n}}{1 - \dfrac{m - n}{m + n}} = \frac{2m}{2n} = \frac{m}{n}.$$

Substituting these values in (9), we obtain

$$\log_e\frac{m}{n} = 2\left[\frac{m - n}{m + n} + \frac{1}{3}\left(\frac{m - n}{m + n}\right)^3 + \frac{1}{5}\left(\frac{m - n}{m + n}\right)^5 + \cdots\right].$$

But by § 590, $\log_e\dfrac{m}{n} = \log_e m - \log_e n$; whence,

$$\log_e m = \log_e n + 2\left[\frac{m - n}{m + n} + \frac{1}{3}\left(\frac{m - n}{m + n}\right)^3 + \frac{1}{5}\left(\frac{m - n}{m + n}\right)^5 + \cdots\right].$$

610. Let it be required, for example, to calculate the Napierian logarithm of 2 to six places of decimals.

Putting $m = 2$ and $n = 1$ in the result of § 609, we have

$$\log_e 2 = \log_e 1 + 2\left[\frac{1}{3} + \frac{1}{3}\left(\frac{1}{3}\right)^3 + \frac{1}{5}\left(\frac{1}{3}\right)^5 + \cdots\right].$$

Or since $\log_e 1 = 0$ (§ 585),

$$\log_e 2 = 2(.3333333 + .0123457 + .0008230 + .0000653$$
$$+ .0000056 + .0000005 + \cdots)$$

$$= 2 \times .3465734 = .6931468.$$

Then, $\log_e 2 = .693147$, to the nearest sixth place of decimals.

Having found $\log_e 2$, we may calculate $\log_e 3$ by putting $m=3$ and $n=2$ in the result of § 609.

Proceeding in this way, we shall find $\log_e 10 = 2.302585....$

611. *To calculate the common logarithm of a number, having given its Napierian logarithm.*

Putting $b = 10$ and $a = e$ in the result of § 594,

$$\log_{10} m = \frac{\log_e m}{\log_e 10} = \frac{1}{2.302585} \times \log_e m = .4342945 \times \log_e m.$$

Thus, $\log_{10} 2 = .4342945 \times .693147 = .301030.$

612. The multiplier by which logarithms of any system are derived from Napierian logarithms, is called the *modulus* of that system.

Thus, .4342945 is the modulus of the common system.

Conversely, to find the Napierian logarithm of a number when its common logarithm is given, we may either divide the common logarithm by the modulus .4342945, or multiply it by 2.302585, the reciprocal of .4342945.

EXERCISE 101

Using the table of common logarithms, find the Napierian logarithm of each of the following to four significant figures :

1. 1000.
3. 9.93.
5. .04568.

2. .0001.
4. 243.6.
6. .56734.

7. What is the characteristic of $\log_5 758$?

8. What is the characteristic of $\log_7 500$?

9. If $\log 3 = .4771$, how many digits are there in 3^{17} ?

10. If $\log 8 = .9031$, how many digits are there in 8^{28} ?

11. If $\log 11 = 1.0414$, how many digits are there in the integral part of $11^{\frac{44}{9}}$?

XXX. COMPOUND INTEREST AND ANNUITIES

613. The principles of logarithms may be applied to the solution of problems in Compound Interest.

Let $P =$ number of dollars in the principal;

$n =$ number of years;

$t =$ the ratio to one year of the time during which simple interest is calculated; thus, if interest is compounded semi-annually, $t = \frac{1}{2}$;

$R =$ number of dollars in the amount of one dollar for t years;

$A =$ number of dollars in the amount of P dollars for n years.

Since one dollar amounts to R dollars in t years, P dollars will amount to PR dollars in t years; that is, the amount at the end of the 1st interval is PR dollars.

In like manner, the amount at the end of the

2d interval is $PR \times R$, or PR^2 dollars;

3d interval is $PR^2 \times R$, or PR^3 dollars; etc.

Since the whole number of intervals is $\frac{n}{t}$, the amount at the end of the last one, in accordance with the law observed above, will be $PR^{\frac{n}{t}}$ dollars.

That is, $A = PR^{\frac{n}{t}}.$ (1)

By §§ 589, 591, $\log A = \log P + \frac{n}{t} \log R.$ (2)

1. What will be the amount of \$7326 for 3 years and 9 months at 7 per cent compound interest, interest being compounded quarterly?

Here, $P = 7326$, $n = 3\frac{3}{4}$, $t = \frac{1}{4}$, $R = 1.0175$, $\frac{n}{t} = 15$.

$$\log P = 3.8649$$
$$\log R = 0.0075; \; \times 15 = 0.1125$$
$$\log A = \overline{3.9774} \quad \therefore A = \$\,9493.$$

2. What sum of money will amount to $\$\,1763.50$ in 3 years at 5 per cent compound interest, interest being compounded semi-annually?

From (2), $\log P = \log A - \dfrac{n}{t}\log R.$

Here, $n = 3$, $t = \dfrac{1}{2}$, $R = 1.025$, $A = 1763.5$, $\dfrac{n}{t} = 6.$

$$\log A = 3.2464$$
$$\log R = 0.0107; \; \times 6 = 0.0642$$
$$\log P = \overline{3.1822} \quad \therefore P = \$\,1521.$$

3. In how many years will $\$\,300$ amount to $\$\,398.60$ at 6 per cent compound interest, interest being compounded quarterly?

From (2), $n = \dfrac{t(\log A - \log P)}{\log R}.$

Here, $P = 300$, $t = \dfrac{1}{4}$, $R = 1.015$, $A = 398.6.$

$$\therefore n = \frac{\log 398.6 - \log 300}{4 \log 1.015} = \frac{2.6006 - 2.4771}{4 \times .0065} = \frac{.1235}{.0260}$$
$$= 4.75 \text{ years.}$$

4. At what rate per cent per annum will $\$\,500$ amount to $\$\,688.83$ in 6 years and 6 months, interest being compounded semi-annually?

From (2), $\log R = \dfrac{\log A - \log P}{\dfrac{n}{t}}.$

Here, $P = 500$, $n = 6\frac{1}{2}$, $t = \dfrac{1}{2}$, $A = 688.83$, $\dfrac{n}{t} = 13.$

$$\log A = \quad 2.8381$$
$$\log P = \quad 2.6990$$
$$13)\overline{0.1391}$$
$$\log R = \quad 0.0107 \quad \therefore R = 1.025.$$

That is, the *interest* on one dollar for 6 months is \$.025, and the rate is 5 per cent per annum.

614. *To find the present worth of A dollars due at the end of n years, interest being compounded annually.*

Putting $t = 1$ in (1), § 613, we have

$$A = PR^n; \text{ whence, } P = \frac{A}{R^n}.$$

ANNUITIES

615. An **Annuity** is a fixed sum of money payable at equal intervals of time.

In the present chapter we shall consider those cases only in which the payments are annual; in finding the present worth of such an annuity, it is customary to compound interest annually.

When we speak of the annuity as *beginning* at a certain epoch, it is understood that the first payment becomes due one year from that time.

616. *To find the present worth of an annuity to continue for n successive years, allowing compound interest.*

Let A = number of dollars in the annuity;

R = number of dollars in the amount of one dollar for one year;

P = number of dollars in the present worth of the annuity.

By § 614, the present worth of the

$$\text{1st payment} = \frac{A}{R};$$

$$\text{2d payment} = \frac{A}{R^2};$$

$$\cdots \cdots$$

$$n\text{th payment} = \frac{A}{R^n}.$$

Hence, the sum of the present worths of the separate payments, or the present worth of the annuity, is

$$\frac{A}{R^n} + \frac{A}{R^{n-1}} + \cdots + \frac{A}{R^2} + \frac{A}{R}.$$

That is, $P = A\left[\dfrac{1}{R^n} + \dfrac{1}{R^{n-1}} + \cdots + \dfrac{1}{R^2} + \dfrac{1}{R}\right].$

The expression in brackets is the sum of the terms of a geometric progression, in which $a = \dfrac{1}{R^n}$, $r = R$, and $l = \dfrac{1}{R}.$

Then, by II, § 527, $P = A\dfrac{1 - \dfrac{1}{R^n}}{R - 1}.$ (3)

Ex. Find the present worth of an annuity of $150 to continue for 20 years, allowing 4 per cent compound interest.

Here, $A = 150$, $n = 20$, $R = 1.04$, $R - 1 = .04$.

Whence, $P = \dfrac{150}{.04}\left[1 - \dfrac{1}{(1.04)^{20}}\right].$

$$\log \frac{1}{(1.04)^{20}} = 20 \text{ colog } 1.04.$$

$$\text{colog } 1.04 = 9.9830 - 10$$
$$\underline{\qquad\qquad\quad 20}$$
$$9.6600 - 10 = \log .4571.$$

Then, $P = \dfrac{150}{.04}(1 - .4571) = 3750 \times .5429.$

$$\log 3750 = 3.5740$$
$$\log .5429 = 9.7347 - 10$$
$$\overline{\log P = 3.3087} \qquad \therefore\ P = \$2036.$$

617. We have from (3), § 616,

$$A = \frac{P(R - 1)}{1 - \dfrac{1}{R^n}} = \frac{PR^n(R - 1)}{R^n - 1};$$ (4)

which is a formula for finding the annuity to continue for n successive years, when the present worth and the amount of one dollar for one year are given.

Formula (4) may also be used to find what fixed annual payment must be made to cancel a note of P dollars due n years hence, R being the number of dollars in the amount of one dollar for one year.

618. If in (3), § 616, n be indefinitely increased, the limiting value of the second member is

$$\frac{A}{R-1} \text{ (§ 248)}.$$

That is, *the present worth of a perpetual annuity is equal to the amount of the annuity divided by the interest on one dollar for one year.*

619. *To find the present worth of an annuity to begin after m years, and continue for n years, allowing compound interest.*

With the notation of § 616, the number of dollars in the value of the annuity one year before the first payment becomes due, is

$$A\frac{1-\dfrac{1}{R^n}}{R-1}, \text{ or } \frac{A(R^n-1)}{R^n(R-1)}.$$

By § 614, the present worth of this amount, due m years hence, is

$$\frac{A(R^n-1)}{R^n(R-1)} \div R^m.$$

Therefore,

$$P = \frac{A(R^n-1)}{R^{m+n}(R-1)}.$$

620. By § 618, the present worth of a perpetual annuity to begin after m years, is given by the formula

$$P = \frac{A}{R^m(R-1)}.$$

EXERCISE 102

1. What will be the amount of $1300 for 16 years at 5 per cent compound interest, the interest being compounded annually?

2. What sum of money will amount to $981.75 in 8 years and 9 months at 4 per cent compound interest, the interest being compounded quarterly?

3. In how many years will $859 amount to $1012.80 at 3 per cent compound interest, the interest being compounded semi-annually?

4. What is the present worth of a note for $625.34 due 12 years hence, allowing $3\frac{3}{4}$ per cent compound interest, the interest being compounded annually?

5. At what rate per cent per annum will $3700 gain $678 in 4 years and 3 months, the interest being compounded quarterly?

6. In how many years will a sum of money double itself at 6 per cent compound interest, the interest being compounded annually?

7. In how many years will a sum of money treble itself at $4\frac{1}{2}$ per cent compound interest, the interest being compounded semi-annually?

8. What is the present worth of an annuity of $300 to continue 14 years, allowing 4 per cent compound interest?

9. What is the present worth of a perpetual annuity of $506.70, allowing $3\frac{1}{2}$ per cent compound interest?

10. What is the present worth of an annuity of $2238 to continue 4 years, allowing 6 per cent compound interest?

11. What is the present worth of an annuity of $2680 to begin after 10 years and continue for 7 years, allowing 5 per cent compound interest?

12. What fixed annual payment must be made in order to cancel a note for $3500 in 5 years, allowing $4\frac{1}{2}$ per cent compound interest?

13. What is the present worth of a perpetual annuity of $297.50, to begin after 8 years, allowing $3\frac{3}{4}$ per cent compound interest?

14. What annuity to continue 12 years can be purchased for $3149, allowing 7 per cent compound interest?

15. A person borrows $6365; how much must he pay in annual instalments in order that the whole debt may be discharged in 10 years, allowing $4\frac{1}{4}$ per cent compound interest?

XXXI. PERMUTATIONS AND COMBINA-TIONS

621. The different orders in which things can be arranged are called their **Permutations**.

Thus, the permutations of the letters a, b, c, taken two at a time, are ab, ac, ba, bc, ca, cb; and their permutations taken three at a time, are abc, acb, bac, bca, cab, cba.

622. The **Combinations** of things are the different collections which can be formed from them without regard to the order in which they are placed.

Thus, the combinations of the letters a, b, c, taken two at a time are ab, bc, ca; for though ab and ba are different permutations, they form the same combination.

623. *To find the number of permutations of n different things taken two at a time.*

Consider the n letters a, b, c, $\cdots$.

In making any particular permutation of two letters, the first letter may be any one of the n; that is, the first place can be filled in n different ways.

After the first place has been filled, the second place can be filled with any one of the remaining $n-1$ letters.

Then, the whole number of permutations of the letters taken two at a time is $n(n-1)$.

We will now consider the general case.

624. *To find the number of permutations of n different things taken r at a time.*

Consider the n letters a, b, c, $\cdots$.

In making any particular permutation of r letters, the first letter may be any one of the n.

After the first place has been filled, the second place can be filled with any one of the remaining $n-1$ letters.

After the second place has been filled, the third place can be filled in $n-2$ different ways.

Continuing in this way, the rth place can be filled in

$$n-(r-1), \text{ or } n-r+1 \text{ different ways.}$$

Then, the whole number of permutations of the letters taken r at a time is given by the formula

$$_nP_r = n(n-1)(n-2)\cdots(n-r+1). \tag{1}$$

The number of permutations of n different things taken r at a time is usually denoted by the symbol $_nP_r$.

625. If *all* the letters are taken together, $r=n$, and (1) becomes
$$_nP_n = n(n-1)(n-2)\cdots 3\cdot 2\cdot 1 = \lfloor n. \tag{2}$$

Hence, *the number of permutations of n different things taken n at a time equals the product of the natural numbers from 1 to n inclusive.*

626. *To find the number of combinations of n different things taken r at a time.*

The number of *permutations* of n different things taken r at a time, is $\quad n(n-1)(n-2)\cdots(n-r+1)$ (§ 624).

But by § 625; each combination of r different things may have $\lfloor r$ permutations.

Hence, the number of *combinations* of n different things taken r at a time equals the number of permutations divided by $\lfloor r$.

That is, $\quad _nC_r = \dfrac{n(n-1)(n-2)\cdots(n-r+1)}{\lfloor r}.$

The number of combinations of n different things taken r at a time is usually denoted by the symbol $_nC_r$.

627. Multiplying both terms of the fraction (3) by the product of the natural numbers from 1 to $n-r$ inclusive, we have

$$_nC_r = \frac{n(n-1)\cdots(n-r+1)\cdot(n-r)\cdots 2\cdot 1}{\lfloor r \times 1\cdot 2\cdots(n-r)} = \frac{\lfloor n}{\lfloor r \lfloor n-r};$$

which is another form of the result.

628. *The number of combinations of n different things taken r at a time equals the number of combinations taken n − r at a time.*

For in making a selection of r things out of n, we leave a selection of $n − r$ things.

The theorem may also be proved by using the result of § 627.

629. Examples.

1. How many changes can be rung with 10 bells, taking 7 at a time?

Putting $n = 10$, $r = 7$, in (1), § 624,

$$_{10}P_7 = 10 \cdot 9 \cdot 8 \cdot 7 \cdot 6 \cdot 5 \cdot 4 = 604800.$$

2. How many different combinations can be formed with 16 letters, taking 12 at a time?

By § 628, the number of combinations of 16 different things, taken 12 at a time, equals the number of combinations of 16 different things, taken 4 at a time.

Putting $n = 16$, $r = 4$, in (3), § 626,

$$_{16}C_4 = \frac{16 \cdot 15 \cdot 14 \cdot 13}{1 \cdot 2 \cdot 3 \cdot 4} = 1820.$$

3. How many different words, each consisting of 4 consonants and 2 vowels, can be formed from 8 consonants and 4 vowels?

The number of combinations of the 8 consonants, taken 4 at a time, is $\dfrac{8 \cdot 7 \cdot 6 \cdot 5}{1 \cdot 2 \cdot 3 \cdot 4}$, or 70.

The number of combinations of the 4 vowels, taken 2 at a time, is $\dfrac{4 \cdot 3}{1 \cdot 2}$, or 6.

Any one of the 70 sets of consonants may be associated with any one of the 6 sets of vowels; hence, there are in all 70×6, or 420 sets, each containing 4 consonants and 2 vowels.

But each set of 6 letters may have $\underline{|6}$, or 720 different permutations (§ 625).

Therefore, the whole number of different words is

$$420 \times 720, \text{ or } 302400.$$

Find the values of the following :

1. $_{14}P_6$.

3. $_{17}P_7$.

5. $_{17}C_{11}$.

2. $_9P_9$.

4. $_{15}C_7$.

6. $_{29}C_{24}$.

7. In a certain play, there are five parts to be taken by a company of twelve persons. In how many different ways can they be assigned ?

8. How many different words, of nine different letters each, can be formed from the letters in the word *flowering*, if the vowels retain their places ?

9. How many different numbers, of seven different figures each, can be formed from the digits 1, 2, 3, 4, 5, 6, 7, 8, 9, if each number begins with 1 and ends with 9 ?

10. How many even numbers, of five different figures each, can be formed from the digits 4, 5, 6, 7, 8 ?

11. How many different committees, of 8 persons each, can be formed from a corporation of 14 persons ? In how many will any particular individual be found ? In how many will any particular individual be excluded ?

12. A and B are in a company of 72 men. If the company is divided into squads of 6, in how many of them will A and B be in the same squad ?

13. In how many different ways can six persons be seated at a round table ?

14. There are 15 points in a plane, no three in the same straight line. How many quadrilaterals can be formed, having four of the points for vertices ?

15. If 32 soldiers are drawn up in line 4 deep, in how many different ways can they be arranged so as to have a different set in the front rank ? In how many ways, if the front rank is always to contain 3 particular men ?

16. If the number of combinations of $2n$ different things taken $n-1$ at a time, is to the number of combinations of $2n-2$ different things taken n at a time as 132 : 35, find the value of n.

17. How many different crews, each consisting of eight oarsmen and a steersman, can be formed from 16 boys, of whom 12 can row but cannot steer, and the others can steer but cannot row ?

18. A person has 22 acquaintances, of whom 14 are males. In how many ways can he invite 17 guests from them so that 10 may be males ?

19. Out of 10 soldiers and 15 sailors, how many different parties can be formed, each consisting of 3 soldiers and 3 sailors ?

20. From 3 sergeants, 8 corporals, and 16 privates, how many different parties can be formed, each consisting of 1 sergeant, 2 corporals, and 5 privates ?

21. Out of 3 capitals, 6 consonants, and 4 vowels, how many different words of six letters each can be formed, each beginning with a capital, and having 3 consonants and 2 vowels ?

22. How many different words of 8 letters each can be formed from eight letters, if 4 of the letters cannot be separated ? How many if these four can only be in one order ?

23. In how many different ways can ten soldiers be drawn up in double rank, if three particular men are always in the front rank, and three others always in the rear ?

24. How many different numbers of seven figures each can be formed from the digits 1, 2, 3, 4, 5, 6, 7, 8, 9, if the first, fourth, and last digits are odd numbers ?

25. How many different words of six letters each can be formed from the letters in the word *percolating*, if each word has a consonant for its first and last letter, and a vowel for its second and fifth ?

26. There are 2 n guests at a dinner-party. If the host and hostess have fixed places opposite to each other, and two specified guests cannot sit next each other, in how many ways can the company be seated ?

630. *To find the number of permutations of n things which are not all different, taken all together.*

Let there be n letters, of which p are a's, q are b's, and r are c's, the rest being all different.

Let N denote the number of permutations of these letters taken all together.

Suppose that, in any assigned permutation of the n letters, the p a's were replaced by p new letters, differing from each other and also from the remaining $n - p$ letters.

Then by simply altering the order of these p letters among themselves, without changing the positions of any of the other letters, we could from the original permutation form $\lfloor p$ different permutations (§ 625).

If this were done in the case of each of the N original permutations, the whole number of permutations would be

$$N \times \lfloor p.$$

Again, if in any one of the latter the q b's were replaced by q new letters, differing from each other and from the remaining $n - q$ letters, then by altering the order of these q letters among themselves, we could from the original permutation form $\lfloor q$ different permutations; and if this were done in the case of each of the $N \times \lfloor p$ original permutations, the whole number of permutations would be $N \times \lfloor p \times \lfloor q$.

In like manner, if in each of the latter the r c's were replaced by r new letters, differing from each other and from the remaining $n - r$ letters, and these r letters were permuted among themselves, the whole number of permutations would be $N \times \lfloor p \times \lfloor q \times \lfloor r$.

But the number of permutations on the hypothesis that the n letters are all different, is $\lfloor n$ (§ 625).

Therefore, $N \times \lfloor p \times \lfloor q \times \lfloor r = \lfloor n$; or, $N = \dfrac{\lfloor n}{\lfloor p \lfloor q \lfloor r}$.

Any other case may be treated in a similar manner.

Ex. How many permutations can be formed from the letters in the word *Tennessee*, taken all together?

Here there are 4 e's, 2 n's, 2 s's, and 1 t.

Putting in the above formula $n = 9$, $p = 4$, $q = 2$, $r = 2$, we have

$$\frac{\lfloor 9}{\lfloor 4 \lfloor 2 \lfloor 2} = \frac{5 \cdot 6 \cdot 7 \cdot 8 \cdot 9}{2 \cdot 2} = 3780.$$

631. *To find the number of permutations of n different things, taken r at a time, when each may occur any number of times from once up to r times, inclusive.*

Consider the n letters a, b, c, ⋯.

In making any particular permutation of r letters, the first letter may be any one of the n; that is, the first place can be filled in n different ways.

The second letter can also be any one of the n; that is, the second place can be filled in n different ways.

Continuing in this way, the rth place can be filled in n different ways.

Then, the number of permutations is

$$n \times n \times \cdots \text{ to } r \text{ factors, or } n^r.$$

Ex. How many different words of four letters each can be formed from nine letters, if each letter may occur any number of times from once up to four times, inclusive?

Here, $n = 9$, $r = 4$.

Then, the number of different words is

$$9^4, \text{ or } 6561.$$

632. *To find the entire number of combinations of n different things, when each may be taken any number of times from once to n times, inclusive.*

Consider the n letters a, b, c, $\cdots$.

We can take them one at a time in n ways.

We can take them 2 at a time in $\dfrac{n(n-1)}{\underline{2}}$ ways (§ 626).

. . . . . .

We can take them all in one way.

Then, the entire number of ways is

$$n + \frac{n(n-1)}{\underline{2}} + \cdots + 1 = 2^n - 1 \ (\S \ 289, \text{ I}).$$

Ex. In how many ways can a selection of one or more volumes be made from 5 books?

Here, $n = 5$; then, the entire number of selections is

$$2^5 - 1, \text{ or } 31.$$

EXERCISE 104

1. In how many different orders may the letters of the word *denomination* be written?

2. There are four white billiard balls exactly alike, and three red balls, also alike. In how many different ways can they be arranged?

3. In how many ways can six things be given to five persons, if there is no restriction as to the number each may receive?

4. How many different numbers less than 10000 can be formed from the digits 1, 2, 3, 4, 5, 6, 7, 8?

5. In how many different orders may the letters of the word *independence* be written?

6. How many different signals can be made with 7 flags, of which 2 are blue, 3 red, and 2 white, if all are hoisted for each signal?

7. A railway signal has m arms, and each can be placed in n positions. How many different signals can be made with it?

8. A man has eight friends. In how many ways can he invite one or more of them to dinner?

9. How many different words of eight letters each can be formed from the letters in the word *arranged*, if the first, fourth, and seventh letters are always vowels?

10. A house has nine windows in front. How many different signals can be given by having one or more of the windows open?

11. In how many ways can 13 books be arranged on a shelf, when five volumes are alike, and four other volumes are also alike?

12. How many different numbers greater than 1000000 can be formed from the digits 4, 3, 3, 3, 2, 2, 0?

13. In how many ways can two dimes, three quarters, four halves, and five dollars be distributed among 14 persons, so that each may receive a coin?

14. A bag contains a cent, a half-dime, a dime, a twenty-cent piece, a quarter-dollar, a half-dollar, and a dollar. In how many ways can a sum of money be drawn from the bag?

XXXII. PROBABILITY

633. Suppose that a bag contains 5 white balls, 4 red balls, and 3 black balls, and that one ball is drawn at random.

Any one ball is as likely to be drawn as any other.

The *drawing of a ball* can occur in 12 different ways; for any one of the balls may be drawn.

The *drawing of a white ball* can occur in 5 different ways; for any one of the white balls may be drawn.

We may then consider $\frac{5}{12}$ as the likelihood that, if a ball is drawn, it is a white ball.

The *drawing of a white ball* can fail to occur in 7 different ways; for any one of the red or black balls may be drawn.

We may then consider $\frac{7}{12}$ as the likelihood that, if a ball is drawn, it is not a white ball.

634. We may take the following definition for the term *probability:*

If an event can happen in a different ways, and fail to happen in b different ways, *and all these ways are equally likely to occur,* the probability of the happening of the event is $\frac{a}{a+b}$, and the probability of its failing is $\frac{b}{a+b}$.

We say the *odds* are a to b in *favor* of the event, if a is greater than b, and a to b *against* the event, if a is less than b.

It follows that if the probability of the happening of an event is p, the probability of its failing is $1-p$.

635. Examples.

1. A bag contains 5 white, 4 red, and 3 black balls.

(*a*) If 3 balls are drawn, what is the probability that they are all white?

The number of combinations of the 5 white balls, taken 3 at a time, is $\dfrac{5 \cdot 4 \cdot 3}{1 \cdot 2 \cdot 3}$ (§ 626), or 10; that is, the drawing of 3 white balls can happen in 10 different ways.

The number of combinations of the 12 balls, taken 3 at a time, is $\dfrac{12 \cdot 11 \cdot 10}{1 \cdot 2 \cdot 3}$, or 220; that is, the drawing of 3 balls can occur in 220 different ways.

Then, the probability of drawing 3 white balls is $\dfrac{10}{220}$, or $\dfrac{1}{22}$.

(b) If 6 balls are drawn, what is the probability that 2 are white, 3 red, and 1 black?

The number of combinations of the 5 white balls, taken 2 at a time, is $\dfrac{5 \cdot 4}{1 \cdot 2}$, or 10; the number of combinations of the 4 red balls, taken 3 at a time, is $\dfrac{4 \cdot 3 \cdot 2}{1 \cdot 2 \cdot 3}$, or 4.

We may associate together any one of the 10 combinations of white balls, any one of the 4 combinations of red balls, and any one of the 3 black balls; hence, there are in all $10 \times 4 \times 3$, or 120, different combinations, each consisting of 2 white balls, 3 red balls, and 1 black ball.

Also, the number of combinations of the 12 balls, taken 6 at a time, is $\dfrac{12 \cdot 11 \cdot 10 \cdot 9 \cdot 8 \cdot 7}{1 \cdot 2 \cdot 3 \cdot 4 \cdot 5 \cdot 6}$, or 924.

Hence, the required probability is $\dfrac{120}{924}$, or $\dfrac{10}{77}$.

2. A bag contains 30 tickets numbered 1, 2, 3, $\cdot$, 30.

(a) If four tickets are drawn, what is the chance that *both* 1 *and* 2 will be among them ?

The number of combinations of the 28 tickets numbered 3, 4, ..., 30, taken 2 at a time, is $\dfrac{28 \cdot 27}{1 \cdot 2}$; that is, there are $\dfrac{28 \cdot 27}{1 \cdot 2}$ different ways of drawing four tickets, two of which are numbered 1 and 2.

The number of combinations of the 30 tickets, taken 4 at a time, is $\dfrac{30 \cdot 29 \cdot 28 \cdot 27}{1 \cdot 2 \cdot 3 \cdot 4}$.

Hence, the probability that, if four tickets are drawn, two of them will be 1 and 2, is

$$\frac{28 \cdot 27}{1 \cdot 2} \div \frac{30 \cdot 29 \cdot 28 \cdot 27}{1 \cdot 2 \cdot 3 \cdot 4} = \frac{3 \cdot 4}{30 \cdot 29} = \frac{2}{145}.$$

(b) If four tickets are drawn, what is the chance that *either* 1 *or* 2 will be among them?

Either 1 or 2 will be among the tickets drawn, unless each ticket drawn bears a number from 3 to 30 inclusive.

The number of combinations of the 28 tickets numbered 3, 4, ..., 30, taken 4 at a time, is $\dfrac{28 \cdot 27 \cdot 26 \cdot 25}{1 \cdot 2 \cdot 3 \cdot 4}$.

The number of combinations of the 30 tickets, taken 4 at a time, is $\dfrac{30 \cdot 29 \cdot 28 \cdot 27}{1 \cdot 2 \cdot 3 \cdot 4}$.

Hence, the probability that each of the 4 tickets drawn bears a number from 3 to 30 inclusive, is $\dfrac{28 \cdot 27 \cdot 26 \cdot 25}{30 \cdot 29 \cdot 28 \cdot 27}$, or $\dfrac{65}{87}$.

Then, the probability that *none* of the tickets drawn bears a number from 3 to 30 inclusive, is $1 - \dfrac{65}{87}$ (§ 634), or $\dfrac{22}{87}$.

This then is the probability that either 1 or 2 will be among the tickets drawn.

EXERCISE 105

1. A bag contains 6 white balls, 5 red balls, and 4 black balls; find the probability of drawing :

(a) One black ball.   (d) Four white balls.

(b) Two white balls.   (e) Two balls of each color.

(c) Three red balls.   (f) Four red and three white balls.

          (g) Two red, five white, and two black balls.

2. A bag contains 24 tickets numbered 1, 2, 3, ..., 24; if three tickets are drawn, find the probability :

(a) That they are 1, 2, and 3.

(b) That either 1, 2, or 3 is among them.

3. What is the probability of throwing not more than 5 in a single throw with two dice ?

4. What is the probability of throwing at least 5 in a single throw with two dice ?

5. What is the probability of throwing 10 in a single throw with three dice ?

6. If six persons seat themselves at random at a round·table, what is the probability that two specified persons will sit together ?

7. If four cards are drawn from a pack, what is the probability that they are of the same suit ?

8. There are 8 books, of which 4 are on mathematics and 3 on science. If the books are placed together on a shelf, what is the probability that the mathematical volumes, and also the scientific, will be together?

636. Mutually Exclusive Events.

If an event can happen in more than one way, and if it happens in any of the ways, cannot at the same time happen in any of the other ways, these various ways are said to be *mutually exclusive.*

If an event can happen in more than one way, and these ways are mutually exclusive, the probability of the happening of the event equals the sum of the probabilities of its happening in the separate ways.

Suppose that an event can happen in a certain way a times out of b, and in another way a' times out of b; all these ways being equally likely to occur.

Also, suppose that the two ways in which the event can happen are mutually exclusive.

Since the event happens $a + a'$ times out of b, the probability of its happening is $\dfrac{a + a'}{b}$ (§ 634), or $\dfrac{a}{b} + \dfrac{a'}{b}$.

But $\dfrac{a}{b}$ is the probability that the event happens in the first way, and $\dfrac{a'}{b}$ the probability that it happens in the second way.

Hence, the probability that it happens equals the sum of the probabilities of its happening in the separate ways.

In like manner, the theorem may be proved when there are more than two ways in which the event can happen.

637. Examples.

1. Find the probability of throwing 4 in a single throw with two dice.

The event can happen in two ways; either by throwing 3 and 1, or by throwing double-twos; and these ways are mutually exclusive.

Each die can come up in 6 ways; and hence the pair can be thrown in 6 × 6, or 36 ways.

Of these different throws, two will be 3 and 1; hence, the probability of throwing 3 and 1 is $\frac{2}{36}$.

Again, double-twos can be thrown in only one way; hence, the probability of throwing double-twos is $\frac{1}{36}$.

Therefore, the probability of throwing 4 is $\frac{2}{36} + \frac{1}{36}$, or $\frac{1}{12}$.

This example can be solved more easily by the method of § 635; the above method is given simply as an illustration of § 636.

2. A bag contains four $10 gold pieces and six silver dollars. If a person is entitled to draw two coins at random, what is the value of his expectation?

If a person has a chance of winning a certain sum of money, the product of the sum by the probability of his winning it is called his *expectation.*

The number of combinations of the four gold pieces, taken 2 at a time, is $\frac{4 \cdot 3}{1 \cdot 2}$, and the number of combinations of the ten coins, taken 2 at a time, is $\frac{10 \cdot 9}{1 \cdot 2}$; hence the probability of drawing two gold coins is $\frac{4 \cdot 3}{10 \cdot 9}$, or $\frac{2}{15}$.

Then the value of the expectation, so far as it depends on the drawing of two gold coins, is $\frac{2}{15} \times 20$, or $\frac{8}{3}$ dollars.

The probability of drawing two silver coins is $\frac{6 \cdot 5}{10 \cdot 9}$, or $\frac{1}{3}$; the value of the corresponding expectation is $\frac{2}{3}$ dollars.

Again, the probability of drawing a gold coin and a silver coin is $(6 \cdot 4) \div \frac{10 \cdot 9}{1 \cdot 2}$, or $\frac{8}{15}$; the value of the corresponding expectation is $\frac{8}{15} \times 11$, or $\frac{88}{15}$ dollars.

Hence, the value of the expectation is $\left(\frac{8}{3} + \frac{2}{3} + \frac{88}{15}\right)$ dollars, or $9.20.

EXERCISE 106

1. A bag contains 20 tickets numbered 1, 2, 3, ···, 20; if a ticket be drawn, what is the probability that its number is a multiple of 3 or 7 ?

2. Find the probability of throwing at least 9 in a single throw with two dice.

3. A bag contains 4 half-dollars and 6 quarter-dollars. If a person is entitled to draw a single coin, find the value of his expectation.

4. Find the probability of throwing 13 in a single throw with three dice.

5. A bag contains 3 dimes, 4 five-cent pieces, and 2 twenty-cent pieces. If a person is entitled to draw two coins, what is the value of his expectation ?

6. Find the probability of throwing 7 in a single throw with four dice.

7. A bag contains 7 gold dollars, and 5 five-dollar gold pieces. If a person is entitled to draw four coins, what is the value of his expectation ?

8. A bag contains 6 fifty-cent pieces, and four other coins which have all the same value. If a person's expectation on drawing three coins is $120\frac{3}{5}$ cents, find the value of each of the unknown coins.

COMPOUND EVENTS

638. Independent Events.

If there are two independent events whose respective probabilities are known, the probability that both will happen is the product of their separate probabilities.

Two events are said to be *independent* when the occurrence of one is not affected by the occurrence of the other.

Let a be the number of ways in which the first event can happen, and b the number of ways in which it can fail; all these ways being equally likely to occur.

Also, let a' be the number of ways in which the second event can happen, and b' the number of ways in which it can fail; all these ways being equally likely to occur.

We may associate together any one of the $a + b$ cases in which the first event happens or fails, and any one of the $a' + b'$ cases in which the second happens or fails; hence there are $(a + b)(a' + b')$ cases, equally likely to occur.

In aa' of these cases both events happen.

Therefore, the probability that both events happen is

$$\frac{aa'}{(a + b)(a' + b')}.$$

But $\dfrac{a}{a + b}$ is the probability that the first event happens,

and $\dfrac{a'}{a' + b'}$ the probability that the second happens.

Hence, the probability that both events happen is the product of their separate probabilities.

And in general, if $p_1, p_2, p_3, \cdot$, are the respective probabilities of any number of independent events, the probability that all the events happen is $p_1 p_2 p_3 \cdots$.

639. Examples.

1. Find the probability of throwing an ace in the first only of two successive throws with a single die.

The probability of throwing an ace at the first trial is $\dfrac{1}{6}$.

The probability of not throwing one at the second is $\dfrac{5}{6}$.

Hence, the probability of throwing an ace in the first only of two successive throws is $\dfrac{1}{6} \times \dfrac{5}{6}$, or $\dfrac{5}{36}$.

2. Find the probability of throwing an ace at least once in three throws with a single die.

There will be an ace unless there are three failures.

The probability of failing at the first trial is $\dfrac{5}{6}$; and this is also the probability of failing at each of the other trials.

Hence, the probability that there will be three failures is

$$\frac{5}{6} \times \frac{5}{6} \times \frac{5}{6}, \text{ or } \frac{125}{216}.$$

Then the probability that there will *not* be three failures is
$1 - \frac{125}{216}$ (§ 634), or $\frac{91}{216}$.

3. A bag contains 5 red balls, 4 white balls, and 3 black balls. Three balls are drawn in succession, each being replaced before the next is drawn. What is the probability that the balls drawn are one of each color?

The probability that the first ball is red is $\frac{5}{12}$; the probability that the second is white is $\frac{4}{12}$, or $\frac{1}{3}$; and the probability that the third is black is $\frac{3}{12}$, or $\frac{1}{4}$.

Hence, the probability of drawing a red ball, a white ball, and a black ball, *in this assigned order*, is $\frac{5}{12} \times \frac{1}{3} \times \frac{1}{4}$, or $\frac{5}{144}$.

But a red ball, a white ball, and a black ball may be drawn in $\lfloor 3$, or 6 different orders (§ 625); and in each case the probability is $\frac{5}{144}$.

Then by § 636, the probability of drawing a red ball, a white ball, and a black ball, without regard to the order in which they are drawn, is $\frac{5}{144} \times 6$, or $\frac{5}{24}$.

640. Dependent Events.

The probability of the concurrent happening of two dependent events is the probability of the first, multiplied by the probability that when the first has happened the second will follow.

Let a and b have the same meanings as in § 638.

Also, suppose that, after the first event has happened, a' represents the number of ways in which the second will follow, and b' the number of ways in which it will not follow; all these ways being equally likely to occur.

Then there are in all $(a + b)(a' + b')$ cases, equally likely to occur, and in aa' of these both events happen.

Therefore, the probability that both events happen is

$$\frac{aa'}{(a + b)(a' + b')}.$$

Hence, the probability that both events happen is the probability of the first, multiplied by the probability that when it has happened the second will follow.

And in general, if there are any number of dependent events such that p_1 is the probability of the first, p_2 the probability that when the first has happened the second will follow, p_3 the probability that when the first and second have happened the third will follow, and so on, then the probability that all the events happen is $p_1 p_2 p_3 \cdots$.

641. Examples.

1. Solve Ex. 3, § 639, if the balls are *not replaced after being drawn*.

The probability that the first ball is red is $\frac{5}{12}$; the probability that the second is white is $\frac{4}{11}$; and the probability that the third is black is $\frac{3}{10}$.

Hence, the probability of drawing a red ball, a white ball, and a black ball, in this assigned order, is $\frac{5}{12} \times \frac{4}{11} \times \frac{3}{10}$.

But the balls may be drawn in $\lfloor 3$, or 6 different orders.

Therefore, the probability of drawing a red ball, a white ball, and a black ball, without regard to the order in which they are drawn, is $\frac{5}{12} \times \frac{4}{11} \times \frac{3}{10} \times 6$, or $\frac{3}{11}$.

2. An urn contains 5 white balls and 3 black balls; another contains 4 white balls and 7 black balls. What is the probability of obtaining a white ball by a single drawing from one of the urns taken at random?

Since the urns are equally likely to be taken, the probability of taking the first urn is $\frac{1}{2}$; and the probability of then drawing a white ball from it is $\frac{5}{8}$.

Hence, the probability of obtaining a white ball from the first urn is $\frac{1}{2} \times \frac{5}{8}$, or $\frac{5}{16}$.

In like manner, the probability of obtaining a white ball from the second urn is $\frac{1}{2} \times \frac{4}{11}$, or $\frac{2}{11}$.

Hence, the required probability is $\frac{5}{16} + \frac{2}{11}$, or $\frac{87}{176}$.

642. *Given the probability of the happening of an event in one trial, to find the probability of its happening exactly r times in n trials.*

Let p be the probability of the happening of the event in one trial.

Then $1 - p$ is the probability of its failing (§ 634).

The probability that the event will happen in each of the first r trials, and fail in each of the remaining $n - r$ trials, is $p^r(1 - p)^{n-r}$.

But the number of ways in which the event may happen exactly r times in n trials is equal to the number of combinations of n things taken r at a time, or

$$\frac{n(n-1)\cdots(n-r+1)}{\underline{|r}} \text{ (§ 626).}$$

Hence, the probability that the event will happen exactly r times in n trials is

$$\frac{n(n-1)\cdots(n-r+1)}{\underline{|r}}p^r(1-p)^{n-r}. \tag{1}$$

Ex. What is the probability of throwing exactly three aces in five throws with a single die?

Here, $p = \dfrac{1}{6}$, $r = 3$, $n = 5$, and $n - r + 1 = 3$.

Substituting in (1), the required probability is

$$\frac{5 \cdot 4 \cdot 3}{1 \cdot 2 \cdot 3} \times \left(\frac{1}{6}\right)^3 \times \left(\frac{5}{6}\right)^2, \text{ or } \frac{125}{3888}.$$

643. It follows from § 642 that, if the probability of the happening of the event in one trial is p, the probability of its failing exactly r times in n trials is

$$\frac{n(n-1)\cdots(n-r+1)}{\lfloor r} p^{n-r}(1-p)^r.$$

644. *Given the probability of the happening of an event in one trial, to find the probability of its happening at least r times in n trials.*

The event happens at least r times if it happens exactly n times, or fails exactly once, twice, $\cdot$, $n - r$ times.

Then the probability that it happens at least r times equals the sum of the probabilities of its happening exactly n times, or failing exactly once, twice, $\cdot$, $n - r$ times.

By §§ 642, 643, the required probability is

$$p^n + np^{n-1}(1-p) + \cdots + \frac{n(n-1)\cdots(r+1)}{\lfloor n-r} p^r(1-p)^{n-r}.$$

Ex. What is the probability of throwing at least three aces in five throws with a single die ?

Here, $p = \dfrac{1}{6}$, $r = 3$, $n = 5$; then the required probability is

$$\left(\frac{1}{6}\right)^5 + 5 \times \left(\frac{1}{6}\right)^4 \times \left(\frac{5}{6}\right) + \frac{5 \cdot 4}{1 \cdot 2} \times \left(\frac{1}{6}\right)^3 \times \left(\frac{5}{6}\right)^2, \text{ or } \frac{23}{648}.$$

EXERCISE 107

1. Find the probability of throwing exactly four sixes in six throws with a single die.

2. Find the probability of throwing at least four doublets in six throws with a pair of dice.

3. A purse contains 5 dollars and 7 five-cent pieces, and another 3 dollars and 12 five-cent pieces. Find the probability of obtaining a dollar by drawing a single coin from one of the purses taken at random.

4. If a coin is tossed eight times, what is the probability that the head will turn up at least five times?

5. A bag contains 5 white and 3 black balls. If 4 balls are drawn and not replaced, what is the probability that the balls drawn are alternately of different colors?

6. What is the probability of throwing 10 with a pair of dice exactly three times in four trials?

7. The probability of a certain event is $\frac{2}{7}$, and of another independent of the first $\frac{6}{11}$. Find the probability that one at least of the events will happen.

8. If two coins are tossed up five times, find the probability that there will be five heads and five tails.

9. Each of four persons draws a card from a pack. Find the probability that there will be one of each suit.

10. A, B, C. and D throw a die in succession, in the order named, until one throws an ace. Find their respective chances of throwing an ace at the first trial.

11. A bag contains three white and six black balls. A person draws three balls, the balls when drawn not being replaced. What is the probability of drawing a white ball?

12. A person has four tickets in a lottery in which there are three prizes and seven blanks. Find his chance of drawing a prize.

13. A box contains ten counters numbered 1, 2, 3, ..., 10. After one is drawn, it is put back, and the process is repeated indefinitely. Find the probability that No. 1 will be drawn in four trials.

14. A bag contains six balls. A person takes one out, and replaces it. After he has done this six times, find the probability that he has had in his hand every ball in the bag.

15. In a series of games, the probability that the winner of any game wins the next game is $\frac{2}{3}$. Find the probability that the winner of the first game wins three or more of the next four.

16. A bag contains three tickets numbered 1, 2, 3. A ticket is drawn, and replaced. After this has been done four times, what is the probability that the sum of the numbers drawn is even?

17. A purse contains a silver dollar and four dimes; another contains five dimes. Four coins are taken from the former and put in the latter; and then four coins are taken from the latter and put in the former. Find the probability that the dollar is still in the first purse.

18. A and B, with six others, draw lots for partners, and play four two-handed games, all the players being of equal skill. The four winners draw lots for partners, and play two games, and the winners in these games play a final game. Find the probability that A and B have played together.

19. If four whole numbers taken at random be multiplied together, find the chance that the last digit in the product is 1, 3, 7, or 9.

20. An urn contains 3 white and 3 black balls, and another 4 white and 4 black balls. A ball is taken from one and put in the other. If a ball be drawn from one of the urns chosen at a random, what is the probability that it is white?

XXXIII. CONTINUED FRACTIONS

645. A **Continued Fraction** is an expression of the form

$$a + \cfrac{b}{c + \cfrac{d}{e + \cdots}}; \quad \text{or,} \quad a + \cfrac{b}{c+} \cfrac{d}{e+} \cdots,$$

as it is usually written.

We shall consider in the present work only continued fractions of the form

$$a + \cfrac{1}{b+} \cfrac{1}{c+} \cdots;$$

where each numerator is unity, a a positive integer or 0, and each of the numbers b, c, $\cdots$, a positive integer.

646. A *terminating* continued fraction is one in which the number of denominators is finite; as,

$$a + \cfrac{1}{b+} \cfrac{1}{c+} \cfrac{1}{d}.$$

An *infinite* continued fraction is one in which the number of denominators is indefinitely great.

647. In the continued fraction

$$a_1 + \cfrac{1}{a_2+} \cfrac{1}{a_3+} \cfrac{1}{a_4+} \cdots,$$

a_1 is called the *first convergent;*

$a_1 + \cfrac{1}{a_2}$ the *second convergent;*

$a_1 + \cfrac{1}{a_2+} \cfrac{1}{a_3}$ the *third convergent;* and so on.

If $a_1 = 0$, as in the continued fraction

$$\cfrac{1}{a_2+} \cfrac{1}{a_3+} \cfrac{1}{a_4+} \cdots,$$

then 0 is considered the first convergent.

648. *Any ordinary fraction in its lowest terms may be converted into a terminating continued fraction.*

Let the given fraction be $\dfrac{a}{b}$, where a and b are prime to each other.

Divide a by b, and let a_1 denote the quotient and b_1 the remainder; then,

$$\frac{a}{b} = a_1 + \frac{b_1}{b} = a_1 + \frac{1}{\dfrac{b}{b_1}}.$$

Divide b by b_1, and let a_2 denote the quotient and b_2 the remainder; then,

$$\frac{a}{b} = a_1 + \frac{1}{a_2 + \dfrac{b_2}{b_1}} = a_1 + \frac{1}{a_2 + \dfrac{1}{\dfrac{b_1}{b_2}}}.$$

Again, divide b_1 by b_2, and let a_3 denote the quotient and b_3 the remainder; then,

$$\frac{a}{b} = a_1 + \frac{1}{a_2 + \dfrac{1}{a_3 + \dfrac{b_3}{b_2}}} = a_1 + \frac{1}{a_2 + \dfrac{1}{a_3 + \dfrac{1}{\dfrac{b_2}{b_3}}}}.$$

The process is the same as that of finding the H. C. F. of a and b (§ 188); and since a and b are prime to each other, we must eventually obtain a remainder unity, at which point the operation terminates.

Hence, any ordinary fraction in its lowest terms can be converted into a *terminating* continued fraction.

Ex.   Convert $\dfrac{62}{23}$ into a continued fraction.

$$
\begin{array}{l}
23)62(2 = a_1 \\
\quad 46 \\
\quad \overline{16)}23(1 = a_2 \\
\qquad 16 \\
\qquad \overline{7)}16(2 = a_3 \\
\qquad\quad 14 \\
\qquad\quad \overline{2)}7(3 = a_4 \\
\qquad\qquad \underline{6}
\end{array}
$$

Therefore, $\dfrac{62}{23} = 2 + \dfrac{1}{1+}\dfrac{1}{2+}\dfrac{1}{3+}\dfrac{1}{2}.$

649. *A quadratic surd (§ 368) may be converted into an infinite continued fraction.*

Ex. Convert $\sqrt{6}$ into a continued fraction.

The greatest integer in $\sqrt{6}$ is 2; we then write

$$\sqrt{6} = 2 + (\sqrt{6} - 2).$$

Reducing $\sqrt{6} - 2$ to an equivalent fraction with a rational numerator (§ 387), we have

$$\sqrt{6} = 2 + \frac{(\sqrt{6}-2)(\sqrt{6}+2)}{\sqrt{6}+2} = 2 + \frac{2}{\sqrt{6}+2}$$

$$= 2 + \frac{1}{\dfrac{\sqrt{6}+2}{2}}. \qquad (1)$$

The greatest integer in $\dfrac{\sqrt{6}+2}{2}$ is 2; we then write

$$\frac{\sqrt{6}+2}{2} = 2 + \frac{\sqrt{6}-2}{2} = 2 + \frac{(\sqrt{6}-2)(\sqrt{6}+2)}{2(\sqrt{6}+2)} = 2 + \frac{1}{\sqrt{6}+2}.$$

Substituting in (1), $\sqrt{6} = 2 + \dfrac{1}{2 + \dfrac{1}{\sqrt{6}+2}}.$ \qquad (2)

The greatest integer in $\sqrt{6} + 2$ is 4; we then write

$$\sqrt{6} + 2 = 4 + (\sqrt{6} - 2) = 4 + \frac{(\sqrt{6}-2)(\sqrt{6}+2)}{\sqrt{6}+2}$$

$$= 4 + \frac{2}{\sqrt{6}+2} = 4 + \frac{1}{\dfrac{\sqrt{6}+2}{2}}.$$

Substituting in (2), we have

$$\sqrt{6} = 2 + \cfrac{1}{2 + \cfrac{1}{4 + \cfrac{1}{\dfrac{\sqrt{6}+2}{2}}}}.$$

The steps now recur, and we have

$$\sqrt{6} = 2 + \frac{1}{2+} \frac{1}{4+} \frac{1}{2+} \frac{1}{4+} \cdots.$$

An infinite continued fraction in which the denominators recur is called a *periodic* continued fraction.

650. *A periodic continued fraction may always be expressed as an irrational number.*

Ex.   Express $\dfrac{1}{1+} \dfrac{1}{3+} \dfrac{1}{1+} \dfrac{1}{3+} \cdots$ as an irrational number.

Let x denote the value of the fraction; then,

$$x = \frac{1}{1+} \frac{1}{3+x} = \frac{3+x}{3+x+1} = \frac{3+x}{4+x}.$$

Clearing of fractions,

$$4x + x^2 = 3 + x, \text{ or } x^2 + 3x = 3.$$

Solving this equation, $x = \dfrac{-3 + \sqrt{9+12}}{2} = \dfrac{-3 + \sqrt{21}}{2}.$

It is evident that the positive sign must be taken before the radical.

PROPERTIES OF CONVERGENTS

651. In §§ 652 to 657, inclusive, we shall suppose the continued fraction to be

$$a_1 + \frac{1}{a_2+} \frac{1}{a_3+} \cdots \frac{1}{a_n+} \frac{1}{a_{n+1}+} \cdots.$$

And we shall let p_r denote the numerator, and q_r the denominator, of the rth convergent (§ 647), when expressed in its simplest form.

652. *To determine the law of formation of the successive convergents.*

The first convergent is a_1.

The second is $a_1 + \dfrac{1}{a_2} = \dfrac{a_1 a_2 + 1}{a_2}.$

The third is $\quad a_1 + \dfrac{1}{a_2+}\ \dfrac{1}{a_3} = a_1 + \dfrac{a_3}{a_2 a_3 + 1} = \dfrac{a_1 a_2 a_3 + a_1 + a_3}{a_2 a_3 + 1}$.

The third convergent may be written in the form

$$\frac{(a_1 a_2 + 1)a_3 + a_1}{a_2 a_3 + 1};$$

in which we observe that:

I. *The numerator equals the numerator of the preceding convergent, multiplied by the last denominator taken, plus the numerator of the convergent next but one preceding.*

II. *The denominator equals the denominator of the preceding convergent, multiplied by the last denominator taken, plus the denominator of the convergent next but one preceding.*

We will now prove by Mathematical Induction that the above laws hold for all convergents after the second, when expressed in their simplest forms.

Assume that the laws hold for all convergents as far as the nth inclusive.

The nth convergent is $\dfrac{p_n}{q_n} = a_1 + \dfrac{1}{a_2+}\ \dfrac{1}{a_3+}\ \cdots\ \dfrac{1}{a_n}$.

Then, since the last denominator is a_n, we have

$$p_n = a_n p_{n-1} + p_{n-2}, \text{ and } q_n = a_n q_{n-1} + q_{n-2}. \qquad (1)$$

Whence, $\qquad\qquad \dfrac{p_n}{q_n} = \dfrac{a_n p_{n-1} + p_{n-2}}{a_n q_{n-1} + q_{n-2}}. \qquad\qquad (2)$

The $(n+1)$th convergent is

$$a_1 + \frac{1}{a_2+}\ \frac{1}{a_3+}\ \cdots\ \frac{1}{a_n+}\ \frac{1}{a_{n+1}},$$

which differs from the nth only in having $a_n + \dfrac{1}{a_{n+1}}$, or $\dfrac{a_n a_{n+1}+1}{a_{n+1}}$, in place of a_n.

Substituting $\dfrac{a_n a_{n+1}+1}{a_{n+1}}$ for a_n in (2), we have

$$\frac{p_{n+1}}{q_{n+1}} = \frac{\dfrac{a_n a_{n+1}+1}{a_{n+1}} p_{n-1} + p_{n-2}}{\dfrac{a_n a_{n+1}+1}{a_{n+1}} q_{n-1} + q_{n-2}}.$$

Then,
$$\frac{p_{n+1}}{q_{n+1}} = \frac{a_{n+1}(a_n p_{n-1} + p_{n-2}) + p_{n-1}}{a_{n+1}(a_n q_{n-1} + q_{n-2}) + q_{n-1}}$$

$$= \frac{a_{n+1}p_n + p_{n-1}}{a_{n+1}q_n + q_{n-1}}, \text{ by (1)}. \tag{3}$$

It is evident that the second member of (3) is the simplest form of the $(n + 1)$th convergent, and therefore

$$p_{n+1} = a_{n+1}p_n + p_{n-1}, \text{ and } q_{n+1} = a_{n+1}q_n + q_{n-1}.$$

These results are in accordance with laws I and II.

Hence, if the laws hold for all convergents as far as the nth inclusive, they also hold for the $(n + 1)$th.

But we know that they hold for the third convergent, and hence they hold for the fourth; and since they hold as far as the fourth, they also hold for the fifth; and so on.

Hence, the laws hold for all convergents after the second.

Ex. Find the first five convergents of

$$1 + \frac{1}{1+} \frac{1}{2+} \frac{1}{3+} \frac{1}{4+ \cdots}.$$

The first convergent is 1, and the second is $1 + 1$, or 2.

Then, by aid of the laws just proved,

$$\text{the third is } \frac{2 \cdot 2 + 1}{1 \cdot 2 + 1} = \frac{5}{3};$$

$$\text{the fourth is } \frac{5 \cdot 3 + 2}{3 \cdot 3 + 1} = \frac{17}{10};$$

$$\text{the fifth is } \frac{17 \cdot 4 + 5}{10 \cdot 4 + 3} = \frac{73}{43}.$$

653. *The difference between two consecutive convergents* $\frac{p_n}{q_n}$ *and* $\frac{p_{n+1}}{q_{n+1}}$ *is* $\frac{1}{q_n q_{n+1}}$.

The difference between the first and second convergents is

$$\left(a_1 + \frac{1}{a_2}\right) - a_1 = \frac{1}{a_2}.$$

Thus the theorem holds for the first and second convergents.

Assume that it holds for the nth and $(n+1)$th convergents.

That is, $\dfrac{p_n}{q_n} \sim \dfrac{p_{n+1}}{q_{n+1}} = \dfrac{1}{q_n q_{n+1}}$, or $p_n q_{n+1} \sim p_{n+1} q_n = 1.$ (1)

Then, $\dfrac{p_{n+1}}{q_{n+1}} \sim \dfrac{p_{n+2}}{q_{n+2}} = \dfrac{p_{n+1}}{q_{n+1}} \sim \dfrac{a_{n+2} p_{n+1} + p_n}{a_{n+2} q_{n+1} + q_n}$ (§ 652)

$$= \frac{(a_{n+2} p_{n+1} q_{n+1} + p_{n+1} q_n) \sim (a_{n+2} p_{n+1} q_{n+1} + p_n q_{n+1})}{q_{n+1}(a_{n+2} q_{n+1} + q_n)}$$

$$= \frac{p_{n+1} q_n \sim p_n q_{n+1}}{q_{n+1} q_{n+2}} \quad (\text{§ 652}) = \frac{1}{q_{n+1} q_{n+2}}, \text{ by (1).}$$

Hence, if the theorem holds for any pair of consecutive convergents, it also holds for the next pair.

But we know that it holds for the first and second convergents, and hence it also holds for the second and third; and since it holds for the second and third, it also holds for the third and fourth; and so on.

Therefore, the theorem holds universally.

As an example of the theorem, the difference between the fourth and fifth convergents, in the example in § 652, is

$$\frac{17}{10} - \frac{73}{43} = \frac{731 - 730}{10 \times 43} = \frac{1}{10 \times 43}.$$

654. It follows from § 653 that p_n and q_n can have no common divisor except unity; for if they had, it would be a divisor of $p_n q_{n+1} \sim p_{n+1} q_n$, or unity, which is impossible.

Therefore, all convergents formed in accordance with the laws of § 652 are in their *lowest terms*.

655. *The even convergents are greater, and the odd convergents less, than the fraction itself.*

I. The first convergent, a_1, is *less* than the fraction itself, since $\dfrac{1}{a_2 + \cdots}$ is omitted.

II. The second, $a_1 + \dfrac{1}{a_2}$, is *greater*, because its denominator a_2 is less than $a_2 + \dfrac{1}{a_3 + \cdots}$, the denominator of the fraction.

III. The third, $a_1 + \dfrac{1}{a_2 +} \dfrac{1}{a_3}$, is *less*, because, by II, the denominator $a_2 + \dfrac{1}{a^3}$ is greater than $a_2 + \dfrac{1}{a_3 +} \dfrac{1}{a_4 + \cdots}$, the denominator of the fraction; and so on.

Hence, the first, third, $\cdots$, convergents are less, and the second, fourth, $\cdots$, convergents greater than the fraction itself.

656. *Any convergent is nearer than the preceding convergent to the value of the fraction itself.*

By § 652, $\dfrac{p_{n+2}}{q_{n+2}} = \dfrac{a_{n+2}p_{n+1} + p_n}{a_{n+2}q_{n+1} + q_n}.$

The fraction itself is obtained from its $(n+2)$th convergent by putting $a_{n+2} + \dfrac{1}{a_{n+3} + \cdots}$ in place of a_{n+2}.

Hence, denoting the value of the fraction by x, we have

$$x = \frac{\left[a_{n+2} + \dfrac{1}{a_{n+3} + \cdots}\right]p_{n+1} + p_n}{\left[a_{n+2} + \dfrac{1}{a_{n+3} + \cdots}\right]q_{n+1} + q_n} = \frac{mp_{n+1} + p_n}{mq_{n+1} + q_n},$$

where m stands for $a_{n+2} + \dfrac{1}{a_{n+3} + \cdots}$.

Now, $x \sim \dfrac{p_n}{q_n} = \dfrac{mp_{n+1} + p_n}{mq_{n+1} + q_n} \sim \dfrac{p_n}{q_n}$

$$= \frac{m(p_{n+1}q_n \sim p_n q_{n+1})}{q_n(mq_{n+1} + q_n)}$$

$$= \frac{m}{q_n(mq_{n+1} + q_n)} \quad (\S\ 653). \qquad\qquad (1)$$

Also, $x \sim \dfrac{p_{n+1}}{q_{n+1}} = \dfrac{mp_{n+1} + p_n}{mq_{n+1} + q_n} \sim \dfrac{p_{n+1}}{q_{n+1}}$

$$= \frac{p_n q_{n+1} \sim p_{n+1} q_n}{q_{n+1}(mq_{n+1} + q_n)} = \frac{1}{q_{n+1}(mq_{n+1} + q_n)}. \qquad (2)$$

Since a_{n+2} is a positive integer, $a_{n+2} + \dfrac{1}{a_{n+3} + \cdots}$ is >1; that is, m is >1.

And since $q_{n+1} = a_{n+1}q_n + q_{n-1}$ (§ 652), q_{n+1} is $> q_n$.

Therefore, the fraction (2) is less than the fraction (1), for it has a smaller numerator and a greater denominator.

Hence, the $(n+1)$th convergent is nearer than the nth to the value of the fraction itself.

657. *To determine limits to the error made in taking the nth convergent for the fraction itself.*

With the notation of § 656, the difference between the fraction itself and its nth convergent is

$$\frac{m}{q_n(mq_{n+1}+q_n)}, \text{ or } \frac{1}{q_n\left(q_{n+1}+\dfrac{q_n}{m}\right)}. \tag{1}$$

Since m is > 1 (§ 656), the denominator $q_n\left(q_{n+1}+\dfrac{q_n}{m}\right)$ is $< q_n(q_{n+1}+q_n)$.

The denominator is also $> q_n q_{n+1}$.

Hence, the fraction (1) is $> \dfrac{1}{q_n(q_{n+1}+q_n)}$, and $< \dfrac{1}{q_n q_{n+1}}$.

That is, the *error* made in taking the nth convergent for the fraction itself lies between

$$\frac{1}{q_n(q_{n+1}+q_n)} \text{ and } \frac{1}{q_n q_{n+1}}.$$

As an example of the above theorem, the error made in taking the fourth convergent for the fraction itself, in the example in § 652, lies between

$$\frac{1}{10(43+10)} \text{ and } \frac{1}{10 \times 43}, \text{ or } \frac{1}{530} \text{ and } \frac{1}{430}.$$

EXERCISE 108

Convert each of the following into a continued fraction, and find in each case the first five convergents.

1. $\dfrac{118}{91}$. 3. $\dfrac{445}{612}$. 5. $\dfrac{418}{571}$. 7. $\dfrac{715}{1561}$.

2. $\dfrac{253}{179}$. 4. 5.83. 6. $\dfrac{743}{611}$. 8. $\dfrac{832}{5151}$.

Convert each of the following into a continued fraction, find in each case the first four convergents, and determine limits to the error made in taking the third convergent for the fraction itself.

9. $\sqrt{26}$.   **12.** $\sqrt{46}$.   **15.** $\sqrt{53}$.   **18.** $\sqrt{23}$.

10. $\sqrt{37}$.   **13.** $\sqrt{\dfrac{3}{2}}$.   **16.** $\sqrt{19}$.   **19.** $2\sqrt{7}$.

11. $\sqrt{8}$.   **14.** $\sqrt{27}$.   **17.** $\dfrac{1+\sqrt{46}}{5}$.   **20.** $3\sqrt{14}$.

Express each of the following in the form of a surd :

21. $\dfrac{1}{4+}\dfrac{1}{3+}\dfrac{1}{4+}\dfrac{1}{3+}\cdots$.   **23.** $4+\dfrac{1}{2+}\dfrac{1}{2+}\cdots$.

22. $\dfrac{1}{2+}\dfrac{1}{5+}\dfrac{1}{2+}\dfrac{1}{5+}\cdots$.   **24.** $1+\dfrac{1}{1+}\dfrac{1}{6+}\dfrac{1}{1+}\dfrac{1}{6+}\cdots$.

25. $a+\dfrac{1}{a+}\dfrac{1}{2a+}\dfrac{1}{a+}\dfrac{1}{2a+}\cdots$.

26. The sidereal year is approximately 365.25636 days ; express the excess above 365 days as a continued fraction, and find its first four convergents.

27. A kilometer is approximately .62138 mile ; express this decimal as a continued fraction, find its fifth convergent, and determine limits to the error made in taking this convergent for the fraction itself.

28. A meter is approximately 1.09363 yards ; express this decimal as a continued fraction, find its sixth convergent, and determine limits to the error made in taking this convergent for the fraction itself.

29. Express the greatest root of the equation

$$2x^2 - 10x = -5$$

as a continued fraction, and find the first five convergents.

Convert each of the following into a continued fraction, and find in each case the first four convergents:

30. $\sqrt{74}$.   **31.** $\dfrac{1}{\sqrt{55}}$.   **32.** $\sqrt{a^2+a}$.   **33.** $\sqrt{57}$.

XXXIV. SUMMATION OF SERIES

658. The **Summation** of an infinite literal series is the process of finding an expression from which the series may be developed.

In § 530, we gave a method for finding the sum of an infinite geometric series.

RECURRING SERIES

659. Consider the infinite series

$$1 + 2x + 3x^2 + 4x^3 + 5x^4 + \cdots.$$

Here, $\quad (3x^2) - 2x(2x) + x^2(1) = 0,$

$$(4x^3) - 2x(3x^2) + x^2(2x) = 0, \text{ etc.}$$

That is, any three consecutive terms, as for example $2x$, $3x^2$, and $4x^3$, are so related that the third, minus $2x$ times the second, plus x^2 times the first, equals 0.

660. A **Recurring Series** is an infinite series of the form

$$a_0 + a_1 x + a_2 x^2 + \cdots,$$

where any $r + 1$ consecutive terms, as for example

$$a_n x^n, \; a_{n-1}x^{n-1}, \; a_{n-2}x^{n-2}, \; \cdot \; , \; a_{n-r}x^{n-r},$$

are so related that

$$a_n x^n + px(a_{n-1}x^{n-1}) + qx^2(a_{n-2}x^{n-2}) + \cdots + sx^r(a_{n-r}x^{n-r}) = 0;$$

p, q, $\cdots$, s being constants.

The above recurring series is said to be of the *rth order,* and the expression $\quad 1 + px + qx^2 + \cdots + sx^r$

is called its *scale of relation.*

The recurring series of § 659 is of the second order, and its scale of relation is $1 - 2x + x^2$.

An infinite geometric series is a recurring series of the first order.

Thus, in the infinite geometric series

$$1 + x + x^2 + x^3 + \cdots,$$

any two consecutive terms, as for example x^3 and x^2, are so related that $(x^3) - x(x^2) = 0$; and the scale of relation is $1 - x$.

661. *To find the scale of relation of a recurring series.*

If the series is of the first order, the scale of relation may be found by dividing any term by the preceding term, and subtracting the result from 1.

If the series is of the second order, $a_0, a_1, a_2, a_3, \cdots$, its consecutive coefficients, and $1 + px + qx^2$ its scale of relation, we shall have

$$\begin{cases} a_2 + pa_1 + qa_0 = 0, \\ a_3 + pa_2 + qa_1 = 0 ; \end{cases} \tag{1}$$

from which p and q may be determined.

If the series is of the third order, $a_0, a_1, a_2, a_3, a_4, a_5, \cdots$, its consecutive coefficients, and $1 + px + qx^2 + rx^3$ its scale of relation, we shall have

$$\begin{cases} a_3 + pa_2 + qa_1 + ra_0 = 0, \\ a_4 + pa_3 + qa_2 + ra_1 = 0, \\ a_5 + pa_4 + qa_3 + ra_2 = 0 ; \end{cases}$$

from which p, q, and r may be determined.

It is evident from the above that the scale of relation of a recurring series of the rth order may be determined when any $2r$ consecutive terms are given.

To ascertain the order of a series, we may first make trial of a scale of relation of three terms; if the result does not agree with the series, try a scale of four terms, five terms, and so on until the correct scale of relation is found.

If the series is assumed to be of too high an order, the equations corresponding to the assumed scale will not be independent. (Compare § 269.)

662. *To find the sum of a recurring series when its scale of relation is known.*

Let $1 + px + qx^2$ be the scale of relation of the series

$$a_0 + a_1 x + a_2 x^2 + \cdots.$$

Denoting the sum of the first n terms by S_n, we have
$$S_n = a_0 + a_1 x + a_2 x^2 + \cdots + a_{n-1} x^{n-1}.$$

Then, $pxS_n = pa_0 x + pa_1 x^2 + \cdots + pa_{n-2} x^{n-1} + pa_{n-1} x^n,$

and $qx^2 S_n = qa_0 x^2 + \cdots + qa_{n-3} x^{n-1} + qa_{n-2} x^n + qa_{n-1} x^{n+1}.$

Adding these equations, and remembering that, by virtue of the scale of relation,
$$a_2 + pa_1 + qa_0 = 0, \cdots, a_{n-1} + pa_{n-2} + qa_{n-3} = 0,$$
the coefficients of x^2, x^3, $\cdot$, x^{n-1} become 0, and we have

$S_n(1 + px + qx^2)$

$\quad = a_0 + (a_1 + pa_0) x + (pa_{n-1} + qa_{n-2}) x^n + qa_{n-1} x^{n+1}.$

Whence,
$$S_n = \frac{a_0 + (a_1 + pa_0) x + (pa_{n-1} + qa_{n-2}) x^n + qa_{n-1} x^{n+1}}{1 + px + qx^2}; \quad (1)$$

which is a formula for the sum of the first n terms of a recurring series of the second order.

If x is so taken that the given series is convergent, the expression $(pa_{n-1} + qa_{n-2}) x^n + qa_{n-1} x^{n+1}$

approaches the limit 0 when n is indefinitely increased (§ 542), and (1) becomes
$$S = \frac{a_0 + (a_1 + pa_0) x}{1 + px + qx^2}; \quad (2)$$

which is a formula for the *value* (§ 540) of a recurring series of the second order.

If $q = 0$, the series is of the first order, and therefore $a_1 + pa_0 = 0$; whence,
$$S = \frac{a_0}{1 + px}; \quad (3)$$

which is a formula for the value of a recurring series of the first order.   (Compare § 530.)

In like manner, we shall find the formula
$$S = \frac{a_0 + (a_1 + pa_0) x + (a_2 + pa_1 + qa_0) x^2}{1 + px + qx^2 + rx^3} \quad (4)$$

for the value of a recurring series of the third order.

It will be observed, in formulæ (1), (3), and (4), that the denominator is the *scale of relation*.

A recurring series is formed by the expansion, in an infinite series, of a fraction, called the *generating fraction*. The operation of summation reproduces the fraction; the process being just the reverse of that of § 564.

Ex.   Find the sum of the series

$$2 + x + 5\,x^2 + 7\,x^3 + 17\,x^4 + \cdots.$$

To determine the scale of relation, we first assume the series to be of the second order (§ 661).

Substituting $a_0 = 2$, $a_1 = 1$, $a_2 = 5$, $a_3 = 7$, in (1), § 661,

$$\begin{cases} 5 + \quad p + 2\,q = 0, \\ 7 + 5\,p + \quad q = 0. \end{cases}$$

Solving these equations, $p = -1$, $q = -2$.

To ascertain if $1 - x - 2\,x^2$ is the correct scale of relation, consider the fifth term.

Since $17\,x^4 + (-x)(7\,x^3) + (-2\,x^2)(5\,x^2)$ is 0, it follows that $1 - x - 2\,x^2$ is the correct scale.

Substituting the values of a_0, a_1, p, and q in (2),

$$S = \frac{2 + (1 - 2)\,x}{1 - x - 2\,x^2} = \frac{2 - x}{1 - x - 2\,x^2}.$$

The result may be verified by expansion.

The series expresses the value of the fraction only for such values of x as make the series convergent.

To find for what values of x the given series is convergent, we proceed as in § 572; we find by the method of § 567,

$$\frac{2 - x}{1 - x - 2\,x^2} = \frac{1}{1 - 2\,x} + \frac{1}{1 + x}$$
$$= (1 + 2\,x + 2^2 x^2 + \cdots) + (1 - x + x^2 - \cdots).$$

The nth term of the given series is $[2^{n-1} + (-1)^{n-1}]\,x^{n-1}$.

The ratio of the $(n + 1)$th term to the nth term is

$$\frac{[2^n + (-1)^n]\,x^n}{[2^{n-1} + (-1)^{n-1}]\,x^{n-1}}, \text{ or } \frac{\left[2 + \dfrac{(-1)^n}{2^{n-1}}\right]x}{1 + \dfrac{(-1)^{n-1}}{2^{n-1}}}.$$

This approaches the limit $2x$, when n is indefinitely increased.

Then, the series is convergent if x is numerically $< \dfrac{1}{2}$ (§ 555, I.).

EXERCISE 109

In each of the following find the generating fraction, and the expression for the nth term, and determine for what values of x the series is convergent: .

1. $4 - x + 7x^2 - 5x^3 + 19x^4 + \cdots$.
2. $1 - 13x - 23x^2 - 85x^3 - 239x^4 + \cdots$.
3. $1 + 5x + 21x^2 + 85x^3 + 341x^4 + \cdots$.
4. $5 - 13x + 35x^2 - 97x^3 + 275x^4 + \cdots$.
5. $3 + 10x + 36x^2 + 136x^3 + 528x^4 + \cdots$.
6. $1 - 2x + x^2 + 22x^3 - 191x^4 + \cdots$.
7. $3 + x + 33x^2 + 109x^3 + 657x^4 + \cdots$.
8. $1 + 31x - 19x^2 + 391x^3 - 619x^4 + \cdots$.

In each of the following find the generating fraction, and continue the series to two more terms :

9. $1 + 2x - 3x^2 + 6x^3 - 7x^4 + 10x^5 - 11x^6 + \cdots$.
10. $1 - 2x - x^2 - 7x^3 - 18x^4 - 59x^5 - 181x^6 + \cdots$.
11. $2 - 11x + 15x^2 + 20x^3 - 133x^4 + 231x^5 + 130x^6 + \cdots$.

THE DIFFERENTIAL METHOD

663. If the first term of a series be subtracted from the second, the second from the third, and so on, a series is formed which is called the *first order of differences* of the given series.

The first order of differences of this new series is called the *second order of differences* of the given series; and so on.

Thus, in the series

$$1, \quad 8, \quad 27, \quad 64, \quad 125, \quad 216, \quad \cdots,$$

the successive orders of differences are as follows :

1st order,	7,	19,	37,	61,	91,	$\cdots$.
2d order,		12,	18,	24,	30,	$\cdots$.
3d order,			6,	6,	6,	$\cdots$.
4th order,				0,	0,	$\cdots$.

The **Differential Method** is a method for finding any term, or the sum of any number of terms of a series, by means of its successive orders of differences.

664. *To find any term of the series*

$$a_1, \quad a_2, \quad a_3, \quad a_4, \quad \cdots, \quad a_n, \quad a_{n+1}, \quad \cdots.$$

The successive orders of differences are as follows:

1st order, $a_2 - a_1$, $a_3 - a_2$, $a_4 - a_3$, $\cdots$, $a_{n+1} - a_n$, $\cdots$.

2d order, $a_3 - 2a_2 + a_1$, $a_4 - 2a_3 + a_2$, $\cdots$.

3d order, $a_4 - 3a_3 + 3a_2 - a_1$, $\cdots$; etc.

Denoting the first terms of the 1st, 2d, 3d, $\cdots$, orders of differences by $d_1, d_2, d_3, \cdots$, respectively, we have

$d_1 = a_2 - a_1$; whence, $a_2 = a_1 + d_1$.

$d_2 = a_3 - 2a_2 + a_1$; whence,

$a_3 = -a_1 + 2a_2 + d_2 = -a_1 + 2a_1 + 2d_1 + d_2 = a_1 + 2d_1 + d_2$.

$d_3 = a_4 - 3a_3 + 3a_2 - a_1$; whence,

$a_4 = a_1 - 3a_2 + 3a_3 + d_3 = a_1 + 3d_1 + 3d_2 + d_3$; etc.

It will be observed, in the values of a_2, a_3, and a_4, that the coefficients of the terms are the same as the coefficients of the terms in the expansion by the Binomial Theorem of $a + x$ to the *first*, *second*, and *third* powers, respectively.

We will now prove by Mathematical Induction that this law holds for any term of the given series.

Assume the law to hold for the nth term, a_n; then the coefficients of the terms will be the same as the coefficients of the terms in the expansion by the Binomial Theorem of $a + x$ to the $(n-1)$th power; that is,

$$a_n = a_1 + (n-1)d_1 + \frac{(n-1)(n-2)}{\lfloor 2} d_2$$

$$+ \frac{(n-1)(n-2)(n-3)}{\lfloor 3} d_3 + \cdots. \qquad (1)$$

If the law holds for the nth term of any series, it must also hold for the nth term of the first order of differences.

Or, $a_{n+1}-a_n=d_1+(n-1)d_2+\dfrac{(n-1)(n-2)}{\lfloor 2}d_3+\cdots.$ (2)

Adding (1) and (2), we have

$$a_{n+1}=a_1+[(n-1)+1]d_1+\dfrac{n-1}{\lfloor 2}[(n-2)+2]d_2$$
$$+\dfrac{(n-1)(n-2)}{\lfloor 3}[(n-3)+3]d_3+\cdots$$
$$=a_1+nd_1+\dfrac{n(n-1)}{\lfloor 2}d_2+\dfrac{n(n-1)(n-2)}{\lfloor 3}d_3+\cdots.$$ (3)

This result is in accordance with the above law.

Hence, if the law holds for the nth term of the given series, it holds for the $(n+1)$th term; but we know that it holds for the fourth term, and hence it holds for the fifth term; and so on.

Therefore, (1) holds for any term of the given series.

If the differences finally become zero, the value of a_n can be obtained exactly.

665. *To find the sum of the first n terms of the series*

$$a_1,\ a_2,\ a_3,\ a_4,\ a_5,\ \cdots.$$ (1)

Let S denote the sum of the first n terms.

Then S is the $(n+1)$th term of the series

$$0,\ a_1,\ a_1+a_2,\ a_1+a_2+a_3,\ \cdots.$$ (2)

The first order of differences of (2) is series (1); whence, the rth order of differences of (2) is the same as the $(r-1)$th order of differences of (1).

Then, if $d_1, d_2, \cdot$, represent the first terms of the 1st, 2d, $\cdots$, orders of differences of (1), $a_1, d_1, d_2, \cdot$, will be the first terms of the 1st, 2d, 3d, $\cdots$, orders of differences of (2).

Putting $a_1=0, d_1=a_1, d_2=d_1$, etc., in (3), § 664,

$$S=na_1+\dfrac{n(n-1)}{\lfloor 2}d_1+\dfrac{n(n-1)(n-2)}{\lfloor 3}d_2+\cdots.$$ (3)

666. *Ex.* Find the twelfth term, and the sum of the first twelve terms, of the series 1, 8, 27, 64, 125, $\cdots$.

Here, $n = 12$, $a_1 = 1$.

Also, $d_1 = 7$, $d_2 = 12$, $d_3 = 6$, and $d_4 = 0$ (§ 663).

Substituting in (1), § 664, the twelfth term

$$= 1 + 11 \cdot 7 + \frac{11 \cdot 10}{1 \cdot 2} \cdot 12 + \frac{11 \cdot 10 \cdot 9}{1 \cdot 2 \cdot 3} \cdot 6 = 1728.$$

Substituting in (3), § 665, the sum of the first twelve terms

$$= 12 + \frac{12 \cdot 11}{1 \cdot 2} \cdot 7 + \frac{12 \cdot 11 \cdot 10}{1 \cdot 2 \cdot 3} \cdot 12 + \frac{12 \cdot 11 \cdot 10 \cdot 9}{1 \cdot 2 \cdot 3 \cdot 4} \cdot 6 = 6084.$$

667. Piles of Shot.

Ex. If shot be piled in the shape of a pyramid with a triangular base, each side of which exhibits 9 shot, find the number in the pile.

The number of shot in the first five courses are 1, 3, 6, 10, and 15, respectively; we have then to find the sum of the first nine terms of the series 1, 3, 6, 10, 15, ⋯.

The successive orders of differences are as follows:

1st order,   2, 3, 4, 5, ⋯.

2d order,   1, 1, 1, ⋯.

3d order,   0, 0, ⋯.

Putting $n = 9$, $a_1 = 1$, $d_1 = 2$, $d_2 = 1$ in (3), § 665,

$$S = 9 + \frac{9 \cdot 8}{1 \cdot 2} \cdot 2 + \frac{9 \cdot 8 \cdot 7}{1 \cdot 2 \cdot 3} \cdot 1 = 165.$$

EXERCISE 110

1. Find the first term of the sixth order of differences of the series 3, 5, 11, 27, 67, 159, 375, ⋯.

2. Find the 15th term, and the sum of the first 15 terms, of the series 1, 9, 21, 37, 57, ⋯.

3. Find the 14th term, and the sum of the first 14 terms, of the series 5, 14, 15, 8, − 7, ⋯.

4. Find the sum of the first n multiples of 3.

5. Find the nth term, and the sum of the first n terms, of the series 2, − 1, 1, 8, 20, ⋯.

6. If shot be piled in the shape of a pyramid with a square base, each side of which exhibits 25 shot, find the number in the pile.

7. Find the 13th term, and the sum of the first 13 terms, of the series 1, 3, 9, 25, 57, 111, ….

8. Find the 10th term, and the sum of the first 10 terms, of the series 4, − 2, 10, 4, − 56, − 206, ….

9. Find the sum of the squares of the first n multiples of 2.

10. Find the nth term, and the sum of the first n terms, of the series 1, − 3, − 13, − 17, − 3, 41, ….

11. Find the number of shot in a pile of 9 courses, with a rectangular base, if the number of shot in the longest side of the base is 24.

12. Find the number of shot in a truncated pile of 10 courses, with a square base, if the number of shot in each side of the lower base is 16.

13. Find the number of shot in a truncated pile of 8 courses, with a rectangular base, if the number of shot in the length and breadth of the base are 20 and 14, respectively.

14. Find the 12th term, and the sum of the first 12 terms, of the series 1, 13, 49, 139, 333, 701, 1333, ….

15. Find the 9th term, and the sum of the first 9 terms, of the series 20, 4, − 36, − 132, − 356, − 820, − 1676, ….

16. Find the sum of the fourth powers of the first n natural numbers.

17. Find the number of shot in a pile with a rectangular base, if the number of shot in the length and breadth of the base are m and n, respectively.

18. Find the number of shot in a truncated pile of n courses, with a triangular base, if the number of shot in each side of the lower base is m.

INTERPOLATION

668. Interpolation is the process of introducing between the terms of a series other terms conforming to the law of the series.

Its usual application is in finding intermediate numbers between those given in Mathematical Tables.

The operation is effected by giving *fractional* values to n in (1), § 664.

The method of Interpolation rests on the assumption that a formula which has been proved for an integral value of n, holds also when n is fractional.

468 ADVANCED COURSE IN ALGEBRA

Ex. Given $\sqrt{5} = 2.2361$, $\sqrt{6} = 2.4495$, $\sqrt{7} = 2.6458$, $\sqrt{8} = 2.8284$, $\cdots$; find $\sqrt{6.3}$.

In this case the successive orders of differences are:

$$.2134, \quad .1963, \quad .1826, \quad \cdots.$$
$$-.0171, \quad -.0137, \quad \cdots.$$
$$.0034, \quad \cdots.$$

Whence, $d_1 = .2134$, $d_2 = -.0171$, $d_3 = .0034$, $\cdots$.

Now, the required term is distant 1.3 intervals from $\sqrt{5}$.

Substituting $n = 2.3$ in (1), § 664, we have, approximately,

$$\sqrt{6.3} = 2.2361 + 1.3 \times .2134 + \frac{1.3 \times .3}{1 \times 2}(-.0171)$$
$$+ \frac{1.3 \times .3 \times -.7}{1 \times 2 \times 3} \times .0034$$
$$= 2.2361 + .2774 - .0033 - .0002 = 2.5100.$$

EXERCISE III

1. Given $\log 26 = 1.4150$, $\log 27 = 1.4314$, $\log 28 = 1.4472$, $\log 29 = 1.4624$, $\cdots$; find $\log 26.7$.

2. Given $\sqrt[3]{91} = 4.49794$, $\sqrt[3]{92} = 4.51436$, $\sqrt[3]{93} = 4.53066$, $\sqrt[3]{94} = 4.54684$, $\cdots$; find $\sqrt[3]{92.5}$.

3. The reciprocal of 35 is .02857; of 36, .02778; of 37, .02703; of 38, .02632; etc. Find the reciprocal of 36.28.

4. Given $\log 124 = 2.09342$, $\log 125 = 2.09691$, $\log 126 = 2.10037$, $\log 127 = 2.10380$, $\cdots$; find $\log 125.36$.

5. Given $21^3 = 9261$, $22^3 = 10648$, $23^3 = 12167$, $24^3 = 13824$, and $25^3 = 15625$; find the cube of $21\frac{1}{2}$.

6. Given $\log 61 = 1.78533$, $\log 62 = 1.79239$, $\log 63 = 1.79934$, $\log 64 = 1.80618$, $\cdots$; find $\log 63.527$.

SUMMATION OF SERIES BY SEPARATION INTO PARTIAL FRACTIONS

318. 1. Find the sum of the first n terms of the infinite series

$$\frac{1}{2 \cdot 3} + \frac{1}{3 \cdot 4} + \frac{1}{4 \cdot 5} + \cdots,$$

and determine whether the series is convergent or divergent.

The nth term of the above series is $\dfrac{1}{(n+1)(n+2)}$.

Separating into partial fractions by the method of § 567, we have

$$\frac{1}{(n+1)(n+2)} = \frac{1}{n+1} - \frac{1}{n+2}.$$

Then the sum of the first n terms of the given series is

$$\left(\frac{1}{2}-\frac{1}{3}\right)+\left(\frac{1}{3}-\frac{1}{4}\right)+\left(\frac{1}{4}-\frac{1}{5}\right)+\cdots+\left(\frac{1}{n+1}-\frac{1}{n+2}\right)$$

$$=\frac{1}{2}-\frac{1}{n+2}=\frac{n}{2(n+2)}.$$

Since $\dfrac{1}{2}-\dfrac{1}{n+2}$ approaches the limit $\dfrac{1}{2}$, when n is indefinitely increased, the series is convergent (§ 543).

2. Find the sum of the first n terms of the infinite series

$$\frac{1}{1\cdot 3}+\frac{1}{2\cdot 4}+\frac{1}{3\cdot 5}+\cdots,$$

and determine whether the series is convergent or divergent.

The nth term of the series is $\dfrac{1}{n(n+2)}$, which, by the method of § 567, equals $\dfrac{1}{2n}-\dfrac{1}{2(n+2)}$.

Then the sum of the first n terms is

$$\left(\frac{1}{2}-\frac{1}{6}\right)+\left(\frac{1}{4}-\frac{1}{8}\right)+\left(\frac{1}{6}-\frac{1}{10}\right)+\cdots+\left[\frac{1}{2n}-\frac{1}{2(n+2)}\right].$$

All the terms cancel except the first two positive, and the last two negative.

Thus the sum of the first n terms is

$$\frac{1}{2}+\frac{1}{4}-\frac{1}{2(n+1)}-\frac{1}{2(n+2)}, \text{ or } \frac{3}{4}-\frac{1}{2(n+1)}-\frac{1}{2(n+2)}.$$

The latter expression approaches the limit $\dfrac{3}{4}$ when n is indefinitely increased.

Hence, the series is convergent.

EXERCISE II2

In each of the following, find the sum of the first n terms, and determine whether the series is convergent or divergent :

1. $\dfrac{1}{1\cdot 3}+\dfrac{1}{3\cdot 5}+\dfrac{1}{5\cdot 7}+\cdots.$

3. $\dfrac{1}{1\cdot 4}+\dfrac{1}{4\cdot 7}+\dfrac{1}{7\cdot 10}+\cdots.$

2. $\dfrac{1}{2\cdot 5}+\dfrac{1}{3\cdot 10}+\dfrac{1}{4\cdot 15}+\cdots.$

4. $\dfrac{1}{1\cdot 4}+\dfrac{1}{2\cdot 5}+\dfrac{1}{3\cdot 6}+\cdots.$

5. $\dfrac{3}{1^2\cdot 2^2}+\dfrac{5}{2^2\cdot 3^2}+\dfrac{7}{3^2\cdot 4^2}+\cdots.$

In each of the following, find the sum of the first n terms, and determine for what values of x the series is convergent :

6. $\dfrac{1}{x(x+1)}+\dfrac{1}{(x+1)(x+2)}+\dfrac{1}{(x+2)(x+3)}+\cdots.$

7. $\dfrac{x}{(1+x)(1+2\,x)}+\dfrac{x}{(1+2\,x)(1+3\,x)}+\dfrac{x}{(1+3\,x)(1+4\,x)}+\cdots.$

8. Find the sum of the first n terms of :

$$\dfrac{1}{x(x+1)(x+2)}+\dfrac{1}{(x+1)(x+2)(x+3)}+\cdots.$$

XXXV. THEORY OF NUMBERS

670. In the present chapter, the word *number* will signify a *positive integer;* and every letter will be understood as representing a positive integer.

One number is said to *divide* another when it is contained in it without a remainder; in this case, the second number is said to be a *multiple* of the first.

A *prime number* is a number which cannot be divided, without a remainder, by any number except itself and unity.

One number is said to be *prime* to another when there is no number, except unity, which will divide each of them without a remainder.

671. *If a number divides the product of two others, and is prime to one of them, it must divide the other.*

Let the number n divide the product ab, and be prime to a.

Since n divides ab, the prime factors of ab must be the same as those of n, with certain additional prime factors.

But since n is prime to a, n and a have no common factor except unity.

Then, the prime factors of b must be either the same as those of n, or with certain additional prime factors; and n divides b.

672. *If a prime number divides the product of any number of factors, it must divide some factor of the product.*

Let p be a prime number which divides the product $abc \cdots$.

Then, the prime factors of $abc \cdots$ must be p, with certain additional prime factors.

Then, some one of the numbers $a, b, c, \cdots$, must have p as a prime factor, and therefore p divides some factor of the product.

673. It follows from § 672 that

If a prime number divides a positive integral power of a number a, it must divide a.

674. *If the numerator and denominator of a fraction are prime to each other, the fraction is in its lowest terms.*

Let a be prime to b.

If possible, let $\dfrac{a}{b} = \dfrac{a'}{b'}$, where b' is $< b$.

Multiplying both members by b', $a' = \dfrac{ab'}{b}$.

Whence, since a' is an integer, b divides ab'.

But a is prime to b, and hence b divides b' (§ 671).

But this is impossible if b' is $< b$.

Hence, b' cannot be $< b$, and $\dfrac{a}{b}$ is in its lowest terms.

675. It was proved, in § 674, that b divides b'.

Whence, $b' = mb$, where m is an integer.

Then,
$$a' = \frac{ab'}{b} = \frac{amb}{b} = am.$$

Hence, *if a is prime to b, and $\dfrac{a}{b} = \dfrac{a'}{b'}$, a' and b' are equimultiples of a and b.*

676. *A number can be resolved into prime factors in only one way.*

Let n be a composite number; and suppose $n = abc \cdot$, where a, b, c, $\cdot$, are prime numbers.

Suppose also, if possible, that $n = a'b'c' \cdot$, where a', b', c', $\cdots$, is a different set of prime numbers.

We have, $abc \cdots = a'b'c' \cdots.$ (1)

Then, a divides $a'b'c' \cdot$, and therefore divides some one of the numbers a', b', c', $\cdots$ (§ 672).

Then, since a, b, c, $\cdot$, and a', b', c', $\cdots$, are prime numbers, a must *equal* some one of the numbers a', b', c', $\cdots$.

Suppose, then, $a = a'$; dividing the members of (1) by a and a', respectively, $bc \cdots = b'c' \cdots;$

and, as before, b equals one of the numbers b', c', $\cdots$.

Proceeding in this way, we can prove each of the numbers a, b, c, $\cdot$, equal to one of the numbers a', b', c', $\cdots$.

677. To find the highest power of 2 which is contained in $\lfloor 14$.

Of the factors 1, 2, 3, $\cdot$, 14, the numbers 2, 2×2, 3×2, $\cdot$, 7×2 contain 2 as a factor at least once.

The numbers 2^2, 2×2^2, 3×2^2 contain 2^2 as a factor at least once.

The number 2^3 contains 2^3 as a factor once.

Then, the highest power of 2 in $\lfloor 14$ is evidently

$$7 + 3 + 1, \text{ or } 11.$$

We will now consider the general case.

To find the highest power of a, where a is any prime number, which is contained in $\lfloor n$.

Of the factors 1, 2, 3, $\cdot$, n, the numbers a, $2\,a$, $3\,a$, $\cdots$, contain a as a factor at least once.

Let the last term of this series be pa.

Then, pa either equals n, or is $< n$; whence,

$$p = \frac{n}{a}, \text{ or } p < \frac{n}{a}.$$

Therefore, p is the *greatest integer* in $\dfrac{n}{a}$.

Again, the numbers a^2, $2\,a^2$, $3\,a^2$, $\cdot$, contain a^2 as a factor at least once; let the last term of this series be qa^2.

Then, as before, $\qquad q = \dfrac{n}{a^2}$, or $q < \dfrac{n}{a^2}$.

Whence, q is the greatest integer in $\dfrac{n}{a^2}$.

Continuing in this way, the highest power of a in $\lfloor n$ is

$$p + q + r + \cdots,$$

where p is the greatest integer in $\dfrac{n}{a}$, q in $\dfrac{n}{a^2}$, r in $\dfrac{n}{a^3}$, etc.

We will now solve the example of § 677 by this method.

In this case, $a = 2$, $n = 14$; then, $\dfrac{n}{a} = 7$, $\dfrac{n}{a^2} = \dfrac{7}{2}$, $\dfrac{n}{a^3} = \dfrac{7}{4}$.

The greatest integer in 7 is 7 ; in $\dfrac{7}{2}$, is 3 ; in $\dfrac{7}{4}$, is 1.

Then, the highest power of 2 in $\lfloor 14$ is $7 + 3 + 1$, or 11.

678. *The product of any n consecutive integers is divisible by* $\lfloor n$.

Let the integers be $m+1,\ m+2,\ \cdots,\ m+n$.

Multiplying both numerator and denominator by the product of the natural numbers from 1 to m, inclusive, the fraction

$$\frac{(m+1)(m+2)\cdots(m+n)}{\lfloor n} = \frac{\lfloor m+n}{\lfloor m \lfloor n}.$$

If a is any prime number, the exponent of a in $\lfloor m+n$ is $p+q+r+\cdots$, where p is the greatest integer in $\dfrac{m+n}{a}$, q in $\dfrac{m+n}{a^2}$, r in $\dfrac{m+n}{a^3}$, etc. (§ 677).

The exponent of a in $\lfloor m$ is $p_1+q_1+r_1+\cdot$, where p_1 is the greatest integer in $\dfrac{m}{a}, q_1$ in $\dfrac{m}{a^2}, r_1$ in $\dfrac{m}{a^3}$, etc.

The exponent of a in $\lfloor n$ is $p_2+q_2+r_2+\cdot$, where p_2 is the greatest integer in $\dfrac{n}{a}, q_2$ in $\dfrac{n}{a^2}, r_2$ in $\dfrac{n}{a^3}$, etc.

Then, the exponent of a in $\lfloor m \lfloor n$ is $(p_1+p_2)+(q_1+q_2)+\cdots$.

Now, the greatest integer in $\dfrac{m+n}{a}$ is either the sum of the greatest integers in $\dfrac{m}{a}$ and $\dfrac{n}{a}$, or else it exceeds this sum by unity.

That is, p equals p_1+p_2, or p_1+p_2+1.

Similarly, q equals q_1+q_2, or q_1+q_2+1; etc.

Then, $p+q+r+\cdots$ is not $<(p_1+q_1)+(p_2+q_2)+\cdots$; that is, the exponent of a in $\lfloor m+n$ is not $<$ its exponent in $\lfloor m \lfloor n$.

Then, $\dfrac{\lfloor m+n}{\lfloor m \lfloor n}$ must be an integer.

Whence, $(m+1)(m+2)\cdots(m+n)$ is divisible by $\lfloor n$.

679. *If n is a prime number, the coefficient of any term, except the first and last, in the expansion by the Binomial Theorem of* $(a+x)^n$, *is divisible by n.*

By § 287, the coefficient of the $(r + 1)$th term of $(a + x)^n$ is

$$\frac{n(n-1)\cdots(n-r+1)}{\lfloor r}. \tag{1}$$

By § 678, $n(n-1)\cdots(n-r+1)$ is divisible by $\lfloor r$.

If r has any value from 1 to $n-1$, none of the factors of $\lfloor r$ can divide n; for, by hypothesis, n is a prime number.

Then, $\lfloor r$ must divide $(n-1)\cdots(n-r+1)$.

Therefore, expression (1) is an integer, and divisible by n.

680. Fermat's Theorem.

If n is a prime number, and m is prime to n, $m^{n-1}-1$ is a multiple of n.

Let $a, b, c, \cdot, k$ be any m numbers.

Expanding by the Binomial Theorem, we have

$$(a + b + c + \cdots + k)^n = [a + (b + c + \cdots + k)]^n$$

$$= a^n + na^{n-1}(b + c + \cdots + k) + \frac{n(n-1)}{\lfloor 2}a^{n-2}(b + c + \cdots + k)^2$$

$$+ \cdots + (b + c + \cdots + k)^n. \tag{1}$$

By § 679, each coefficient n, $\dfrac{n(n-1)}{\lfloor 2}$, $\cdots$, is divisible by n.

Then, every term in the expansion (1), which is not a power of $a, b, c, \cdots, k$, is a multiple of n; and (1) can be written

$$(a + b + c + \cdots + k)^n = (a^n + b^n + c^n + \cdots + k^n) + pn,$$

where p is an integer.

Putting $a = b = c = \cdots = k = 1$, we have

$$m^n = m + pn, \text{ or } m^n - m = pn, \text{ or } m(m^{n-1}-1) = pn.$$

Since m is prime to n, it cannot be a multiple of n.

Then, $m^{n-1}-1$ must be a multiple of n.

681. The result $m^n - m = pn$, of § 680, holds if m is not prime to n.

That is, $m^n - m$ is a multiple of n when n is prime, whether m is prime to n or not.

EXAMPLES

682. **1.** If two consecutive numbers are not multiples of 3, their sum is a multiple of 3.

The numbers must be in the forms $3m+1$ and $3m+2$.

Then their sum is $6m+3$, which is a multiple of 3.

It follows from the above that any number of the form

$$n(n+1)\,[n+(n+1)], \text{ or } n(n+1)(2n+1),$$

is divisible by 6.

For either n or $n+1$ must be even; and if neither n nor $n+1$ is a multiple of 3, their sum is a multiple of 3.

2. Every perfect square is in the form $5n$, or $5n \pm 1$.

For any number is in the form $5m$, or $5m \pm a$, where a may be 1 or 2.

$(5m)^2$ is in the form $5n$.

Again, $(5m \pm a)^2$ equals a multiple of 5, plus a^2.

But a^2 is either 1 or 4; and $4 = 5 - 1$.

Hence, $(5m \pm a)^2$ differs by 1 from a multiple of 5, and is therefore in the form $5n+1$ or $5n-1$.

3. If n is even, and not a multiple of 3, n^2+2 is divisible by 6.

For n must be in the form $3m \pm 1$, where m is odd.

Then, $n^2+2 = 9m^2 \pm 6m + 1 + 2$, which is divisible by 3.

Again, n^2+2 is *even;* hence, it is divisible by 6.

4. Every even power of an odd number is in the form $8n+1$.

Now, any odd number is in one of the forms

$$8m \pm 1, \text{ or } 8m \pm 3.$$

If this be raised to any even power, the result will be a multiple of 8 plus 1, or a multiple of 8 plus an even power of 3.

Now any even power of 3 is in the form of a multiple of 8, plus 1.

Hence, any even power of an odd number is in the form $8n+1$.

5. Prove that $n^7 - n$ is divisible by 42.

By § 681, since 7 is prime, $n^7 - n$ is divisible by 7.

Again, $n^7 - n = n (n^6 - 1) = n (n^2 - 1) (n^4 + n^2 + 1)$
$$= (n - 1) n (n + 1) (n^4 + n^2 + 1).$$

By § 678, $(n - 1) n (n + 1)$ is divisible by $\lfloor 3$, or 6.
Hence, $n^7 - n$ is divisible by 7 and 6, or by 42.

6. Prove that the fourth power of any number is in the form $5n$ or $5n + 1$.

If m is prime to 5, $m^4 - 1$ is a multiple of 5 (§ 680).

That is, m^4 is a multiple of 5, increased by 1 ; and is therefore in the form $5n + 1$.

If m is not prime to 5, it contains 5 as a factor; and m^4 is in the form $5n$.

EXERCISE 113

1. If n is odd, and greater than 1, $(n - 1) n (n + 1)$ is divisible by 24.

2. Prove that $n^5 - n$ is divisible by 30, if n is greater than 1.

3. Prove that $n (n + 1) (n + 5)$ is a multiple of 6.

4. Find the highest power of 2 in $\lfloor 50$.

5. Find the highest power of 3 in $\lfloor 80$.

6. Prove that every perfect square is in the form $3n$, or $3n + 1$.

7. Prove that every perfect sixth power is in the form $7n$, or $7n + 1$.

8. Prove that, if n is odd, and not a multiple of 3, $n^2 + 5$ is divisible by 6.

9. Prove that, if n is odd, $(n^2 + 3) (n^2 + 7)$ is divisible by 32.

10. Prove that any odd power of 7 is in the form $8n - 1$.

11. Prove that $n^5 - 5 n^3 + 4 n$ is divisible by 120, if n is greater than 2.

12. Prove that, if n is odd, and greater than 1, $n^5 - n$ is divisible by 240.

13. Prove that every perfect cube is in the form $7n$, or $7n \pm 1$.

14. Prove that every perfect cube is in the form $9n$, or $9n \pm 1$.

XXXVI. DETERMINANTS

683. The solution of the equations

$$\begin{cases} a_1 x + b_1 y = c_1, \\ a_2 x + b_2 y = c_2, \end{cases}$$

is
$$x = \frac{b_2 c_1 - b_1 c_2}{a_1 b_2 - a_2 b_1}, \quad y = \frac{c_2 a_1 - c_1 a_2}{a_1 b_2 - a_2 b_1}.$$

The common denominator may be written in the form

$$\begin{vmatrix} a_1, & b_1 \\ a_2, & b_2 \end{vmatrix}. \tag{1}$$

This is understood as signifying the product of the upper left-hand and lower right-hand numbers, minus the product of the lower left-hand and upper right-hand.

The expression (1) is called a **Determinant of the Second Order.**

The numerators of the above fractions can also be expressed as determinants; thus,

$$b_2 c_1 - b_1 c_2 = \begin{vmatrix} c_1, & b_1 \\ c_2, & b_2 \end{vmatrix}, \text{ and } c_2 a_1 - c_1 a_2 = \begin{vmatrix} a_1, & c_1 \\ a_2, & c_2 \end{vmatrix}.$$

684. The solution of the equations

$$\begin{cases} a_1 x + b_1 y + c_1 z = d_1, \\ a_2 x + b_2 y + c_2 z = d_2, \\ a_3 x + b_3 y + c_3 z = d_3, \end{cases}$$

is
$$x = \frac{d_1 b_2 c_3 - d_1 b_3 c_2 + d_2 b_3 c_1 - d_2 b_1 c_3 + d_3 b_1 c_2 - d_3 b_2 c_1}{a_1 b_2 c_3 - a_1 b_3 c_2 + a_2 b_3 c_1 - a_2 b_1 c_3 + a_3 b_1 c_2 - a_3 b_2 c_1}; \tag{1}$$

with results of similar form for y and z.

The denominator of (1) may be written in the form

$$\begin{vmatrix} a_1, & b_1, & c_1 \\ a_2, & b_2, & c_2 \\ a_3, & b_3, & c_3 \end{vmatrix}. \tag{2}$$

This is understood as signifying the sum of the products of
the numbers connected by lines parallel to a line joining the
upper left-hand corner to the lower right-hand, in the following diagram, minus the sum of the products of the numbers
connected by lines parallel to a line joining the lower left-hand
corner to the upper right-hand.

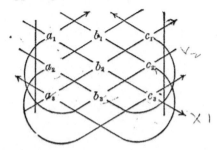

The expression (2) is called a **Determinant of the Third Order**.

The numerator of the value of x can also be expressed as a determinant,
as follows:

$$\begin{vmatrix} d_1, & b_1, & c_1 \\ d_2, & b_2, & c_2 \\ d_3, & b_3, & c_3 \end{vmatrix};$$

as may be verified by expanding it by the above rule.

685. The numbers in the first, second, etc., horizontal lines,
of a determinant, are said to be in the *first, second,* etc., *rows,*
respectively; and the numbers in the first, second, etc., vertical
columns, in the *first, second,* etc., *columns.*

The numbers constituting the determinant are called its
elements, and the products in the expanded form its *terms.*

Thus, in the determinant (2), of § 684, the elements are
$a_1, a_2, a_3,$ etc., and the terms $a_1b_2c_3, -a_1b_3c_2,$ etc.

EXERCISE 114

Evaluate the following determinants:

1. $\begin{vmatrix} x+y, & x-y \\ x-y, & x+y \end{vmatrix}.$

2. $\begin{vmatrix} a-b, & -2a \\ 2b, & a-b \end{vmatrix}.$

3. $\begin{vmatrix} 1, & 5, & 2 \\ 4, & 7, & 3 \\ 9, & 8, & 6 \end{vmatrix}.$

4. $\begin{vmatrix} 6, & 4, & 7 \\ 9, & 0, & 8 \\ 5, & 3, & 2 \end{vmatrix}$.　　**5.** $\begin{vmatrix} 2, & -3, & 1 \\ -2, & 4, & 5 \\ 3, & -1, & -4 \end{vmatrix}$.　　**6.** $\begin{vmatrix} 1, & x, & a \\ 1, & y, & b \\ 1, & z, & c \end{vmatrix}$.

7. $\begin{vmatrix} a, & b, & c \\ b, & a, & d \\ c, & d, & a \end{vmatrix}$.　　**8.** $\begin{vmatrix} x+y, & z, & z \\ x, & y+z, & x \\ y, & y, & z+x \end{vmatrix}$.

Verify the following by expanding the determinants :

9. $\begin{vmatrix} a_1, & b_1, & c_1 \\ a_2, & b_2, & c_2 \\ a_3, & b_3, & c_3 \end{vmatrix} = \begin{vmatrix} c_3, & b_3, & a_3 \\ c_2, & b_2, & a_2 \\ c_1, & b_1, & a_1 \end{vmatrix}$.　　**10.** $\begin{vmatrix} ma_1, & b_1, & c_1 \\ ma_2, & b_2, & c_2 \\ ma_3, & b_3, & c_3 \end{vmatrix} = \begin{vmatrix} a_1, & mb_1, & c_1 \\ a_2, & mb_2, & c_2 \\ a_3, & mb_3, & c_3 \end{vmatrix}$.

11. $\begin{vmatrix} a_1, & b_1, & c_1 \\ a_2, & b_2, & c_2 \\ a_3, & b_3, & c_3 \end{vmatrix} = a_1 \begin{vmatrix} b_2, & c_2 \\ b_3, & c_3 \end{vmatrix} - b_1 \begin{vmatrix} a_2, & c_2 \\ a_3, & c_3 \end{vmatrix} + c_1 \begin{vmatrix} a_2, & b_2 \\ a_3, & b_3 \end{vmatrix}$.

686. If, in any permutation of the numbers 1, 2, 3, ···, n, a greater number precedes a less, there is said to be an *inversion*.

Thus, in the case of five numbers, the permutation 4, 3, 1, 5, 2 has six inversions ; 4 before 1, 3 before 1, 4 before 2, 3 before 2, 5 before 2, and 4 before 3.

Consider, now, the n^2 elements

$$\begin{vmatrix} a_{1,1}, & a_{1,2}, & a_{1,3}, & \cdots, & a_{1,n} \\ a_{2,1}, & a_{2,2}, & a_{2,3}, & \cdots, & a_{2,n} \\ \cdot & \cdot & \cdot & \cdot & \cdot \\ a_{n,1}, & a_{n,2}, & a_{n,3}, & \cdots, & a_{n,n} \end{vmatrix}. \qquad (1)$$

The notation in regard to suffixes, in (1), is that the first suffix denotes the row, and the second the column, in which the element is situated.

Thus, $a_{k,r}$ is the element in the kth row and rth column.

Let all possible products of the elements taken n at a time be formed, subject to the restriction that each product shall contain one and only one element from each row, and one and only one from each column, and write them so that the *first suffixes* shall be in the order 1, 2, 3, · , n.

This is equivalent to writing all the permutations of the numbers 1, 2, ···, n in the *second suffixes*.

Make each product + or − according as the number of inversions in the *second* suffixes is *even* or *odd*.

The expression (1) is called a **Determinant of the nth Order.**

The number of terms in the expanded form of a determinant of the nth order is $\lfloor n$ (§ 625).

The elements lying in the diagonal joining the upper left-hand to the lower right hand corner are said to be in the

Printed in Great Britain
by Amazon

57060098R00280